THE BOOK

Ford Fiesta
Service and Repair Manual

A K Legg LAE MIMI, Steve Rendle and Mark Coombs

Models covered

All Ford Fiesta models with petrol and diesel engines,
including Van, Courier and Combi models, and special/limited editions

1242 cc, 1298 cc & 1388 cc petrol engines

1753 cc diesel engine

(3397 - 304 - 2AD1)

© Haynes Publishing 2000

ABCDE
FGHIJ
KLMN

A book in the **Haynes Service and Repair Manual Series**

ISBN 1 85960 397 1

British Library Cataloguing in Publication Data
A catalogue record for this book is available from the British Library

Printed in the USA

Haynes Publishing
Sparkford Nr Yeovil, Somerset BA22 7JJ, England

Haynes North America, Inc.
861 Lawrence Drive, Newbury Park, California 91320, USA

Editions Haynes S.A.
Tour Aurore - IBC, 18 Place des Reflets
92975 Paris La Defense 2 Cedex, France

Haynes Publishing Nordiska AB
Box 1504, 751 45 UPPSALA, Sverige

Contents

LIVING WITH YOUR FORD FIESTA

Roadside Repairs

Weekly Checks

MAINTENANCE

Routine Maintenance and Servicing

Contents

REPAIRS AND OVERHAUL

The Ford Fiesta model range covered by this manual was introduced into the UK in October 1995 to supersede the previous Fiesta range. 3-door and 5-door Hatchback models are available, along with 3-door Van, and Courier and Combi light commercial variants (the Combi model is basically a Courier light commercial fitted with rear passenger seats and windows).

1.25 and 1.4 litre 16-valve, and 1.3 litre 8-valve petrol engines are available, as well as a 1.8 litre diesel engine. All engines are mounted transversely at the front of the vehicle.

Models may be fitted with five-speed manual, or CTX continuously variable automatic transmissions, mounted at the left-hand side of the engine.

All models have front-wheel-drive with fully-independent front and semi-independent rear suspension. The front suspension is of conventional McPherson strut type, incorporating lower arms, and an anti-roll bar. Hatchback and Van models use a rear beam axle with trailing arms and McPherson struts, whereas the Courier and Combi models use a torsion bar rear suspension to provide a more spacious load area.

All models have a high trim level, which is very comprehensive in the upper model range. Driver's and passenger's air bag systems, central locking, electric windows, an electric sunroof, anti-lock brakes, and air conditioning are all available.

For the home mechanic, the Ford Fiesta is a straightforward vehicle to maintain and repair since design features have been incorporated to reduce the actual cost of ownership to a minimum, and most of the items requiring frequent attention are easily accessible.

Ford Fiesta Si

Ford Courier

The Ford Fiesta Team

Haynes manuals are produced by dedicated and enthusiastic people working in close co-operation. The team responsible for the creation of this book included:

Authors	**Andy Legg**
	Steve Rendle
	Mark Coombs
Sub-editor	**Sophie Yar**
Editor & Page Make-up	**Steve Churchill**
Workshop manager	**Paul Buckland**
Photo Scans	**John Martin**
	Paul Tanswell
Cover illustration & Line Art	**Roger Healing**
Wiring diagrams	**Matthew Marke**

We hope the book will help you to get the maximum enjoyment from your car. By carrying out routine maintenance as described you will ensure your car's reliability and preserve its resale value.

Your Ford Fiesta Manual

The aim of this manual is to help you get the best value from your vehicle. It can do so in several ways. It can help you decide what work must be done (even should you choose to get it done by a garage), provide information on routine maintenance and servicing, and give a logical course of action and diagnosis when random faults occur. However, it is hoped that you will use the manual by tackling the work yourself. On simpler jobs, it may even be quicker than booking the car into a garage and going there twice, to leave and collect it. Perhaps most important, a lot of money can be saved by avoiding the costs a garage must charge to cover its labour and overheads.

The manual has drawings and descriptions to show the function of the various components, so that their layout can be understood. Then the tasks are described and photographed in a clear step-by-step sequence.

References to the "left" or "right" of the vehicle are in the sense of a person in the driving seat, facing forwards.

Acknowledgements

Thanks are due to Champion Spark Plug who supplied the illustrations showing spark plug conditions and to Duckhams Oils, who provided lubrication data. Certain other illustrations are the copyright of the Ford Motor Company, and are used with their permission. Thanks are also due to Draper Tools Limited, who provided some of the workshop tools, and to all those people at Sparkford who helped in the production of this manual.

We take great pride in the accuracy of information given in this manual, but vehicle manufacturers make alterations and design changes during the production run of a particular vehicle of which they do not inform us. No liability can be accepted by the authors or publishers for loss, damage or injury caused by any errors in, or omissions from, the information given.

Working on your car can be dangerous. This page shows just some of the potential risks and hazards, with the aim of creating a safety-conscious attitude.

General hazards

Scalding

• Don't remove the radiator or expansion tank cap while the engine is hot.
• Engine oil, automatic transmission fluid or power steering fluid may also be dangerously hot if the engine has recently been running.

Burning

• Beware of burns from the exhaust system and from any part of the engine. Brake discs and drums can also be extremely hot immediately after use.

Crushing

• When working under or near a raised vehicle, always supplement the jack with axle stands, or use drive-on ramps. *Never venture under a car which is only supported by a jack.*

• Take care if loosening or tightening high-torque nuts when the vehicle is on stands. Initial loosening and final tightening should be done with the wheels on the ground.

Fire

• Fuel is highly flammable; fuel vapour is explosive.
• Don't let fuel spill onto a hot engine.
• Do not smoke or allow naked lights (including pilot lights) anywhere near a vehicle being worked on. Also beware of creating sparks (electrically or by use of tools).
• Fuel vapour is heavier than air, so don't work on the fuel system with the vehicle over an inspection pit.
• Another cause of fire is an electrical overload or short-circuit. Take care when repairing or modifying the vehicle wiring.
• Keep a fire extinguisher handy, of a type suitable for use on fuel and electrical fires.

Electric shock

• Ignition HT voltage can be dangerous, especially to people with heart problems or a pacemaker. Don't work on or near the ignition system with the engine running or the ignition switched on.

• Mains voltage is also dangerous. Make sure that any mains-operated equipment is correctly earthed. Mains power points should be protected by a residual current device (RCD) circuit breaker.

Fume or gas intoxication

• Exhaust fumes are poisonous; they often contain carbon monoxide, which is rapidly fatal if inhaled. Never run the engine in a confined space such as a garage with the doors shut.

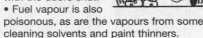

• Fuel vapour is also poisonous, as are the vapours from some cleaning solvents and paint thinners.

Poisonous or irritant substances

• Avoid skin contact with battery acid and with any fuel, fluid or lubricant, especially antifreeze, brake hydraulic fluid and Diesel fuel. Don't syphon them by mouth. If such a substance is swallowed or gets into the eyes, seek medical advice.
• Prolonged contact with used engine oil can cause skin cancer. Wear gloves or use a barrier cream if necessary. Change out of oil-soaked clothes and do not keep oily rags in your pocket.
• Air conditioning refrigerant forms a poisonous gas if exposed to a naked flame (including a cigarette). It can also cause skin burns on contact.

Asbestos

• Asbestos dust can cause cancer if inhaled or swallowed. Asbestos may be found in gaskets and in brake and clutch linings. When dealing with such components it is safest to assume that they contain asbestos.

Special hazards

Hydrofluoric acid

• This extremely corrosive acid is formed when certain types of synthetic rubber, found in some O-rings, oil seals, fuel hoses etc, are exposed to temperatures above 400ºC. The rubber changes into a charred or sticky substance containing the acid. *Once formed, the acid remains dangerous for years. If it gets onto the skin, it may be necessary to amputate the limb concerned.*
• When dealing with a vehicle which has suffered a fire, or with components salvaged from such a vehicle, wear protective gloves and discard them after use.

The battery

• Batteries contain sulphuric acid, which attacks clothing, eyes and skin. Take care when topping-up or carrying the battery.
• The hydrogen gas given off by the battery is highly explosive. Never cause a spark or allow a naked light nearby. Be careful when connecting and disconnecting battery chargers or jump leads.

Air bags

• Air bags can cause injury if they go off accidentally. Take care when removing the steering wheel and/or facia. Special storage instructions may apply.

Diesel injection equipment

• Diesel injection pumps supply fuel at very high pressure. Take care when working on the fuel injectors and fuel pipes.

⚠ *Warning: Never expose the hands, face or any other part of the body to injector spray; the fuel can penetrate the skin with potentially fatal results.*

Remember...

DO

• Do use eye protection when using power tools, and when working under the vehicle.

• Do wear gloves or use barrier cream to protect your hands when necessary.

• Do get someone to check periodically that all is well when working alone on the vehicle.

• Do keep loose clothing and long hair well out of the way of moving mechanical parts.

• Do remove rings, wristwatch etc, before working on the vehicle – especially the electrical system.

• Do ensure that any lifting or jacking equipment has a safe working load rating adequate for the job.

DON'T

• Don't attempt to lift a heavy component which may be beyond your capability – get assistance.

• Don't rush to finish a job, or take unverified short cuts.

• Don't use ill-fitting tools which may slip and cause injury.

• Don't leave tools or parts lying around where someone can trip over them. Mop up oil and fuel spills at once.

• Don't allow children or pets to play in or near a vehicle being worked on.

The following pages are intended to help in dealing with common roadside emergencies and breakdowns. You will find more detailed fault finding information at the back of the manual, and repair information in the main chapters.

If your car won't start and the starter motor doesn't turn

- ☐ If it's a model with automatic transmission, make sure the selector is in 'P' or 'N'.
- ☐ Open the bonnet and make sure that the battery terminals are clean and tight.
- ☐ Switch on the headlights and try to start the engine. If the headlights go very dim when you're trying to start, the battery is probably flat. Get out of trouble by jump starting (see next page) using a friend's car.

If your car won't start even though the starter motor turns as normal

- ☐ Is there fuel in the tank?
- ☐ Is there moisture on electrical components under the bonnet? Switch off the ignition, then wipe off any obvious dampness with a dry cloth. Spray a water-repellent aerosol product (WD-40 or equivalent) on ignition and fuel system electrical connectors like those shown in the photos. Pay special attention to the ignition coil wiring connector and HT leads. (Note that Diesel engines don't normally suffer from damp.)

A Check the condition and security of the battery connections.

B Check that the spark plug HT leads are securely connected by pushing them onto the ignition coil (petrol models).

C Check that the wiring connectors are securely connected to the ignition coil (petrol models).

Check that electrical connections are secure (with the ignition switched off) and spray them with a water dispersant spray like WD40 if you suspect a problem due to damp

D Check that the throttle position sensor wiring plug is securely connected (petrol models).

E Check that the fuel cut-off switch has not been activated (petrol models).

Jump starting

When jump-starting a car using a booster battery, observe the following precautions:

✔ Before connecting the booster battery, make sure that the ignition is switched off.

✔ Ensure that all electrical equipment (lights, heater, wipers, etc) is switched off.

✔ Take note of any special precautions printed on the battery case.

✔ Make sure that the booster battery is the same voltage as the discharged one in the vehicle.

✔ If the battery is being jump-started from the battery in another vehicle, the two vehicles MUST NOT TOUCH each other.

✔ Make sure that the transmission is in neutral (or PARK, in the case of automatic transmission).

1 Connect one end of the red jump lead to the positive (+) terminal of the flat battery

2 Connect the other end of the red lead to the positive (+) terminal of the booster battery.

3 Connect one end of the black jump lead to the negative (-) terminal of the booster battery

4 Connect the other end of the black jump lead to a bolt or bracket on the engine block, well away from the battery, on the vehicle to be started.

5 Make sure that the jump leads will not come into contact with the fan, drive-belts or other moving parts of the engine.

6 Start the engine using the booster battery and run it at idle speed. Switch on the lights, rear window demister and heater blower motor, then disconnect the jump leads in the reverse order of connection. Turn off the lights etc.

Wheel changing

Some of the details shown here will vary according to model. For instance, the location of the jack is not the same on all cars. However, the basic principles apply to all vehicles.

> ⚠️ **Warning: Do not change a wheel in a situation where you risk being hit by another vehicle. On busy roads, try to stop in a lay-by or a gateway. Be wary of passing traffic while changing the wheel - it is easy to become distracted by the job in hand.**

Preparation

- ☐ When a puncture occurs, stop as soon as it is safe to do so.
- ☐ Park on firm level ground, if possible, and well out of the way of other traffic.
- ☐ Use hazard warning lights if necessary.

- ☐ If you have one, use a warning triangle to alert other drivers of your presence.
- ☐ Apply the handbrake and engage first or reverse gear (or Park on models with automatic transmission).

- ☐ Chock the wheel diagonally opposite the one being removed – a couple of large stones will do for this.
- ☐ If the ground is soft, use a flat piece of wood to spread the load under the jack.

Changing the wheel

1 On Hatchback and Van models, the jack and wheel brace are behind the trim panel on the right-hand side of the luggage compartment. Release the securing clip and fold back the trim panel from the side of the luggage compartment, then unhook the securing strap, and lift out the jack and wheel brace. The wheel brace is clipped to the jack.

2 On Courier/Combi models, the jack, wheel brace and jack handle are located behind the trim panel in front of the right-hand rear light assembly. Release the securing clip at the top of the trim panel, then lift the panel out. Unscrew the wing nut securing the jack retaining bracket, then swivel the bracket round until the jack and wheel brace can be removed. Pull the jack handle from the retaining clips.

3 The spare wheel is in a cradle, under the rear of the vehicle. Pull up the cover in the luggage compartment for access to the spare wheel cradle securing screw. Using the wheel brace, loosen the screw by 6 to 8 turns then unhook the spare wheel cradle from the securing bracket under the back of the vehicle, and lower the cradle until it is resting on the floor.

4 On some models, it may be necessary to unclip a safety cord from the cradle before it can be fully lowered. Lift the spare wheel from the cradle.

5 Where applicable, prise off the wheel trim from the punctured wheel, using the end of the wheel brace, then loosen each wheel nut by half a turn.

6 Locate the jack head below the reinforced jacking point nearest the wheel to be changed, and on firm ground. Ensure that the lug on the jack head engages with the cut-out in the jacking point.

Finally...

- ☐ Remove the wheel chocks.

- ☐ Stow the jack and tools in the correct locations in the car.

- ☐ Check the tyre pressure on the wheel just fitted. If it is low, or if you don't have a pressure gauge with you, drive slowly to the nearest garage and inflate the tyre to the right pressure.

- ☐ Have the damaged tyre or wheel repaired as soon as possible.

7 Turn the jack handle clockwise (on Courier and Combi models, engage the end of the jack handle with the jack) until the wheel is raised clear of the ground. Remove the nuts and lift the wheel clear, then fit the spare wheel. Refit the wheel nuts and tighten moderately with the wheel brace.

8 Lower the car to the ground, then finally tighten the wheel nuts in a diagonal sequence, and where applicable, fit the wheel trim. Note that the wheel bolts should be slackened and retightened to the specified torque at the earliest opportunity (see Chapter 1A or 1B).

dentifying leaks

Puddles on the garage floor or drive, or obvious wetness under the bonnet or underneath the car, suggest a leak that needs investigating. It can sometimes be difficult to decide where the leak is coming from, especially if the engine bay is very dirty already. Leaking oil or fluid can also be blown rearwards by the passage of air under the car, giving a false impression of where the problem lies.

 Warning: Most automotive oils and fluids are poisonous. Wash them off skin, and change out of contaminated clothing, without delay.

 The smell of a fluid leaking from the car may provide a clue to what's leaking. Some fluids are distinctively coloured. It may help to clean the car carefully and to park it over some clean paper overnight as an aid to locating the source of the leak.
Remember that some leaks may only occur while the engine is running.

Sump oil

Engine oil may leak from the drain plug...

Oil from filter

...or from the base of the oil filter.

Gearbox oil

Gearbox oil can leak from the seals at the inboard ends of the driveshafts.

Antifreeze

Leaking antifreeze often leaves a crystalline deposit like this.

Brake fluid

A leak occurring at a wheel is almost certainly brake fluid.

Power steering fluid

Power steering fluid may leak from the pipe connectors on the steering rack.

Towing

When all else fails, you may find yourself having to get a tow home – or of course you may be helping somebody else. Long-distance recovery should only be done by a garage or breakdown service. For shorter distances, DIY towing using another car is easy enough, but observe the following points:
☐ Use a proper tow-rope – they are not expensive. The vehicle being towed must display an 'ON TOW' sign in its rear window.
☐ Always turn the ignition key to the 'on' position when the vehicle is being towed, so that the steering lock is released, and that the direction indicator and brake lights will work.
☐ Before being towed, release the handbrake and select neutral on the transmission.

☐ Note that greater-than-usual pedal pressure will be required to operate the brakes, since the vacuum servo unit is only operational with the engine running.
☐ On models with power steering, greater-than-usual steering effort will also be required.
☐ The driver of the car being towed must keep the tow-rope taut at all times to avoid snatching.
☐ Make sure that both drivers know the route before setting off.
☐ Only drive at moderate speeds and keep the distance towed to a minimum. Drive smoothly and allow plenty of time for slowing down at junctions.

☐ On models with automatic transmission, special precautions apply. If in doubt, do not tow, or transmission damage may result.
☐ A towing eye is supplied as part of the vehicle tool kit. The towing eye is located with the jack and wheel brace in the luggage compartment (see "Wheel changing").
☐ To fit the towing eye, prise the cover from the relevant bumper, then screw in the towing eye, anticlockwise as far as it will go. **Note that the towing eye has a left-hand thread.** Tighten the towing eye with the wheel brace. On Courier and Combi models, a fixed rear towing eye is welded to the rear of the chassis.

Introduction

There are some very simple checks which need only take a few minutes to carry out, but which could save you a lot of inconvenience and expense.

These "Weekly checks" require no great skill or special tools, and the small amount of time they take to perform could prove to be very well spent, for example;

☐ Keeping an eye on tyre condition and pressures, will not only help to stop them wearing out prematurely, but could also save your life.

☐ Many breakdowns are caused by electrical problems. Battery-related faults are particularly common, and a quick check on a regular basis will often prevent the majority of these.

☐ If your car develops a brake fluid leak, the first time you might know about it is when your brakes don't work properly. Checking the level regularly will give advance warning of this kind of problem.

☐ If the oil or coolant levels run low, the cost of repairing any engine damage will be far greater than fixing the leak, for example.

Underbonnet check points

◀ **1.25 litre Zetec SE petrol**

A *Engine oil level dipstick*

B *Engine oil filler cap*

C *Coolant reservoir (expansion tank)*

D *Brake and clutch fluid reservoir*

E *Washer fluid reservoir*

F *Battery*

◀ **1.8 litre Endura DE diesel**

A *Engine oil level dipstick*

B *Engine oil filler cap*

C *Coolant reservoir (expansion tank)*

D *Brake and clutch fluid reservoir*

E *Washer fluid reservoir*

F *Battery*

Engine oil level

Before you start

✔ Make sure that your car is on level ground.
✔ Check the oil level before the car is driven, or at least 5 minutes after the engine has been switched off.

 HAYNES HiNT *If the oil is checked immediately after driving the vehicle, some of the oil will remain in the upper engine components, resulting in an inaccurate reading on the dipstick!*

The correct oil

Modern engines place great demands on their oil. It is very important that the correct oil for your car is used (See "Lubricants, fluids and tyre pressures").

Car Care

● If you have to add oil frequently, you should check whether you have any oil leaks. Place some clean paper under the car overnight, and check for stains in the morning. If there are no leaks, the engine may be burning oil *(see "Fault Finding")*.

● Always maintain the level between the upper and lower dipstick marks (see photo 3). If the level is too low severe engine damage may occur. Oil seal failure may result if the engine is overfilled by adding too much oil.

1 The dipstick is located in a tube at the front of the engine on Zetec-SE petrol engines and Endura-DE diesel engines, or at the rear of the engine on Endura-E petrol engines (see "*Underbonnet Check Points*" on page 0•10 for exact location). Withdraw the dipstick.

2 Using a clean rag or paper towel, wipe all the oil from the dipstick. Insert the clean dipstick into the tube as far as it will go, then withdraw it again.

3 Note the oil level on the end of the dipstick, which should be between the upper ("MAX") mark and the lower ("MIN") mark. The dipstick will vary according to the type of engine fitted.

4 Oil is added through the filler cap. Unscrew the filler cap, then top-up the level. A funnel may help to reduce spillage. Add the oil slowly, checking the level on the dipstick often. Don't overfill.

Coolant level

 Warning: DO NOT attempt to remove the expansion tank pressure cap when the engine is hot, as there is a very great risk of scalding. Do not leave open containers of coolant about, as it is poisonous.

Car Care

● With a sealed-type cooling system, adding coolant should not be necessary on a regular basis. If frequent topping-up is required, it is likely there is a leak. Check the radiator, all hoses and joint faces for signs of staining or wetness, and rectify as necessary.

● It is important that antifreeze is used in the cooling system all year round, not just during the winter months. Don't top-up with water alone, as the antifreeze will become too diluted.

1 The coolant level varies with the temperature of the engine. The expansion tank has "MAX" and "MIN" level markings. When cold, the level should be between the two marks. When the engine is hot, the level may rise slightly above the "MAX" mark.

2 If topping up is necessary, wait until the engine is cold, then turn the pressure cap on the expansion tank slowly anticlockwise, and pause until any pressure remaining in the system is released. Unscrew the cap and lift off.

3 Add a mixture of water and antifreeze to the expansion tank, until the coolant is up to the "MAX" mark. Refit the cap, turning it clockwise as far as it will go until it is secure. Re-check that the cap is securely tightened once the engine is warm.

Brake fluid level

Warning:
● *Brake fluid can harm your eyes and damage painted surfaces, so use extreme caution when handling and pouring it.*
● *Do not use fluid that has been standing open for some time, as it absorbs moisture from the air, which can cause a dangerous loss of braking effectiveness.*

● *Make sure that your car is on level ground.*
● *The fluid level in the reservoir will drop slightly as the brake pads wear down, but the fluid level must never be allowed to drop below the "MIN" mark.*

Safety First!

● If the reservoir requires repeated topping-up this is an indication of a fluid leak somewhere in the system, which should be investigated immediately.

● If a leak is suspected, the car should not be driven until the braking system has been checked. Never take any risks where brakes are concerned.

1 The "MAX" and "MIN" marks are indicated on the side of the reservoir, which is located at the rear left-hand side of the engine compartment. The fluid level must be kept between these two marks.

2 If topping-up is necessary, first wipe the area around the filler cap with a clean rag, then hold the fluid level sensor wiring plug as the cap is unscrewed. When adding fluid, it's a good idea to inspect the reservoir. The fluid should be changed if dirt is visible.

3 Carefully add fluid, avoiding spilling it on surrounding paintwork. Use only the specified hydraulic fluid; mixing different types of fluid can cause damage to the system and/or a loss of braking effectiveness. Bear in mind that the level in the reservoir will rise slightly when the cap/float assembly is refitted. After filling to the correct level, refit the cap securely. Wipe off any spilt fluid.

4 When checking the fluid level, also check the operation of the low fluid level warning light. Switch on the ignition and ask an assistant to press the button on top of the reservoir cap. The brake fluid level/handbrake "on" warning light should come on - if not, the level switch, wiring or bulb may be faulty. If the warning light comes on and the fluid level is not low, check that the handbrake is not on. Switch off the ignition after testing.

Screen washer fluid level

Screenwash additives not only keep the windscreen clean during foul weather, they also prevent the washer system freezing in cold weather - which is when you are likely to need it most. Don't top up using plain water as the screenwash will become too diluted, and will freeze during cold weather.

Warning: On no account use coolant antifreeze in the washer system - this could discolour or damage paintwork.

1 The windscreen / tailgate / headlight washer fluid reservoir is located at the rear right-hand corner of the engine compartment. If topping-up is necessary, open the cap.

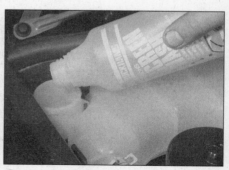

2 When topping-up the reservoir a screenwash additive should be added in the quantities recommended on the bottle.

Power steering fluid level

Before you start:
✔ Park the vehicle on level ground.
✔ Set the steering wheel straight-ahead.
✔ The engine should be turned off.

HAYNES HINT *For the check to be accurate, the steering must not be turned once the engine has been stopped.*

Safety First!
● The need for frequent topping-up indicates a leak, which should be investigated immediately.

1 The power steering fluid reservoir is located at the front right-hand corner of the engine compartment. The fluid level should be checked with the engine stopped. A translucent reservoir is fitted, with "MAX" and "MIN" markings on the side of the reservoir.

2 The fluid level should be between the "MAX" and "MIN" marks. If topping-up is necessary, and before removing the cap, wipe the surrounding area so that dirt does not enter the reservoir.

3 Unscrew the cap, allowing the fluid to drain from the bottom of the cap as it is removed. Top up the fluid level to the "MAX" mark, using the specified type of fluid (do not overfill the reservoir), then refit and tighten the filler cap.

Wiper blades

1 Check the condition of the wiper blades; if they are cracked or show any signs of deterioration, or if the glass swept area is smeared, renew them. For maximum clarity of vision, wiper blades should be renewed annually, as a matter of course.

2 To remove a windscreen wiper blade, pull the arm fully away from the screen until it locks. Swivel the blade through 90°, then depress the locking clip at the base of the mounting block, and slide the blade out of the hooked end of the arm. Where applicable, don't forget to check the tailgate wiper blade as well. The blade can be removed by swivelling the blade through 90°, then sliding the blade from the arm.

Tyre condition and pressure

It is very important that tyres are in good condition, and at the correct pressure - having a tyre failure at any speed is highly dangerous. Tyre wear is influenced by driving style - harsh braking and acceleration, or fast cornering, will all produce more rapid tyre wear. As a general rule, the front tyres wear out faster than the rears. Interchanging the tyres from front to rear ("rotating" the tyres) may result in more even wear. However, if this is completely effective, you may have the expense of replacing all four tyres at once! Remove any nails or stones embedded in the tread before they penetrate the tyre to cause deflation. If removal of a nail does reveal that the tyre has been punctured, refit the nail so that its point of penetration is marked. Then immediately change the wheel, and have the tyre repaired by a tyre dealer.

Regularly check the tyres for damage in the form of cuts or bulges, especially in the sidewalls. Periodically remove the wheels, and clean any dirt or mud from the inside and outside surfaces. Examine the wheel rims for signs of rusting, corrosion or other damage. Light alloy wheels are easily damaged by "kerbing" whilst parking; steel wheels may also become dented or buckled. A new wheel is very often the only way to overcome severe damage.

New tyres should be balanced when they are fitted, but it may become necessary to re-balance them as they wear, or if the balance weights fitted to the wheel rim should fall off. Unbalanced tyres will wear more quickly, as will the steering and suspension components. Wheel imbalance is normally signified by vibration, particularly at a certain speed (typically around 50 mph). If this vibration is felt only through the steering, then it is likely that just the front wheels need balancing. If, however, the vibration is felt through the whole car, the rear wheels could be out of balance. Wheel balancing should be carried out by a tyre dealer or garage.

1 Tread Depth - visual check
The original tyres have tread wear safety bands (B), which will appear when the tread depth reaches approximately 1.6 mm. The band positions are indicated by a triangular mark on the tyre sidewall (A).

2 Tread Depth - manual check
Alternatively, tread wear can be monitored with a simple, inexpensive device known as a tread depth indicator gauge.

3 Tyre Pressure Check
Check the tyre pressures regularly with the tyres cold. Do not adjust the tyre pressures immediately after the vehicle has been used, or an inaccurate setting will result.

Tyre tread wear patterns

Shoulder Wear

Underinflation (wear on both sides)
Under-inflation will cause overheating of the tyre, because the tyre will flex too much, and the tread will not sit correctly on the road surface. This will cause a loss of grip and excessive wear, not to mention the danger of sudden tyre failure due to heat build-up.
Check and adjust pressures
Incorrect wheel camber (wear on one side)
Repair or renew suspension parts
Hard cornering
Reduce speed!

Centre Wear

Overinflation
Over-inflation will cause rapid wear of the centre part of the tyre tread, coupled with reduced grip, harsher ride, and the danger of shock damage occurring in the tyre casing.
Check and adjust pressures

If you sometimes have to inflate your car's tyres to the higher pressures specified for maximum load or sustained high speed, don't forget to reduce the pressures to normal afterwards.

Uneven Wear

Front tyres may wear unevenly as a result of wheel misalignment. Most tyre dealers and garages can check and adjust the wheel alignment (or "tracking") for a modest charge.
Incorrect camber or castor
Repair or renew suspension parts
Malfunctioning suspension
Repair or renew suspension parts
Unbalanced wheel
Balance tyres
Incorrect toe setting
Adjust front wheel alignment
Note: *The feathered edge of the tread which typifies toe wear is best checked by feel.*

Battery

Caution: *Before carrying out any work on the vehicle battery, read the precautions given in "Safety first" at the start of this manual.*

✔ Make sure that the battery tray is in good condition, and that the clamp is tight. Corrosion on the tray, retaining clamp and the battery itself can be removed with a solution of water and baking soda. Thoroughly rinse all cleaned areas with water. Any metal parts damaged by corrosion should be covered with a zinc-based primer, then painted.

✔ Periodically (approximately every three months), check the charge condition of the battery as described in Chapter 5A.

✔ If the battery is flat, and you need to jump start your vehicle, see *Roadside Repairs*.

1 The battery is located on the left-hand side of the engine compartment. The exterior of the battery should be inspected periodically for damage such as a cracked case or cover.

2 Check the tightness of the battery cable clamps to ensure good electrical connections. You should not be able to move them. Also check each cable for cracks and frayed conductors.

HAYNES HINT

Battery corrosion can be kept to a minimum by applying a layer of petroleum jelly to the clamps and terminals after they are reconnected.

3 If corrosion (white, fluffy deposits) is evident, remove the cables from the battery terminals, clean them with a small wire brush, then refit them. Automotive stores sell a tool for cleaning the battery post . . .

4 . . . as well as the battery cable clamps

Electrical systems

✔ Check all external lights and the horn. Refer to the appropriate Sections of Chapter 12 for details if any of the circuits are found to be inoperative.

✔ Visually check all accessible wiring connectors, harnesses and retaining clips for security, and for signs of chafing or damage.

HAYNES HINT

If you need to check your brake lights and indicators unaided, back up to a wall or garage door and operate the lights. The reflected light should show if they are working properly.

1 If a single indicator light, brake light or headlight has failed, it is likely that a bulb has blown and will need to be replaced. Refer to Chapter 12 for details. If both brake lights have failed, it is possible that the brake light switch operated by the brake pedal has failed. Refer to Chapter 9 for details.

2 If more than one indicator light or headlight has failed, it is likely that either a fuse has blown or that there is a fault in the circuit (see Chapter 12). The main fuses are mounted in a panel located at the lower driver's side of the facia under a cover. Pull the cover to release it from the facia. Additional fuses are located in the auxiliary fusebox at the rear left-hand corner of the engine compartment.

3 To replace a blown fuse, remove it, where applicable, using the plastic tool provided. Fit a new fuse of the same rating, available from car accessory shops. It is important that you find the reason that the fuse blew (see *"Electrical fault finding"* in Chapter 12).

Lubricants and fluids

Engine (1.3 litre Endura-E)	Multigrade engine oil, viscosity SAE 5W-40 to 15W-40, to API SG *(Duckhams QXR Premium Petrol Engine Oil, or Duckhams Hypergrade Petrol Engine Oil)*
Engine (1.25 & 1.4 litre Zetec-SE)	Multigrade engine oil, viscosity SAE 5W-30 to 10W-40, to API SG *(Duckhams QXR Premium Petrol Engine Oil)*
Engine (1.8 litre Endura-DE diesel)	Multigrade engine oil, viscosity SAE 5W-40 to 15W-40, to CCMC-PD2 or API CD *(Duckhams QXR Premium Diesel Engine Oil, or Duckhams Hypergrade Diesel Engine Oil)**
Cooling system	Ethylene glycol antifreeze *(Duckhams Antifreeze & Summer Coolant)*
Manual transmission	Synthetic gear oil, viscosity 75W-90 to Ford specification WSD-M2C200-B
Automatic transmission	Automatic transmission fluid to Ford specification ESP-M2C166-H or Tutela WSD-M2C199-A *(Duckhams ATF Autotrans III)*
Braking system	Hydraulic fluid to DOT 4 and Ford specification SAM-6C9103-A *(Duckhams Universal Brake and Clutch Fluid)*
Power steering	Automatic transmission fluid to Ford Specification ESP-M2C 166-H *(Duckhams ATF Autotrans III)*

Note: Vehicles using a 10 000 mile service interval must use a high-quality oil (such as Duckhams QXR Premium Diesel Engine Oil) only

Choosing your engine oil

Engines need oil, not only to lubricate moving parts and minimise wear, but also to maximise power output and to improve fuel economy. By introducing a simplified and improved range of engine oils, Duckhams has taken away the confusion and made it easier for you to choose the right oil for your engine.

HOW ENGINE OIL WORKS

• Beating friction

Without oil, the moving surfaces inside your engine will rub together, heat up and melt, quickly causing the engine to seize. Engine oil creates a film which separates these moving parts, preventing wear and heat build-up.

• Cooling hot-spots

Temperatures inside the engine can exceed 1000° C. The engine oil circulates and acts as a coolant, transferring heat from the hot-spots to the sump.

• Cleaning the engine internally

Good quality engine oils clean the inside of your engine, collecting and dispersing combustion deposits and controlling them until they are trapped by the oil filter or flushed out at oil change.

OIL CARE - FOLLOW THE CODE

To handle and dispose of used engine oil safely, always:

• **Avoid skin contact with used engine oil.** Repeated or prolonged contact can be harmful.
• **Dispose of used oil and empty packs in a responsible manner in an authorised disposal site.** Call 0800 663366 to find the one nearest to you. Never tip oil down drains or onto the ground.

Tyre pressures

Note: *Pressures given here are a guide only, and apply to original-equipment tyres – the recommended pressures may vary if any other make or type of tyre is fitted; check with the vehicle handbook, or the tyre manufacturer or supplier for latest recommendations.*

Normal load (up to 3 people)	Front	Rear
155/70 R 13 tyres:		
Hatchback models	2.4 bar (35 psi)	1.8 bar (26 psi)
Van (petrol engine) models	2.1 bar (31 psi)	1.8 bar (26 psi)
165/70 R 13 tyres:		
Hatchback models:		
1.25 litre and 1.4 litre Zetec-SE petrol engine models:		
Manual transmission models	2.1 bar (31 psi)	1.8 bar (26 psi)
Automatic transmission models	2.2 bar (32 psi)	1.8 bar (26 psi)
1.3 Endura-E petrol engine models	2.2 bar (32 psi)	1.8 bar (26 psi)
1.8 Endura-DE diesel engine models	2.4 bar (35 psi)	1.8 bar (26 psi)
Van (diesel engine) models	2.1 bar (31 psi)	1.8 bar (26 psi)
Courier and Combi models	2.0 bar (29 psi)	1.8 bar (26 psi)
185/55 R 14 tyres	2.2 bar (32 psi)	1.8 bar (26 psi)

Full load (more than 3 people)		
All except Van, Courier and Combi models with 165/70 R 13 tyres	2.5 bar (37 psi)	2.8 bar (41 psi)
Van, Courier and Combi models with 165/70 R 13 tyres	2.3 bar (34 psi)	2.8 bar (41 psi)

Chapter 1 Part A:
Routine maintenance and servicing – petrol engine models

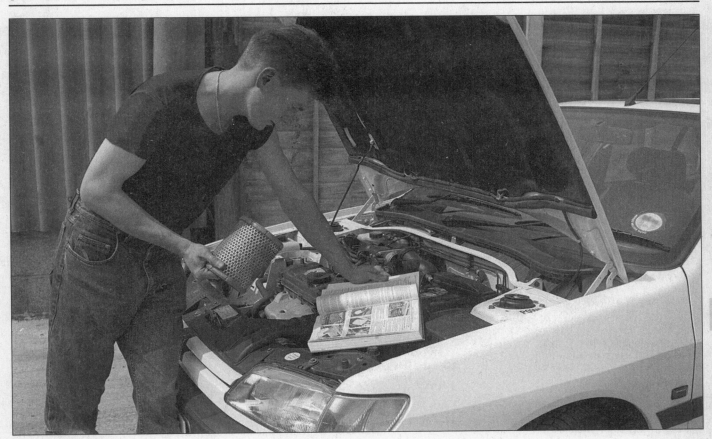

Contents

Degrees of difficulty

Easy, suitable for novice with little experience | **Fairly easy,** suitable for beginner with some experience | **Fairly difficult,** suitable for competent DIY mechanic | **Difficult,** suitable for experienced DIY mechanic | **Very difficult,** suitable for expert DIY or professional

Lubricants and fluids

Refer to "Weekly checks"

Capacities

Engine oil
Including oil filter:
Endura-E engine (approximate)	3.25 litres
Zetec-SE engine (approximate)	4.0 litres

Excluding oil filter:
Endura-E engine (approximate)	2.75 litres
Zetec-SE engine (approximate)	3.5 litres

Cooling system
Endura-E engine (approximate)	7.1 litres
Zetec-SE engine (approximate)	6.0 litres

Transmission
Manual transmission (approximate)	2.8 litres
Automatic transmission (approximate):	
From dry	5.6 litres
At fluid change	5.0 litres

Washer fluid reservoir
Without headlight washers	4.0 litres
With headlight washers	8.0 litres

Fuel tank
All models	42.0 litres

Engine

Oil filter:
Endura-E (JJA / 50 PS)	Champion C140
Endura-E (J4C / 60 PS)	Champion C104
Zetec-SE	Champion C104

Valve clearances (cold):	Inlet	Exhaust
Endura-E engine	0.20 mm	0.30 mm
Zetec-SE engine	0.17 to 0.23 mm	0.27 to 0.33 mm

Cooling system

Antifreeze mixture:
50% antifreeze	Protection down to -37°C
55% antifreeze	Protection down to -45°C

Note: *Refer to antifreeze manufacturer for latest recommendations.*

Fuel system

Air filter element	Champion U671
Fuel filter	Champion type not available

Ignition system

Spark plugs:	Type	Gap
Endura-E engine	Champion RS9PYC4	1.2 mm
Zetec-SE engine	Champion RE7PYC5	1.3 mm

The spark plug gap quoted is that recommended by Champion for their specified plug listed above. If spark plugs of any other type are to be fitted, refer to their manufacturer's recommendations.

Brakes

Friction material minimum thickness
Front brake pads	1.5 mm
Rear brake shoes	1.0 mm

Torque wrench settings

	Nm	lbf ft
Roadwheel nuts	85	63
Spark plugs:		
Endura-E engine	17	13
Zetec-SE engine	15	11
Manual transmission filler/level plug	35	26
Automatic transmission:		
Fluid strainer	8	6
Sump	8	6
Drain plug	33	25

The maintenance intervals in this manual are provided with the assumption that you, not the dealer, will be carrying out the work. These are the minimum maintenance intervals recommended by us for vehicles driven daily. If you wish to keep your vehicle in peak condition at all times, you may wish to perform some of these procedures more often. We encourage frequent maintenance, because it enhances the efficiency, performance and resale value of your vehicle.

If the vehicle is driven in dusty areas, used to tow a trailer, or driven frequently at slow speeds (idling in traffic) or on short journeys, more frequent maintenance intervals are recommended.

When the vehicle is new, it should be serviced by a factory-authorised dealer service department, in order to preserve the factory warranty.

Every 5000 miles or 6 months, whichever comes first
☐ Renew the engine oil and filter (Section 3)

Note: *Ford recommend that the engine oil and filter are changed every 10 000 miles or 12 months. However, oil and filter changes are good for the engine and we recommend that the oil and filter are renewed more frequently, especially if the vehicle is used on a lot of short journeys.*

Every 10 000 miles or 12 months, whichever comes first
☐ Check and, if necessary, adjust the valve clearances – models with Endura-E engine (Section 4)
☐ Check and, if necessary, adjust the selector cable – models with automatic transmission (Section 5)
☐ Check the condition and tension of the auxiliary drivebelt(s) (Section 6)
☐ Check all components, pipes and hoses for fluid leaks (Section 7)
☐ Check the front brake pads and discs for wear (Section 8)
☐ Check the rear brake shoes and drums for wear (Section 9)
☐ Check the steering and suspension components for condition and security (Section 10)
☐ Check the condition of the driveshaft gaiters (Section 11)
☐ Lubricate all hinges and locks (Section 12)
☐ Check the roadwheel nuts are tightened to the specified torque (Section 13)
☐ Carry out a road test (Section 14)

Every 20 000 miles
☐ Renew the pollen filter (Section 15)

Note: *If the vehicle is used in dusty conditions, the pollen filter should be renewed more frequently.*

Every 30 000 miles
☐ Renew the spark plugs – models with Endura-E engine (Section 16)
☐ Renew the air filter (Section 17)
☐ Renew the automatic transmission fluid and strainer (Section 18)
☐ Check the crankcase ventilation system – models with Endura-E engine (Section 19)
☐ Check the oil filler cap – models with Endura-E engine (Section 20)
☐ Check the manual transmission oil level (Section 21)

Every 40 000 miles
☐ Renew the spark plugs – models with Zetec-SE engine (Section 22)

Every 60 000 miles
☐ Renew the fuel filter (Section 23)

Every 100 000 miles
☐ Adjust the valve clearances - models with Zetec-SE engine (Section 24)

Every 100 000 miles or 10 years, whichever comes sooner
☐ Renew the timing belt – models with Zetec-SE engine (Section 25)

Every 3 years, regardless of mileage
☐ Renew the brake fluid (Section 26)

Every 4 years, regardless of mileage
☐ Renew the coolant and check the condition of the expansion tank pressure cap (Section 27)

1A

Underbonnet view of a 1.25 litre Zetec-SE engine model

1 Engine oil filler cap
2 Suspension strut top cover
3 Windscreen washer fluid reservoir
4 Coolant reservoir (expansion tank)
5 Windscreen wiper motor
6 MAP sensor
7 Brake fluid reservoir
8 Auxiliary fuse/relay box
9 Air cleaner casing
10 Battery
11 Ignition coil
12 Engine oil level dipstick
13 Alternator

Front underbody view of a 1.25 litre Zetec-SE engine model

1 Brake caliper
2 Engine oil drain plug
3 Engine oil filter
4 Cooling fan
5 Horn
6 Track-rod end
7 Suspension lower arm
8 Gearchange rod
9 Exhaust system
10 Suspension subframe
11 Driveshaft

Rear underbody view – Hatchback and Van models

1 Suspension trailing arm
2 Shock absorber
3 Spare wheel cradle
4 Exhaust rear silencer
5 Suspension beam
6 Fuel tank

1A

Rear underbody view – Courier and Combi models

1 Suspension torsion beam
2 Shock absorber
3 Exhaust rear silencer
4 Spare wheel cradle
5 Brake pressure proportioning valve
6 Suspension beam
7 Fuel tank

1 General information

1 This Chapter is designed to help the home mechanic maintain his/her vehicle for safety, economy, long life and peak performance.

2 The Chapter contains a master maintenance schedule, followed by Sections dealing specifically with each task in the schedule. Visual checks, adjustments, component renewal and other helpful items are included. Refer to the accompanying illustrations of the engine compartment and the underside of the vehicle for the locations of the various components.

3 Servicing your vehicle in accordance with the mileage/time maintenance schedule and the following Sections will provide a planned maintenance programme, which should result in a long and reliable service life. This is a comprehensive plan, so maintaining some items but not others at the specified service intervals, will not produce the same results.

4 As you service your vehicle, you will discover that many of the procedures can - and should - be grouped together, because of the particular procedure being performed, or because of the proximity of two otherwise-unrelated components to one another. For example, if the vehicle is raised for any reason, the exhaust can be inspected at the same time as the suspension and steering components.

5 The first step in this maintenance programme is to prepare yourself before the actual work begins. Read through all the Sections relevant to the work to be carried out, then make a list and gather all the parts and tools required. If a problem is encountered, seek advice from a parts specialist, or a dealer service department.

2 Intensive maintenance

1 If, from the time the vehicle is new, the routine maintenance schedule is followed closely, and frequent checks are made of fluid levels and high-wear items, as suggested throughout this manual, the engine will be kept in relatively good running condition, and the need for additional work will be minimised.

2 It is possible that there will be times when the engine is running poorly due to the lack of regular maintenance. This is even more likely if a used vehicle, which has not received regular and frequent maintenance checks, is purchased. In such cases, additional work may need to be carried out, outside of the regular maintenance intervals.

3 If engine wear is suspected, a compression test (refer to Chapter 2A or 2B, as applicable) will provide valuable information regarding the overall performance of the main internal components. Such a test can be used as a basis to decide on the extent of the work to be carried out. If, for example, a compression test indicates serious internal engine wear, conventional maintenance as described in this Chapter will not greatly improve the performance of the engine, and may prove a waste of time and money, unless extensive overhaul work is carried out first.

4 The following series of operations are those most often required to improve the performance of a generally poor-running engine:

Primary operations

a) Clean, inspect and test the battery (refer to "Weekly checks").
b) Check all the engine-related fluids (refer to "Weekly checks").
c) Check the condition and tension of the auxiliary drivebelt (Section 6).
d) Renew the spark plugs (Sections 16 or 22).
e) Check the condition of the air filter, and renew if necessary (Section 17).
f) Renew the fuel filter (Section 23).
g) Check the condition of all hoses, and check for fluid leaks (Section 7).

5 If the above operations do not prove fully effective, carry out the following secondary operations:

Secondary operations

All items listed under "Primary operations", plus the following:

a) Check the charging system (refer to Chapter 5A).
b) Check the ignition system (refer to Chapter 5B).
c) Check the fuel system (refer to Chapter 4A).

Every 5000 miles or 6 months, whichever comes first

3 Engine oil and filter renewal

1 Frequent oil and filter changes are the most important preventative maintenance procedures which can be undertaken by the DIY owner. As engine oil ages, it becomes diluted and contaminated, which leads to premature engine wear.

2 Before starting this procedure, gather together all the necessary tools and materials. Also make sure that you have plenty of clean rags and newspapers handy, to mop up any spills. Ideally, the engine oil should be warm, as it will drain more easily, and more built-up sludge will be removed with it. Take care not to touch the exhaust or any other hot parts of the engine when working under the vehicle. To avoid any possibility of scalding, and to protect yourself from possible skin irritants and other harmful contaminants in used engine oils, it is advisable to wear gloves when carrying out this work.

3 Firmly apply the handbrake then jack up the front of the vehicle and support it on axle stands (see "Jacking and Vehicle Support").

4 Remove the oil filler cap **(see illustration)**.

5 Using a spanner, or preferably a socket and bar, slacken the drain plug about half a turn. Position the draining container under the drain plug, then remove the plug completely.

 As the plug releases from the threads, move it away sharply, so that the stream of oil from the sump runs into the container, not up your sleeve!

3.4 Removing the oil filler cap

6 Allow some time for the oil to drain, noting that it may be necessary to reposition the container as the oil flow slows to a trickle.

7 After all the oil has drained, wipe the drain plug and the sealing washer with a clean rag. Examine the condition of the sealing washer, and renew it if it shows signs of scoring or other damage which may prevent an oil-tight seal. Clean the area around the drain plug opening, and refit the plug complete with the washer and tighten it securely.

8 Move the container into position under the oil filter which is located on the rear of the cylinder block on the Endura-E engine and on the front of the cylinder block on the Zetec-SE engine.

9 Use an oil filter removal tool to slacken the filter initially, then unscrew it by hand the rest of the way **(see illustration)**. Empty the oil from the old filter into the container.

10 Use a clean rag to remove all oil, dirt and sludge from the filter sealing area on the engine.

11 Apply a light coating of clean engine oil to the sealing ring on the new filter, then screw the filter into position on the engine **(see illustration)**. Tighten the filter firmly by hand only - **do not** use any tools.

12 Remove the old oil and all tools from under the vehicle then lower the vehicle to the ground.

13 Fill the engine through the filler hole, using the correct grade and type of oil (refer to "Weekly Checks" for details of topping-up). Pour in half the specified quantity of oil first, then wait a few minutes for the oil to drain into the sump. Continue to add oil, a small quantity at a time, until the level is up to the lower mark on the dipstick. Adding approximately a further 1.0 litre will bring the level up to the upper mark on the dipstick.

14 Start the engine and run it for a few minutes, while checking for leaks around the oil filter seal and the sump drain plug. Note that there may be a delay of a few seconds before the low oil pressure warning light goes out when the engine is first started, as the oil

3.9 Using an oil filter removal tool to loosen the filter

circulates through the new oil filter and the engine oil galleries before the pressure builds up.

15 Stop the engine, and wait a few minutes for the oil to settle in the sump once more.

3.11 Apply a light coating of engine oil to the sealing ring on the new filter

With the new oil circulated and the filter now completely full, recheck the level on the dipstick, and add more oil as necessary.

16 Dispose of the used engine oil safely with reference to "General repair procedures".

Every 10 000 miles or 12 months, whichever comes first

4 Valve clearance check and adjustment – Endura-E engine

This procedure is described in Chapter 2A.

5 Selector cable check and adjustment – models with automatic transmission

This procedure is described in Chapter 7B.

6 Auxiliary drivebelt check and renewal

Checking

1 A single auxiliary drivebelt is fitted at the right-hand side of the engine. The length of the drivebelt varies according to whether air conditioning and/or power steering is fitted. An automatic adjuster is fitted so checking of the drivebelt tension is unnecessary.

2 Due to their function and material makeup, drivebelts are prone to failure after a long period of time and should therefore be inspected regularly.

3 Since the drivebelt is located very close to the right-hand side of the engine compartment, it is possible to gain better access by raising the front of the vehicle and removing the right-hand wheel, then unbolting the crankshaft pulley lower cover from the underbody.

4 With the engine stopped, inspect the full length of the drivebelt for cracks and separation of the belt plies. It will be necessary to turn the engine (using a spanner or socket and bar on the crankshaft pulley bolt) in order to move the belt from the pulleys

so that the belt can be inspected thoroughly. Twist the belt between the pulleys so that both sides can be viewed. Also check for fraying, and glazing which gives the belt a shiny appearance. Check the pulleys for nicks, cracks, distortion and corrosion.

Renewal

5 To remove the drivebelt, first raise the front of the vehicle and support on axle stands (see "Jacking and Vehicle Support"). Unbolt and remove the crankshaft pulley cover.

6 Using a spanner on the tensioner centre bolt, turn the tensioner anti-clockwise to release the drivebelt tension. Note how the drivebelt is routed, then remove the belt from the pulleys (see illustration).

7 Fit the new drivebelt onto the crankshaft, alternator, power steering pump, and air conditioning compressor pulleys as applicable, then turn the tensioner anti-clockwise and locate the drivebelt on the pulley. Make sure that the drivebelt is correctly seated in all of the pulley grooves, then release the tensioner.

8 Refit the crankshaft pulley cover and lower the vehicle to the ground.

6.6 Using a spanner, turn the tensioner anti-clockwise to release the tension then remove the belt from the pulleys

7 Hose and fluid leak check

1 Visually inspect the engine joint faces, gaskets and seals for any signs of water or oil leaks. Pay particular attention to the areas around the cylinder head cover, cylinder head, oil filter and sump joint faces. Bear in mind that, over a period of time, some very slight seepage from these areas is to be expected - what you are really looking for is any indication of a serious leak. Should a leak be found, renew the offending gasket or oil seal by referring to the appropriate Chapters in this manual.

2 Also check the security and condition of all the engine-related pipes and hoses, and all braking system pipes and hoses. Ensure that all cable ties or securing clips are in place, and in good condition. Clips which are broken or missing can lead to chafing of the hoses, pipes or wiring, which could cause more serious problems in the future.

3 Carefully check the radiator hoses and heater hoses along their entire length. Renew any hose which is cracked, swollen or deteriorated. Cracks will show up better if the hose is squeezed. Pay close attention to the hose clips that secure the hoses to the cooling system components. Hose clips can pinch and puncture hoses, resulting in cooling system leaks. If the crimped-type hose clips are used, it may be a good idea to replace them with standard worm-drive clips.

4 Inspect all the cooling system components (hoses, joint faces, etc) for leaks.

 HAYNES HiNT | *A leak in the cooling system will usually show up as white- or rust-coloured deposits on the area adjoining the leak.*

1A

5 Where any problems are found on system components, renew the component or gasket with reference to Chapter 3.

6 With the vehicle raised, inspect the fuel tank and filler neck for punctures, cracks and other damage. The connection between the filler neck and tank is especially critical. Sometimes a rubber filler neck or connecting hose will leak due to loose retaining clamps or deteriorated rubber.

7 Carefully check all rubber hoses and metal fuel lines leading away from the fuel tank. Check for loose connections, deteriorated hoses, crimped lines, and other damage. Pay particular attention to the vent pipes and hoses, which often loop up around the filler neck and can become blocked or crimped. Follow the lines to the front of the vehicle, carefully inspecting them all the way. Renew damaged sections as necessary. Similarly, whilst the vehicle is raised, take the opportunity to inspect all underbody brake fluid pipes and hoses.

8 From within the engine compartment, check the security of all fuel, vacuum and brake hose attachments and pipe unions, and inspect all hoses for kinks, chafing and deterioration.

9 Where applicable, check the condition of the power steering and automatic transmission fluid pipes and hoses.

8 Front brake pad and disc wear check

1 Apply the handbrake, then jack up the front of the car and support it securely on axle stands (see "*Jacking and Vehicle Support*"). Remove the front roadwheels.

For a quick check, the thickness of friction material remaining on the inner brake pad can be measured through the aperture in the caliper body.

2 For a comprehensive check, the brake pads should be removed and cleaned. The operation of the caliper can then also be checked, and the condition of the brake disc itself can be fully examined on both sides. Refer to Chapter 9 for further information.

3 On completion refit the roadwheels and lower the car to the ground.

9 Rear brake shoe and drum wear check

Remove the rear brake drums, and check the brake shoes for signs of wear or contamination. At the same time, also inspect the wheel cylinders for signs of leakage, and the brake drum for signs of wear. Refer to the relevant Sections of Chapter 9 for further information.

10 Steering and suspension check

Front suspension and steering check

1 Raise the front of the vehicle, and securely support it on axle stands (see "*Jacking and Vehicle Support*").

2 Visually inspect the balljoint dust covers and the steering rack-and-pinion gaiters for splits, chafing or deterioration. Any wear of these components will cause loss of lubricant, together with dirt and water entry, resulting in rapid deterioration of the balljoints or steering gear.

3 On vehicles with power steering, check the fluid hoses for chafing or deterioration, and the pipe and hose unions for fluid leaks. Also check for signs of fluid leakage under pressure from the steering gear rubber gaiters, which would indicate failed fluid seals within the steering gear.

4 Grasp the roadwheel at the 12 o'clock and 6 o'clock positions, and try to rock it **(see illustration)**. Very slight free play may be felt, but if the movement is appreciable, further investigation is necessary to determine the source. Continue rocking the wheel while an assistant depresses the footbrake. If the movement is now eliminated or significantly reduced, it is likely that the hub bearings are at fault. If the free play is still evident with the footbrake depressed, then there is wear in the suspension joints or mountings.

5 Now grasp the wheel at the 9 o'clock and 3 o'clock positions, and try to rock it as before.

10.4 Check for wear in the hub bearings by grasping the wheel and trying to rock it

Any movement felt now may again be caused by wear in the hub bearings or the steering track-rod balljoints. If the outer balljoint is worn, the visual movement will be obvious. If the inner joint is suspect, it can be felt by placing a hand over the rack-and-pinion rubber gaiter and gripping the track-rod. If the wheel is now rocked, movement will be felt at the inner joint if wear has taken place.

6 Using a large screwdriver or flat bar, check for wear in the suspension mounting bushes by levering between the relevant suspension component and its attachment point. Some movement is to be expected, as the mountings are made of rubber, but excessive wear should be obvious. Also check the condition of any visible rubber bushes, looking for splits, cracks or contamination of the rubber.

7 With the car standing on its wheels, have an assistant turn the steering wheel back and forth, about an eighth of a turn each way. There should be very little, if any, lost movement between the steering wheel and roadwheels. If this is not the case, closely observe the joints and mountings previously described. In addition, check the steering column universal joints for wear, and also check the rack-and-pinion steering gear itself.

Rear suspension check

8 Chock the front wheels, then jack up the rear of the vehicle and support securely on axle stands (see "*Jacking and Vehicle Support*").

9 Working as described previously for the front suspension, check the rear hub bearings, the suspension bushes and the strut or shock absorber mountings (as applicable) for wear.

Shock absorber check

10 Check for any signs of fluid leakage around the shock absorber body, or from the rubber gaiter around the piston rod. Should any fluid be noticed, the shock absorber is defective internally, and should be renewed. **Note:** *Shock absorbers should always be renewed in pairs on the same axle.*

11 The efficiency of the shock absorber may be checked by bouncing the vehicle at each corner. Generally speaking, the body will return to its normal position and stop after being depressed. If it rises and returns on a rebound, the shock absorber is probably suspect. Also examine the shock absorber upper and lower mountings for any signs of wear.

11 Driveshaft gaiter check

1 With the vehicle raised and securely supported on stands, turn the steering onto full lock then slowly rotate the roadwheel. Inspect the condition of the outer constant

11.1 Check the condition of the driveshaft gaiters

12.2 Lubricate the bonnet lock with grease

1A

velocity (CV) joint rubber gaiters while squeezing the gaiters to open out the folds **(see illustration)**. Check for signs of cracking, splits or deterioration of the rubber which may allow the grease to escape and lead to water and grit entry into the joint. Also check the security and condition of the retaining clips. Repeat these checks on the inner CV joints. If any damage or deterioration is found, the gaiters should be renewed as described in Chapter 8.

2 At the same time check the general condition of the CV joints themselves by first holding the driveshaft and attempting to rotate the wheel. Repeat this check by holding the inner joint and attempting to rotate the driveshaft. Any appreciable movement indicates wear in the joints, wear in the driveshaft splines or loose driveshaft retaining nut.

12 Hinge and lock lubrication

1 Work around the vehicle and lubricate the hinges of the bonnet, doors and tailgate with a light machine oil.

2 Lightly lubricate the bonnet release mechanism and exposed section of inner cable with a smear of grease **(see illustration)**.

3 Check carefully the security and operation of all hinges, latches and locks, adjusting them where required. Check the operation of the central locking system (if fitted).

4 Check the condition and operation of the tailgate struts, renewing them if either is leaking or no longer able to support the tailgate securely when raised.

13 Roadwheel nut tightness check

1 Where applicable, remove the wheel trims, and slacken the roadwheel nuts slightly.

2 Tighten the nuts to the specified torque, using a torque wrench.

14 Road test

Instruments and electrical equipment

1 Check the operation of all instruments and electrical equipment.

2 Make sure that all instruments read correctly, and switch on all electrical equipment in turn, to check that it functions properly.

Steering and suspension

3 Check for any abnormalities in the steering, suspension, handling or road "feel".

4 Drive the vehicle, and check that there are no unusual vibrations or noises.

5 Check that the steering feels positive, with no excessive "sloppiness", or roughness, and check for any suspension noises when cornering and driving over bumps.

Drivetrain

6 Check the performance of the engine, clutch, transmission and driveshafts.

7 Listen for any unusual noises from the engine, clutch and transmission.

8 Make sure that the engine runs smoothly when idling, and that there is no hesitation when accelerating.

9 Check that, where applicable, the clutch action is smooth and progressive, that the drive is taken up smoothly, and that the pedal

travel is not excessive. Also listen for any noises when the clutch pedal is depressed.

10 Check that all gears can be engaged smoothly without noise, and that the gear lever action is not abnormally vague or "notchy".

11 On automatic transmission models, make sure that all gear changes occur smoothly, without snatching, and without an increase in engine speed between changes. Check that all of the gear positions can be selected with the vehicle at rest. If any problems are found, they should be referred to a Ford dealer.

12 Listen for a metallic clicking sound from the front of the vehicle, as the vehicle is driven slowly in a circle with the steering on full-lock. Carry out this check in both directions. If a clicking noise is heard, this indicates wear in a driveshaft joint (see Chapter 8).

Check the operation and performance of the braking system

13 Make sure that the vehicle does not pull to one side when braking, and that the wheels do not lock prematurely when braking hard.

14 Check that there is no vibration through the steering when braking.

15 Check that the handbrake operates correctly, without excessive movement of the lever, and that it holds the vehicle stationary on a slope.

16 Test the operation of the brake servo unit as follows. Depress the footbrake four or five times to exhaust the vacuum, then start the engine. As the engine starts, there should be a noticeable "give" in the brake pedal as vacuum builds up. Allow the engine to run for at least two minutes, and then switch it off. If the brake pedal is now depressed again, it should be possible to detect a hiss from the servo as the pedal is depressed. After about four or five applications, no further hissing should be heard, and the pedal should feel considerably harder.

Every 20 000 miles

15 Pollen filter renewal

1 Open the bonnet, and locate the pollen filter housing, at the left-hand corner of the scuttle at the rear of the engine compartment.
2 Release the two clips, and open the pollen filter cover **(see illustration)**.
3 Pull the filter from the housing, using the tab provided **(see illustration)**.
4 Fit the new filter using a reversal of the removal procedure. Make sure that the filter is fitted with the removal tab and the "TOP/OBEN" marking visible.

15.2 Releasing a pollen filter cover securing clip

15.3 Pulling out the pollen filter

Every 30 000 miles

16 Spark plug renewal and ignition system check - Endura-E engine

Spark plug renewal

1 The correct functioning of the spark plugs is vital for the correct running and efficiency of the engine. It is essential that the plugs fitted are appropriate for the engine; suitable types are specified at the beginning of this Chapter, on the Vehicle Emissions Control Information (VECI) label located on the underside of the

16.4 Tools required for changing spark plugs

bonnet (only on models sold in some areas) or in the vehicle's Owner's Handbook. If the correct type is used and the engine is in good condition, the spark plugs should not need attention between scheduled replacement intervals. Spark plug cleaning is rarely necessary, and should not be attempted unless specialised equipment is available, as damage can easily be caused to the firing ends.
2 If the marks on the original-equipment spark plug (HT) leads cannot be seen, mark the leads to correspond to the cylinder the lead serves. Pull the leads from the plugs by gripping the end fitting, not the lead, otherwise the lead connection may be fractured.
3 It is advisable to remove the dirt from the spark plug recesses using a clean brush, vacuum cleaner or compressed air before removing the plugs, to prevent dirt dropping into the cylinders.
4 Unscrew the plugs from the front of the cylinder head using a spark plug spanner, suitable box spanner or a deep socket and extension bar **(see illustration)**. Keep the socket aligned with the spark plug - if it is forcibly moved to one side, the ceramic insulator may be broken off. As each plug is removed, examine it as follows.
5 Examination of the spark plugs will give a good indication of the condition of the engine.

If the insulator nose of the spark plug is clean and white, with no deposits, this is indicative of a weak mixture or too hot a plug (a hot plug transfers heat away from the electrode slowly, a cold plug transfers heat away quickly).
6 If the tip and insulator nose are covered with hard black-looking deposits, then this is indicative that the mixture is too rich. Should the plug be black and oily, then it is likely that the engine is fairly worn, as well as the mixture being too rich.
7 If the insulator nose is covered with light tan to greyish-brown deposits, then the mixture is correct and it is likely that the engine is in good condition.
8 The spark plug electrode gap is of considerable importance as, if it is too large or too small, the size of the spark and its efficiency will be seriously impaired. The gap should be set to the value given in the Specifications at the beginning of this Chapter.
9 To set the gap, measure it with a feeler blade and then bend open, or closed, the outer plug electrode until the correct gap is achieved. The centre electrode should never be bent, as this may crack the insulator and cause plug failure, if nothing worse. If using feeler blades, the gap is correct when the appropriate-size blade is a firm sliding fit **(see illustrations)**.

16.9a Using a wire-type gauge when checking the gap

16.9b Measuring a spark plug gap with a feeler blade

16.9c To change the gap, bend the outer electrode only

10 Special spark plug electrode gap adjusting tools are available from most motor accessory shops, or from some spark plug manufacturers.

11 Before fitting the spark plugs, check that the threaded connector sleeves are tight, and that the plug exterior surfaces and threads are clean (see Haynes Hint).

It's often difficult to insert spark plugs into their holes without cross-threading them. To avoid this possibility, fit a short length of rubber or plastic hose over the end of the spark plug. The flexible hose acts as a universal joint, to help align the plug with the plug hole. Should the plug begin to cross thread, the hose will slip on the spark plug, preventing thread damage to the aluminium cylinder head

12 Remove the rubber hose (if used), and tighten the plug to the specified torque using the spark plug socket and a torque wrench. Refit the remaining spark plugs in the same manner.

13 Connect the HT leads in their correct order.

Ignition system check

 Warning: Voltages produced by an electronic ignition system are considerably higher than those produced by conventional ignition systems. Extreme care must be taken when working on the system with the ignition switched on. Persons with surgically-implanted cardiac pacemaker devices should keep well clear of the ignition circuits, components and test equipment.

14 The spark plug (HT) leads should be checked whenever new spark plugs are fitted.

15 Ensure that the leads are numbered before removing them, to avoid confusion when refitting. Pull the leads from the plugs by gripping the end fitting, not the lead, otherwise the lead connection may be fractured.

16 Check inside the end fitting for signs of corrosion, which will look like a white crusty powder. Push the end fitting back onto the spark plug, ensuring that it is a tight fit on the

plug. If not, remove the lead again and use pliers to carefully crimp the metal connector inside the end fitting until it fits securely on the end of the spark plug.

17 Using a clean rag, wipe the entire length of the lead to remove any built-up dirt and grease. Once the lead is clean, check for burns, cracks and other damage. Do not bend the lead excessively, nor pull the lead lengthwise - the conductor inside might break.

18 Disconnect the other end of the lead from the ignition coil by squeezing the clips. Check for corrosion and a tight fit. If an ohmmeter is available, check the resistance of the lead by connecting the meter between each end of the lead. Refit the lead securely on completion.

19 Check the remaining leads one at a time, in the same way.

20 If new spark plug (HT) leads are required, purchase a set for your specific car and engine.

21 Even with the ignition system in first-class condition, some engines may still occasionally experience poor starting attributable to damp ignition components. To disperse moisture, a water-dispersant aerosol can be very effective.

17 Air filter element renewal

1 The air cleaner is located in the left-hand front corner of the engine compartment. First release the clips (Endura-E engine) or unscrew the screws (Zetec-SE engine) securing the cover to the air cleaner housing (see illustration).

2 Lift the cover and remove the filter element from the base (see illustration). Note which way round it is fitted.

3 Wipe clean the interior surfaces of the cover and base.

4 Insert the new element making sure that it is seated correctly in the base.

5 Refit the cover and secure with the clips or retaining screws.

18 Automatic transmission fluid and strainer renewal

1 The transmission fluid should only be changed when the transmission is cold.

2 Position the vehicle over an inspection pit, on vehicle ramps, or jack it up, but make sure that it is level.

3 Place a suitable container beneath the drain plug on the transmission sump pan. Remove the transmission fluid dipstick to speed up the draining operation.

4 Thoroughly clean the area around the drain plug in the transmission sump pan then unscrew the plug and allow the fluid to drain into the container.

5 When all the fluid has drained (this may take some time) clean the drain plug, then refit it together with a new seal and tighten securely.

6 Unscrew the mounting bolts and lower the sump from the bottom of the automatic transmission. If it is stuck, use a screwdriver to free it taking care not to damage the mating surfaces of the sump and transmission.

7 Recover the gasket, and clean the mating surfaces of the sump and transmission.

8 With the sump removed, clean the magnet of any accumulation of metallic particles. The inside of the sump will give an indication of the condition of the transmission, also if the fluid is discoloured or burnt this indicates problems which should be diagnosed by an automatic transmission specialist. Clean out the inside of the sump with cloth rags.

9 Unscrew the retaining bolt and lower the strainer from the transmission. Recover the sealing ring and discard it; a new one must be fitted on reassembly.

10 Fit the new strainer together with a new sealing ring and tighten the retaining bolt to the specified torque.

11 Refit the sump together with a new gasket and tighten the retaining bolts to the specified torque.

12 Place a funnel with a fine mesh screen in the transmission dipstick tube, and fill the transmission with the specified type of fluid. It is essential that no dirt is introduced into the transmission during this operation.

1A

17.1 Remove the screws from both sides . . .

17.2 . . . then lift the cover and remove the filter element (Zetec-SE engine shown)

13 Depending on the extent to which the fluid was allowed to drain, it is possible that the amount of fluid required when filling the transmission may be more than the specified amount (see "*Lubricants and fluids*"). However, due to fluid remaining in the system, it is more likely that less than the specified amount will be required. Add about half the specified amount, then with Park (P) engaged run the engine up to its normal operating temperature and check the level on the dipstick (with the engine idling). Add fluid through the transmission dipstick tube until the level is up to the MAX mark, then refit the dipstick and switch off the engine.

19 Crankcase ventilation system check – Endura-E engine

Refer to Chapter 4C, and check that all crankcase ventilation hoses are clear and unblocked.

20 Oil filler cap check – models with Endura-E engine

1 Remove and inspect the oil filler cap to ensure that it is in good condition, and not blocked up with sludge.
2 Disconnect the hoses at the cap, and clean the cap if necessary by brushing the inner mesh filter with petrol, and blowing through with light pressure from an air line. Renew the cap if it is badly congested.
3 Refit the hoses and cap.

21 Manual transmission oil level check

1 Position the vehicle over an inspection pit, on vehicle ramps, or jack it up, but make sure that it is level.

2 Remove all traces of dirt then unscrew the filler/level plug from the front face of the transmission. Note it is the plug furthest from the engine - do not confuse it with the blanking plug near the bellhousing.

3 The level must be between 10 mm and 15 mm below the bottom edge of the filler/level plug hole (use a cranked tool such as an Allen key to check the level). If necessary, top up the level with the specified grade of oil (see "*Lubricants and fluids*").

4 When the level is correct, clean and refit the filler level plug and tighten it to the specified torque.

5 Lower the car to the ground.

Every 40 000 miles

22 Spark plug renewal and ignition system check – Zetec-SE engine

Spark plug renewal

1 The correct functioning of the spark plugs is vital for the correct running and efficiency of the engine. It is essential that the plugs fitted are appropriate for the engine; suitable types are specified at the beginning of this Chapter, on the Vehicle Emissions Control Information (VECI) label located on the underside of the bonnet (only on models sold in some areas) or in the vehicle's Owner's Handbook. If the correct type is used and the engine is in good condition, the spark plugs should not need attention between scheduled replacement intervals. Spark plug cleaning is rarely necessary, and should not be attempted unless specialised equipment is available, as damage can easily be caused to the firing ends.

2 Remove the oil filler cap then unscrew the bolts and remove the plastic cover from the top of the cylinder head cover. Temporarily refit the filler cap.
3 If the marks on the original-equipment spark plug (HT) leads cannot be seen, mark the leads to correspond to the cylinder the lead serves. Pull the leads from the plugs by gripping the end fitting, not the lead, otherwise the lead connection may be fractured **(see illustration)**.
4 It is advisable to remove any dirt from the spark plug recesses using a clean brush, vacuum cleaner or compressed air before removing the plugs, to prevent dirt dropping into the cylinders.
5 Unscrew the plugs from the cylinder head using a spark plug spanner, suitable box spanner or a deep socket and extension bar **(see illustrations)**. Keep the socket aligned with the spark plug - if it is forcibly moved to one side, the ceramic insulator may be broken off. As each plug is removed, examine it as follows.

6 Examination of the spark plugs will give a good indication of the condition of the engine. If the insulator nose of the spark plug is clean and white, with no deposits, this is indicative of a weak mixture or too hot a plug (a hot plug transfers heat away from the electrode slowly, a cold plug transfers heat away quickly).
7 If the tip and insulator nose are covered with hard black-looking deposits, then this is indicative that the mixture is too rich. Should the plug be black and oily, then it is likely that the engine is fairly worn, as well as the mixture being too rich.
8 If the insulator nose is covered with light tan to greyish-brown deposits, then the mixture is correct and it is likely that the engine is in good condition.
9 The spark plug electrode gap is of considerable importance as, if it is too large or too small, the size of the spark and its efficiency will be seriously impaired. The gap should be set to the value given in the Specifications at the beginning of this Chapter.

22.3 Disconnecting the HT leads from the spark plugs - plastic cover removed (Zetec-SE engine)

22.5a Tools required for changing spark plugs

22.5b Unscrewing the spark plugs from the cylinder head

22.10a Using a wire-type gauge when checking the gap

22.10b Measuring a spark plug gap with a feeler blade

22.10c To change the gap, bend the outer electrode only

10 To set the gap, measure it with a feeler blade and then bend open, or closed, the outer plug electrode until the correct gap is achieved. The centre electrode should never be bent, as this may crack the insulator and cause plug failure, if nothing worse. If using feeler blades, the gap is correct when the appropriate-size blade is a firm sliding fit **(see illustrations)**.

11 Special spark plug electrode gap adjusting tools are available from most motor accessory shops, or from some spark plug manufacturers.

12 Before fitting the spark plugs, check that the threaded connector sleeves are tight, and that the plug exterior surfaces and threads are clean **(see Haynes Hint)**.

13 Remove the rubber/plastic hose (if used), and tighten the plug to the specified torque using the spark plug socket and a torque wrench. Refit the remaining spark plugs in the same manner.

14 Connect the HT leads in their correct order.

15 Refit the plastic cover and tighten the retaining bolts. Refit the oil filler cap.

Ignition system check

Warning: Voltages produced by an electronic ignition system are considerably higher than those produced by conventional ignition systems. Extreme care must be taken when working on the system with the ignition switched on. Persons with surgically-implanted cardiac pacemaker devices should keep well clear of the ignition circuits, components and test equipment.

16 The spark plug (HT) leads should be checked whenever new spark plugs are fitted.

17 Ensure that the leads are numbered before removing them, to avoid confusion when refitting. With the plastic top cover removed, pull the leads from the plugs by gripping the end fitting, not the lead, otherwise the lead connection may be fractured.

18 Check inside the end fitting for signs of corrosion, which will look like a white crusty powder. Push the end fitting back onto the spark plug, ensuring that it is a tight fit on the plug. If not, remove the lead again and use pliers to carefully crimp the metal connector inside the end fitting until it fits securely on the end of the spark plug.

19 Using a clean rag, wipe the entire length of the lead to remove any built-up dirt and grease. Once the lead is clean, check for burns, cracks and other damage. Do not bend the lead excessively, nor pull the lead lengthwise - the conductor inside might break.

20 Disconnect the other end of the lead from the ignition coil by squeezing the clips **(see illustration)**. Check for corrosion and a tight fit. If an ohmmeter is available, check the resistance of the lead by connecting the meter between each end of the lead. Refit the lead securely on completion.

21 Check the remaining leads one at a time, in the same way.

22 If new spark plug (HT) leads are required, purchase a set for your specific car and engine.

23 Even with the ignition system in first-class condition, some engines may still occasionally experience poor starting attributable to damp ignition components. To disperse moisture, a water-dispersant aerosol can be very effective.

HAYNES HINT

It's often difficult to insert spark plugs into their holes without cross-threading them. To avoid this possibility, fit a short length of rubber or plastic hose over the end of the spark plug. The flexible hose acts as a universal joint, to help align the plug with the plug hole. Should the plug begin to cross thread, the hose will slip on the spark plug, preventing thread damage to the aluminium cylinder head

1A

22.20 Squeeze the clips to disconnect the HT leads from the ignition coil

Every 60 000 miles

23 Fuel filter renewal

1 The fuel filter is located on the front left-hand corner of the fuel tank. First, chock the front roadwheels, then jack up the rear of the vehicle and support on axle stands.

2 Squeeze the tabs and disconnect the quick-release fittings from each end of the filter. Plug the fuel lines to prevent loss of fuel.

3 Note the fuel flow arrow on the filter, then unscrew and remove the clamp bolt and remove the filter from the mounting bracket which is riveted to the fuel tank flange.

4 Fit the new filter using a reversal of the removal procedure. Make sure the quick-release fittings are pushed fully onto the inlet and outlet stubs, and tighten the clamp bolt securely. Also make sure the filter is fitted the correct way around with the directional arrow pointing towards the fuel line leading to the engine compartment.

Every 100 000 miles

24 Valve clearance check and adjustment – Zetec-SE engine

The procedure is described in Chapter 2B.

Every 100 000 miles or 10 years, whichever comes sooner

25 Timing belt renewal – Zetec-SE engine

The procedure is described in Chapter 2B.

Every 3 years, regardless of mileage

26 Brake fluid renewal

 Warning: Brake hydraulic fluid can harm your eyes and damage painted surfaces, so use extreme caution when handling and pouring it. Do not use fluid that has been standing open for some time, as it absorbs moisture from the air. Excess moisture can cause a dangerous loss of braking effectiveness.

1 The procedure is similar to that for the bleeding of the hydraulic system as described in Chapter 9 except that, on models with a conventional braking system, the brake fluid reservoir should be emptied by siphoning, using a clean poultry baster or similar before starting, and allowance should be made for the old fluid to be expelled when bleeding a section of the circuit. On models fitted with ABS, reduce the fluid level in the reservoir (by siphoning or using a poultry baster), but do not allow the fluid level to drop far enough to allow air into the system – if air enters the ABS hydraulic unit, the unit must be bled using special Ford test equipment (see Chapter 9).

2 Working as described in Chapter 9, open the first bleed screw in the sequence, and pump the brake pedal gently until nearly all the old fluid has been emptied from the master cylinder reservoir. Top-up to the "MAX" level with new fluid, and continue pumping until only the new fluid remains in the reservoir, and new fluid can be seen emerging from the bleed screw. Tighten the screw, and top the reservoir level up to the "MAX" level line.

 Old hydraulic fluid is invariably much darker in colour than the new, making it easy to distinguish the two.

3 Work through all the remaining bleed screws in the sequence until new fluid can be seen at all of them. Be careful to keep the master cylinder reservoir topped-up to above the "MIN" level at all times, or air may enter the system and greatly increase the length of the task.

4 When the operation is complete, check that all bleed screws are securely tightened, and that their dust caps are refitted. Wash off all traces of spilt fluid, and recheck the master cylinder reservoir fluid level.

5 Check the operation of the brakes before taking the car on the road.

Every 4 years, regardless of mileage

27 Coolant renewal and pressure cap check

Cooling system draining

 Warning: Wait until the engine is cold before starting this procedure. Do not allow anti-freeze to come in contact with your skin, or with the painted surfaces of the vehicle. Rinse off spills immediately with plenty of water. Never leave antifreeze lying around in an open container, or in a puddle in the driveway or on the garage floor. Children and pets are attracted by its sweet smell, but antifreeze can be fatal if ingested.

1 With the engine completely cold, remove the expansion tank filler cap. Turn the cap anti-clockwise, wait until any pressure remaining in the system is released, then unscrew it and lift it off.

2 Where applicable, remove the engine undershield, then position a suitable container beneath the radiator drain screw, at the bottom left-hand corner of the radiator.

3 Slacken the drain screw, and allow the coolant to drain into the container **(see illustration)**.

4 When the flow of coolant stops, tighten the radiator drain screw.

5 If the coolant has been drained for a reason other than renewal, then provided it is clean and less than two years old, it can be re-used, though this is not recommended.

27.3 Radiator drain screw (arrowed)

27.15 Removing the expansion tank filler cap

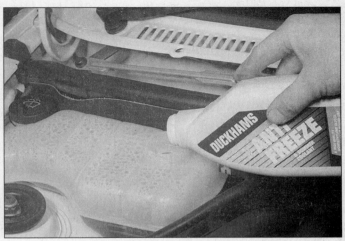

27.17 Fill the cooling system through the expansion tank

Cooling system flushing

6 If coolant renewal has been neglected, or if the antifreeze mixture has become diluted, then in time, the cooling system may gradually lose efficiency, as the coolant passages become restricted due to rust, scale deposits, and other sediment. The cooling system efficiency can be restored by flushing the system clean.

7 The radiator should be flushed independently of the engine, to avoid unnecessary contamination.

Radiator flushing

8 Disconnect the top and bottom hoses and any other relevant hoses from the radiator, with reference to Chapter 3.

9 Insert a garden hose into the radiator top inlet. Direct a flow of clean water through the radiator, and continue flushing until clean water emerges from the radiator bottom outlet.

10 If after a reasonable period, the water still does not run clear, the radiator can be flushed with a good proprietary cleaning agent. It is important that their manufacturer's instructions are followed carefully. If the contamination is particularly bad, insert the hose in the radiator bottom outlet, and reverse-flush the radiator.

Engine flushing

11 Remove the thermostat as described in Chapter 3 then, if the radiator top hose has been disconnected from the engine, temporarily reconnect the hose.

12 With the top and bottom hoses disconnected from the radiator, insert a garden hose into the radiator top hose. Direct a clean flow of water through the engine, and continue flushing until clean water emerges from the radiator bottom hose.

13 On completion of flushing, refit the thermostat and reconnect the hoses with reference to Chapter 3.

Cooling system filling

14 Before attempting to fill the cooling system, make sure that all hoses and clips are in good condition, and that the clips are tight. Note that an antifreeze mixture must be used all year round, to prevent corrosion of the engine components. Also check that the cylinder block drain plug is in place and tight.

15 Remove the expansion tank filler cap (see illustration).

16 Place a container under the vehicle, below the expansion tank, to catch any coolant which may be spilt during the topping up procedure. Also place a wad of rags around the expansion tank.

17 Slowly fill the system until the coolant level reaches the "MAX" mark on the side of the expansion tank (see illustration).

18 Refit and tighten the expansion tank filler cap.

19 Start the engine, and allow it to run until it reaches normal operating temperature (until the cooling fan cuts in and out).

20 Stop the engine, and allow it to cool, then re-check the coolant level with reference to

27.26 Inspect the pressure (expansion tank) cap seal (arrowed)

"Weekly checks". Top-up the level if necessary and refit the expansion tank filler cap. Where applicable, refit the engine undershield.

Antifreeze mixture

21 The antifreeze should always be renewed at the specified intervals. This is necessary not only to maintain the antifreeze properties, but also to prevent corrosion which would otherwise occur as the corrosion inhibitors become progressively less effective.

22 Always use an ethylene-glycol based antifreeze which is suitable for use in mixed-metal cooling systems. The quantity of antifreeze and levels of protection are given in the Specifications.

23 Before adding antifreeze, the cooling system should be completely drained, preferably flushed, and all hoses checked for condition and security.

24 After filling with antifreeze, a label should be attached to the expansion tank, stating the type and concentration of antifreeze used, and the date installed. Any subsequent topping-up should be made with the same type and concentration of antifreeze.

25 Do not use engine antifreeze in the windscreen/tailgate washer system, as it will cause damage to the vehicle paintwork. A screenwash additive should be added to the washer system in the quantities stated on the bottle.

Pressure (expansion tank) cap check

26 Clean the pressure cap, and inspect the seal inside the cap for damage or deterioration. If there is any sign of damage or deterioration to the seal, fit a new pressure cap (see illustration).

1A

Chapter 1 Part B:
Routine maintenance and servicing – diesel engine models

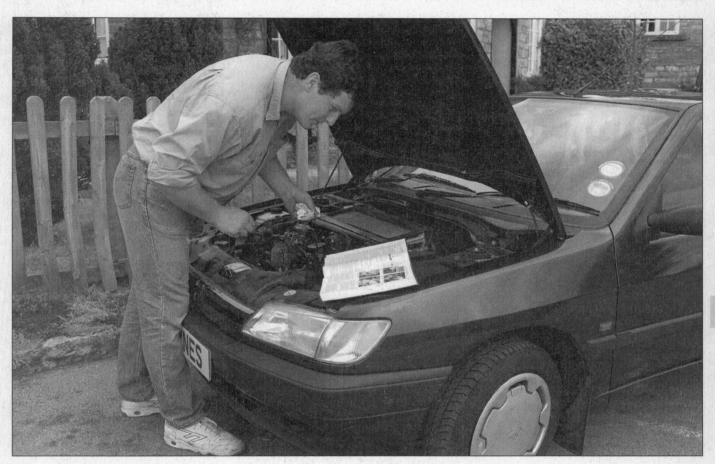

Contents

Degrees of difficulty

| Easy, suitable for novice with little experience | Fairly easy, suitable for beginner with some experience | Fairly difficult, suitable for competent DIY mechanic | Difficult, suitable for experienced DIY mechanic | Very difficult, suitable for expert DIY or professional |

Lubricants and fluids
Refer to "*Weekly checks*"

Capacities

Engine oil
Including oil filter .... 4.5 litres
Excluding oil filter .... 4.1 litres

Cooling system
All models (approximate) .... 9.3 litres

Transmission
Manual transmission (approximate) .... 2.8 litres

Engine
Oil filter .... Champion C115
Valve clearances:
Inlet .... 0.285 to 0.415 mm
Exhaust .... 0.435 to 0.565 mm

Cooling system
Antifreeze mixture:
50% antifreeze .... Protection down to -37°C
55% antifreeze .... Protection down to -45°C
Note: *Refer to antifreeze manufacturer for latest recommendations.*

Fuel system
Air filter element .... Champion U663
Fuel filter .... Champion L138

Brakes
Friction material minimum thickness
Front brake pads .... 1.5 mm
Rear brake shoes .... 1.0 mm

Torque wrench settings

	Nm	lbf ft
Manual transmission filler/level plug	35	26
Roadwheel nuts	85	63

The maintenance intervals in this manual are provided with the assumption that you, not the dealer, will be carrying out the work. These are the minimum maintenance intervals recommended by us for vehicles driven daily. If you wish to keep your vehicle in peak condition at all times, you may wish to perform some of these procedures more often. We encourage frequent maintenance, because it enhances the efficiency, performance and resale value of your vehicle.

If the vehicle is driven in dusty areas, used to tow a trailer, or driven frequently at slow speeds (idling in traffic) or on short journeys, more frequent maintenance intervals are recommended.

When the vehicle is new, it should be serviced by a factory-authorised dealer service department, in order to preserve the factory warranty.

Every 5000 miles or 6 months, whichever comes first

☐ Renew the engine oil and filter (Section 3)

Note: *Ford recommend that the engine oil and filter are changed every 10 000 miles or 12 months. However, oil and filter changes are good for the engine and we recommend that the oil and filter are renewed more frequently, especially if the vehicle is used on a lot of short journeys.*

Every 10 000 miles or 12 months, whichever comes first

☐ Drain water from the fuel filter (Section 4)
☐ Check the condition and tension of the auxiliary drivebelt(s) (Section 5)
☐ Check all components, pipes and hoses for fluid leaks (Section 6)
☐ Check the front brake pads and discs for wear (Section 7)
☐ Check the rear brake shoes and drums for wear (Section 8)
☐ Check the steering and suspension components for condition and security (Section 9)
☐ Check the condition of the driveshaft gaiters (Section 10)
☐ Lubricate all hinges and locks (Section 11)
☐ Check the roadwheel nuts are tightened to the specified torque (Section 12)
☐ Carry out a road test (Section 13)

Every 20 000 miles

☐ Renew the fuel filter (Section 14)
☐ Renew the pollen filter (Section 15)

Note: *If the vehicle is used in dusty conditions, the pollen filter should be renewed more frequently.*

Every 30 000 miles

☐ Check and, if necessary, adjust the valve clearances (Section 16)
☐ Renew the air filter (Section 17)
☐ Check the manual transmission oil level (Section 18)

Every 40 000 miles

☐ Renew the timing belt and injection pump belt (Section 19)

Every 3 years, regardless of mileage

☐ Renew the brake fluid (Section 20)

Every 4 years, regardless of mileage

☐ Renew the coolant and check the condition of the expansion tank pressure cap (Section 21)

1B

Underbonnet view of a 1.8 litre Endura-DE engine model

1 *Engine oil filler cap*
2 *Suspension strut top mounting*
3 *Windscreen washer fluid reservoir*
4 *Coolant reservoir (expansion tank)*
5 *Windscreen wiper motor*
6 *Brake fluid reservoir*
7 *Auxiliary fuse/relay box*
8 *Air cleaner casing*
9 *Battery*
10 *Fuel filter*
11 *Engine oil level dipstick*
12 *Fuel injection pump*

Front underbody view of a 1.8 litre Endura-DE engine model

1 *Brake caliper*
2 *Engine oil drain plug*
3 *Starter motor*
4 *Cooling fan*
5 *Horn*
6 *Track-rod end*
7 *Suspension lower arm*
8 *Gearchange rod*
9 *Exhaust system*
10 *Suspension subframe*
11 *Driveshaft*

Rear underbody view – Hatchback and Van models

1 Suspension trailing
  arm
2 Shock absorber
3 Spare wheel cradle
4 Exhaust rear silencer
5 Suspension beam
6 Fuel tank

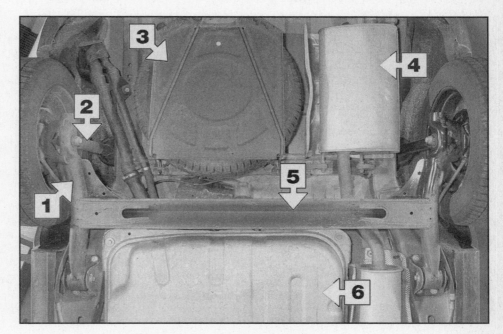

1B

Rear underbody view – Courier and Combi models

1 Suspension torsion
  beam
2 Shock absorber
3 Exhaust rear silencer
4 Spare wheel cradle
5 Brake pressure
  proportioning valve
6 Suspension beam
7 Fuel tank

1 General information

1 This Chapter is designed to help the home mechanic maintain his/her vehicle for safety, economy, long life and peak performance.

2 The Chapter contains a master maintenance schedule, followed by Sections dealing specifically with each task in the schedule. Visual checks, adjustments, component renewal and other helpful items are included. Refer to the accompanying illustrations of the engine compartment and the underside of the vehicle for the locations of the various components.

3 Servicing your vehicle in accordance with the mileage/time maintenance schedule and the following Sections will provide a planned maintenance programme, which should result in a long and reliable service life. This is a comprehensive plan, so maintaining some items but not others at the specified service intervals, will not produce the same results.

4 As you service your vehicle, you will discover that many of the procedures can - and should - be grouped together, because of the particular procedure being performed, or because of the proximity of two otherwise-unrelated components to one another. For example, if the vehicle is raised for any reason, the exhaust can be inspected at the same time as the suspension and steering components.

5 The first step in this maintenance programme is to prepare yourself before the actual work begins. Read through all the Sections relevant to the work to be carried out, then make a list and gather all the parts and tools required. If a problem is encountered, seek advice from a parts specialist, or a dealer service department.

2 Intensive maintenance

1 If, from the time the vehicle is new, the routine maintenance schedule is followed closely, and frequent checks are made of fluid levels and high-wear items, as suggested throughout this manual, the engine will be kept in relatively good running condition, and the need for additional work will be minimised.

2 It is possible that there will be times when the engine is running poorly due to the lack of regular maintenance. This is even more likely if a used vehicle, which has not received regular and frequent maintenance checks, is purchased. In such cases, additional work may need to be carried out, outside of the regular maintenance intervals.

3 If engine wear is suspected, a compression test or leakdown test (refer to Chapter 2C) will provide valuable information regarding the overall performance of the main internal components. Such a test can be used as a basis to decide on the extent of the work to be carried out. If, for example, a compression or leakdown test indicates serious internal engine wear, conventional maintenance as described in this Chapter will not greatly improve the performance of the engine, and may prove a waste of time and money, unless extensive overhaul work is carried out first.

4 The following series of operations are those most often required to improve the performance of a generally poor-running engine:

Primary operations

a) Clean, inspect and test the battery (refer to "Weekly checks").
b) Check all the engine-related fluids (refer to "Weekly checks").
c) Check the condition and tension of the auxiliary drivebelt (Section 5).
d) Check the condition of the air filter, and renew if necessary (Section 17).
e) Renew the fuel filter (Section 14).
f) Check the condition of all hoses, and check for fluid leaks (Section 6).

5 If the above operations do not prove fully effective, carry out the following secondary operations:

Secondary operations

All items listed under "Primary operations", plus the following:

a) Check the charging system (refer to Chapter 5A).
b) Check the pre-heating system (refer to Chapter 5C).
c) Check the fuel system (refer to Chapter 4B).

Every 5000 miles or 6 months, whichever comes first

3 Engine oil and filter renewal

1 Frequent oil and filter changes are the most important preventative maintenance procedures which can be undertaken by the DIY owner. As engine oil ages, it becomes diluted and contaminated, which leads to premature engine wear.

2 Before starting this procedure, gather together all the necessary tools and materials. Also make sure that you have plenty of clean rags and newspapers handy, to mop up any spills. Ideally, the engine oil should be warm, as it will drain more easily, and more built-up sludge will be removed with it. Take care not to touch the exhaust or any other hot parts of the engine when working under the vehicle. To avoid any possibility of scalding, and to protect yourself from possible skin irritants and other harmful contaminants in used engine oils, it is advisable to wear gloves when carrying out this work.

3 Firmly apply the handbrake then jack up the front of the vehicle and support it on axle stands (see "Jacking and Vehicle Support").

4 Remove the oil filler cap.

5 Using a spanner, or preferably a suitable socket and bar, slacken the drain plug about half a turn **(see illustration)**. Position the draining container under the drain plug, then remove the plug completely.

6 Allow some time for the oil to drain, noting that it may be necessary to reposition the container as the oil flow slows to a trickle.

7 After all the oil has drained, wipe the drain plug and the sealing washer with a clean rag. Examine the condition of the sealing washer, and renew it if it shows signs of scoring or other damage which may prevent an oil-tight seal. Clean the area around the drain plug opening, and refit the plug complete with the washer and tighten it securely.

8 Move the container into position under the oil filter which is located on the rear of the cylinder block **(see illustration)**.

3.5 Engine oil drain plug on the sump

3.8 View of the oil filter from under the rear of the engine

9 Use an oil filter removal tool to slacken the filter initially, then unscrew it by hand the rest of the way. Empty the oil from the old filter into the container.
10 Use a clean rag to remove all oil, dirt and sludge from the filter sealing area on the engine.
11 Apply a light coating of clean engine oil to the sealing ring on the new filter, then screw the filter into position on the engine. Tighten the filter firmly by hand only - **do not** use any tools.
12 Remove the old oil and all tools from under the vehicle then lower the vehicle to the ground.

13 Fill the engine through the filler hole, using the correct grade and type of oil (refer to "Weekly Checks" for details of topping-up). Pour in half the specified quantity of oil first, then wait a few minutes for the oil to drain into the sump. Continue to add oil, a small quantity at a time, until the level is up to the lower mark on the dipstick. Adding approximately a further 1.0 litre will bring the level up to the upper mark on the dipstick.
14 Start the engine and run it for a few minutes, while checking for leaks around the oil filter seal and the sump drain plug. Note

that there may be a delay of a few seconds before the low oil pressure warning light goes out when the engine is first started, as the oil circulates through the new oil filter and the engine oil galleries before the pressure builds up.
15 Stop the engine, and wait a few minutes for the oil to settle in the sump once more. With the new oil circulated and the filter now completely full, recheck the level on the dipstick, and add more oil as necessary.
16 Dispose of the used engine oil safely with reference to "General repair procedures".

Every 10 000 miles or 12 months, whichever comes first

4 Fuel filter water draining

Caution: *Before starting any work on the fuel filter, wipe clean the filter assembly and the area around it; it is essential that no dirt or other foreign matter is allowed into the system. Obtain a suitable container into which the filter can be drained and place rags or similar material under the filter assembly to catch any spillages. Do not allow diesel fuel to leak into the clutch bellhousing or it will contaminate the clutch driven plate friction material which will cause severe clutch slip which can be cured only by the renewal of the clutch plate and the degreasing of all fouled surfaces. Similarly, diesel fuel should never be allowed to contaminate components such as the alternator and starter motor, the coolant hoses and engine mountings, and any wiring.*

1 In addition to taking the precautions noted above to catch any fuel spillages, connect a tube to the drain spigot on the base of the fuel filter. Place the other end of the tube in a clean jar or can.
2 Open the drain cock by unscrewing the knurled wheel.
3 Allow the filter to drain until clean fuel, free of dirt or water, emerges from the tube (approximately 100 cc is usually sufficient). Close the drain cock and remove the tube, containers and rag, mopping up any spilt fuel.
4 If, as often happens, no fuel emerges on opening the drain cock, slacken the vent screw on the filter head to allow sufficient air into the filter for fuel to flow. If this does not work, remove the filter cartridge and check it carefully until the reason for the lack of flow can be identified and is cured. It is unwise simply to probe the drain cock with a piece of wire in an attempt to clear the obstruction; the small seals in the drain cock may be damaged or dislodged. Note that the system may require bleeding if the vent screw is disturbed or the filter unscrewed (refer to Chapter 4B).

5 On completion, dispose safely of the drained. Check carefully all disturbed components to ensure that there are no leaks (of air or fuel) when the engine is restarted.

5 Auxiliary drivebelt check and renewal

Checking

1 The auxiliary drivebelt is fitted at the right-hand side of the engine and drives the alternator, air conditioning compressor and power steering pump (as applicable).
2 Due to their function and material makeup, drivebelts are prone to failure after a long period of time and should therefore be inspected regularly.
3 Since the drivebelt is located very close to the right-hand side of the engine compartment, it is possible to gain better access by raising the front of the vehicle and removing the right-hand wheel, then unbolting the crankshaft pulley lower cover from the underbody.
4 With the engine stopped, inspect the full length of the drivebelt for cracks and separation of the belt plies. It will be necessary to turn the engine (using a spanner or socket and bar on the crankshaft pulley bolt) in order to move the belt away from the pulleys so that the belt can be inspected thoroughly. Twist the belt between the pulleys so that both sides can be viewed. Also check for fraying, and glazing which gives the belt a shiny appearance. Check the pulleys for nicks, cracks, distortion and corrosion.

Renewal

5 To remove the drivebelt, raise the front of the vehicle (if not already done) and support on axle stands (see "Jacking and Vehicle Support"). Unbolt and remove the crankshaft pulley cover.
6 Loosen only the adjustment clamping bolt located in the centre of the tensioner pulley.
7 Back off the adjustment bolt **(see illustration)** to release the tension on the belt,

then release it from the crankshaft, alternator, power steering pump, and air conditioning compressor pulleys (as applicable) and remove it from under the vehicle.
8 Locate the new drivebelt on the pulleys and around the tensioner. Make sure that the drivebelt is correctly seated in all of the pulley grooves.
9 Tighten the adjustment bolt until it is possible to deflect the drivebelt midway between the pulleys on the longest run approximately 3 mm under firm thumb pressure.
10 Tighten the adjustment clamping bolt securely, then refit the crankshaft pulley cover and lower the vehicle to the ground.

6 Hose and fluid leak check

1 Visually inspect the engine joint faces, gaskets and seals for any signs of water or oil leaks. Pay particular attention to the areas around the cylinder head cover, cylinder head, oil filter and sump joint faces. Bear in mind that, over a period of time, some very slight seepage from these areas is to be expected - what you are really looking for is any indication of a serious leak. Should a leak be found, renew the offending gasket or oil seal by referring to the appropriate Chapters in this manual.

5.7 Auxiliary drivebelt tension adjustment bolt

1B

2 Also check the security and condition of all the engine-related pipes and hoses, and all braking system pipes and hoses. Ensure that all cable ties or securing clips are in place, and in good condition. Clips which are broken or missing can lead to chafing of the hoses, pipes or wiring, which could cause more serious problems in the future.

3 Carefully check the radiator hoses and heater hoses along their entire length. Renew any hose which is cracked, swollen or deteriorated. Cracks will show up better if the hose is squeezed. Pay close attention to the hose clips that secure the hoses to the cooling system components. Hose clips can pinch and puncture hoses, resulting in cooling system leaks. If the crimped-type hose clips are used, it may be a good idea to replace them with standard worm-drive clips.

4 Inspect all the cooling system components (hoses, joint faces, etc) for leaks.

 A leak in the cooling system will usually show up as white- or rust-coloured deposits on the area adjoining the leak.

5 Where any problems are found on system components, renew the component or gasket with reference to Chapter 3.

6 With the vehicle raised, inspect the fuel tank and filler neck for punctures, cracks and other damage. The connection between the filler neck and tank is especially critical. Sometimes a rubber filler neck or connecting hose will leak due to loose retaining clamps or deteriorated rubber.

7 Carefully check all rubber hoses and metal fuel lines leading away from the fuel tank. Check for loose connections, deteriorated hoses, crimped lines, and other damage. Pay particular attention to the vent pipes and hoses, which often loop up around the filler neck and can become blocked or crimped. Follow the lines to the front of the vehicle, carefully inspecting them all the way. Renew damaged sections as necessary. Similarly, whilst the vehicle is raised, take the opportunity to inspect all underbody brake fluid pipes and hoses.

8 From within the engine compartment, check the security of all fuel, vacuum and brake hose attachments and pipe unions, and inspect all hoses for kinks, chafing and deterioration.

9 Where applicable, check the condition of the power steering fluid pipes and hoses.

7 Front brake pad and disc wear check

1 Apply the handbrake, then jack up the front of the car and support it securely on axle stands (see "*Jacking and Vehicle Support*"). Remove the front roadwheels.

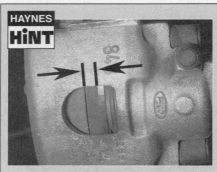

For a quick check, the thickness of friction material remaining on each brake pad can be measured through the aperture in the caliper body.

2 For a comprehensive check, the brake pads should be removed and cleaned. The operation of the caliper can then also be checked, and the condition of the brake disc itself can be fully examined on both sides. Refer to Chapter 9 for further information.

3 On completion refit the roadwheels and lower the car to the ground.

8 Rear brake shoe and drum wear check

Remove the rear brake drums, and check the brake shoes for signs of wear or contamination. At the same time, also inspect the wheel cylinders for signs of leakage, and the brake drum for signs of wear. Refer to the relevant Sections of Chapter 9 for further information.

9 Steering and suspension check

Front suspension and steering check

1 Raise the front of the vehicle, and securely support it on axle stands (see "*Jacking and Vehicle Support*").

9.4 Check for wear in the hub bearings by grasping the wheel and trying to rock it

2 Visually inspect the balljoint dust covers and the steering rack-and-pinion gaiters for splits, chafing or deterioration. Any wear of these components will cause loss of lubricant, together with dirt and water entry, resulting in rapid deterioration of the balljoints or steering gear.

3 On vehicles with power steering, check the fluid hoses for chafing or deterioration, and the pipe and hose unions for fluid leaks. Also check for signs of fluid leakage under pressure from the steering gear rubber gaiters, which would indicate failed fluid seals within the steering gear.

4 Grasp the roadwheel at the 12 o'clock and 6 o'clock positions, and try to rock it **(see illustration)**. Very slight free play may be felt, but if the movement is appreciable, further investigation is necessary to determine the source. Continue rocking the wheel while an assistant depresses the footbrake. If the movement is now eliminated or significantly reduced, it is likely that the hub bearings are at fault. If the free play is still evident with the footbrake depressed, then there is wear in the suspension joints or mountings.

5 Now grasp the wheel at the 9 o'clock and 3 o'clock positions, and try to rock it as before. Any movement felt now may again be caused by wear in the hub bearings or the steering track-rod balljoints. If the outer balljoint is worn, the visual movement will be obvious. If the inner joint is suspect, it can be felt by placing a hand over the rack-and-pinion rubber gaiter and gripping the track-rod. If the wheel is now rocked, movement will be felt at the inner joint if wear has taken place.

6 Using a large screwdriver or flat bar, check for wear in the suspension mounting bushes by levering between the relevant suspension component and its attachment point. Some movement is to be expected, as the mountings are made of rubber, but excessive wear should be obvious. Also check the condition of any visible rubber bushes, looking for splits, cracks or contamination of the rubber.

7 With the car standing on its wheels, have an assistant turn the steering wheel back and forth, about an eighth of a turn each way. There should be very little, if any, lost movement between the steering wheel and roadwheels. If this is not the case, closely observe the joints and mountings previously described. In addition, check the steering column universal joints for wear, and also check the rack-and-pinion steering gear itself.

Rear suspension check

8 Chock the front wheels, then jack up the rear of the vehicle and support securely on axle stands (see "*Jacking and Vehicle Support*").

9 Working as described previously for the front suspension, check the rear hub bearings, the suspension bushes and the strut or shock absorber mountings (as applicable) for wear.

Shock absorber check

10 Check for any signs of fluid leakage around the shock absorber body, or from the rubber gaiter around the piston rod. Should any fluid be noticed, the shock absorber is defective internally, and should be renewed. **Note:** *Shock absorbers should always be renewed in pairs on the same axle.*

11 The efficiency of the shock absorber may be checked by bouncing the vehicle at each corner. Generally speaking, the body will return to its normal position and stop after being depressed. If it rises and returns on a rebound, the shock absorber is probably suspect. Also examine the shock absorber upper and lower mountings for any signs of wear.

10 Driveshaft gaiter check

1 With the vehicle raised and securely supported on stands, turn the steering onto full lock then slowly rotate the roadwheel. Inspect the condition of the outer constant velocity (CV) joint rubber gaiters while squeezing the gaiters to open out the folds **(see illustration)**. Check for signs of cracking, splits or deterioration of the rubber which may allow the grease to escape and lead to water and grit entry into the joint. Also check the security and condition of the retaining clips. Repeat these checks on the inner CV joints. If any damage or deterioration is found, the gaiters should be renewed as described in Chapter 8.

2 At the same time check the general condition of the CV joints themselves by first holding the driveshaft and attempting to rotate the wheel. Repeat this check by holding the inner joint and attempting to rotate the driveshaft. Any appreciable movement indicates wear in the joints, wear in the driveshaft splines or loose driveshaft retaining nut.

11 Hinge and lock lubrication

1 Work around the vehicle and lubricate the hinges of the bonnet, doors and tailgate with a light machine oil.
2 Lightly lubricate the bonnet release mechanism and exposed section of inner cable with a smear of grease **(see illustration)**.
3 Check carefully the security and operation of all hinges, latches and locks, adjusting them where required. Check the operation of the central locking system (if fitted).
4 Check the condition and operation of the tailgate struts, renewing them if either is leaking or no longer able to support the tailgate securely when raised.

12 Roadwheel nut tightness check

1 Where applicable, remove the wheel trims, and slacken the roadwheel nuts slightly.
2 Tighten the nuts to the specified torque, using a torque wrench.

13 Road test

Instruments and electrical equipment

1 Check the operation of all instruments and electrical equipment.
2 Make sure that all instruments read correctly, and switch on all electrical equipment in turn, to check that it functions properly.

Steering and suspension

3 Check for any abnormalities in the steering, suspension, handling or road "feel".
4 Drive the vehicle, and check that there are no unusual vibrations or noises.
5 Check that the steering feels positive, with no excessive "sloppiness", or roughness, and

check for any suspension noises when cornering and driving over bumps.

Drivetrain

6 Check the performance of the engine, clutch, transmission and driveshafts.
7 Listen for any unusual noises from the engine, clutch and transmission.
8 Make sure that the engine runs smoothly when idling, and that there is no hesitation when accelerating.
9 Check that the clutch action is smooth and progressive, that the drive is taken up smoothly, and that the pedal travel is not excessive. Also listen for any noises when the clutch pedal is depressed.
10 Check that all gears can be engaged smoothly without noise, and that the gear lever action is not abnormally vague or "notchy".
11 Listen for a metallic clicking sound from the front of the vehicle, as the vehicle is driven slowly in a circle with the steering on full-lock. Carry out this check in both directions. If a clicking noise is heard, this indicates wear in a driveshaft joint (see Chapter 8).

Check the operation and performance of the braking system

12 Make sure that the vehicle does not pull to one side when braking, and that the wheels do not lock prematurely when braking hard.
13 Check that there is no vibration through the steering when braking.
14 Check that the handbrake operates correctly, without excessive movement of the lever, and that it holds the vehicle stationary on a slope.
15 Test the operation of the brake servo unit as follows. Depress the footbrake four or five times to exhaust the vacuum, then start the engine. As the engine starts, there should be a noticeable "give" in the brake pedal as vacuum builds up. Allow the engine to run for at least two minutes, and then switch it off. If the brake pedal is now depressed again, it should be possible to detect a hiss from the servo as the pedal is depressed. After about four or five applications, no further hissing should be heard, and the pedal should feel considerably harder.

1B

10.1 Check the condition of the driveshaft gaiters

11.2 Lubricate the bonnet lock with grease

14.1 The fuel filter is located on a bracket at the left-hand end of the cylinder head

15.2 Releasing a pollen filter cover securing clip

15.3 Pulling out the pollen filter

Every 20 000 miles

14 Fuel filter renewal

Caution: Before starting any work on the fuel filter, wipe clean the filter assembly and the area around it; it is essential that no dirt or other foreign matter is allowed into the system. Obtain a suitable container into which the filter can be drained and place rags or similar material under the filter assembly to catch any spillages. Do not allow diesel fuel to leak into the clutch bellhousing or it will contaminate the clutch driven plate friction material which will cause severe clutch slip which can be cured only by the renewal of the clutch plate and the degreasing of all fouled surfaces. Similarly, diesel fuel

should never be allowed to contaminate components such as the alternator and starter motor, the coolant hoses and engine mountings, and any wiring.

1 The fuel filter is located on a bracket on the left-hand end of the cylinder head (see illustration).
2 Drain the fuel filter with reference to Section 4.
3 Loosen the clamp bolt retaining the filter to the mounting bracket.
4 Note the location of the fuel lines then squeeze the tabs and disconnect the quick-release fittings from the inlet and outlet stubs on the filter. The inlet fuel line is the line from the fuel heater, and the outlet fuel line is the line leading to the injection pump.
5 Remove the filter from the retaining bracket and withdraw from the engine compartment.
6 Fit the new filter using a reversal of the removal procedure. Make sure the quick-

release fittings are pushed fully onto the inlet and outlet stubs, and tighten the clamp bolt securely. The direction of fuel flow is indicated on the top of the filter by arrows.

15 Pollen filter renewal

1 Open the bonnet, and locate the pollen filter, at the left-hand corner of the scuttle at the rear of the engine compartment.
2 Release the two clips, and open the pollen filter cover (see illustration).
3 Pull the filter from the housing, using the tab provided (see illustration).
4 Fit the new filter using a reversal of the removal procedure. Make sure that the filter is fitted with the removal tab and the "TOP/OBEN" marking visible.

Every 30 000 miles

16 Valve clearance check and adjustment

This procedure is described in Chapter 2C.

17 Air filter element renewal

1 The air cleaner is located in the left-hand front corner of the engine compartment. First unscrew the screws securing the cover to the air cleaner housing, and disconnect the air inlet duct from the cover.
2 Lift the cover and remove the filter element from the base (see illustration). Note which way round it is fitted. Due to the position of the battery, the element is best removed from the rear of the base.

3 Wipe clean the interior surfaces of the cover and base.
4 Insert the new element making sure that it is seated correctly in the base.
5 Refit the cover and secure with the retaining screws. Reconnect the air inlet duct.

17.2 Removing the element from the base of the air cleaner

18 Manual transmission oil level check

1 Position the vehicle over an inspection pit, on vehicle ramps, or jack it up, but make sure that it is level.
2 Remove all traces of dirt then unscrew the filler/level plug from the front face of the transmission. Note it is the plug furthest from the engine - do not confuse it with the blanking plug near the bellhousing.
3 The level must be between 10 mm and 15 mm below the bottom edge of the filler/level plug hole (use a cranked tool such as an Allen key to check the level). If necessary, top up the level with the specified grade of oil (see "Weekly Checks").
4 When the level is correct, clean and refit the filler level plug and tighten it to the specified torque.
5 Lower the car to the ground.

Every 40 000 miles

19 Timing belt and injection pump belt renewal

The procedure is described in Chapter 2C.

Every 3 years, regardless of mileage

20 Brake fluid renewal

 Old hydraulic fluid is invariably much darker in colour than the new, making it easy to distinguish the two.

⚠ *Warning: Brake hydraulic fluid can harm your eyes and damage painted surfaces, so use extreme caution when handling and pouring it. Do not use fluid that has been standing open for some time, as it absorbs moisture from the air. Excess moisture can cause a dangerous loss of braking effectiveness.*

1 The procedure is similar to that for the bleeding of the hydraulic system as described in Chapter 9 except that, on models with a conventional braking system, the brake fluid reservoir should be emptied by siphoning, using a clean poultry baster or similar before starting, and allowance should be made for the old fluid to be expelled when bleeding a section of the circuit. On models fitted with ABS, reduce the fluid level in the reservoir (by siphoning or using a poultry baster), but do not allow the fluid level to drop far enough to allow air into the system – if air enters the ABS hydraulic unit, the unit must be bled using special Ford test equipment (see Chapter 9).

2 Working as described in Chapter 9, open the first bleed screw in the sequence, and pump the brake pedal gently until nearly all the old fluid has been emptied from the master cylinder reservoir. Top-up to the "MAX" level with new fluid, and continue pumping until only the new fluid remains in the reservoir, and new fluid can be seen emerging from the bleed screw. Tighten the screw, and top the reservoir level up to the "MAX" level line.

3 Work through all the remaining bleed screws in the sequence until new fluid can be seen at all of them. Be careful to keep the master cylinder reservoir topped-up to above the "MIN" level at all times, or air may enter the system and greatly increase the length of the task.

4 When the operation is complete, check that all bleed screws are securely tightened, and that their dust caps are refitted. Wash off all traces of spilt fluid, and recheck the master cylinder reservoir fluid level.

5 Check the operation of the brakes before taking the car on the road.

1B

Every 4 years, regardless of mileage

21 Coolant renewal and pressure cap check

Cooling system draining

⚠ *Warning: Wait until the engine is cold before starting this procedure. Do not allow antifreeze to come in contact with your skin, or with the painted surfaces of the vehicle. Rinse off spills immediately with plenty of water. Never leave antifreeze lying around in an open container, or in a puddle in the driveway or on the garage floor. Children and pets are attracted by its sweet smell, but antifreeze can be fatal if ingested.*

1 With the engine completely cold, remove the expansion tank filler cap. Turn the cap anti-clockwise, wait until any pressure remaining in the system is released, then unscrew it and lift it off.

2 Where applicable, remove the engine undershield, then position a suitable container beneath the radiator drain screw, at the bottom left-hand corner of the radiator.

3 Slacken the drain screw, and allow the coolant to drain into the container **(see illustration)**.

4 When the flow of coolant stops, tighten the radiator drain screw.

5 If the coolant has been drained for a reason other than renewal, then provided it is clean and less than two years old, it can be re-used, though this is not recommended.

Cooling system flushing

6 If coolant renewal has been neglected, or if the antifreeze mixture has become diluted, then in time, the cooling system may gradually lose efficiency, as the coolant passages become restricted due to rust, scale deposits, and other sediment. The cooling system efficiency can be restored by flushing the system clean.

7 The radiator should be flushed independently of the engine, to avoid unnecessary contamination.

Radiator flushing

8 Disconnect the top and bottom hoses and any other relevant hoses from the radiator, with reference to Chapter 3.

9 Insert a garden hose into the radiator top inlet. Direct a flow of clean water through the radiator, and continue flushing until clean water emerges from the radiator bottom outlet.

10 If after a reasonable period, the water still does not run clear, the radiator can be flushed with a good proprietary cleaning agent. It is important that their manufacturer's instructions are followed carefully. If the contamination is particularly bad, insert the hose in the radiator bottom outlet, and reverse-flush the radiator.

Engine flushing

11 Remove the thermostat as described in Chapter 3 then, if the radiator top hose has been disconnected from the engine, temporarily reconnect the hose.

12 With the top and bottom hoses disconnected from the radiator, insert a garden hose into the radiator top hose. Direct a clean flow of water through the engine, and continue flushing until clean water emerges from the radiator bottom hose.

21.3 Radiator drain screw (arrowed)

21.15 Removing the expansion tank filler cap

21.17 Fill the cooling system through the expansion tank

21.26 Inspect the pressure (expansion tank) cap seal (arrowed)

13 On completion of flushing, refit the thermostat and reconnect the hoses with reference to Chapter 3.

Cooling system filling

14 Before attempting to fill the cooling system, make sure that all hoses and clips are in good condition, and that the clips are tight. Note that an antifreeze mixture must be used all year round, to prevent corrosion of the engine components. Also check that the cylinder block drain plug is in place and tight.

15 Remove the expansion tank filler cap **(see illustration)**.

16 Place a container under the vehicle, below the expansion tank, to catch any coolant which may be spilt during the topping up procedure. Also place a wad of rags around the expansion tank.

17 Slowly fill the system until the coolant level reaches the "MAX" mark on the side of the expansion tank **(see illustration)**.

18 Refit and tighten the expansion tank filler cap.

19 Start the engine, and allow it to run until it reaches normal operating temperature (until the cooling fan cuts in and out).

20 Stop the engine, and allow it to cool, then re-check the coolant level with reference to "*Weekly checks*". Top-up the level if necessary and refit the expansion tank filler cap. Where applicable, refit the engine undershield.

Antifreeze mixture

21 The antifreeze should always be renewed at the specified intervals. This is necessary not only to maintain the antifreeze properties, but also to prevent corrosion which would otherwise occur as the corrosion inhibitors become progressively less effective.

22 Always use an ethylene-glycol based antifreeze which is suitable for use in mixed-metal cooling systems. The quantity of antifreeze and levels of protection are given in the Specifications.

23 Before adding antifreeze, the cooling system should be completely drained, preferably flushed, and all hoses checked for condition and security.

24 After filling with antifreeze, a label should be attached to the expansion tank, stating the type and concentration of antifreeze used, and the date installed. Any subsequent topping-up should be made with the same type and concentration of antifreeze.

25 Do not use engine antifreeze in the windscreen/tailgate washer system, as it will cause damage to the vehicle paintwork. A screenwash additive should be added to the washer system in the quantities stated on the bottle.

Pressure (expansion tank) cap check

26 Clean the pressure cap, and inspect the seal inside the cap for damage or deterioration **(see illustration)**. If there is any sign of damage or deterioration to the seal, fit a new pressure cap.

Chapter 2 Part A:
Endura-E petrol engine in-car repair procedures

Contents

Degrees of difficulty

Easy, suitable for novice with little experience	**Fairly easy,** suitable for beginner with some experience	**Fairly difficult,** suitable for competent DIY mechanic	**Difficult,** suitable for experienced DIY mechanic	**Very difficult,** suitable for expert DIY or professional

Specifications

General

Engine type	Four-cylinder, in-line overhead valve
Designation	Endura-E
Engine code:	
50PS engine	JJA
60PS engine	J4C
Capacity	1298 cc
Bore	73.96 mm
Stroke	75.48 mm
Compression ratio	9.5:1
Firing order	1-2-4-3 (No 1 cylinder at timing chain end)
Direction of crankshaft rotation	Clockwise (seen from right-hand side of vehicle)

Valves

	Inlet	Exhaust
Valve clearance (cold)	0.20 mm	0.30 mm
Valve length	103.70 to 104.40 mm	104.02 to 104.72 mm
Valve head diameter	34.40 to 34.60 mm	28.90 to 29.10 mm
Valve stem diameter:		
Standard	7.025 to 7.043 mm	6.999 to 7.017 mm
Oversize 0.2 mm	7.225 to 7.243 mm	7.199 to 7.217 mm
Oversize 0.4 mm	7.425 to 7.443 mm	7.399 to 7.417 mm
Valve stem-to-guide clearance	0.020 to 0.069 mm	0.046 to 0.095 mm

Valve springs

Free length	41.0 mm

Cylinder head

Maximum permissible gasket surface distortion (measured over full length)	0.25 mm
Valve seat angle (inlet and exhaust)	45°
Valve seat width (inlet and exhaust)	1.18 to 1.75 mm*

*The inlet and exhaust valves have special inserts which cannot be recut using conventional tools.

Camshaft

Camshaft bearing diameter . . . . 39.615 to 39.635 mm
Bearing bush inside diameter:
    Standard . . . . 39.662 to 39.682 mm
    Oversize . . . . 39.662 to 39.713 mm
Camshaft thrust plate thickness . . . . 4.457 to 4.508 mm
Endfloat . . . . 0.02 to 0.19 mm

Cylinder block

Cylinder bore diameter:
    Standard 1 . . . . 73.94 to 73.95 mm
    Standard 2 . . . . 73.95 to 73.96 mm
    Standard 3 . . . . 73.96 to 73.97 mm
    Oversize 0.5 mm . . . . 75.00 to 75.01 mm
Valve tappet diameter . . . . 13.081 to 13.094 mm
Valve tappet clearance in cylinder block . . . . 0.016 to 0.062 mm

Pistons and piston rings

Piston diameter:
    Standard 1 . . . . 73.91 to 73.92 mm
    Standard 2 . . . . 73.92 to 73.93 mm
    Standard 3 . . . . 73.93 to 73.94 mm
    Oversize 0.5 mm . . . . 74.46 to 74.49 mm
    Oversize 1.0 mm . . . . 74.96 to 74.99 mm
Piston-to-cylinder bore clearance . . . . 0.015 to 0.050 mm
Piston ring end gap - installed:
    Top compression ring . . . . 0.25 to 0.45 mm
    Second compression ring . . . . 0.45 to 0.75 mm
    Oil control ring . . . . 0.20 to 0.50 mm
Piston ring-to-groove clearance:
    Compression rings . . . . 0.20 mm (maximum)
    Oil control ring . . . . 0.10 mm (maximum)
Ring gap position:
    Top compression ring . . . . Offset 180° from oil control ring gap
    Second compression ring . . . . Offset 90° from oil control ring gap
    Oil control ring . . . . Aligned with gudgeon pin

Gudgeon pin

Length . . . . 63.6 to 64.4 mm
Diameter:
    White colour code . . . . 18.026 to 18.029 mm
    Red colour code . . . . 18.029 to 18.032 mm
    Blue colour code . . . . 18.032 to 18.035 mm
    Yellow colour code . . . . 18.035 to 18.038 mm
Clearance in piston . . . . 0.008 to 0.014 mm
Interference fit in connecting rod . . . . 0.016 to 0.048 mm

Crankshaft and bearings

Main bearings 5
Main bearing journal diameter:
    Standard . . . . 56.980 to 57.000 mm
    0.254 mm undersize (green) . . . . 56.726 to 56.746 mm
Main bearing journal-to-shell running clearance . . . . 0.009 to 0.056 mm
Crankpin (big-end) bearing journal diameter:
    Standard . . . . 40.99 to 41.01 mm
    0.254 mm undersize (green) . . . . 40.74 to 40.76 mm
    0.508 mm undersize . . . . 40.49 to 40.51 mm
    0.762 mm undersize . . . . 40.24 to 40.26 mm
Crankpin (big-end) bearing journal-to-shell running clearance . . . . 0.006 to 0.060 mm
Crankpin (big-end) bearing side clearance . . . . 0.100 to 0.25 mm
Crankshaft endfloat . . . . 0.05 to 0.26 mm
Thrustwasher thickness:
    Standard . . . . 2.80 to 2.85 mm
    Oversize . . . . 2.99 to 3.04 mm

Lubrication

Oil pressure:
    At idle speed . . . . 0.60 bar
    At 2000 rpm . . . . 1.50 bar

Oil pump clearances:
Outer rotor-to-body . . . .   0.14 to 0.26 mm
Inner rotor-to-outer rotor . . . .   0.051 to 0.127 mm
Rotor endfloat . . . .   0.025 to 0.06 mm

Torque wrench settings

	Nm	lbf ft
Main bearing cap	95	70
*Crankpin (big-end) bearing cap bolts:		
Stage 1	4	3
Stage 2	Angle-tighten a further 90°	
* New bolts must be used		
Crankshaft rear oil seal housing	18	13
Flywheel bolts	67	49
Timing chain tensioner	8	6
Camshaft thrust plate bolts	11	8
Camshaft sprocket bolt	28	21
Timing chain cover	9	7
Crankshaft pulley bolt	115	85
Oil pump	18	13
Oil pump cover	10	7
Sump:		
Stage 1	7	5
Stage 2	10	7
Stage 3 (with engine warm)	10	7
Oil pressure switch	14	10
Oil dipstick tube to inlet manifold	2	1
Rocker shaft pedestal bolts	43	32
Cylinder head bolts (may be re-used once only):		
Stage 1	30	22
Stage 2	Angle-tighten a further 90°	
Stage 3	Angle-tighten a further 90°	
Rocker cover bolts	6	4
Front engine mounting bracket to cylinder head	69	51
Engine/transmission mountings:		
Right-hand mounting-to-cylinder block bracket	120	88
Right-hand mounting bracket-to-cylinder block	69	51
Right-hand mounting brace	69	51
Right-hand mounting-to-body	84	62
Left-hand rear mounting bracket-to-transmission	50	37
Left-hand rear mounting bracket-to-mounting	68	50
Left-hand front mounting bracket-to-mounting	68	50
Left-hand front mounting bracket brace	49	36
Engine-to-transmission bolts	40	30

2A

1 General information

How to use this Chapter

This Part of Chapter 2 is devoted to in-car repair procedures on the Endura-E petrol engine. All procedures concerning engine removal and refitting, and engine block/cylinder head overhaul can be found in Chapter 2D.

Refer to *"Buying spare parts and vehicle identification numbers"* in the Reference Section at the end of this manual for details of engine code locations.

Most of the operations included in this chapter are based on the assumption that the engine is still installed in the car. Therefore, if this information is being used during a complete engine overhaul, with the engine already removed, many of the steps included here will not apply.

Engine description

The engine is an overhead valve, water-cooled, four cylinder in-line design, designated Endura-E. The Endura-E engine replaces the HCS engine fitted to earlier Fiesta models and, apart from an aluminium sump and modifications to the inlet manifold and inlet system, is virtually identical. The engine is mounted transversely at the front of the vehicle together with the transmission to form a combined power unit.

The crankshaft is supported in five shell-type main bearings. The connecting rod big-end bearings are also split shell-type, and are attached to the pistons by interference-fit gudgeon pins. Each piston is fitted with two compression rings and one oil control ring.

The camshaft, which runs on bearings within the cylinder block, is chain-driven from the crankshaft, and operates the valves via pushrods and rocker arms. The valves are each closed by a single valve spring, and operate in guides integral in the cylinder head.

The oil pump is mounted externally on the crankcase, incorporates a full-flow oil filter, and is driven by a skew gear on the camshaft.

Repair operations possible with the engine in the car

The following work can be carried out with the engine in the car:
a) Rocker shaft assembly - removal, inspection and refitting.
b) Cylinder head - removal and refitting.
c) Crankshaft pulley - removal and refitting.
d) Crankshaft oil seals - renewal.
e) Timing chain, sprockets and tensioner - removal, inspection and refitting.
f) Oil pump - removal and refitting.
g) Sump - removal and refitting.
h) Connecting rods and pistons - removal and refitting*.
i) Flywheel - removal, inspection and refitting.

j) *Engine/transmission mountings -
inspection and renewal.*

*Although the operation marked with an
asterisk can be carried out with the engine in
the car after removal of the sump, it is better
for the engine to be removed in the interests
of cleanliness and improved access. For this
reason, the procedure is described in Part D
of this Chapter.*

2 Compression test - description and interpretation

1 When engine performance is down, or if
misfiring occurs which cannot be attributed to
the ignition or fuel systems, a compression
test can provide diagnostic clues as to the
engine's condition. If the test is performed
regularly, it can give warning of trouble before
any other symptoms become apparent.

2 The engine must be fully warmed-up to
operating temperature, the oil level must be
correct and the battery must be fully charged.
The help of an assistant will also be required.

3 Refer to Chapter 12 and remove the fuel
pump fuse from the fusebox. Now start the
engine and allow it to run until it stalls.

4 Disable the ignition system by
disconnecting the 3-pin multi-plug from the
DIS ignition coil. Remove all the spark plugs
with reference to Chapter 1A.

5 Fit a compression tester to the No 1
cylinder spark plug hole - the type of tester
which screws into the spark plug thread is to
be preferred.

6 Arrange for an assistant to hold the
accelerator pedal fully depressed to the floor,
while at the same time cranking the engine
over for several seconds on the starter motor.
Observe the compression gauge reading. The
compression will build up fairly quickly in a
healthy engine. Low compression on the first
stroke, followed by gradually-increasing
pressure on successive strokes, indicates
worn piston rings. A low compression on the
first stroke which does not rise on successive
strokes, indicates leaking valves or a blown
head gasket (a cracked cylinder head could
also be the cause). Deposits on the underside
of the valve heads can also cause low
compression. Record the highest gauge
reading obtained, then repeat the procedure
for the remaining cylinders.

7 Due to the variety of testers available, and
the fluctuation in starter motor speed when
cranking the engine, different readings are
often obtained when carrying out the
compression test. For this reason, actual
compression pressure figures are not quoted
by Ford. However, the most important factor
is that the compression pressures are uniform
in all cylinders, and that is what this test is
mainly concerned with.

8 Add some engine oil (about three squirts
from a plunger type oil can) to each cylinder

**3.4 Timing mark on the crankshaft pulley
aligned with the TDC (0) mark on the
timing cover**

through the spark plug holes, and then repeat
the test.

9 If the compression increases after the oil is
added, the piston rings are probably worn. If
the compression does not increase
significantly, the leakage is occurring at the
valves or the head gasket. Leakage past the
valves may be caused by burned valve seats
and/or faces, or warped, cracked or bent
valves.

10 If two adjacent cylinders have equally low
compressions, it is most likely that the head
gasket has blown between them. The
appearance of coolant in the combustion
chambers or on the engine oil dipstick would
verify this condition.

11 If one cylinder is about 20 percent lower
than the other, and the engine has a slightly
rough idle, a worn lobe on the camshaft could
be the cause.

12 On completion of the checks, refit the
spark plugs and reconnect the HT leads and
the DIS ignition coil plug. Refit the fuel pump
fuse to the fusebox.

3 Top Dead Centre (TDC) for No 1 piston - locating

1 Top dead centre (TDC) is the highest point
of the cylinder that each piston reaches as the
crankshaft turns. Each piston reaches its TDC
position at the end of its compression stroke,
and then again at the end of its exhaust
stroke. For the purpose of engine timing, TDC
at the end of the compression stroke for No 1
piston is used. On the Endura-E engine, No 1
cylinder is at the crankshaft pulley/timing
chain end of the engine. Proceed as follows.

2 Ensure that the ignition is switched off.
Disconnect the HT leads from the spark plugs,
then unscrew and remove the plugs as
described in Chapter 1A.

3 Unbolt and remove the auxiliary drivebelt
lower cover for access to the crankshaft
pulley, and unclip the coolant hose from the
cover. If necessary for improved access,
apply the handbrake, then jack up the front of
the vehicle and support it on axle stands (see
"Jacking and Vehicle Support").

4 Turn the engine over by hand (using a
spanner on the crankshaft pulley) to the point
where the timing mark on the crankshaft
pulley aligns with the TDC (0) mark on the
timing cover **(see illustration)**. As the pulley
mark nears the timing mark, the No 1 piston is
simultaneously approaching the top of its
cylinder. To ensure that it is on its
compression stroke, place a finger over the
No 1 cylinder plug hole, and feel to ensure
that air pressure exits from the cylinder as the
piston reaches the top of its stroke.

5 A further check to ensure that the piston is
on its compression stroke can be made by
removing the rocker cover (see Section 4), so
that the movement of the valves and rockers
can be observed.

6 With the TDC timing marks on the
crankshaft pulley and timing cover in
alignment, rock the crankshaft back and forth
a few degrees each side of this position, and
observe the action of the valves and rockers
for No 1 cylinder. When No 1 piston is at the
TDC firing position, the inlet and exhaust valve
of No 1 cylinder will be fully closed, but the
corresponding valves of No 4 cylinder will be
seen to rock open and closed.

7 If the inlet and exhaust valves of No 1
cylinder are seen to rock whilst those of No 4
cylinder are shut, the crankshaft will need to
be turned one full rotation to bring No 1 piston
up to the top of its cylinder on the
compression stroke.

8 Once No 1 cylinder has been positioned at
TDC on the compression stroke, TDC for any
of the other cylinders can then be located by
rotating the crankshaft clockwise (in its
normal direction of rotation), 180° at a time,
and following the firing order (see
Specifications).

9 On completion, clip the coolant hose to the
auxiliary drivebelt lower cover then refit the
cover and tighten the mounting bolts. Where
applicable, lower the vehicle to the ground.

10 Refit the spark plugs (see Chapter 1A) and
reconnect the HT leads.

4 Cylinder head rocker cover - removal and refitting

Removal

1 Remove the air inlet duct from between the
air cleaner and throttle housing (see Chapter 4A).

2 Detach the HT leads from the spark plugs
and position them clear of the rocker cover.
Pull on the connector of each lead (not the
lead itself), and note the order of fitting.

3 Remove the engine oil filler cap, and
disconnect the crankcase ventilation hose
from the Tee-piece. Position the filler cap to
one side.

4 Unscrew the four retaining bolts, and lift the
rocker cover clear of the cylinder head.
Remove the gasket.

4.6a Engage tags of rocker cover gasket into the cut-outs in the cover

4.6b Refitting the rocker cover

Refitting

5 Thoroughly clean the rocker cover, and scrape away any traces of old gasket remaining on the cover and cylinder head mating surfaces.

6 Fit a new gasket to the rocker cover, then refit the rocker cover **(see illustrations)**. Tighten the cover retaining bolts to the specified torque wrench setting, in a diagonal sequence.

7 Refit the engine oil filler cap.

8 Reconnect the HT leads, and refit the air inlet duct (see Chapter 4A).

5 Valve clearances - checking and adjustment

Note: *The valve clearances must be checked and adjusted only when the engine is cold.*

1 The importance of having the valve clearances correctly adjusted cannot be overstressed, as they vitally affect the performance of the engine. If the clearances are too great, the engine will be noisy (characteristic rattling or tapping noises) and engine efficiency will be reduced, as the valves open too late and close too early. A more serious problem arises if the clearances are too small, however. If this is the case, the valves may not close fully when the engine is hot, resulting in serious damage to the engine (eg. burnt valve seats and/or cylinder head warping/cracking). The clearances are checked and adjusted as follows.

5.6 Adjusting the valve clearances

2 Set the engine to TDC for No 1 piston, as described in Section 3. It is not essential to remove the spark plugs, although if they are removed the engine will be easier to turn when adjusting the valve clearances.

3 Remove the rocker cover as described in Section 4.

4 Starting from the thermostat end of the cylinder head, the valves are numbered as follows:

Valve No	Cylinder No
1 - Exhaust	1
2 - Inlet	1
3 - Exhaust	2
4 - Inlet	2
5 - Inlet	3
6 - Exhaust	3
7 - Inlet	4
8 - Exhaust	4

5 Adjust the valve clearances following the sequence given in the following table. Turn the crankshaft pulley 180° (half a turn) after adjusting each pair of valve clearances.

Valves "rocking"	Valves to adjust
7 and 8	1 (exhaust), 2 (inlet)
5 and 6	3 (exhaust), 4 (inlet)
1 and 2	8 (exhaust), 7 (inlet)
3 and 4	6 (exhaust), 5 (inlet)

6 The clearances for the inlet and exhaust valves differ (refer to the Specifications). Use a feeler blade of the appropriate thickness to check each clearance between the end of the valve stem and the rocker arm **(see illustration)**. The blade should be a firm sliding fit between the valve and rocker arm.

6.4 Rocker shaft partially dismantled for inspection

Where adjustment is necessary, turn the adjuster bolt as required with a ring spanner to set the clearance to that specified. The adjuster bolts are of stiff-thread type, and require no locking nut.

7 On completion, refit the rocker cover as described in Section 4.

6 Cylinder head rocker gear - removal, inspection and refitting

Removal

1 Remove the rocker cover as described in Section 4.

2 Unscrew the four retaining bolts, and lift the rocker gear assembly from the cylinder head. As the assembly is withdrawn, ensure that the pushrods remain seated in their positions in the engine.

HAYNES
HiNT

If the pushrods are to be removed, keep them in the correct order of fitting by labelling them 1 to 8, starting from the thermostat end of the cylinder head, or locate them in a card.

2A

Inspection

3 To dismantle the rocker shaft assembly, extract the split pin from one end of the shaft, then withdraw the spring- and plain-washers from the shaft.

4 Slide off the rocker arms, the support pedestals and coil springs from the shaft, but take care to keep them in their original order of fitting **(see illustration)**.

5 Clean the respective components, and inspect them for signs of excessive wear or damage. Check that the oil lubrication holes in the shaft are clear.

6 Check the rocker shaft and arm pads which bear on the valve stem end faces for wear and scoring, and check each rocker arm on the shaft for excessive wear. Renew any components as necessary.

Refitting

7 Apply clean engine oil to the rocker shaft prior to reassembling.

6.8 Flat on the rocker shaft (arrowed) to same side as rocker arm adjusting screws

8 Reassemble in the reverse order of dismantling. Make sure that the "flat" on the rear end of the rocker shaft is to the same side as the rocker arm adjusting screws (closest to the thermostat end of the cylinder head when fitted) **(see illustration)**. This is essential for the correct lubrication of the cylinder head components.
9 Refit the rocker shaft assembly. As it is fitted, ensure that the rocker adjuster screws engage with their corresponding pushrods.
10 Refit the rocker shaft retaining bolts, hand-tighten them and then tighten them to the specified torque wrench setting. As they are tightened, some of the rocker arms will apply pressure to the ends of the valve stems, and some of the rocker pedestals will not initially be in contact with the cylinder head - these should pull down as the bolts are tightened to their specified torque. If for any reason they do not, avoid the temptation to overtighten in order to pull them into position; loosen off the bolts, and check the cause of the problem.
11 Adjust the valve clearances as described in Section 5.

7 Cylinder head -
removal and refitting

Removal

Note: *The following procedure describes removal and refitting of the cylinder head complete with inlet and exhaust manifolds. If wished, the manifolds may be removed first, as described in the relevant Part of Chapter 4, and the cylinder head then removed on its own.*
1 Depressurise the fuel system as described in Chapter 4A.
2 Disconnect the battery negative (earth) lead (see Chapter 5A).
3 Refer to Chapter 1A and drain the cooling system.
4 Remove the air inlet duct from the throttle housing and air cleaner as described in Chapter 4A.
5 Refer to Section 6 and remove the rocker cover and rocker shaft complete with rocker gear.

6 Disconnect the 3-pin multi-plug from the DIS ignition coil.
7 Disconnect the accelerator cable from the throttle housing and supports (see Chapter 4A).
8 Loosen the clip and disconnect the coolant top hose from the thermostat housing. At the same time release the wiring loom from the support clips then remove the clips from the hose.
9 Disconnect the oxygen sensor wiring at the multi-plug.
10 Disconnect the two engine wiring loom multi-plugs at the rear of the engine.
11 Disconnect the brake servo vacuum pipe from the rear of the inlet manifold.
12 Disconnect the evaporative canister purge valve vacuum pipe from the inlet manifold.
13 Unclip and remove the wiring loom support bracket.
14 Disconnect the wiring from the camshaft position sensor, oil pressure switch and engine coolant temperature sensor.
15 Disconnect the heater hose by releasing the quick-release fitting.

> **HAYNES HiNT**
> *Whenever you disconnect any vacuum lines, coolant or emissions hoses, wiring connectors and fuel lines, always label them clearly, so that they can be correctly reassembled. Masking tape and/or a touch-up paint applicator work well for marking the locations of components and brackets.*

16 Unscrew the support bolt then withdraw the oil level dipstick tube.
17 Identify the fuel feed and return lines for position, then disconnect them from the fuel rail by squeezing the lugs on the quick-release couplings. Be prepared for some loss of fuel by placing cloth rags beneath the couplings.
18 Remove the spark plugs from the cylinder head as described in Chapter 1A.
19 Remove the pushrods by twisting them to release them from the tappets in the cylinder block. Keep them in order of fitting by labelling them 1 to 8, starting from the thermostat end of the cylinder head. Alternatively, push them through a piece of card in their fitted sequence.
20 Unbolt and remove the heatshield from the top of the exhaust manifold.
21 Undo the screws securing the exhaust downpipe to the exhaust manifold.
22 Unbolt and remove the cover from the crankshaft position sensor on the front of the cylinder block. Disconnect the wiring from the sensor.
23 Unbolt the wiring loom guide from the left-hand end of the cylinder head.
24 Using a trolley jack and block of wood, support the weight of the engine. Alternatively, use a hoist attached to a lifting eye bolted to the right-hand side of the cylinder block. Note that the lifting eye on the inlet manifold cannot be used since it will be removed together with the cylinder head.

25 Undo the screws and remove the right-hand front engine mounting upper bracket.
26 Progressively unscrew and loosen off the cylinder head retaining bolts in the reverse sequence to that shown for tightening **(see illustration 7.36a)**. When they are all loosened off, remove the bolts, then lift the cylinder head clear and remove the gasket. The gasket must always be renewed; it should be noted that the cylinder head retaining bolts may be re-used, but only once. They should be marked accordingly with a punch or paint mark. If there is any doubt as to how many times the bolts have been used, they must be renewed.
27 If necessary, remove the two dowel pins from the cylinder block.
28 To dismantle/overhaul the cylinder head, refer to Part D of this Chapter. It is normal for the cylinder head to be decarbonised and the valves to be reground whenever the head is removed.

Preparation for refitting

29 The mating faces of the cylinder head and cylinder block must be perfectly clean before refitting the head. Use a hard plastic or wood scraper to remove all traces of gasket and carbon; also clean the piston crowns. Take particular care during the cleaning operations, as aluminium alloy is easily damaged. Also, make sure that the carbon is not allowed to enter the oil and water passages - this is particularly important for the lubrication system, as carbon could block the oil supply to the engine's components. Using adhesive tape and paper, seal the water, oil and bolt holes in the cylinder block.

> **HAYNES HiNT**
> *To prevent carbon entering the gap between the pistons and bores, smear a little grease in the gap. After cleaning each piston, use a small brush to remove all traces of grease and carbon from the gap, then wipe away the remainder with a clean rag.*

30 Check the mating surfaces of the cylinder block and the cylinder head for nicks, deep scratches and other damage. If slight, they may be removed carefully with a file, but if excessive, machining may be the only alternative to renewal.
31 If warpage of the cylinder head gasket surface is suspected, use a straight-edge to check it for distortion. Refer to Part D of this Chapter if necessary.
32 Clean the threads of the cylinder head bolts or fit new ones (as applicable) and clean out the bolt holes in the block. Screwing a bolt into an oil-filled hole can (in extreme cases) cause the block to fracture, due to the hydraulic pressure created.

Refitting

33 Make sure that the two dowel pins are correctly located in the cylinder block.

7.34 Cylinder head gasket top-face marking ("OBEN")

7.36a Cylinder head bolt tightening sequence

34 Check that the new cylinder head gasket is the same type as the original, and that the "TOP" (or "OBEN") marking is facing upwards. Locate the new cylinder head gasket onto the top face of the cylinder block and over the dowels. Ensure that it is correctly aligned with the coolant passages and oilways **(see illustration)**.

35 Lower the cylinder head carefully into position, then insert the retaining bolts and hand-tighten them.

36 Tightening of the cylinder head bolts must be done in three stages, and in the correct sequence. First tighten all of the bolts in the sequence shown to the Stage 1 torque setting. When all of the bolts are tightened to the Stage 1 setting, further tighten each bolt (in sequence) through the Stage 2 specified angle of rotation. When the second stage tightening is completed on all of the bolts, further tighten them to the Stage 3 angle setting (in sequence) to complete. Where possible, use an angle-tightening setting gauge attachment tool for accurate tightening of stages two and three **(see illustrations)**.

37 Lubricate the pushrods with clean engine oil, and then insert them into their original locations.

38 Refit the rocker shaft assembly. As it is fitted, ensure that the rocker adjuster screws engage with their corresponding pushrods.

39 Refit the rocker shaft retaining bolts, hand-tighten them and then tighten them to the specified torque wrench setting. As they are tightened, some of the rocker arms will apply pressure to the ends of the valve stems, and some of the rocker pedestals will not initially be in contact with the cylinder head - these should pull down as the bolts are tightened. If for any reason they do not, avoid the temptation to overtighten in order to pull them into position; loosen off the bolts, and check the cause of the problem.

40 Adjust the valve clearances as described in Section 5.

41 Refit the rocker cover as described in Section 4.

42 The remainder of the refitting procedure is a reversal of the removal process. Tighten all fastenings to their specified torque setting (where given). Refer to Chapters 4A and 4C for details on reconnecting the fuel system

and exhaust system components. Ensure that all coolant, fuel, vacuum and electrical connections are securely made.

43 On completion, refill the cooling system and top-up the engine oil (see Chapter 1A and *"Weekly Checks"*). When the engine is restarted, check for any sign of fuel, oil and/or coolant leakage from the various cylinder head joints.

8 Crankshaft pulley - removal and refitting

Removal

1 Disconnect the battery negative (earth) lead (see Chapter 5A).

2 Apply the handbrake, then jack up the front of the vehicle and support it on axle stands (see *"Jacking and Vehicle Support"*). Remove the right-hand front roadwheel.

3 Working beneath the vehicle, unbolt and remove the drivebelt lower cover, and unclip the coolant hose from the bracket.

4 Remove the auxiliary drivebelt as described in Chapter 1A.

5 Loosen off the crankshaft pulley retaining bolt. To prevent the crankshaft from turning, remove the starter motor (Chapter 5A) and lock

the ring gear through the starter motor aperture using a large screwdriver or similar tool.

6 Fully unscrew the crankshaft pulley bolt, and withdraw the pulley from the front end of the crankshaft. If it does not pull off by hand, lever it free using a pair of suitable levers positioned diagonally opposite each other behind the pulley.

7 If required, the crankshaft front oil seal can be renewed at this stage, as described in Section 14.

Refitting

8 Refitting is a reversal of the removal procedure ensuring that the pulley retaining bolt is tightened to the specified torque setting.

9 Refit the auxiliary drivebelt (see Chapter 1A), and lower the vehicle to the ground.

9 Timing chain cover - removal and refitting

Removal

1 Remove the sump as described in Section 11.

2 Remove the crankshaft pulley as described in Section 8.

7.36b Tightening the cylinder head bolts (Stage 1)

7.36c Cylinder head bolt tightening (Stages 2 and 3) using an angle gauge

2A

10.2 Oil slinger removal from crankshaft

10.3 Chain tensioner arm removal from the pivot pin. Note tensioner retaining bolts (arrowed)

3 Disconnect the camshaft position sensor wiring multi-plug.

4 Unscrew the retaining bolts, and carefully prise free the timing chain cover. Note that one of the bolt holes is split and the bolt also secures the water pump.

5 A combined timing cover and water pump gasket is fitted during production; if this is still fitted, it will be necessary to cut away the old gasket using a sharp knife keeping as close as possible to the water pump. If the timing cover has been removed at any time, the single gasket used originally will have been replaced by an individual gasket.

6 Clean the mating faces of the timing chain cover and cylinder block.

7 If necessary, renew the crankshaft front oil seal in the timing cover prior to refitting the cover (see Section 14).

Refitting

8 Lightly lubricate the front end of the crankshaft and the radial lip of the timing chain cover oil seal (already installed in the cover). Using a new gasket, fit the timing chain cover, centring it with the aid of the crankshaft pulley - lubricate the seal contact surfaces beforehand. Refit the retaining bolts and tighten them to the specified torque. Note that the sump mating faces of the cover and

cylinder block must be level with each other.

9 Refit the crankshaft pulley (see Section 8).

10 Reconnect the camshaft position sensor multi-plug.

11 Refit the sump as described in Section 11.

10 Timing chain, sprockets and tensioner - removal, inspection and refitting

Removal

1 Remove the timing chain cover as described in Section 9.

2 Remove the oil slinger from the front face of the crankshaft, noting its orientation **(see illustration)**.

3 Retract the chain tensioner cam back against its spring pressure, then slide the chain tensioner arm from its pivot pin on the front main bearing cap **(see illustration)**.

4 Unbolt and remove the chain tensioner.

5 Note the fitted position of the camshaft position sender plate, then unscrew and remove the camshaft sprocket bolts and remove the plate. Hold the sprocket stationary using a suitable tool engaged with the holes in the sprocket.

6 Withdraw the camshaft sprocket and

unhook the timing chain from the crankshaft sprocket.

7 Slide the sprocket from the key on the nose of the crankshaft. If it is tight use a suitable puller. If necessary, remove the Woodruff key from the groove in the crankshaft.

Inspection

8 Examine the teeth on the timing sprockets for any signs of excessive wear or damage.

9 The timing chain should always be renewed during a major engine overhaul. Slack links and pins are indicative of a worn chain. Unless the chain is known to be relatively new, it should be renewed.

10 Examine the rubber cushion on the tensioner spring leaf. If grooved or deteriorated, it must be renewed.

Refitting

11 Commence reassembly by locating the Woodruff key in the crankshaft groove, making sure that it is parallel to the surface of the crankshaft.

12 Slide on the crankshaft sprocket and engage it with the Woodruff key. If it is tight, use the pulley together with its bolt to press on the sprocket. Make sure the timing mark is on the outer face of the sprocket.

13 Fit the timing chain tensioner and tighten the mounting bolts to the specified torque. Check that the face of the tensioner cam is parallel with the face of the cylinder block, ideally using a dial gauge. The maximum permissible error between two measuring points 20 mm apart is 0.16 mm. If necessary, loosen the mounting bolts, turn the tensioner as required, then tighten the bolts and recheck.

14 Turn the crankshaft so that the timing mark on the crankshaft sprocket is directly in line with the centre of the camshaft sprocket mounting flange.

15 Engage the camshaft sprocket with the timing chain, then engage the chain around the teeth of the crankshaft sprocket. Push the

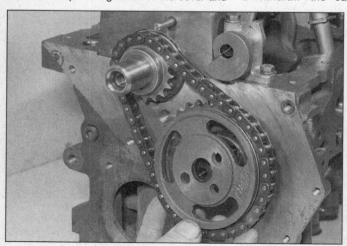

10.15a Fit the timing chain to the crankshaft and camshaft sprockets . . .

10.15b . . . and check that the timing marks on the sprockets are in alignment

camshaft sprocket onto its mounting flange, and check that the sprocket retaining bolt holes are in alignment. Also check that the timing marks of both sprockets face each other. If required, turn the camshaft/sprocket as required to achieve this. It may also be necessary to remove the camshaft sprocket from the chain in order to reposition it in the required location in the chain to align the timing marks. This is a "trial and error" procedure, which must be continued until the exact alignment of the bolt holes and the timing marks is made **(see illustrations)**.

16 Locate the camshaft position sender plate on the sprocket in its previously noted position, then insert the sprocket bolts and tighten them to the specified torque.

17 Retract the timing chain tensioner cam, and then slide the tensioner arm onto its pivot pin. Release the cam so that it bears on the arm.

18 Refit the oil slinger to the front of the crankshaft sprocket so that its convex side faces the sprocket.

19 Refit the timing chain cover as described in Section 9.

11 Sump -
removal and refitting

Removal

1 Disconnect the battery negative (earth) lead (see Chapter 5A). Apply the handbrake, then jack up the front of the vehicle and support it on axle stands (see *"Jacking and Vehicle Support"*). Where applicable, remove the engine undershield.

2 Refer to Chapter 1A and drain the engine oil. Refit the sump drain plug.

3 Trace the wiring back from the oxygen sensor on the downpipe and disconnect it at the wiring connector. Unbolt and remove the heatshields from the exhaust manifold, then unscrew the nuts securing the downpipe to the exhaust manifold, separate the downpipe and remove the ring gasket. Release the exhaust mounting rubber and lower the downpipe from the engine.

4 Remove the starter motor (see Chapter 5A).

5 Working beneath the vehicle, unbolt and remove the auxiliary drivebelt lower cover, and unclip the coolant hose from the bracket.

6 On models with air conditioning, remove the auxiliary drivebelt (Chapter 1A), unbolt the compressor from the sump mounting and position the compressor to one side. Do not disconnect any refrigerant hoses.

7 Unscrew the bolts securing the sump flange to the transmission.

8 Undo the eighteen bolts securing the sump to the base of the engine crankcase, then prise free and lower the sump. If the sump is stuck tight to the engine, cut around the flange gasket with a sharp knife, then lightly tap and prise it free. Keep the sump upright as

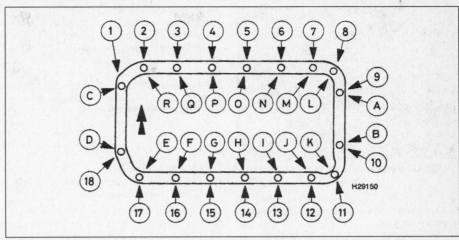

11.15 Sump bolt tightening sequence (Endura-E engines) - arrow indicates front of car
Refer to Specifications for torque wrench settings

Stage 1 - Tighten in alphabetical order
Stage 2 - Tighten in numerical order

Stage 3 - Tighten in alphabetical order

it is lowered, to prevent spillage of any remaining oil in it. Also be prepared for oil drips from the crankcase when the sump is removed.

9 Remove the one-piece sump gasket.

10 Remove any dirt and old gasket from the contact faces of the sump and crankcase, and wash the sump out thoroughly before refitting. Check that the mating faces of the sump are not distorted. Check that the oil pick-up strainer is clear, cleaning it if necessary.

Refitting

11 Thoroughly clean the sump and cylinder block mating faces.

12 Apply sealing compound (available from Ford dealers) to the cylinder block mating face in the area of the joint between the timing chain cover and cylinder block, and the rear oil seal housing and cylinder block. Also apply sealer into the corners of the semi-circular areas on the timing chain cover and rear oil seal housing.

13 Locate the one-piece gasket on the sump, then fit the sump to the crankcase. Fit the retaining bolts and tighten them initially finger-tight.

14 Using a straight-edge, check that the sump flange is level with the surface of the cylinder block. If necessary reposition the sump.

15 Tighten the bolts in the sequence shown through Stages 1 and 2, to the torques specified **(see illustration)**. Note that different tightening sequences are specified for the tightening stages. Final (Stage 3) tightening is carried out after the engine has been started and warmed up.

16 Refit and tighten the bolts securing the sump flange to the transmission.

17 Where applicable, refit the air conditioning compressor, then refit and adjust the auxiliary drivebelt as described in Chapter 1A.

18 Refit the auxiliary drivebelt lower cover and clip the coolant hose into position.

19 Refit the starter motor.

20 Check that the downpipe and manifold mating faces are clean, then locate a new ring gasket and reconnect the exhaust downpipe to the manifold. Where applicable, use new self-locking nuts, and tighten securely. Refit the rubber mounting, and reconnect the oxygen sensor wiring.

21 Check that the sump drain plug is fitted and tightened securely, then refill the engine with oil as described in Chapter 1A.

22 Reconnect the battery, then start the engine and run it up to its normal operating temperature. Check that no oil leaks are evident around the sump joint.

23 After the engine has warmed up for approximately 15 minutes, switch it off. Tighten the sump bolts to the Stage 3 torque wrench setting given in the Specifications, in the correct sequence.

24 Refit the undershield and lower the vehicle to the ground.

12 Oil pump -
removal and refitting

Removal

1 The oil pump is externally-mounted, on the rear-facing side of the crankcase.

2 Apply the handbrake, then jack up the front of the vehicle and support it on axle stands (see *"Jacking and Vehicle Support"*).

3 Unscrew and remove the oil filter cartridge. It should unscrew by hand, but will probably be tight. Use a strap wrench to loosen it off, if required. Catch any oil spillage in a suitable container.

2A

12.4 Unscrewing the oil pump retaining bolts

4 Undo the three retaining bolts and withdraw the oil pump from the engine **(see illustration)**.
5 Clean all traces of the old gasket from the mating surfaces of the pump and engine.

Refitting

6 If the original oil pump has been dismantled and reassembled and is to be re-used, or if a new pump is to be fitted, it must first be primed with engine oil prior to fitting. To do this, turn its driveshaft and simultaneously

inject clean engine oil into it.
7 Locate a new gasket into position on the pump mounting flange, then insert the pump, engaging the drivegear as it is fitted **(see illustration)**. Fit the retaining bolts, and tighten to the specified torque wrench setting.
8 Fit a new oil filter into position on the oil pump body, as described in Chapter 1A.
9 Lower the vehicle to the ground, and top-up the engine oil as described in *"Weekly Checks"*.

13 Oil pump - dismantling, inspection and reassembly

Dismantling

1 To inspect the oil pump components for excessive wear, undo the retaining bolts and remove the cover plate from the pump body. Remove the O-ring seal from the cover face **(see illustration)**.
2 Wipe the exterior of the pump housing clean housing.

Inspection

3 Noting their orientation, extract and clean the rotors and the inner body of the pump housing. Inspect them for signs of severe scoring or excessive wear, which if evident will necessitate renewal of the complete pump.
4 Using feeler blades, check the clearances between the pump body and the outer rotor, the inner-to-outer rotor clearance, and the amount of rotor endfloat **(see illustrations)**.
5 Check the drivegear for signs of excessive wear or damage.
6 If the clearances measured are outside the specified maximum clearances and/or the drivegear is in poor condition, the complete pump unit must be renewed.

Reassembly

7 Refit the rotors into the pump (in their original orientation), lubricate the rotors and the new O-ring seal with clean engine oil, and refit the cover. Tighten the retaining bolts to the specified torque wrench setting.

12.7 Refitting the oil pump. Note the new gasket

13.1 Extract the O-ring from the groove in the oil pump

13.4a Checking the outer body-to-rotor clearance

13.4b Checking the inner rotor-to-outer rotor clearance

13.4c Checking the rotor endfloat

14 Crankshaft oil seals - renewal

Front oil seal

1 Remove the crankshaft pulley as described in Section 8.

2 Using a suitable claw tool, extract the oil seal from the timing chain cover, but take care not to damage the seal housing. As it is removed, note the fitted orientation of the seal in the cover.

 If a claw tool is not available, screw two self-tapping screws into the seal, and pull on the screws to remove the seal.

3 Clean the oil seal housing in the timing chain cover. Lubricate the sealing lips of the new seal and the crankshaft nose with clean engine oil.

4 Locate the new seal into position so that it is squarely located on the crankshaft stub and in the housing, and is correctly orientated. Drift it into position using a large socket, another suitable tool, or the old seal, until the new seal is flush with the edge of the timing chain cover.

5 Lightly lubricate the oil seal contact surface of the crankshaft pulley, then refit the pulley as described in Section 8.

Rear oil seal

6 Remove the flywheel as described in Section 15.

7 Note the orientation and fitted depth of the oil seal to ensure correct fitting of the new seal.

8 Using a suitable claw tool, lever the seal from the rear seal housing (taking care not to damage the housing) - see Haynes Hint.

9 Clean the seal housing, the crankshaft rear flange face and the flywheel mating surface.

10 Lubricate the crankshaft flange and the oil seal inner lip with clean engine oil.

11 If Ford service tool No 21-011F is

15.5 Tightening the flywheel retaining bolts to the specified torque

Note the "peg" tool locking the ring gear teeth to prevent rotation as the bolts are tightened.

available, position the seal on the service tool (ensuring correct orientation), then press the seal into its housing using two diagonally opposite flywheel bolts. Tighten the bolts progressively to ensure that the oil seal enters correctly. Remove the tool on completion.

12 If the service tool is not available, start the oil seal in its housing using finger pressure initially then carefully tap it into the housing to its previously noted position making sure it is kept square. If a suitable length of metal tube is available use this to drive in the seal.

13 Check that the crankshaft rear flange and the flywheel mating faces are clean, then refit the flywheel as described in Section 15.

15 Flywheel - removal, inspection and refitting

Removal

1 Remove the transmission as described in Chapter 7A, then remove the clutch as described in Chapter 6.

2 Unscrew the six retaining bolts, and remove the flywheel from the rear flange of the crankshaft - take care not to drop the flywheel, as it is heavy. A tool similar to that shown in illustration 15.5 can be fitted to prevent the flywheel/crankshaft from rotating as the bolts are removed. If on removal, the retaining bolts are found to be in poor condition (stretched threads, etc) they must be renewed.

Inspection

3 Inspect the starter ring gear on the flywheel for any broken or excessively worn teeth. If evident, the ring gear must be renewed; this is a task best entrusted to a Ford dealer or a competent garage. Alternatively, obtain a complete new flywheel.

4 The clutch friction surface on the flywheel must be carefully inspected for grooving or hairline cracks (caused by overheating). If these conditions are evident, it may be possible to have the flywheel surface-ground, however this work must be carried out by an engine overhaul specialist. If surface-grinding is not possible, the flywheel must be renewed.

Refitting

5 Check that the mating faces of the flywheel and crankshaft are clean before refitting. Lubricate the threads of the retaining bolts with engine oil before they are screwed into position. Locate the flywheel onto the crankshaft so that the hole engages with the dowel, then insert the bolts. Hand-tighten them initially, then tighten them in a progressive sequence to the specified torque **(see illustration)**.

6 Refit the clutch as described in Chapter 6 and the transmission as described in Chapter 7A.

16 Engine/transmission mountings - inspection and renewal

Inspection

1 The engine/transmission mountings seldom require attention, but broken or deteriorated mountings should be renewed immediately, or the added strain placed on the driveline components may cause damage or wear.

2 During the check, the engine/transmission must be raised slightly, to remove its weight from the mountings.

3 Apply the handbrake, then jack up the front of the vehicle and support it on axle stands (see *"Jacking and Vehicle Support"*). Position a jack under the sump, with a large block of wood between the jack head and the sump, then carefully raise the engine/transmission just enough to take the weight off the mountings.

4 Check the mountings to see if the rubber is cracked, hardened or separated from the metal components. Sometimes, the rubber will split right down the centre.

5 Check for relative movement between each mounting's brackets and the engine/transmission or body (use a large screwdriver or lever to attempt to move the mountings). If movement is noted, lower the engine and check the mounting nuts and bolts for tightness.

Renewal

6 The engine mountings can be removed if the weight of the engine/transmission is supported by one of the following alternative methods.

7 Either support the weight of the assembly from underneath using a jack and a suitable piece of wood between the jack and the sump (to prevent damage), or from above by attaching a hoist to the engine. A third method is to use a suitable support bar with end pieces which will engage in the water channel each side of the bonnet lid aperture. Using an adjustable hook and chain connected to the engine, the weight of the engine and transmission can then be taken from the mountings.

8 Once the weight of the engine and transmission is suitably supported, any of the mountings can be unbolted and removed.

9 To remove the right-hand engine mounting, unscrew the nuts and remove the upper bracket, then unscrew the bolts and remove the lower bracket from the cylinder head. Unbolt the insulator from the right-hand side of the engine compartment.

10 To remove the left-hand mounting first remove the battery and battery tray as described in Chapter 5A, then loosen the clips and remove the air inlet duct from between

2A

the air mass air flow sensor on the air cleaner and the throttle housing. Unscrew the mounting nuts from the left-hand engine mounting, then unscrew the bolts and remove the upper bracket. Unscrew the bolts and remove the insulator from the left-hand side of the engine compartment.

11 To remove the rear engine mounting/link, apply the handbrake, then jack up the front of the vehicle and support it on axle stands (see *"Jacking and Vehicle Support"*). Unscrew the through-bolts and remove the rear engine mounting link from the bracket on the transmission and from the bracket on the underbody. Hold the engine stationary while the bolts are being removed since the link will be under tension.

12 Refitting of all mountings is a reversal of the removal procedure. Do not fully tighten the mounting nuts/bolts until all of the mountings are in position. Check that the mounting rubbers do not twist or distort as the mounting bolts and nuts are tightened to their specified torques.

Chapter 2 Part B:
Zetec-SE petrol engine in-car repair procedures

Contents

Degrees of difficulty

| Easy, suitable for novice with little experience | | Fairly easy, suitable for beginner with some experience | | Fairly difficult, suitable for competent DIY mechanic | 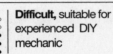 | Difficult, suitable for experienced DIY mechanic | | Very difficult, suitable for expert DIY or professional | |

Specifications

2B

General

Engine type	Four-cylinder, in-line, double overhead camshafts
Designation	Zetec-SE
Engine code:	
1.25 litre	DHA
1.4 litre	FHA
Capacity:	
1.25 litre	1242 cc
1.4 litre	1388 cc
Bore:	
1.25 litre	71.8 mm
1.4 litre	75.9 mm
Stroke (all engines)	76.5 mm
Compression ratio:	
1.25 litre	10.0:1
1.4 litre	10.3:1
Firing order	1-3-4-2 (No 1 cylinder at timing belt end)
Direction of crankshaft rotation	Clockwise (seen from right-hand side of vehicle)

Valves

	Inlet	Exhaust
Valve clearance (cold)	0.17 to 0.23 mm	0.27 to 0.33 mm
Valve length:		
1.25 litre	97.65 mm	99.70 mm
1.4 litre	97.35 mm	99.40 mm

Valve springs

Free length	53.2 mm

Cylinder head

Maximum permissible gasket surface distortion	0.05 mm

Cylinder block

Cylinder bore diameter:
   1.25 litre engine:
Class 1	71.900 to 71.910 mm
Class 2	71.910 to 71.920 mm
Class 3	71.920 to 71.930 mm

   1.4 litre engine:
Class 1	76.000 to 76.010 mm
Class 2	76.010 to 76.020 mm
Class 3	76.020 to 76.030 mm

Pistons and piston rings

Piston diameter:
   1.25 litre engine:
Class 1	71.875 to 71.885 mm
Class 2	71.885 to 71.895 mm
Class 3	71.895 to 71.905 mm
1.4 litre engine	Unavailable at time of writing
Oversizes - all engines	None available
Piston-to-cylinder bore clearance	Not specified

Piston ring end gaps - installed:	**1.25 litre**	**1.4 litre**
Top compression ring	0.2 to 0.3 mm	0.2 to 0.3 mm
Second compression ring	0.3 to 0.7 mm	0.3 to 0.7 mm
Oil control ring	0.3 to 0.7 mm	0.15 to 0.65 mm

Crankshaft

Note: *The crankshaft cannot be removed from the cylinder block (see text).*

Crankshaft endfloat	0.220 to 0.430 mm

Camshafts

Camshaft bearing journal diameter	Unavailable at time of writing
Camshaft bearing journal-to-cylinder head running clearance	Unavailable at time of writing
Camshaft endfloat (typical)	0.05 to 0.13 mm

Lubrication

Oil pressure (warm engine):
Idling (800 rpm)	1.4 bars
At 2000 rpm	3.0 bars
Pressure relief valve opens at	5.0 bars
Oil pump clearances	Not specified

Torque wrench settings

	Nm	lbf ft
Crankshaft sprocket/timing belt retainer plate to cylinder block	9	7
Battery box	25	18
Camshaft pulley bolt	60	44
Coolant outlet to cylinder head	19	14
Cover on cylinder head cover	6	4
Crankcase breather to cylinder block	9	7
Crankshaft rear oil seal housing	9	7
Cylinder head cover	10	7
Earth lead to alternator	11	8
Earth lead to transmission	30	15
Engine mounting brackets	55	41
Fluid pipes to transmission	21	15
Flywheel	85	63
Left-hand engine mounting bracket bolts	49	36
Left-hand engine mounting bracket nuts	69	51
Lifting eye to cylinder head	19	14
Lower timing belt cover	9	7
Oil baffle to cylinder block	9	7
Oil dipstick tube	9	7
Oil drain plug	37	27
Oil filter connector	45	33
Oil intake pipe to oil baffle	9	7
Oil pressure switch	15	11
Oil pump to cylinder block	9	7
Rear engine mounting link to crossmember	70	51
Rear engine mounting link to engine	50	36

Torque wrench settings (continued)

	Nm	lbf ft
Right-hand engine mounting bracket	69	51
Sump	20	15
TDC pin blanking hole	25	18
Thermostat housing to cylinder block	9	7
Timing belt tensioner	20	15
Timing belt tensioning pulley	35	26
Upper timing belt cover	9	7
Big-end bearing cap:		
Stage 1	8	6
Stage 2	Angle-tighten through 90°	
Camshaft bearing cap:		
Stage 1	6	4
Stage 2	15	11
Cylinder head:		
Stage 1	15	11
Stage 2	30	22
Stage 3	Angle-tighten through 90°	
Crankshaft pulley/vibration damper:		
Stage 1	40	30
Stage 2	Angle-tighten through 90°	

1 General information

How to use this Chapter

This Part of Chapter 2 is devoted to in-car repair procedures on the Zetec-SE petrol engine. All procedures concerning engine removal and refitting, and engine block/cylinder head overhaul can be found in Chapter 2D.

Refer to *"Buying spare parts and vehicle identification numbers"* in the Reference Section at the end of this manual for details of engine code locations.

Most of the operations included in this chapter are based on the assumption that the engine is still installed in the car. Therefore, if this information is being used during a complete engine overhaul, with the engine already removed, many of the steps included here will not apply.

Engine description

The Zetec-SE engine, (formerly Zeta), is of sixteen-valve, double overhead camshaft (DOHC), four-cylinder, in-line type, mounted transversely at the front of the vehicle, with the transmission on its left-hand end. It is available in 1.25 litre and 1.4 litre versions.

Apart from the plastic timing belt covers and plastic inlet manifold, and the cast iron cylinder liners, the engine (including the sump) is manufactured entirely of aluminium alloy.
Caution: When tightening bolts into aluminium castings, it is important to adhere to the specified torque wrench settings, to avoid stripping threads with the resultant time-consuming consequences.

The crankshaft runs in five main bearings, the centre main bearing's upper half incorporating thrustwashers to control crankshaft endfloat. Due to the very fine bearing clearances and bearing shell tolerances incorporated during manufacture, it is not possible to renew the crankshaft separate to the cylinder block; in fact it is not possible to remove and refit the crankshaft accurately using conventional tooling. This means that if the crankshaft is worn excessively, it must be renewed together with the cylinder block.
Caution: Do not unbolt the main bearing cap/ladder from the cylinder block, as it is not possible to refit it accurately using conventional tooling. Additionally, the manufacturers do not supply torque settings for the main bearing cap/ladder retaining bolts.

The connecting rods rotate on horizontally-split bearing shells at their big-ends, however the big-ends are of unusual design in that the caps are sheared from the rods during manufacture thus making each cap individually matched to its own connecting rod. The big-end bearing shells are also unusual in that they do not have any locating tabs and must be accurately positioned during refitting. The pistons are attached to the connecting rods by gudgeon pins which are an interference fit in the connecting rod small-end eyes. The aluminium alloy pistons are fitted with three piston rings: two compression rings and an oil control ring. After manufacture, the cylinder bores and pistons are measured and classified into three grades, which must be carefully matched together, to ensure the correct piston/cylinder clearance; no oversizes are available to permit reboring.

The inlet and exhaust valves are each closed by coil springs; they operate in guides which are shrink-fitted into the cylinder head, as are the valve seat inserts.

Both camshafts are driven by the same toothed timing belt, each operating eight valves via bucket tappets and shims. Each camshaft rotates in five bearings that are line-bored directly in the cylinder head and the (bolted-on) bearing caps; this means that the bearing caps are not available separately from the cylinder head, and must not be interchanged with caps from another engine.

The water pump is bolted to the right-hand end of the cylinder block, beneath the front run of the timing belt, and is driven by the auxiliary drivebelt from the crankshaft pulley.

Lubrication is by means of an eccentric-rotor trochoidal pump, which is mounted on the crankshaft right-hand end, and draws oil through a strainer located in the sump. The pump forces oil through an externally-mounted full-flow cartridge-type filter.

Repair operations possible with the engine in the car

The following work can be carried out with the engine in the car:
a) Cylinder head cover - removal and refitting.
b) Timing belt - renewal.
c) Timing belt tensioner and sprockets - removal and refitting.
d) Camshaft oil seals - renewal.
e) Camshafts, tappets and shims - removal and refitting.
f) Cylinder head - removal and refitting.
g) Sump - removal and refitting.
h) Crankshaft oil seals - renewal.
i) Oil pump - removal and refitting.
j) Flywheel/driveplate - removal and refitting.
k) Engine/transmission mountings - removal and refitting.

Note: *It is possible to remove the pistons and connecting rods (after removing the cylinder head and sump) without removing the engine. However, this is not recommended. Work of this nature is more easily and thoroughly completed with the engine on the bench, as described in Chapter 2D.*

2B

2 Compression test - description and interpretation

1 When engine performance is down, or if misfiring occurs which cannot be attributed to the ignition or fuel systems, a compression test can provide diagnostic clues as to the engine's condition. If the test is performed regularly, it can give warning of trouble before any other symptoms become apparent.

2 The engine must be fully warmed-up to operating temperature, the oil level must be correct and the battery must be fully charged. The help of an assistant will also be required.

3 Refer to Chapter 12 and remove the fuel pump fuse from the fusebox. Now start the engine and allow it to run until it stalls.

4 Unscrew and remove the oil filler cap, then unbolt the plastic cover for access to the spark plugs. Refit the oil filler cap.

5 Disable the ignition system by disconnecting the 3-pin multi-plug from the DIS ignition coil. Remove all the spark plugs with reference to Chapter 1A.

6 Fit a compression tester to the No 1 cylinder spark plug hole - the type of tester which screws into the spark plug thread is to be preferred.

7 Arrange for an assistant to hold the accelerator pedal fully depressed to the floor, while at the same time cranking the engine over for several seconds on the starter motor. Observe the compression gauge reading. The compression will build up fairly quickly in a healthy engine. Low compression on the first stroke, followed by gradually-increasing pressure on successive strokes, indicates worn piston rings. A low compression on the first stroke which does not rise on successive strokes, indicates leaking valves or a blown head gasket (a cracked cylinder head could also be the cause). Deposits on the underside of the valve heads can also cause low compression. Record the highest gauge reading obtained, then repeat the procedure for the remaining cylinders.

8 Due to the variety of testers available, and the fluctuation in starter motor speed when cranking the engine, different readings are often obtained when carrying out the compression test. For this reason, actual compression pressure figures are not quoted by Ford. However, the most important factor is that the compression pressures are uniform in all cylinders, and that is what this test is mainly concerned with.

9 Add some engine oil (about three squirts from a plunger type oil can) to each cylinder through the spark plug holes, and then repeat the test.

10 If the compression increases after the oil is added, the piston rings are probably worn. If the compression does not increase significantly, the leakage is occurring at the valves or the head gasket. Leakage past the valves may be caused by burned valve seats and/or faces, or warped, cracked or bent valves.

11 If two adjacent cylinders have equally low compressions, it is most likely that the head gasket has blown between them. The appearance of coolant in the combustion chambers or on the engine oil dipstick would verify this condition.

12 If one cylinder is about 20 percent lower than the other, and the engine has a slightly rough idle, a worn lobe on the camshaft could be the cause.

13 On completion of the checks, refit the spark plugs and reconnect the HT leads and the DIS ignition coil plug. Refit the plastic cover and oil filler cap. Refit the fuel pump fuse to the fusebox.

3 Top Dead Centre (TDC) for No 1 piston - locating

Note: *A timing pin and camshaft setting bar are required for this procedure (see text).*

1 Top dead centre (TDC) is the highest point of the cylinder that each piston reaches as the crankshaft turns. Each piston reaches its TDC position at the end of its compression stroke, and then again at the end of its exhaust stroke. For the purpose of engine timing, TDC on the compression stroke for No 1 piston is used. No 1 cylinder is at the timing belt end of the engine. Proceed as follows.

2 Disconnect the battery negative (earth) lead (refer to Chapter 5A).

3 Apply the handbrake, then jack up the front of the vehicle and support it on axle stands (see *"Jacking and Vehicle Support"*). If the engine is to be turned using the right-hand front roadwheel with 4th gear engaged, it is only necessary to raise the right-hand front roadwheel off the ground.

4 Where necessary, remove the engine undershield, then remove the auxiliary drivebelt lower cover for access to the crankshaft pulley and bolt.

5 Remove the cylinder head cover as described in Section 4.

6 The piston of No 1 cylinder must now be positioned just before top dead centre (TDC). To do this, have an assistant turn the crankshaft until the slots in the left-hand ends of the camshafts are parallel with the upper surface of the cylinder head. Note that the slots are slightly offset so make sure that the lower edges of the slots are aligned with the cylinder head. Turn the crankshaft slightly anticlockwise (viewed from the right-hand end of the engine).

7 Unscrew the blanking plug from the right-hand rear side of the engine cylinder block. A timing pin must now be inserted and tightened into the hole. If the special Ford timing pin (21-210) is unavailable, a home-made tool can be fabricated out of a bolt having the same thread as the blanking plug. The length of the pin must be 38.24 mm, and this measurement can be accurately adjusted using a self-locking nut screwed onto the bolt as shown **(see illustrations)**. Use vernier calipers to set the position of the nut on the bolt.

8 With the timing pin in position, turn the crankshaft clockwise until the specially machined surface on the crank web just touches the timing pin. No 1 piston is now at TDC on its compression stroke. To confirm this, check that the camshaft lobes for No 4 cylinder are 'rocking' (ie exhaust valves closing and inlet valves opening).

9 It should now be possible to insert the camshaft setting bar into the slots in the left-hand ends of the camshafts. If the Ford setting tool (2-162) is unavailable, a home-made tool can be fabricated out of a length of flat metal bar 5.00 mm thick. The bar must be a good fit in the slots and should be approximately 180 to 230 mm long by 20 to 30 mm wide **(see illustration)**.

3.7a Unscrew the blanking plug from the right-hand rear side of the cylinder block . . .

3.7b . . . then insert the timing pin

3.9 Home-made camshaft setting bar located in the camshaft slots

4.2a Lift the flap . . .

4.2b . . . and disconnect the crankcase breather hose

10 If the bar cannot be inserted in the slots with the crankshaft at TDC, the valve timing must be adjusted as described in Section 8 of this Chapter.

4.3a Undo the screws . . .

11 Once the work requiring the TDC setting has been completed, remove the metal bar from the camshaft slots then unscrew the timing pin and refit the blanking plug. Refit the cylinder head cover (Section 4), auxiliary drivebelt lower cover, and where necessary the engine undershield. Lower the vehicle to the ground and reconnect the battery negative lead.

4   Cylinder head cover - removal and refitting

Removal

1 Disconnect the battery negative (earth) lead (see Chapter 5A).

2 Lift the flap over the centre of the fuel rail at the front of the cylinder head cover, then disconnect the crankcase breather hose **(see illustrations)**.
3 Unscrew and remove the oil filler cap, then undo the screws and lift the plastic cover for access to the spark plug HT leads **(see illustrations)**.
4 Disconnect the HT leads from the spark plugs and ignition coil, and position them to the left-hand side of the engine compartment. Also disconnect the camshaft position sensor wiring and remove it from the channel in the cylinder head cover **(see illustrations)**.
5 Unscrew the nuts securing the cylinder head cover to the top of the cylinder head. Also undo the screw securing the upper timing cover to the cylinder head cover **(see illustration)**.
6 Carefully lift the cover from the top of the cylinder head **(see illustration)**. Note that the gasket is vulcanised to the cover and cannot be renewed separately. Take care not to damage the gasket otherwise it will be necessary to obtain a new cover. Note also that the four rubber plugs in the cover locate on extensions on the camshaft bearing caps.
7 Check the condition of the vulcanised gasket and the rubber plugs. If necessary, renew the plugs. The new plugs come together with a special plastic installer which is located on the lower lip of the plug. After pressing the plug into the cover, remove the installer **(see illustrations)**.

2B

4.3b . . . and remove the plastic cover from the cylinder head cover

4.4a Disconnect the HT leads from the spark plugs . . .

4.4b . . . and from the ignition coil

4.4c Removing the camshaft position sensor wiring from the channel in the cylinder head cover

4.5 Unscrew the nuts . . .

4.6 . . . and remove the cylinder head cover

4.7a Locate the plastic installer on the rubber plug . . .

Refitting

8 Clean the surface of the cylinder head and the gasket on the cover.
9 Lower the cover onto the cylinder head and over the location studs. Refit and tighten the securing nuts to the specified torque.
10 Insert and tighten the screw securing the upper timing cover to the cylinder head cover.
11 Reconnect the HT leads to the spark plugs.
12 Refit the plastic cover and tighten the securing screws, then refit the oil filler cap.
13 Reconnect the crankcase breather hose and refit the covering flap.
14 Reconnect the battery negative lead.

5 Valve clearances - checking and adjustment

1 Remove the cylinder head cover as described in Section 4.
2 Remove the spark plugs (Chapter 1A) in order to make turning the engine easier. The engine may be turned using a spanner on the crankshaft pulley bolt or by raising the front right-hand roadwheel clear of the ground, engaging 4th gear (manual transmission models only) and turning the wheel. If the former method is used, jack up and support the front of the vehicle (see *"Jacking and Vehicle Support"*) then unbolt the lower cover for access to the pulley bolt; if the latter method is used, apply the handbrake then jack up the front right-hand side of the vehicle

5.9 Depressing a tappet with a screwdriver and removing a shim

4.7b . . . then press the plug into the cylinder head cover, and remove the installer

until the roadwheel is clear of the ground and support with an axle stand.
3 Draw the valve positions on a piece of paper, numbering them 1 to 8 inlet and exhaust, from the timing belt (right-hand) end of the engine (ie 1E, 1I, 2E, 2I and so on). As there are two inlet and two exhaust valves for each cylinder, draw the cylinders as large circles and the four valves as smaller circles. The inlet valves are at the front of the cylinder head, and the exhaust valves are at the rear. As the valve clearances are adjusted, cross them off.
4 Turn the engine in a clockwise direction until both inlet valves of No 1 cylinder are fully shut and the apex of the camshaft lobes are pointing upwards away from the valve positions.
5 Insert a feeler blade of the correct thickness (see *Specifications*) between the heel of the camshaft lobe and the shim on the tappet. It should be a firm sliding fit. If this is the case, the clearance is correct and the valve position can be crossed off. If the clearance is not correct, use feeler blades to determine the exact clearance and record this on the drawing. From this clearance it will be possible to calculate the thickness of the new shim to be fitted.
6 Check the clearance of the second inlet valve for No 1 cylinder and if necessary record the existing clearance on the drawing.
7 Now turn the engine until the inlet valves of No 2 cylinder are fully shut and the camshaft lobes pointing away from the valve positions. Check the clearances as described previously and record any that are incorrect.

5.11 Valve clearance adjustment shim

8 After checking all of the inlet valve clearances, check the exhaust valve clearances in the same way but note that the clearances are different.
9 Where adjustment is required, the procedure is to remove the shim from the top of the tappet and fit a new shim to provide the correct clearance. Ford technicians use a special tool (21-218) consisting of a bar bolted to the left and right-hand camshaft bearing caps. A sliding lever on the bar is used, together with a pushrod, to depress the relevant tappet in order to remove the old shim and fit the new one. Use of this tool (or a similar tool) will save a considerable amount of time, as the alternative is to remove the camshafts with the additional time of disconnecting the timing belt and resetting the valve timing **(see illustration)**. However, if TDC setting tools are available (see Section 3) removal of the camshafts is to be preferred to using an ill-fitting tool to depress the tappets.
10 If the recorded clearance was too small, a thinner shim must be fitted, and conversely if the clearance was too large, a thicker shim must be fitted. To calculate the thickness of the new shim, first use a micrometer to measure the thickness of the existing shim (C) and add this to the measured clearance (B). Deduct the desired clearance (A) to provide the thickness (D) of the new shim. The thickness of the shim should be etched on the downward facing surface, however use the micrometer to verify this. The formula is as follows.

D (new shim thickness) = ((C (existing shim thickness) + B (measured clearance)) - A (desired clearance)

All measurements in mm.
Sample calculation - clearance too small
Desired clearance (A)   = 0.20
Measured clearance (B)   = 0.15
Existing shim thickness (C) = 2.725
Shim thickness reqd. (D) = C+B-A = 2.675

Sample calculation - clearance too large
Desired clearance (A)   = 0.30
Measured clearance (B)   = 0.40
Existing shim thickness (C) = 2.550
Shim thickness reqd. (D) = C+B-A = 2.650

11 The shims are available in thicknesses from 2.000 mm to 3.300 mm in increments of 0.025 mm **(see illustration)**. If the Ford tool (or similar) is being used to remove the shims without removing the camshafts, turn the tappets so that the slot is facing towards the centre of the engine. It will then be possible to use a small screwdriver to lift out the old shim. Fit the new shim then release the tool.
12 When fitting the new shim make sure that the etched thickness is facing downwards onto the tappet.
13 It will be helpful for future adjustment if a record is kept of the thickness of shim fitted at each position. The shims required can be purchased in advance once the clearances and the existing shim thicknesses are known.

6.4 Removing the auxiliary drivebelt lower cover

6.5 Removing the auxiliary drivebelt from the alternator pulley

6.7 Loosening the crankshaft pulley bolt while holding the pulley with a home-made tool

It is permissible to interchange shims between tappets to achieve the correct clearances but it is not advisable to turn the camshaft with any shims removed, since there is a risk that the cam lobe will jam in the empty tappet.

14 When all the clearances have been checked and adjusted, refit the lower cover (where removed), lower the vehicle to the ground and refit the cylinder head cover as described in Section 4.

6 Crankshaft pulley/vibration damper - removal and refitting

Caution: Removal of the crankshaft pulley effectively loses the valve timing setting, and it will be necessary to reset the timing using the procedure and tools described in Section 3.

6.8a Using a puller to remove the crankshaft pulley

6.8b Remove the retaining bolt . . .

Note: The vibration damper retaining bolt may only be used once. Obtain a new bolt for the refitting procedure.

Removal

1 Disconnect the battery negative (earth) lead (see Chapter 5A).
2 Apply the handbrake, then jack up the front of the vehicle and support it on axle stands (see *"Jacking and Vehicle Support"*). Remove the engine undershield if fitted.
3 Remove the right-hand front roadwheel, then where necessary undo the retaining screws and remove the wheel arch liner.
4 Unbolt and remove the auxiliary drivebelt lower cover for access to the crankshaft pulley **(see illustration)**.
5 Remove the auxiliary drivebelt as described in Chapter 1A **(see illustration)**.
6 Set the engine to the top dead centre (TDC) position as described in Section 3, then remove the camshaft position bar and the crankshaft timing pin. Do not leave the tools in position while the crankshaft pulley bolt is being loosened.
7 Hold the crankshaft pulley stationary using a home-made tool like the one shown **(see illustration)**. The bolt ends locate in the pulley holes and an extension bar and socket can then be used to loosen the bolt. Do not turn the crankshaft otherwise it will be more difficult to reset the valve timing, and also with the bolt loose the crankshaft sprocket may not turn with the crankshaft and the pistons may touch the valves.
8 With the bolt loosened several turns, use a suitable puller to free the pulley from the taper

6.8c . . . and withdraw the pulley from the end of the crankshaft

on the end of the crankshaft. Fully unscrew the bolt and withdraw the pulley **(see illustrations)**.
9 Clean the end of the crankshaft and the pulley.

Refitting

10 The procedure in this paragraph is necessary in order to be able to set the valve timing after the crankshaft/vibration pulley has been refitted. Unbolt and remove the upper timing cover (see Section 7). While holding each of the camshaft sprockets stationary in turn using the home-made tool described in paragraph 7, loosen the sprocket retaining bolts until they are just finger-tight to enable the sprockets to turn on the camshafts. Alternatively the camshafts can be held stationary using a spanner on the special hexagon flats.
11 Locate the pulley on the end of the crankshaft and press it onto the taper as far as it will go. This procedure must always be carried out before inserting and tightening the new bolt. Do not simply insert and tighten the new bolt, as in certain circumstances the torque will not be sufficient to press the pulley fully onto the end of the taper on the crankshaft. Ford technicians use a special installer which consists of a threaded rod screwed into the crankshaft together with a spacer which locates on the pulley. In the absence of this tool, use a long bolt or threaded rod together with washers and a nut **(see illustration)**. As a last resort use the removed (old) bolt, however this is not recommended as the threads may be stretched (see Note at the beginning of this Section).

6.11 Use a long bolt threaded into the crankshaft to draw the pulley onto the taper

2B

6.12 Inserting the new crankshaft pulley retaining bolt

7.2 Removing the upper idler pulley

7.3 Unscrewing the timing cover upper retaining bolt

12 Remove the tool, then insert the new bolt and tighten it to the specified stage 1 torque setting while holding the pulley stationary with the special tool **(see illustration)**.
13 Now angle-tighten the bolt by 90°.
14 The valve timing must now be set and the camshaft sprocket bolts tightened as described in Section 8.
15 Refit the upper timing cover.
16 Refit and tension the auxiliary drivebelt as described in Chapter 1A.
17 Refit the auxiliary drivebelt lower cover and tighten the retaining bolts.
18 Refit the wheel arch liner and where fitted the engine undershield, then refit the wheel and lower the vehicle to the ground.
19 Reconnect the battery negative lead.

7 Timing belt covers - removal and refitting

Upper cover

Removal

1 Remove the auxiliary drivebelt as described in Chapter 1A.
2 Unbolt and remove the upper idler pulley **(see illustration)**.
3 Unscrew the single upper bolt securing the upper timing cover to the cylinder head cover **(see illustration)**.
4 Unscrew the remaining retaining screws - there are three near the top, two half way down and two at the bottom.

7.8a Undo the bolts . . .

5 Manoeuvre the timing cover rearwards from behind the right-hand engine mounting brackets, and withdraw it from the engine compartment **(see illustration)**.

Refitting

6 Refitting is a reversal of removal, but tighten the retaining bolts to the specified torque.

Lower cover

Removal

7 The timing belt lower cover is located around the crankshaft. First remove the crankshaft pulley/vibration damper as described in Section 6.
8 Working beneath the right-hand wheel arch, unscrew the retaining bolts and withdraw the timing cover **(see illustrations)**.

Refitting

9 Refitting is a reversal of removal, but tighten the retaining bolts to the specified torque.

8 Timing belt - removal and refitting

Note: *The timing belt must be renewed after 100 000 miles (150 000 km) or 10 years.*

Removal

1 Remove the crankshaft pulley/vibration damper as described in Section 6. This work includes removing the cylinder head cover and upper timing belt cover, and setting the engine at top dead centre (TDC).

7.8b . . . and remove the lower timing cover

7.5 Removing the upper timing cover

2 With the camshaft timing bar removed, loosen the camshaft sprocket bolts several turns while holding the sprockets with a suitable tool **(see illustration)**. Using a soft-metal drift from behind the sprockets, release the sprockets from the tapers on the ends of the camshafts so that they are free to rotate.
3 Remove the timing belt lower cover as described in Section 7.
4 Remove the timing belt guide disc from the end of the crankshaft. Note which way round the disc is fitted - the concave side faces inwards **(see illustration)**.
5 The timing belt tensioner spring and pushrod must now be compressed to release the tension on the timing belt. A home-made compressor tool can be made out of a long bolt fitted with two short lengths of metal and four nuts. Fit the tool over the tensioner spring body and compress the spring pushrod until a 1.5 mm diameter drill can be inserted through

8.2 Loosening the camshaft sprocket retaining bolts with a home-made tool

8.4 Removing the timing belt guide disc

8.5a Home-made tool for compressing the timing belt tensioner spring

8.5b With the spring compressed, insert a 1.5 mm diameter drill through the body and through the pushrod

8.6 Support the engine with a trolley jack and block of wood

8.7 Removing the right-hand engine mounting upper bracket

8 Unbolt the right-hand engine mounting lower bracket from the cylinder head (see illustrations).

9 If the timing belt is to be re-used, use white paint or similar to mark its direction of rotation, and note from the manufacturer's markings which way round it is fitted. Withdraw the belt from the sprockets and from over the tensioner (see illustrations). *Do not* attempt to turn the crankshaft or camshafts until the timing belt is refitted.

10 If the belt is being removed for reasons other than renewal, check it carefully for any signs of uneven wear, splitting, cracks (especially at the roots of the belt teeth) or contamination with oil or coolant. Renew the belt if there is the slightest doubt about its condition. As a safety measure, the belt should be renewed irrespective of its apparent condition whenever the engine is overhauled.

the upper end of the body through the pushrod. The drill will hold the tension spring in its compressed position and the tool can then be removed (see illustrations).

6 Using a trolley jack and wooden block, support the weight of the engine beneath the right-hand side of the engine (see illustration).

7 Unscrew the nuts and remove the upper bracket from the right-hand engine mounting (see illustration).

2B

8.8a Unscrew the bolts . . .

8.8b . . . and remove the right-hand engine mounting lower bracket

8.9a Showing the manufacturer's markings on the timing belt

8.9b Removing the timing belt from the camshaft sprockets . . .

8.9c . . . tensioner pulley . . .

8.9d . . . and crankshaft sprocket

8.23 Tightening the camshaft sprocket retaining bolts

Check also the sprockets for signs of wear or damage, and ensure that the tensioner pulley rotates smoothly on its bearings; renew any worn or damaged components. If signs of oil or coolant contamination are found, trace the source of the leak and rectify it, then wash down the engine timing belt area and related components, to remove all traces of oil or coolant. If the tensioner spring and pushrod are thought to be worn, renew the tensioner as an assembly.

Refitting

11 Locate the timing belt on the crankshaft sprocket, then feed it over the tensioner pulley and finally over the two camshaft sprockets. If the original belt is being refitted, make sure that it is the correct way round as noted during removal.
12 Refit the right-hand engine mounting lower bracket and tighten the bolts to the specified torque.
13 Refit the upper mounting bracket and tighten the nuts to the specified torque. Withdraw the trolley jack from under the vehicle.
14 Refit the sprocket/belt retainer plate to the cylinder block and tighten the bolt to the specified torque.
15 Fit the compressor tool to the timing belt tensioner body and compress the pushrod until the drill can be removed. Carefully release the compressor to tension the timing belt, then remove the tool.
16 Refit the timing belt guide disc on the end of the crankshaft, making sure that the concave side faces inwards.

17 Refit the timing belt lower cover and tighten the bolts to the specified torque.
18 Locate the crankshaft pulley/vibration damper on the end of the crankshaft and press it onto the taper as far as it will go. This procedure must always be carried out before inserting and tightening the new bolt - it is not sufficient to press on the pulley by hand only. Ford technicians use a special installer which consists of a threaded rod screwed into the crankshaft together with a metal ring which locates on the pulley. In the absence of this tool, use the old pulley bolt together with a suitable metal ring to press the pulley squarely onto the crankshaft as far as it will go. Do not use the new bolt for this initial operation (see Note at the beginning of this Section).
19 Insert the new bolt and tighten it to the specified stage 1 torque setting while holding the pulley stationary with the special tool (see Section 6).
20 Now angle-tighten the bolt by 90°. The crankshaft sprocket is now effectively clamped to the crankshaft.
21 Position No 1 piston at TDC as described in Section 3. The procedure is to insert and tighten the timing pin then turn the crankshaft clockwise until the machined surface on the crank web just touches the timing pin.
22 Set the camshafts at TDC as described in Section 3 and insert the setting bar in the slots.
23 Moderately tighten the bolts retaining the camshaft sprockets to the camshafts, then remove the setting bar and timing pin and fully tighten the bolts while holding the sprockets using the tool described in Section 6 or using a spanner on the hexagon flats provided **(see illustration)**.
24 Check the accuracy of the valve timing by first turning the crankshaft two complete turns. Refit the TDC timing pin and position the crankshaft at TDC, then insert the setting bar in the camshaft slots. On completion remove the timing pin and bar and refit the blanking plug.
25 Refit the timing belt upper cover.
26 Refit and tension the auxiliary drivebelt as described in Chapter 1A.
27 Refit the auxiliary drivebelt lower cover and tighten the retaining bolts.
28 Refit the wheel arch liner and where fitted the engine undershield, then lower the vehicle to the ground.

29 Reconnect the battery negative lead.

9 Timing belt tensioner and sprockets - removal, inspection and refitting

Tensioner and tensioner pulley

Removal

1 Disconnect the battery negative (earth) lead (see Chapter 5A).
2 Apply the handbrake, then jack up the front of the vehicle and support it on axle stands (see *"Jacking and Vehicle Support"*). Remove the engine undershield if fitted.
3 Remove the right-hand front roadwheel, then undo the retaining screws and remove the wheel arch liner.
4 Unbolt and remove the auxiliary drivebelt lower cover for access to the crankshaft pulley.
5 Remove the auxiliary drivebelt as described in Chapter 1A.
6 Remove the timing belt upper cover as described in Section 7.
7 As a precaution against losing the valve timing, use string to tie the front and rear runs of the timing belt together. This will ensure that the belt remains engaged with the camshaft sprockets while the tensioner and pulley are removed.
8 The timing belt tensioner spring and pushrod must now be compressed to release the tension on the timing belt, and a 1.5 mm drill must be inserted through the upper end of the body and through the pushrod. The procedure is described in Section 8.
9 With the tensioner spring and pushrod held in their compressed position with the drill, unscrew the retaining bolts and remove the tensioner body from the cylinder block. If required, unbolt and remove the timing backplate **(see illustrations)**.
10 Unscrew the pivot bolt and remove the tensioner pulley from the cylinder block **(see illustration)**.
11 While the tensioner and pulley are removed, make sure that the timing belt remains fully engaged with the camshaft and crankshaft sprockets.

9.9a Removing the timing belt tensioner body

9.9b Removing the timing backplate

9.10 Removing the timing belt tensioner pulley

Inspection

12 Spin the tensioner pulley and check that it turns freely without any roughness or tightness. Do not attempt to clean the pulley by immersing in any cleaning fluid.

13 If necessary, use the compressor tool to release the tension of the tensioner spring and remove it from the body. Clean the spring and body and inspect them for wear and damage.

14 Renew the components as required, and reassemble the tensioner spring to the body using the compressor tool to compress it. Retain with the drill.

Refitting

15 Clean the cylinder block in the area of the tensioner.

16 Locate the tensioner pulley on the block, insert the pivot bolt and tighten to the specified torque. Make sure that the back of the timing belt is located over the pulley.

17 Refit the tensioner body (with fitted spring) and tighten the retaining bolts to the specified torque. Ensure that the pushrod of the tensioner locates correctly on the pulley contact surface.

18 Fit the compressor tool to the timing belt tensioner body and compress the pushrod until the drill can be removed. Carefully release the compressor to tension the timing belt, then remove the tool. Untie the string.

19 Provided that the timing belt has remained fully engaged with the camshaft and crankshaft sprockets, it should not be necessary to check the valve timing. However, if there is any doubt, check the valve timing as described in Section 3.

20 Refit the timing belt upper cover as described in Section 7.

21 Refit the auxiliary drivebelt as described in Chapter 1A.

22 Refit the auxiliary drivebelt lower cover and tighten the bolts.

23 Refit the wheel arch liner and the right-hand front roadwheel.

24 Refit the engine undershield (if fitted) and lower the vehicle to the ground.

25 Reconnect the battery negative lead.

Camshaft sprockets

Removal

26 Disconnect the battery negative (earth) lead (see Chapter 5A).

27 Apply the handbrake, then jack up the front of the vehicle and support it on axle stands (see *"Jacking and Vehicle Support"*). Remove the engine undershield if fitted.

28 Remove the right-hand front roadwheel, then undo the retaining screws and remove the wheel arch liner.

29 Unbolt and remove the auxiliary drivebelt lower cover.

30 Remove the auxiliary drivebelt as described in Chapter 1A.

31 Remove the timing belt upper cover as described in Section 7.

32 Set the No 1 piston and camshafts to top dead centre (TDC) as described in Section 3.

This procedure includes removal of the cylinder head cover.

33 The timing belt tensioner spring and pushrod must now be compressed to release the tension on the timing belt, and a 1.5 mm drill must be inserted through the upper end of the body and through the pushrod. The procedure is described in Section 8.

34 Using a trolley jack and wooden block, support the weight of the engine beneath the right-hand side of the engine.

35 Unscrew the nuts and remove the upper bracket from the right-hand engine mounting.

36 Unbolt the right-hand engine mounting lower bracket from the cylinder head.

37 Disengage the timing belt from the camshaft sprockets and position it to one side, taking care not to bend it sharply. The belt will remain engaged with the crankshaft sprocket by means of the retainer plate bolted to the cylinder block. However, as a precaution keep a little upward pressure on the belt by tying it to the side of the engine compartment.

38 Hold each of the camshaft sprockets stationary in turn using a home-made tool (see Section 6), then loosen the sprocket retaining bolts. Alternatively the camshafts can be held stationary using a spanner on the special hexagon flats **(see illustration)**. The TDC setting bar must not be used to hold the camshafts stationary.

39 Unscrew the bolts and remove the sprockets from the camshafts. If necessary, use a soft-metal drift to release the sprockets from the taper on the camshafts **(see illustrations)**.

Inspection

40 Examine the teeth of the sprockets for wear and damage, and renew them if necessary.

Refitting

41 Locate the sprockets on the camshafts and screw in the retaining bolts loosely.

42 Engage the timing belt with the camshaft sprockets.

43 Refit the right-hand engine mounting lower bracket and tighten the bolts to the specified torque.

44 Refit the upper mounting bracket and tighten the nuts to the specified torque.

9.38 Using a spanner to hold the camshafts stationary

Withdraw the trolley jack from under the vehicle.

45 Fit the compressor tool to the timing belt tensioner body and compress the pushrod until the drill can be removed. Carefully release the compressor to tension the timing belt, then remove the tool.

46 Position No 1 piston at TDC as described in Section 3. The procedure is to insert and tighten the timing pin then turn the crankshaft clockwise until the machined surface on the crank web just touches the timing pin.

47 Set the camshafts at TDC as described in Section 3 and insert the setting bar in the slots.

48 Moderately tighten the bolts retaining the camshaft sprockets to the camshafts, then remove the setting bar and timing pin and fully tighten the bolts while holding the sprockets using the tool described in Section 6.

49 Check the accuracy of the valve timing by first turning the crankshaft two complete turns. Refit the TDC timing pin and position the crankshaft at TDC, then insert the setting bar in the camshaft slots. On completion remove the timing pin and bar and refit the blanking plug.

50 Refit the timing belt upper cover as described in Section 7.

51 Refit and tension the auxiliary drivebelt as described in Chapter 1A.

52 Refit the auxiliary drivebelt lower cover and tighten the retaining bolts.

53 Refit the wheel arch liner and where fitted the engine undershield, then refit the wheel and lower the vehicle to the ground.

54 Reconnect the battery negative lead.

9.39a Unscrew the bolt . . .

9.39b . . . and remove the camshaft sprocket

9.56 Removing the timing belt/sprocket holder plate

9.57 Slide the sprocket from the end of the crankshaft

5 Working on the first camshaft, dip the new oil seal in fresh oil, then locate it over the camshaft and into the cylinder head/camshaft bearing cap. Make sure that the closed end of the oil seal faces outwards **(see illustration)**.

6 Using a socket or length of metal tubing, drive the oil seals squarely into position to the previously noted depths. Wipe away any excess oil **(see illustration)**.

7 Refit the camshaft sprockets as described in Section 9.

Crankshaft sprocket

Removal

55 Remove the timing belt as described in Section 8.

56 Unbolt the belt/sprocket holder plate **(see illustration)**.

57 Slide the sprocket off the end of the crankshaft **(see illustration)**.

Inspection

58 Examine the teeth of the sprocket for wear and damage, and renew if necessary.

Refitting

59 Wipe clean the end of the crankshaft, then slide on the sprocket.

60 Refit the belt/sprocket holder plate and tighten the bolt.

61 Refit the timing belt as described in Section 8.

10 Camshaft oil seals - renewal

1 Remove the camshaft sprockets as described in Section 9.

2 Note the fitted depths of the oil seals as a guide for fitting the new ones.

3 Using a screwdriver or similar tool, carefully prise the oil seals from the cylinder head/camshaft bearing caps. Take care not to damage the oil seal contact surfaces on the ends of the camshafts or the oil seal seatings. An alternative method of removing the seals is to drill a small hole then insert a self-tapping screw and use pliers to pull out the seal **(see illustrations)**.

4 Wipe clean the oil seal seatings and also the ends of the camshafts.

11 Camshafts and tappets - removal, inspection and refitting

Removal

1 Before removing the camshafts it may be useful to check and record the valve clearances as described in Section 5. If any clearance is not within limits, new shims can be obtained and fitted.

2 Remove the camshaft sprockets as described in Section 9.

3 The camshaft bearing caps are marked for position - the inlet caps have the letter 'I' and exhaust caps have the letter 'E'. On the project vehicle these were not very clear, and if this is the case mark them using paint or a marker pen. Make sure they are identified for inlet and exhaust camshafts **(see illustrations)**.

4 Position the crankshaft so that No 1 piston is approximately 25 mm before TDC.

10.3a Drill a small hole and insert a self-tapping screw . . .

10.3b . . . then pull out the oil seal using a pair of pliers

10.5 Locating the new oil seal into the cylinder head/camshaft bearing cap

10.6 Driving the new oil seal into position with a socket

11.3a No 3 Inlet camshaft bearing cap

11.3b No 3 Exhaust camshaft bearing cap

11.3c Number the camshaft bearing caps with paint if they are not marked

11.6 Unscrew the camshaft bearing cap bolts . . .

5 Position the camshafts so that none of the valves are at full lift. To do this turn each camshaft using a spanner on the hexagon flats provided.

6 Progressively loosen the camshaft bearing cap retaining bolts, noting the location of the extended bolts which secure the cylinder head cover. Work only as described, to release gradually and evenly the pressure of the valve springs on the caps **(see illustration)**.

7 Withdraw the caps, keeping them in order to aid refitting, then lift the camshafts from the cylinder head and withdraw their oil seals. The exhaust camshaft can be identified by the reference lobe for the camshaft position sensor; therefore, there is no need to mark the camshafts **(see illustrations)**.

8 Obtain sixteen small, clean containers, and number them 1 to 8 for both the inlet and exhaust camshafts. Lift the tappets one by

one from the cylinder head keeping the shims with the respective tappets **(see illustration)**.

Inspection

9 With the camshafts and tappets removed, check each for signs of obvious wear (scoring, pitting etc) and for ovality, and renew if necessary.

10 If possible, use a micrometer to measure the outside diameter of each tappet - take measurements at the top and bottom of each tappet, then a second set at right-angles to the first; if any measurement is significantly different from the others, the tappet is tapered or oval (as applicable) and must be renewed. If the tappets or the cylinder head bores are excessively worn, new tappets and/or a new cylinder head will be required.

11 Visually examine the camshaft lobes for score marks, pitting, and evidence of overheating (blue, discoloured areas). Look

for flaking away of the hardened surface layer of each lobe. If any such signs are evident, renew the component concerned.

12 Examine the camshaft bearing journals and the cylinder head bearing surfaces for signs of obvious wear or pitting. If any such signs are evident, renew the component concerned.

13 To check camshaft endfloat, remove the tappets, clean the bearing surfaces carefully, and refit the camshafts and bearing caps. Tighten the bearing cap bolts to the specified torque wrench setting, then measure the endfloat using a dial gauge mounted on the cylinder head so that its tip bears on the camshaft right-hand end.

14 Tap the camshaft fully towards the gauge, zero the gauge, then tap the camshaft fully away from the gauge, and note the gauge reading. If the endfloat measured is found to be more than the typical value given, fit a new camshaft and repeat the check; if the clearance is still excessive, the cylinder head must be renewed.

Refitting

15 Commence reassembly by lubricating the cylinder head tappet bores and the tappets with engine oil. Carefully refit the tappets (together with their respective shims) to the cylinder head, ensuring that each tappet is refitted to its original bore. Some care will be required to enter the tappets squarely into their bores.

16 Liberally oil the camshaft bearings and lobes. Ensuring that each camshaft is in its original location, refit the camshafts, locating each so that the slot in its left-hand end is approximately parallel to, and just above, the cylinder head mating surface. At this stage position the camshafts so that none of the valves are at full lift **(see illustration)**.

17 Clean the mating faces of the cylinder head and camshaft bearing caps, and ensure that the locating dowels are firmly in place.

18 Apply a 2 to 3 mm diameter bead of suitable sealant (Ford recommend WSK-M2G348-A5) to the No 1 camshaft bearing caps at the oil seal ends only **(see illustration)**. If preferred, the oil seals can be located at this stage, otherwise fit them later.

2B

11.7a . . . withdraw the caps . . .

11.7b . . . then remove the camshafts

11.8 Removing the bucket tappets

11.16 Locating the camshafts in the cylinder head

11.18 Apply sealant to the No 1 camshaft bearing caps

11.19a Oil the bearing surfaces . . .

11.19b . . . then refit the camshaft bearing caps

11.20 Camshaft bearing cap bolt tightening sequence

19 Oil the bearing surfaces, then locate the camshaft bearing caps on the camshafts and insert the retaining bolts loosely. Make sure that each cap is located in its previously noted position (see illustrations).

20 Ensuring that each cap is kept square to the cylinder head as it is tightened down, and working in the sequence shown (see illustration), tighten the camshaft bearing cap bolts slowly and by one turn at a time, until each cap touches the cylinder head. Next, go round again in the same sequence, tightening the bolts to the first stage torque wrench setting specified, then once more, tightening them to the second stage setting. Work only in the sequence shown so that pressure is gradually applied to the valve springs.

21 Wipe off all surplus sealant, and if not already done fit the new oil seals with reference to Section 10.

22 Refit the camshaft sprockets (Section 9).

12 Cylinder head - removal, inspection and refitting

Removal

Note: *The following paragraphs assume that the cylinder head will be removed together with the inlet and exhaust manifolds attached. This simplifies the procedure, but makes it a bulky and heavy assembly to handle - ideally an engine hoist will be required, to prevent the risk of injury, and to prevent damage to any delicate components as the assembly is removed and refitted. If it is wished first to remove the manifolds, refer to Chapter 4A, then amend the following procedure accordingly.*

1 Depressurise the fuel system (Chapter 4A).

2 Set the engine to TDC compression on piston No 1 as described in Section 3. This

procedure includes disconnecting the battery and removing the cylinder head cover, then setting the engine to TDC using a timing pin and camshaft setting bar.

3 Remove the right-hand front roadwheel, then undo the retaining screws and remove the wheel arch liner.

4 Remove the auxiliary drivebelt as described in Chapter 1A.

5 Unscrew and remove the bolts securing the heatshield assembly to the catalytic converter and exhaust manifold at the rear of the engine. Access to the lower bolt is best from under the vehicle (see illustration).

6 Drain the cooling system (see Chapter 1A).

7 Remove the battery as described in Chapter 5A, then disconnect the wiring bracket and unbolt the battery box from the body (see illustration).

8 Loosen the clips and remove the air inlet duct from between the mass airflow sensor and throttle body housing (see illustration).

12.5 Removing the heatshield from the top of the exhaust manifold

12.7 Removing the battery box

12.8 Disconnecting the air inlet duct from the mass airflow sensor on the air cleaner

12.11a Disconnecting the accelerator cable from the throttle body housing

12.11b Unbolting the throttle body housing support bracket

12.14a Disconnecting the wiring from the throttle position sensor . . .

9 Unclip the fuel feed and return hoses from their supports, then squeeze together the quick release fittings and disconnect the hoses from the fuel rail.
10 Lift the flap over the centre of the fuel rail at the front of the cylinder head cover, then disconnect the crankcase breather hose.
11 Disconnect the inner accelerator cable from the throttle body housing (refer to Chapter 4A). Also unbolt and remove the throttle body housing support bracket **(see illustrations)**.
12 Unscrew and remove the oil filler cap, then undo the screws and lift the plastic cover for access to the spark plug HT leads.
13 Disconnect the HT leads from the spark plugs and position them to the left-hand side of the engine compartment.
14 Disconnect the wiring from the following components:

a) *The throttle position sensor on the throttle body housing **(see illustration)***
b) *The DIS ignition coil **(see illustration)***
c) *The engine coolant temperature sensor on the left-hand end of the cylinder head **(see illustration)***
d) *The engine wiring loom plug on the left-hand end of the cylinder head*
e) *The camshaft position sensor on the right-hand rear of the cylinder head*
f) *The oxygen sensor wiring on the bulkhead **(see illustration)***
g) *The earth wire from the rear of the cylinder head **(see illustration)***

15 Loosen the clips, and disconnect the following coolant hoses:
a) *The top hose at the thermostat housing.*
b) *The expansion tank vent and heater hoses at the thermostat housing.*

16 Disconnect the vacuum hoses from the throttle body housing.
17 Where applicable, disconnect the vacuum hose from the EGR valve.
18 Unscrew the nuts securing the catalytic converter to the exhaust manifold **(see illustration)**.
19 Remove the alternator as described in Chapter 5A.
20 Unscrew the bolt securing the oil level dipstick tube to the inlet manifold, then withdraw the tube from the cylinder block. Remove the O-ring and discard it **(see illustrations)**.
21 Unscrew and remove the inlet manifold mounting bolts securing the manifold to the cylinder block **(see illustration)**.
22 Unscrew the nuts securing the cylinder head cover to the top of the cylinder head.

2B

12.14b . . . DIS ignition coil . . .

12.14c . . . engine coolant temperature sensor . . .

12.14d . . . oxygen sensor . . .

12.14e . . . and the earth wire on the back of the cylinder head

12.18 Unscrewing the nuts securing the catalytic converter to the exhaust manifold

12.20a Unscrew the upper mounting bolt . . .

12.20b ... remove the dipstick tube from the cylinder block ...

12.20c ... then remove the O-ring

12.21 Removing the bolts securing the inlet manifold to the cylinder block

12.22a Unscrew the upper bolt securing the rear timing cover to the cylinder head ...

12.22b ... and the lower bolt

12.27 Removing the coolant pump drive pulley

Also unscrew the bolts securing the rear timing cover to the cylinder head cover (see illustrations).
23 Carefully lift the cover from the top of the cylinder head. Note that the gasket is vulcanised to the cover and cannot be renewed separately. Take care not to damage the gasket otherwise it will be necessary to obtain a new cover. Note also that the four rubber plugs in the cover locate on extensions on the camshaft bearing caps.
24 Using a trolley jack and wooden block, support the weight of the engine beneath the right-hand side of the engine.
25 Unscrew the nuts and remove the upper bracket from the right-hand engine mounting.
26 Unbolt the right-hand engine mounting lower bracket from the cylinder head.
27 Hold the coolant pump pulley stationary using a strap wrench or oil filter removal tool, then unscrew the bolts and remove the pulley from the coolant pump drive flange (see illustration).

28 Unbolt and remove the auxiliary drivebelt idler pulley.
29 Remove the upper timing belt cover as described in Section 7.
30 The timing belt tensioner spring and pushrod must now be compressed to release the tension on the timing belt, and a 1.5 mm drill must be inserted through the upper end of the body and through the pushrod. The procedure is described in Section 8.
31 Disengage the timing belt from the camshaft sprockets and position it to one side, taking care not to bend it sharply. The belt will remain engaged with the crankshaft sprocket by means of the retainer plate bolted to the cylinder block. However, as a precaution keep a little upward pressure on the belt by tying it to the side of the engine compartment.
32 Hold each of the camshaft sprockets stationary in turn using a home-made tool (see Section 6), then loosen the sprocket retaining bolts. Alternatively the camshafts can be held

stationary using a spanner on the special hexagon flats. The TDC setting bar must not be used to hold the camshafts stationary.
33 Unscrew the bolts and remove the sprockets from the camshafts.
34 Remove the spark plugs (see Chapter 1A).
35 Remove the camshafts and tappets with reference to Section 11.
36 Unscrew and remove the two bolts securing the timing belt cover support bracket to the cylinder head.
37 Working in the reverse of the sequence shown in illustration 12.48a, slacken the ten cylinder head bolts progressively and by one turn at a time; a Torx key (TX 55 size) will be required. Remove all the bolts (see illustrations).
38 Lift the cylinder head away; use assistance if possible, as it is a heavy assembly (see illustration). Remove the gasket, noting the two dowels, and discard it. The gasket is manufactured from laminated steel and cannot be re-used.

12.37a Slacken the cylinder head bolts ...

12.37b ... then remove them together with their washers

12.38 Lifting the cylinder head complete with manifolds from the top of the cylinder block

12.44 Locating the new cylinder head gasket on the cylinder block dowels

12.48a Cylinder head bolt tightening sequence

Inspection

39 The mating faces of the cylinder head and cylinder block must be perfectly clean before refitting the head. Use a hard plastic or wood scraper to remove all traces of gasket and carbon; also clean the piston crowns. Take particular care during the cleaning operations, as aluminium alloy is easily damaged. Also, make sure that the carbon is not allowed to enter the oil and water passages - this is particularly important for the lubrication system, as carbon could block the oil supply to the engine's components. Using adhesive tape and paper, seal the water, oil and bolt holes in the cylinder block. To prevent carbon entering the gap between the pistons and bores, smear a little grease in the gap. After cleaning each piston, use a small brush to remove all traces of grease and carbon from the gap, then wipe away the remainder with a clean rag.

40 Check the mating surfaces of the cylinder block and the cylinder head for nicks, deep scratches and other damage. If slight, they may be removed carefully with a file, but if excessive, renewal is necessary as it is not permissible to machine the surfaces.

41 If warpage of the cylinder head gasket surface is suspected, use a straight-edge to check it for distortion. Refer to Part D of this Chapter if necessary.

Refitting

42 Wipe clean the mating surfaces of the cylinder head and cylinder block. Check that the two locating dowels are in position in the cylinder block, and that all cylinder head bolt holes are free from oil. This is most important, as a hydraulic lock in a cylinder head bolt hole as the bolt is tightened can cause a fracture of the block casting.

43 Turn the crankshaft anticlockwise so that pistons 1 and 4 are approximately 25 mm before TDC, in order to avoid the risk of valve/piston contact. Turn the crankshaft using a spanner on the pulley bolt.

44 Position a new gasket over the dowels on the cylinder block surface - it can only be fitted one way round **(see illustration)**.

45 As the cylinder head is such a heavy and awkward assembly to refit with manifolds, it is helpful to make up a pair of guide studs from

two 10 mm (thread size) studs approximately 90 mm long, with a screwdriver slot cut in one end - two old cylinder head bolts with their heads cut off would make a good starting point. Screw these guide studs, screwdriver slot upwards to permit removal, into the bolt holes at diagonally-opposite corners of the cylinder block surface (or into those where the locating dowels are fitted, as shown); ensure that approximately 70 mm of stud protrudes above the gasket.

46 Refit the cylinder head, sliding it down the guide studs (if used) and locating it on the dowels. Unscrew the guide studs (if used) when the head is in place.

47 Fit the new cylinder head bolts carefully and screw them in by hand only until finger-tight.

48 Working progressively and in the sequence shown **(see illustrations)**, use first a torque wrench, then an ordinary socket extension bar and an angle gauge, to tighten the cylinder head bolts in the stages given in the Specifications of this Chapter. **Note:** *Once tightened correctly, following this procedure, the cylinder head bolts do not require re-checking.*

49 Refit and tighten to the specified torque the two bolts securing the timing belt cover support bracket to the cylinder head.

12.48b Tighten the bolts to the specified torques . . .

12.48c . . . then angle-tighten them

2B

12.61 Using a strap wrench to hold the coolant pump pulley while tightening the bolts

50 Locate the sprockets on the camshafts and screw in the retaining bolts loosely.
51 Engage the timing belt with the camshaft sprockets.
52 Refit the right-hand engine mounting lower bracket and tighten the bolts to the specified torque.
53 Refit the upper mounting bracket and tighten the nuts to the specified torque. Withdraw the trolley jack from under the vehicle.
54 Fit the compressor tool to the timing belt tensioner body and compress the pushrod until the drill can be removed. Carefully release the compressor to tension the timing belt, then remove the tool.
55 Position No 1 piston and the camshafts at TDC as described in Section 3. The procedure is to insert and tighten the timing pin then turn the crankshaft clockwise until the machined surface on the crank web just touches the timing pin, then insert the camshaft setting bar in the slots.
56 Moderately tighten the bolts retaining the camshaft sprockets to the camshafts, then remove the setting bar and timing pin and fully tighten the bolts while holding the sprockets using the tool described in Section 6, or using a spanner on the hexagon flats provided.
57 Check the accuracy of the valve timing by first turning the crankshaft two complete turns. Refit the TDC timing pin and position the crankshaft at TDC, then insert the setting bar in the camshaft slots. On completion remove the timing pin and bar and refit the blanking plug.

58 Refit the spark plugs (see Chapter 1A).
59 Refit the upper timing belt cover as described in Section 7.
60 Refit the auxiliary drivebelt idler pulley, and tighten the mounting bolt to the specified torque.
61 Refit the coolant pump pulley to the drive flange, and tighten the bolts to the torque specified in Chapter 3 **(see illustration)**.
62 Refit the cylinder head cover and tighten the bolts to the specified torque (Section 4).
63 Insert the bolts securing the inlet manifold to the cylinder block and tighten them to the torque specified in Chapter 4A.
64 Refit the oil level dipstick tube in the rubber grommet then secure it to the inlet manifold and tighten the bolt to the specified torque.
65 Locate the catalytic converter onto the exhaust manifold, then tighten the retaining nuts progressively to the torque specified in Chapter 4A.
66 Refit the alternator (see Chapter 5A).
67 Where applicable, reconnect the vacuum hose to the EGR valve.
68 Reconnect the vacuum hoses to the throttle body housing.
69 Reconnect the following coolant hoses and tighten the clips:
a) *The top hose on the thermostat housing.*
b) *The expansion tank vent and heater hoses at the thermostat housing.*
70 Reconnect the wiring to the following components:
a) *The throttle position sensor on the throttle body housing*
b) *The DIS ignition coil*
c) *The engine coolant temperature sensor on the left-hand end of the cylinder head*
d) *The engine wiring loom plug on the left-hand end of the cylinder head*
e) *The camshaft position sensor on the right-hand rear of the cylinder head*
f) *The oxygen sensor on the exhaust manifold*
g) *The earth wire at the rear of the cylinder head*
71 Reconnect the HT leads to the spark plugs.
72 Refit the plastic cover and tighten the screws. Refit the oil filler cap.
73 Reconnect the accelerator cable to the throttle body housing (refer to Chapter 4A).

Refit the throttle body housing support bracket.
74 Reconnect the crankcase breather hose to the cylinder head cover and refit the flap.
75 Reconnect the fuel feed and return hoses to the fuel rail and locate them in the supports.
76 Refit the air intake duct and tighten the clips.
77 Refit the battery box and tighten the bolts, then reconnect the wiring bracket and refit the battery with reference to Chapter 5A.
78 Refit the heatshield to the catalytic converter and exhaust manifold and tighten the bolts.
79 Refit the auxiliary drivebelt as described in Chapter 1A.
80 Refit the wheel arch liner and refit the right-hand front roadwheel.
81 Refill and bleed the cooling system as described in Chapter 1A.
82 Check and if necessary top-up the engine oil level (see *"Weekly Checks"*).
83 Check all disturbed joints for signs of oil or coolant leakage once the engine has been restarted and warmed up to normal operating temperature.

13 Sump - removal and refitting

Removal

1 Apply the handbrake, then jack up the front of the vehicle and support it on axle stands (see *"Jacking and Vehicle Support"*).
2 Drain the engine oil, then check the drain plug sealing washer and renew if necessary **(see illustration)**. Clean and refit the engine oil drain plug together with the washer, and tighten it to the specified torque wrench setting. Although not strictly necessary as part of the dismantling procedure, owners are advised to remove and discard the oil filter, so that it can be renewed with the oil (see Chapter 1A).
3 Unscrew the bolts securing the transmission to the sump.
4 Progressively unscrew the sump retaining bolts, then lower the sump from the crankcase and withdraw it from under the vehicle **(see illustration)**.
5 Recover the sump gasket. Due to its laminated steel and vulcanised rubber construction this gasket is expensive, therefore if it is in good condition it is possible to re-use it. Unlike more conventional gaskets, this gasket releases from the crankcase and sump surfaces easily.
6 While the sump is removed, take the opportunity to remove the oil pump pick-up/strainer pipe and clean it with reference to Section 14.

Refitting

7 Thoroughly clean the contact surfaces of the sump and crankcase. If necessary, use a

13.2 Fitting a new sealing washer to the engine oil drain plug

13.4 Removing the sump retaining bolts

13.8 Apply sealant to the joints between the crankcase and rear oil seal/oil pump housing

13.9 Locate the gasket on the crankcase or sump

13.11 Sump bolt tightening sequence

cloth rag to clean the interior of the sump and crankcase. If the oil pump pick-up/strainer pipe was removed, fit a new gasket and refit the pipe with reference to Section 14.

8 Apply a thin film of suitable sealant (Ford recommend WSK-M4G320-A) to the bottom face of the crankshaft rear oil seal housing. Also apply the sealant over the joints between the crankshaft rear oil seal and crankcase, and oil pump housing and crankcase (**see illustration**).

9 Locate the gasket on the sump or crankcase, then offer the sump onto the crankcase and insert the retaining bolts finger-tight (**see illustration**).

10 Before tightening the bolts, the sump must be accurately aligned with the end face of the cylinder block. If the transmission is still attached to the engine, this presents no problem provided that the sump-to-transmission bolts are tightened before the

sump bolts. However, if the engine is detached from the transmission (eg for overhaul), a straight-edge must be used for alignment.

11 Once the sump is correctly aligned, progressively tighten the sump-to-crankcase bolts to the specified torque using the sequence shown (**see illustration**).

12 If not already done, tighten the sump-to-transmission bolts to the specified torque.

13 Lower the vehicle to the ground, then fit a new oil filter (if necessary) and refill the engine with oil with reference to Chapter 1A.

14 Finally start the engine and check for signs of oil or coolant leaks.

14 Oil pump -
removal, inspection and refitting

Removal

1 Remove the timing belt as described in Section 8.

2 Remove the crankshaft sprocket as described in Section 9.

3 Refit the right-hand engine mounting lower and upper brackets and tighten the mounting bolts/nuts to their specified torques. Remove the trolley jack from under the sump.

4 Remove the sump and gasket as described in Section 13.

5 Unscrew the bolts securing the oil pump pick-up/strainer pipe to the baffle plate/main bearing cap.

6 Unscrew the bolt securing the oil pump

pick-up/strainer pipe to the oil pump, then withdraw the pipe and recover the sealing O-ring (**see illustration**). Discard the O-ring.

7 Unscrew the bolts securing the oil pump to the cylinder block/crankcase (**see illustration**). Withdraw the pump over the nose of the crankshaft.

8 Recover then discard the gasket (**see illustration**).

9 Support the oil pump on wooden blocks, then use a screwdriver to hook or drive out the crankshaft front oil seal.

10 If necessary, unbolt and remove the baffle plate from the main bearing cap/ladder (**see illustration**). Thoroughly clean all components, particularly the mating surfaces of the pump, the sump, and the cylinder block/crankcase.

Inspection

11 It is not possible to obtain individual components of the oil pump, furthermore, there are no torque settings available for tightening the pump cover plate bolts. However, the following procedure is provided for owners wishing to dismantle the oil pump for examination.

12 Unscrew the screws, and remove the pump cover plate; noting any identification marks on the rotors, withdraw the rotors.

13 Inspect the rotors for obvious signs of wear or damage, and renew if necessary; if either rotor, the pump body, or its cover plate are scored or damaged, the complete oil pump assembly must be renewed.

14 The oil pressure relief valve can be dismantled as follows.

2B

14.6 Removing the O-ring from the oil pump pick-up/strainer pipe

14.7 Removing the oil pump mounting bolts

14.8 Removing the oil pump gasket

14.10 Unbolting the baffle plate from the main bearing cap/ladder

15.7 Locating the new front oil seal over the crankshaft

15 Unscrew the threaded plug, and recover the valve spring and plunger. If the plug's sealing O-ring is worn or damaged, a new one must be obtained, to be fitted on reassembly.

16 Reassembly is the reverse of the dismantling procedure; ensure the spring and valve are refitted the correct way round, and tighten the threaded plug securely.

Refitting

17 If removed, refit the oil baffle plate to the crankcase and tighten the bolts.

18 The oil pump must be primed on installation, by pouring clean engine oil into it, and rotating its inner rotor a few turns.

19 Use a little grease to stick the new gasket in place on the cylinder block/crankcase.

20 Offer the oil pump over the nose of the crankshaft and turn the inner rotor as necessary to align its flats with the flats on the crankshaft. Locate the pump on the dowels, then insert the retaining bolts and progressively tighten them to the specified torque.

21 Fit a new crankshaft front oil seal (see Section 15).

22 Locate a new O-ring (dipped in oil) on the pick-up/strainer pipe, then locate the pipe in the oil pump and insert the retaining bolts. Insert the bolts retaining the pipe on the baffle plate/main bearing cap. Tighten the bolts to the specified torque.

23 Refit the sump as described in Section 13.

24 Support the weight of the engine with a trolley jack and wood block beneath the sump, then unscrew the nuts and bolts and

15.18 Locating the new rear oil seal housing (complete with fitting ring) over the rear of the crankshaft

remove the right-hand engine mounting upper and lower brackets.

25 Refit the crankshaft sprocket with reference to Section 9.

26 Refit the timing belt with reference to Section 8.

15 Crankshaft oil seals - renewal

Front (oil pump housing) oil seal

1 Remove the timing belt as described in Section 8.

2 Remove the crankshaft sprocket as described in Section 9.

3 As a safety precaution, refit the right-hand engine mounting lower and upper brackets and tighten the mounting bolts/nuts.

4 Note the fitted depth of the oil seal as a guide for fitting the new one.

5 Using a screwdriver, prise the old oil seal from the oil pump housing. Take care not to damage the seal contact surface on the nose of the crankshaft or the seating in the housing.

6 Wipe clean the seating and the nose of the crankshaft.

7 Dip the new oil seal in fresh oil, then locate it over the crankshaft and into the oil pump housing. Make sure that the closed end of the oil seal faces outwards **(see illustration)**.

8 Using a socket or length of metal tubing, drive the oil seal squarely into position to the previously noted depth. The Ford installation tool (21-171) is used together with an old crankshaft pulley bolt to press the oil seal into position. The same idea may be used with metal tubing and a large washer - do not use a new crankshaft pulley bolt, as it is only permissible to use the bolt once. With the oil seal in position, wipe away any excess oil.

9 Support the weight of the engine with a trolley jack and wood block beneath the sump, then unscrew the nuts and bolts and remove the right-hand engine mounting upper and lower brackets.

10 Refit the crankshaft sprocket with reference to Section 9.

11 Refit the timing belt with reference to Section 8.

15.20 With the oil seal housing bolted in position, remove the fitting ring

Rear oil seal

12 Remove the transmission (see the relevant Part of Chapter 7).

13 On manual transmission models remove the clutch as described in Chapter 6.

14 Remove the flywheel/driveplate as described in Section 16.

15 Unscrew the retaining bolts and withdraw the rear oil seal housing over the end of the crankshaft. Note that the seal and housing are manufactured as one unit incorporating a vulcanised gasket. It is not possible to obtain the seal separately.

16 Clean the housing contact surface on the cylinder block and the end of the crankshaft.

17 The new oil seal housing is supplied complete with a fitting ring which ensures that the oil seal lips are correctly located on the crankshaft.

18 Smear the end of the crankshaft with fresh engine oil, then locate the oil seal housing with fitting ring over the end of the crankshaft. Press the housing into position noting that the centre bolt holes are formed into locating dowels **(see illustration)**.

19 Insert the retaining bolts and progressively tighten them to the specified torque. Wipe away any surplus oil.

20 Remove the fitting ring and check that the oil seal lips are correctly located **(see illustration)**.

21 Refit the flywheel/driveplate as described in Section 16.

22 On manual transmission models refit the clutch as described in Chapter 6.

23 Refit the transmission (see the relevant Part of Chapter 7).

16 Flywheel/driveplate - removal, inspection and refitting

Removal

1 Remove the transmission (see the relevant Part of Chapter 7).

2 On manual transmission models remove the clutch as described in Chapter 6.

3 Hold the flywheel/driveplate stationary using one of the following methods. If an assistant is available, insert one of the transmission mounting bolts into the cylinder block and have the assistant engage a wide-bladed screwdriver with the starter ring gear teeth while the bolts are loosened. Alternatively, a piece of angle-iron can be engaged with the ring gear and located against the transmission mounting bolt. A further method is to fabricate a piece of flat metal bar with a pointed end to engage the ring gear - fit the tool to the transmission bolt and use washers and packing to align it with the ring gear, then tighten the bolt to hold it in position **(see illustration)**.

16.3 Home-made tool for holding the flywheel stationary while loosening the bolts

16.4 Removing the flywheel retaining bolts (note the location dowel in the crankshaft)

16.7 Crankshaft speed/position sensor mounting and retaining bolt

4 Unscrew and remove the retaining bolts, then lift the flywheel/driveplate off of the locating dowel on the crankshaft **(see illustration)**.

Inspection

5 Clean the flywheel/driveplate to remove grease and oil. Inspect the surface for cracks, rivet grooves, burned areas and score marks. Light scoring can be removed with emery cloth. Check for cracked and broken ring gear teeth. Lay the flywheel/driveplate on a flat surface, and use a straight edge to check for warpage.
6 Clean and inspect the mating surfaces of the flywheel/driveplate and the crankshaft. If the crankshaft rear oil seal is leaking, renew it (see Section 15) before refitting the flywheel/driveplate.
7 While the flywheel/driveplate is removed,

16.10 Flywheel bolt tightening sequence

clean carefully its inner face, particularly the recesses which serve as the reference points for the crankshaft speed/position sensor. Clean the sensor's tip, and check that the sensor is securely fastened. The sensor mounting may be removed if necessary by first removing the sensor, then unscrewing the bolt and withdrawing the mounting from the cylinder block **(see illustration)**.

Refitting

8 Make sure that the mating faces of the flywheel/driveplate and crankshaft are clean, then locate the flywheel/driveplate on the crankshaft and engage it with the locating dowel.
9 Insert the retaining bolts finger-tight.
10 Lock the flywheel/driveplate (see paragraph 3), then tighten the bolts to the specified torque using the sequence shown **(see illustration)**.
11 On manual transmission models refit the clutch with reference to Chapter 6.
12 Refit the transmission (see the relevant Part of Chapter 7).

---

17 Engine/transmission mountings - inspection and renewal

Inspection

1 The engine/transmission mountings seldom require attention, but broken or deteriorated mountings should be renewed immediately, or the added strain placed on the driveline components may cause damage or wear.
2 During the check, the engine/transmission must be raised slightly, to remove its weight from the mountings.
3 Apply the handbrake, then jack up the front of the vehicle and support it on axle stands (see "Jacking and Vehicle Support"). Remove the engine undershield where fitted. Position a jack under the sump, with a large block of wood between the jack head and the sump, then carefully raise the engine/transmission just enough to take the weight off the mountings.
4 Check the mountings to see if the rubber is cracked, hardened or separated from the

metal components. Sometimes, the rubber will split right down the centre.
5 Check for relative movement between each mounting's brackets and the engine/transmission or body (use a large screwdriver or lever to attempt to move the mountings). If movement is noted, lower the engine and check the mounting nuts and bolts for tightness.

Renewal

6 The engine mountings can be removed if the weight of the engine/transmission is supported by one of the following alternative methods.
7 Either support the weight of the assembly from underneath using a jack and a suitable piece of wood between the jack and the sump (to prevent damage), or from above by attaching a hoist to the engine. A third method is to use a suitable support bar with end pieces which will engage in the water channel each side of the bonnet lid aperture. Using an adjustable hook and chain connected to the engine, the weight of the engine and transmission can then be taken from the mountings.
8 Once the weight of the engine and transmission is suitably supported, any of the mountings can be unbolted and removed.
9 To remove the right-hand engine mounting, unscrew the nuts and remove the upper bracket, then unscrew the bolts and remove the lower bracket from the cylinder head. Unbolt the insulator from the right-hand side of the engine compartment **(see illustration)**.

17.9 Right-hand engine mounting insulator on the inner wing panel

2B

17.10 Left-hand engine/transmission mounting

17.11 Removing a through-bolt from the rear engine mounting/link

10 To remove the left-hand mounting first remove the battery and battery tray as described in Chapter 5A, then loosen the clips and remove the air inlet duct from between the air mass air flow sensor on the air cleaner and the throttle body housing. Unscrew the mounting nuts from the left-hand engine mounting, then unscrew the bolts and remove the upper bracket. Unscrew the bolts and remove the insulator from the left-hand side of the engine compartment **(see illustration)**.

11 To remove the rear engine mounting/link, apply the handbrake, then jack up the front of the vehicle and support it on axle stands (see *"Jacking and Vehicle Support"*). Unscrew the through-bolts and remove the rear engine mounting link from the bracket on the transmission and from the bracket on the underbody **(see illustration)**. Hold the engine stationary while the bolts are being removed since the link will be under tension.

12 Refitting of all mountings is a reversal of the removal procedure. Do not fully tighten the mounting nuts/bolts until all of the mountings are in position. Check that the mounting rubbers do not twist or distort as the mounting bolts and nuts are tightened to their specified torques.

Chapter 2 Part C:
Endura-DE diesel engine in-car repair procedures

Contents

Degrees of difficulty

Easy, suitable for novice with little experience	**Fairly easy,** suitable for beginner with some experience	**Fairly difficult,** suitable for competent DIY mechanic	**Difficult,** suitable for experienced DIY mechanic	**Very difficult,** suitable for expert DIY or professional 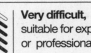

Specifications

General

Engine type	Four-cylinder in-line, four-stroke, overhead camshaft, compression ignition, normally-aspirated
Designation	Endura-DE
Engine code	RTK or RTJ
Capacity	1753 cc
Bore	82.5 mm
Stroke	82.0 mm
Compression ratio	21.5:1
Firing order	1-3-4-2 (No 1 cylinder at timing belt end)
Direction of crankshaft rotation	Clockwise (seen from right-hand side of vehicle)
Compression pressure (at starter motor cranking speed)	28 to 34 bar (406 to 493 lbf/in^2)
Maximum power (DIN)	44 kW (60 PS) @ 4800 rpm
Maximum torque (DIN)	105 Nm (78 lbf ft) @ 2500 rpm

Cylinder block

Cylinder bore diameter:

Class A	82.500 to 82.515 mm
Class B	82.515 to 82.530 mm
Class C	82.660 to 82.675 mm
Class D	82.675 to 82.690 mm
Class E (first rebore)	83.000 to 83.015 mm
Class F (second rebore)	83.500 to 83.515 mm

Crankshaft

Main bearing journal diameter:

Standard	53.970 to 53.990 mm
Undersize (0.25 mm)	53.720 to 53.740 mm
Undersize (0.50 mm)	53.470 to 53.490 mm
Main bearing running clearance	0.025 to 0.085 mm

Big-end bearing journal diameter:

Standard	48.970 to 48.990 mm
Undersize (0.25 mm)	48.720 to 48.740 mm
Undersize (0.50 mm)	48.470 to 48.490 mm
Big-end bearing running clearance	0.025 to 0.085 mm
Crankshaft endfloat	0.1436 to 0.3688 mm
Connecting rod to crank web axial clearance	0.125 to 0.325 mm
Torque to rotate fitted crankshaft (without connecting rods or pistons)	10 Nm (7 lbf ft) max

2C

Connecting rods
Big-end bore diameter .... 52.000 to 52.020 mm
Small-end bore diameter (with bush) .... 26.012 to 26.020 mm

Pistons
Diameter (measured at 90° to gudgeon pin bore):
  Class A .... 82.460 to 82.475 mm
  Class B .... 82.475 to 82.490 mm
  Class C .... 82.621 to 82.639 mm
  Class D .... 82.636 to 82.654 mm
  Class E (first rebore) .... 82.961 to 82.979 mm
  Class F (second rebore) .... 83.461 to 83.479 mm
Clearance in bore (new) .... 0.025 to 0.055 mm
Piston protrusion at TDC .... 0.500 to 0.840 mm
Gudgeon pin diameter .... 25.96 to 26.00 mm

Piston rings
Clearance in groove:
  Top compression .... 0.090 to 0.122 mm
  Second compression .... 0.050 to 0.082 mm
  Oil control .... 0.030 to 0.062 mm
End gap (fitted):
  Top compression .... 0.30 to 0.32 mm
  Second compression .... 0.30 to 0.32 mm
  Oil control .... 0.250 to 0.580 mm

Camshaft
Endfloat .... 0.100 to 0.240 mm
Bearing journal diameter .... 27.960 to 27.980 mm
Bearing running clearance .... 0.020 to 0.079 mm

Valve timing
Inlet opens .... 6° BTDC
Inlet closes .... 32° ABDC
Exhaust opens .... 57° BBDC
Exhaust closes .... 7° ATDC

Valve clearances (cold)
Inlet .... 0.285 to 0.415 mm
Exhaust .... 0.435 to 0.565 mm

Valves
Tappet shim thicknesses available .... 3.00 to 4.75 mm in increments of 0.05 mm
Valve spring free length .... 43 mm approx.

Cylinder head gasket
Selection according to piston protrusion:
  0.500 to 0.680 mm .... 1.36 mm thick (2 tooth marks)
  0.681 to 0.740 mm .... 1.42 mm thick (3 tooth marks)
  0.741 to 0.840 mm .... 1.52 mm thick (4 tooth marks)

Cylinder head
Distortion limit .... 0.08 mm overall
Swirl chamber projection .... 0.000 to 0.061 mm
Valve tappet bore diameter:
  Standard .... 35.000 to 35.030 mm
  Oversize .... 35.500 to 35.530 mm
Valve guide bore diameter:
  Standard .... 8.000 to 8.025 mm
  First oversize .... 8.263 to 8.288 mm
  Second oversize .... 8.463 to 8.488 mm

Lubrication system
Oil pressure:
  At 750 rpm .... 0.75 bar (11 lbf/in^2)
  At 2000 rpm .... 1.50 bars (22 lbf/in^2)
Oil pressure relief valve setting .... 2.0 to 4.0 bars
Oil pump inner-to-outer rotor maximum clearance .... 0.174 mm

Torque wrench settings

	Nm	lbf ft
Big-end bearing cap bolts:		
Stage 1	25	18
Stage 2 (angle-tighten)	60°	60°
Stage 3 (angle-tighten)	20°	20°
Crankshaft sprocket flange bolt (oiled):		
Stage 1	150	111
Stage 2 (loosen by angle)	-90°	-90°
Stage 3	120	88
Stage 4 (angle-tighten)	60°	60°
Cylinder head bolts (M12 and Torx T70 head):		
Stage 1	10	7
Stage 2	100	74
Stage 3 (after waiting 3 minutes):		
a)	Unscrew No 1 bolt 180°	
b)	Tighten No 1 bolt to 70 Nm (52 lbf ft)	
c)	Further tighten the No 1 bolt 120°	
Stage 4	Repeat stage three with each of the remaining bolts in sequence	
Flywheel bolts:		
Stage 1	18	13
Stage 2 (angle-tighten)	45°	45°
Stage 3 (angle-tighten)	45°	45°
Front engine mounting bracket:		
Outer nut	120	89
Inner nut	70	52
Main bearing cap bolts:		
Stage 1	27	20
Stage 2 (angle-tighten)	75°	75°
Alternator bracket to block	46	34
Alternator drivebelt tensioner clamp bolt	6	4
Auxiliary shaft oil seal housing	23	17
Auxiliary shaft thrustplate bolts	9	7
Auxiliary shaft timing pulley	45	33
Camshaft bearing caps	20	15
Camshaft sprocket flange	30	22
Crankshaft position sensor bracket	14	10
Crankshaft pulley/vibration damper to sprocket flange	35	26
Crankshaft rear oil seal carrier	20	15
Cylinder head cover	5	4
Engine lifting eye	23	17
Engine mounting bracket-to-cylinder block	33	24
Front engine mounting bracket	33	24
Front engine mounting reinforcement bracket	50	37
Front plate	24	18
Oil baffle	20	15
Oil dipstick tube bracket	10	7
Oil drain plug	24	18
Oil inlet pipe bracket	22	16
Oil pressure switch	20	15
Oil pump	23	17
Rear cover bolt	24	18
Rear engine mounting bracket bolts	50	37
Rear engine mounting bracket nuts	70	52
Rear engine mounting link to cylinder block	50	37
Rear engine mounting link to front subframe	70	52
Retaining plate for oil separator, fuel filter, and fuel heater	20	15
Right-hand engine mounting bracket	45	33
Side timing belt cover	8	6
Sump	11	8
TDC pin blanking plug	24	18
Tensioning pulley bolt	6	4
Thermostat housing	22	16
Timing belt idler (with automatic tensioner)	35	26
Timing belt idler	9	7
Timing belt tensioner	50	37
Timing belt automatic tensioner	45	33
Transmission-to-engine mounting bolts	44	32
Upper and lower timing belt cover	7	5
Vacuum pump	22	16

2C

1 General information

How to use this Chapter

This Part of Chapter 2 is devoted to in-car repair procedures. All procedures concerning engine removal and refitting, and engine block/cylinder head overhaul can be found in Chapter 2D.

Refer to the *"Buying spare parts and vehicle identification numbers"* Section at the end of this manual for details of engine code locations.

Most of the operations included in Chapter 2C are based on the assumption that the engine is still installed in the car. Therefore, if this information is being used during a complete engine overhaul, with the engine already removed, many of the steps included here will not apply.

Engine description

The 1.8 litre diesel engine is of four-cylinder overhead camshaft design. The engine is mounted transversely, in line with the transmission. Both the cylinder block and the cylinder head are of cast iron.

Two toothed drivebelts (timing belts) are fitted, one to drive the fuel injection pump and the other to drive the camshaft, the oil pump auxiliary shaft and the coolant pump. The valves are operated by bucket tappets. Valve clearance adjustment is by means of selective shims. The cam lobes bear directly on the shims and tappets, which in turn bear directly on the valves. The camshaft runs in five renewable shell bearings.

The oil pump is mounted externally, and is driven by the auxiliary shaft.

The crankshaft runs in five main bearings, of the usual shell type. Endfloat is controlled by separate thrustwashers at the centre bearing. The crankshaft sprocket incorporates a flange for the crankshaft pulley/vibration damper which drives the alternator, power steering pump and air conditioning compressor.

Pistons, gudgeon pins and connecting rods are carefully selected to be of matching weight. The connecting rods are also graded by length. The gudgeon pins are fully floating in the pistons and rods and are retained by circlips. The big-ends of the rods are horizontally split and carry shell bearings.

Crankcase ventilation is by means of a hose which connects the camshaft cover to the inlet manifold. A non-return valve prevents crankcase pressurisation taking place. Another hose connects the camshaft cover to the lower crankcase.

Repair operations possible with the engine in the vehicle

The following operations can be carried out without having to remove the engine from the vehicle:

a) Timing belt and injection pump drivebelt - renewal.
b) Timing belt/drivebelt tensioners and sprockets - removal and refitting.
c) Camshaft oil seal - renewal.
d) Camshafts and tappets - removal and refitting.
e) Auxiliary shaft oil seal - renewal.
f) Cylinder head - removal and refitting.
g) Sump - removal and refitting.
h) Crankshaft oil seals - renewal.
i) Oil pump - removal and refitting.
j) Flywheel - removal and refitting.
k) Engine/transmission mountings - removal and refitting.

Note: *It is possible to remove the pistons and connecting rods (after removing the cylinder head and sump) without removing the engine. However, this is not recommended. Work of this nature is more easily and thoroughly completed with the engine on the bench, as described in Chapter 2D.*

2 Compression and leakdown tests - description and interpretation

Compression test

Note: *A compression tester specifically designed for diesel engines must be used for this test.*

1 When engine performance is down, or if misfiring occurs which cannot be attributed to a fault in the fuel system, a compression test can provide diagnostic clues as to the engine's condition. If the test is performed regularly it can give warning of trouble before any other symptoms become apparent.

2 A compression tester specifically intended for diesel engines must be used, because of the higher pressures involved. The tester is connected to an adapter which screws into the glow plug or injector hole. It is unlikely to be worthwhile buying such a tester for occasional use, but it may be possible to borrow or hire one - if not, have the test performed by a garage.

3 Unless specific instructions to the contrary are supplied with the tester, observe the following points:

a) The battery must be in a good state of charge, the air filter must be clean and the engine should be at normal operating temperature.
b) All the injectors or glow plugs should be removed before starting the test. If removing the injectors, also remove the fire seal washers (which must be renewed when the injectors are refitted - see Chapter 5C), otherwise they may be blown out.
c) It is advisable to disconnect the stop solenoid on the pump to reduce the amount of fuel discharged as the engine is cranked.

4 There is no need to hold the accelerator pedal down during the test because the diesel engine air inlet is not throttled.

5 The actual compression pressures measured are not so important as the balance between cylinders. Values are given in the Specifications.

6 The cause of poor compression is less easy to establish on a diesel engine than on a petrol one. The effect of introducing oil into the cylinders ("wet" testing) is not conclusive, because there is a risk that the oil will sit in the swirl chamber or in the recess on the piston crown instead of passing to the rings. However, the following can be used as a rough guide to diagnosis.

7 All cylinders should produce very similar pressures; any difference greater than that specified indicates the existence of a fault. Note that the compression should build up quickly in a healthy engine; low compression on the first stroke, followed by gradually increasing pressure on successive strokes, indicates worn piston rings. A low compression reading on the first stroke, which does not build up during successive strokes, indicates leaking valves or a blown head gasket (a cracked head could also be the cause).

8 A low reading from two adjacent cylinders is almost certainly due to the head gasket having blown between them.

Leakdown test

9 A leakdown test measures the rate at which compressed air fed into the cylinder is lost. It is an alternative to a compression test and in many ways it is better, since the escaping air provides easy identification of where pressure loss is occurring (piston rings, valves or head gasket).

10 The equipment needed for leakdown testing is unlikely to be available to the home mechanic. If poor compression is suspected, have the test performed by a suitably equipped garage.

3 Top Dead Centre (TDC) for No 1 piston - locating

Note: *A timing pin and, on engines with an automatic tensioner, a camshaft setting bar are required for this procedure (see text).*

1 Top dead centre (TDC) is the highest point of the cylinder that each piston reaches as the crankshaft turns. Each piston reaches its TDC position at the end of its compression stroke, and then again at the end of its exhaust stroke. For the purpose of engine timing, TDC on the compression stroke for No 1 piston is used. No 1 cylinder is at the timing belt end of the engine. Proceed as follows.

2 Disconnect the battery negative (earth) lead (refer to Chapter 5A).

3 Apply the handbrake, then jack up the front of the vehicle and support it on axle stands

3.9 Camshaft rear offset slot (arrowed)

3.11a Remove the blanking plug from the cylinder block . . .

3.11b . . . and insert the TDC timing pin (arrowed)

(see "*Jacking and Vehicle Support*"). If the engine is to be turned using the right-hand front roadwheel with 4th gear engaged, it is only necessary to raise the right-hand front roadwheel off the ground.

4 Where necessary, remove the engine undershield, then remove the auxiliary drivebelt lower cover for access to the crankshaft pulley and bolt.

5 Remove the upper timing belt cover as described in Section 6.

6 Remove the glow plugs as described in Chapter 5C. This will enable the engine to be turned easily.

Engines with an automatic timing belt tensioner

7 Disconnect the crankcase ventilation hoses.

8 Unbolt and remove the cylinder head cover, and remove the gasket.

9 The piston of No 1 cylinder must now be positioned just before top dead centre (TDC). To do this, have an assistant turn the crankshaft until the slot in the left-hand end of the camshaft is parallel with the upper surface of the cylinder head. Note that the slot is

slightly offset so make sure that the lower edges of the slots are aligned with the cylinder head. Turn the crankshaft slightly anticlockwise from this position (viewed from the right-hand end of the engine) **(see illustration)**.

Engines with standard timing belt tensioner

10 The piston of No 1 cylinder must now be positioned just before top dead centre (TDC). To do this, have an assistant turn the crankshaft until the timing hole in the camshaft sprocket is aligned with the corresponding hole in the cylinder head. Turn the crankshaft slightly anticlockwise from this position (viewed from the right-hand end of the engine).

All engines

11 Remove the alternator as described in Chapter 5A, then unscrew the blanking plug from the right-hand front side of the engine cylinder block. Ford timing pin 21-104 must now be inserted and tightened into the hole. If necessary, a home-made pin can be made from an M10 bolt with a dimension of 47.5 mm from beneath its head to the tip, however it

will be necessary to grind and slot the head to allow it to be inserted **(see illustrations)**.

12 With the timing pin in position, turn the crankshaft slowly clockwise until the specially machined surface on the crank web just touches the timing pin. No 1 piston is now at TDC on its compression stroke.

13 On engines with an automatic tensioner, it should now be possible to insert the camshaft setting bar into the slot in the left-hand end of the camshaft.

14 On engines with a standard tensioner, it should now be possible to insert Ford timing pin 23-019 through the camshaft sprocket and into the cylinder head hole.

15 Insert Ford timing pin 23-029 (or suitable drill bit) through the injection pump sprocket timing hole into the housing hole **(see illustration)**.

16 If any of the timing pins cannot be fitted, reset the valve timing as described in Section 7.

17 Once the work requiring the TDC setting has been completed, remove the timing pins and where applicable the camshaft setting bar, then refit the blanking plug. Refit all removed components referring to the relevant Chapters.

2C

3.11c Home-made tools for setting the valve timing

A   Head of bolt and area indicated will need grinding to allow the timing pin to be inserted

3.15 Timing 'pin' inserted through the injection pump sprocket

4.2a Removing the cylinder head cover . . .

4.2b . . . and gasket

4.3 Unscrew the four nuts (arrowed) and remove the oil baffle plate

4 Valve clearances - checking and adjustment

Checking

1 Disconnect the two crankcase ventilation hoses from the left-hand end of the cylinder head cover.

2 Unscrew the mounting bolts and withdraw the cylinder head cover. Check the gasket and if necessary remove it for renewal **(see illustrations)**.

3 Unscrew the nuts and remove the baffle plate from the camshaft bearing caps **(see illustration)**. Temporarily refit and tighten the removed nuts to their specified torque.

4 During the following procedure, the crankshaft must be turned in order to position the peaks of the camshaft lobes away from the

4.8 Measuring a valve clearance with a feeler blade

valves. To do this, either turn the crankshaft on the pulley bolt or alternatively raise the front right-hand corner of the vehicle, engage 4th gear, and turn the front roadwheel. Access to the pulley bolt is gained by jacking up the front of the vehicle and supporting on axle stands, then removing the pulley lower cover.

5 If desired, to enable the crankshaft to be turned more easily, remove the glow plugs (Chapter 5C) or the fuel injectors (Chapter 4B).

6 Draw the valve positions on a piece of paper, numbering them 1 to 8 from the timing end of the engine. Identify them as inlet or exhaust (ie 1I, 2E, 3I, 4E, 5I, 6E, 7I, 8E).

7 Turn the crankshaft until the valves of No 4 cylinder (flywheel end) are "rocking". The exhaust valve will be closing and the inlet valve will be opening. The piston of No 1 cylinder will be at the top of its compression stroke, with both valves fully closed. The clearances for both valves of No 1 cylinder may be checked at the same time.

8 Insert a feeler blade of the correct thickness (see Specifications) between the cam lobe and the shim on the top of the tappet bucket, and check that it is a firm sliding fit **(see illustration)**. If it is not, use the feeler blades to ascertain the exact clearance, and record this for use when calculating the new shim thickness required. Note that the inlet and exhaust valve clearances are different, so it is important that you know which valve clearance you are checking.

9 With No 1 cylinder valve clearances checked, turn the engine through half a turn so that No 2 valves are "rocking", then check the valve clearances of No 3 cylinder in the same

way. Similarly check the valve clearances of No 4 cylinder with No 1 valves 'rocking' and No 2 cylinder with No 3 valves 'rocking'.

Adjustment

10 If adjustment is required, turn the engine in the normal direction of rotation through approximately 90°, to bring the pistons to mid-stroke. If this is not done, the pistons at TDC will prevent the tappets being depressed, and damage may result. Depress the tappets and then either shim can be withdrawn if the peak of the cam does not prevent access. The Ford tools for this operation are Nos 21-106 and 21-107, but with care and patience a C-spanner or screwdriver can be used to depress the tappet and the shim can be flicked out with a small screwdriver **(see illustrations)**.

11 If the valve clearance was too small, a thinner shim must be fitted. If the clearance was too large, a thicker shim must be fitted. The thickness of the shim (in mm) is engraved on the side facing away from the camshaft **(see illustration)**. If the marking is missing or illegible, a micrometer will be needed to establish shim thickness.

12 When the shim thickness and the valve clearance are known, the required thickness of the new shim can be calculated as follows:

All measurements in mm.

Sample calculation - clearance too small

Desired clearance (A)	= 0.50
Measured clearance (B)	= 0.35
Shim thickness found (C)	= 3.95
Shim thickness reqd. (D)	= C+B-A = 3.80

4.10a Maker's tools for tappet depression and shim extraction

4.10b Depressing a tappet with a screwdriver and removing a shim

4.11 Shim thickness marking

Sample calculation - clearance too large
Desired clearance (A) = 0.35
Measured clearance (B) = 0.40
Shim thickness found (C) = 4.05
Shim thickness reqd. (D) = C+B-A = 4.10

13 With the correct shim fitted, release the tappet depressing tool. Turn the engine back so that the cam lobes are again pointing upwards and check that the clearance is now correct.

14 Repeat the process for the remaining valves, turning the engine each time to bring a pair of cam lobes upwards.

15 It will be helpful for future adjustment if a record is kept of the thickness of shim fitted at each position. The shims required can be purchased in advance once the clearances and the existing shim thicknesses are known.

16 It is permissible to interchange shims between tappets to achieve the correct clearances but it is not advisable to turn the camshaft with any shims removed, since there is a risk that the cam lobe will jam in the empty tappet.

17 When all the clearances are correct, refit the fuel injectors or glow plugs (Chapter 4B or 5C), then refit the oil baffle plate and tighten the nuts to the specified torque. Refit the cylinder head cover together with a new gasket and tighten the bolts to the specified torque.

18 Reconnect the crankcase ventilation hoses to the cylinder head cover.

5 Crankshaft pulley/vibration damper - removal and refitting

Removal

1 Disconnect the battery negative (earth) lead (see Chapter 5A).

2 Apply the handbrake, then jack up the front of the vehicle and support it on axle stands (see *"Jacking and Vehicle Support"*). Remove the engine undershield if fitted.

3 Remove the right-hand front roadwheel, then where necessary, undo the retaining screws and remove the wheel arch liner.

4 Unbolt and remove the auxiliary drivebelt lower cover for access to the crankshaft pulley.

5 Remove the auxiliary drivebelt as described in Chapter 1B.

6 Unscrew the bolts and remove the crankshaft pulley/vibration damper from the end of the crankshaft. To hold the crankshaft stationary while loosening the bolts, have an assistant engage 4th gear and depress the footbrake pedal, or alternatively remove the starter motor and have an assistant insert a wide-bladed screwdriver in the teeth of the starter ring gear.

Refitting

7 Refitting is a reversal of removal, but tighten the mounting bolts to the specified torque.

6 Timing belt covers - removal and refitting

Removal

1 Apply the handbrake, then jack up the front of the vehicle and support it on axle stands (see *"Jacking and Vehicle Support"*). Where fitted, remove the engine undershield. Remove the right-hand front roadwheel.

2 The right-hand engine mounting brackets must now be removed for access to the timing belt covers. First support the weight of the engine using a trolley jack and block of wood beneath the sump. Alternatively, use a support bar across the top of the engine resting in the front wing water drain channels. With the engine supported, unscrew the bolts and remove the reinforcement bracket, then unscrew the nuts and remove the upper bracket. Make sure the engine is adequately supported.

3 Unscrew the single retaining bolt and release the clip then remove the upper timing belt cover.

4 Unscrew the bolts retaining the top of the lower timing belt cover. If necessary, slightly raise the engine for access to the bolts.

5 Unbolt and remove the auxiliary drivebelt lower cover for access to the crankshaft pulley.

6 Remove the auxiliary drivebelt as described in Chapter 1B.

7 Unscrew the bolts and remove the crankshaft pulley/vibration damper from the end of the crankshaft. To hold the crankshaft stationary while loosening the bolts, have an assistant engage 4th gear and depress the footbrake pedal, or alternatively remove the starter motor and have an assistant insert a wide-bladed screwdriver in the teeth of the starter ring gear.

8 Unscrew the lower bolts and remove the lower timing belt cover.

9 Unscrew the bolts and remove the cover from over the injection pump pulley.

Refitting

10 Refitting is a reversal of removal, but tighten the bolts to the specified torque.

7.9 Home-made camshaft setting bar inserted in the offset slot

7 Timing belt and injection pump drivebelt - removal, inspection and refitting

> **Warning: Never re-use or re-tension a timing/injection pump drivebelt which has already been used. This could lead to the belt becoming over-tensioned, leading to its failure and resulting in serious engine damage.**

Removal

1 Disconnect the battery negative (earth) lead (see Chapter 5A).

2 Apply the handbrake, then jack up the front of the vehicle and support it on axle stands (see *"Jacking and Vehicle Support"*). Where fitted, remove the engine undershield. Remove the right-hand roadwheel and where necessary the wheel arch liner.

3 Remove the timing belt covers as described in Section 6.

4 Unbolt and remove the auxiliary drivebelt tensioner.

5 Remove the alternator as described in Chapter 5A.

6 Set Piston No 1 to TDC on its compression stroke as described in Section 3.

Engines with an automatic timing belt tensioner

7 Disconnect the crankcase ventilation hoses.

8 Unbolt and remove the cylinder head cover, and remove the gasket.

9 Fit Ford special timing tool 21-162B in the slot at the left-hand end of the camshaft. If the Ford tool is not available, a home-made version may be fabricated out of metal bar, making sure that it is a good fit in the slot **(see illustration)**.

10 Hold the camshaft sprocket stationary using a tool which engages the sprocket holes, then loosen the retaining bolt two or three turns.

11 Loosen the centre bolt of the tensioner sprocket, then turn the adjusting eccentric anticlockwise to the 6 o'clock position to release the belt tension.

12 Remove the timing belt from the crankshaft, camshaft, and tensioner sprockets and from the idler pulley.

13 Insert a screwdriver between the rear timing cover and the camshaft sprocket and apply light pressure to the sprocket. Insert a soft-metal drift through the hole in the rear cover and tap lightly on the sprocket to release it from the taper on the camshaft.

Engines with standard timing belt tensioner

14 Insert Ford timing pin 23-019 (or suitable drill bit) through the camshaft sprocket and into the special hole in the cylinder head **(see illustration)**.

2C

7.14 Drill bit used as a timing pin through the camshaft sprocket

7.27 Screwing in the TDC setting pin

15 Loosen the bolts securing the sprocket to the camshaft.

16 Loosen the tensioner bolt, then compress the tensioner spring and move the tensioner to release the belt tension. Tighten the tensioner bolt to hold it away from the belt.

17 Remove the timing belt from the crankshaft, camshaft and idler sprockets and from the tensioner pulley.

All engines

18 To remove the injection pump drivebelt, loosen the tensioner bolt then lever the tensioner to release the tension and re-tighten the bolt to hold. Remove the belt from the crankshaft and injection pump sprockets and from the tensioner pulley.

Inspection

19 Clean the sprockets, idler wheel and tensioner pulley and wipe them dry, however do not apply excessive amounts of solvent to the idler and tensioner wheels otherwise the bearing lubricant may be contaminated. Also clean the rear timing belt cover, and the front of the cylinder head and block.

20 Examine the timing belt carefully for any signs of oil or coolant - the presence of either would indicate a leak, which must be cured before fitting the new belt. A new timing belt **must** be fitted once the old one has been removed - **never** refit a used timing belt.

Refitting

21 Locate the new injection pump drivebelt on the crankshaft and injection pump sprockets so that it is taut between the two sprockets, and the directional arrows are pointing the correct way.

22 Slacken the injection pump sprocket bolts half a turn, and also slacken the belt tensioner bolt half a turn. Allow the belt tensioner to snap against the belt. Retighten all the slackened bolts and make sure that the bolts are centralised in the elongated holes.

Engines with standard timing belt tensioner

23 Fit the new timing belt, with the directional arrows correct for normal crankshaft rotation. The belt should be slack on the tensioner side and taut between sprockets.

Caution: The engine must be cold, having been switched off for at least 4 hours.

24 Slacken the camshaft sprocket bolts and the tensioner bolts half a turn. Allow the tensioner to snap against the belt.

25 Retighten all slackened bolts, and make sure that the bolts are centralised in the elongated holes. Remove all the timing pins and turn the crankshaft through two revolutions in the normal direction of rotation

until the slot in the injection pump sprocket is again at the highest point (12 o'clock).

26 Now turn the crankshaft anti-clockwise until the slot in the injection pump sprocket is at the 11 o'clock position.

27 Screw in the TDC setting pin **(see illustration)**.

28 Slowly turn the crankshaft clockwise until the crankshaft web contacts the timing pin.

29 Insert the timing pins in the camshaft and the injection pump sprockets.

30 Slacken the bolts (through half a turn) that secure the camshaft and injection pump sprockets and the belt tensioners.

31 Depress both drivebelts on the taut side opposite to the tensioners, and then release them.

32 Retighten all slackened bolts. The valve timing is now set correctly **(see illustration)**.

Engines with an automatic timing belt tensioner

33 Make sure that the crankshaft is positioned at TDC with the crankshaft web in contact with the timing pin.

34 Unscrew the camshaft sprocket bolt and apply engine oil to the head contact face. Screw in the bolt finger-tight then back off a quarter turn. Make sure that the sprocket turns on the camshaft.

35 Fit the new timing belt, with the directional arrows correct for normal crankshaft rotation. Locate it first on the crankshaft sprocket, then over the idler pulley, over the camshaft sprocket, on the tensioner sprocket and on the idler.

Caution: The engine must be cold, having been switched off for at least 4 hours.

36 Turn the tensioner adjusting eccentric clockwise to the 9 o'clock position to tension the timing belt, then tighten the centre bolt to the specified torque.

37 Remove all timing pins and camshaft setting bar, and turn the crankshaft through six revolutions in the normal direction of rotation until the slot in the injection pump sprocket is again at the highest point (12 o'clock).

38 Now turn the crankshaft anti-clockwise until the slot in the injection pump sprocket is at the 11 o'clock position.

39 Screw in the TDC setting pin.

40 Slowly turn the crankshaft clockwise until the crankshaft web contacts the timing pin.

41 Insert the timing pins in the camshaft and the injection pump sprockets.

42 Hold the camshaft sprocket stationary using a tool which engages the sprocket holes, then loosen the retaining bolt two or three turns.

43 Insert a screwdriver between the rear timing cover and the camshaft sprocket and apply light pressure to the sprocket. Insert a soft-metal drift through the hole in the rear cover and tap lightly on the sprocket to release it from the taper on the camshaft.

44 Insert the camshaft setting bar in the slot in the camshaft. If necessary, turn the camshaft using grips to align the slot.

7.32 Timing belt and injection pump belt 'timed' and ready for fitting of the timing covers

1 Camshaft sprocket
2 Idler sprocket
3 Injection pump sprocket
4 Injection pump drivebelt tensioner
5 Crankshaft pulley vibration damper
6 Auxiliary shaft sprocket
7 Coolant pump sprocket
8 Timing belt tensioner

45 Hold the tensioner centre bolt stationary with a spanner, turn the adjustment eccentric until the arrows are aligned, then tighten the centre bolt to the specified torque. Turn the eccentric smoothly and make sure that it is finally set between the 6 o'clock and 12 o'clock positions **(see illustration)**.

46 Turn the crankshaft through four revolutions, then recheck the TDC setting using the timing pins and camshaft setting bar. The arrows on the tensioner must not be offset by more that 3 mm.

47 Remove the setting bar, then refit the cylinder head cover together with a new gasket and tighten the bolts.

48 Reconnect the crankcase ventilation hoses.

All engines

49 Refit and tighten the timing pin blanking plug **(see illustration)**.

50 Refit the alternator with reference to Chapter 5A.

51 Refit the auxiliary drivebelt tensioner and tighten the bolt to the specified torque.

52 Refit the timing belt covers with reference to Section 6.

53 Refit the undershield (where fitted) then refit the roadwheel and lower the vehicle to the ground.

54 Reconnect the battery negative (earth) lead (see Chapter 5A).

---

8 Timing belt/drivebelt tensioners and sprockets - removal, inspection and refitting

Note: *A new timing belt must always be fitted.*

Crankshaft sprockets

Removal

1 Remove the timing belt and injection pump drivebelt as described in Section 7. This procedure includes removal of the crankshaft pulley/vibration damper.

2 Unbolt the auxiliary drivebelt tensioner.

3 Remove the alternator as described in Chapter 5A.

4 Hold the crankshaft stationary using a length of metal bar bolted to the sprocket

7.45 Turn the adjustment eccentric (1) until the arrows (inset) are aligned, then tighten the centre bolt (2)

flange, then unscrew and remove the retaining bolt. **Note:** *The bolt is very tight. Discard the bolt - a new one must be obtained for refitting.*

5 Remove the outer sprocket, using a suitable puller if necessary **(see illustration)**.

6 Remove the inner sprocket from the end of the crankshaft and recover the O-ring from the sprocket **(see illustrations)**. To remove the sprocket, use Ford tool 21-200 or a similar tool which engages the inside of the sprocket. If necessary, remove the locating pin from the end of the crankshaft.

Inspection

7 Examine the sprockets for wear and damage and renew them if necessary. Wipe clean the oil seal surface on the inner sprocket.

8 If there is any sign of oil leakage from the crankshaft front oil seal, renew it with reference to Section 15. Note that the support ring on the new oil seal must remain in position until just before the inner crankshaft sprocket is fitted.

7.49 Refitting the timing pin blanking plug

Refitting

9 Make sure the locating pin is fitted to the end of the crankshaft.

10 Fit the new O-ring to the inner sprocket, then lubricate the crankshaft with engine oil. Remove the oil seal support ring, then slide on the sprocket making sure that the hole is aligned with the locating pin. Press the sprocket fully onto the crankshaft.

11 Fit the outer sprocket onto the inner sprocket making sure that the vee engages with the cut-out. Lubricate the head of the new bolt with oil, then insert it and tighten it while holding the sprocket stationary. Observe the four stages as given in the Specifications, and use an angle gauge where required.

12 Refit the alternator as described in Chapter 5A.

13 Refit the auxiliary drivebelt tensioner and tighten the bolt.

14 Fit the new timing belt and injection pump drivebelt as described in Section 7.

Camshaft sprocket

Removal

15 Remove the timing belt as described in Section 7 - there is no need to remove the injection pump drivebelt. Note that if a support bar is located over the engine, it must be positioned to allow sufficient room to remove the camshaft sprocket.

2C

8.5 Removing the outer (timing belt) crankshaft sprocket

8.6a Removing the inner (injection pump) crankshaft sprocket

8.6b Inner crankshaft sprocket, showing O-ring seal (arrowed)

16 On engines with a standard tensioner, hold the sprocket stationary using a tool engaged with the holes in the sprocket, then loosen the centre flange bolt and the four sprocket retaining bolts **(see illustration)**. Remove the sprocket from the flange, then pull the flange from the end of the camshaft using a suitable puller. Remove the Woodruff key from the groove in the camshaft.

17 On engines with an automatic tensioner, hold the sprocket stationary using a tool engaged with the holes in the sprocket, then loosen the centre bolt several turns. Insert a screwdriver between the rear timing cover and the camshaft sprocket and apply light pressure to the sprocket. Insert a soft-metal drift through the hole in the rear cover and tap lightly on the sprocket to release it from the taper on the camshaft. Fully unscrew the bolt and remove the sprocket from the end of the camshaft.

Inspection

18 Inspect the sprocket for wear and damage and renew it if necessary.

Refitting

19 Refit the sprocket to the camshaft using a reversal of the removal procedure. On engines with an automatic tensioner, leave the centre bolt finger-tight. On engines with a standard tensioner, fully tighten the flange bolt but leave the sprocket bolts finger-tight.

20 Fit the new timing belt with reference to Section 7.

Auxiliary shaft sprocket

Removal

21 Remove the timing belt as described in Section 7 - there is no need to remove the injection pump drivebelt. **Note:** *The timing belt must be renewed.*

22 The auxiliary shaft sprocket must now be held stationary while the bolt is loosened. To do this, engage the old timing belt with the sprocket and locate both runs of the belt over the crankshaft sprocket. Using a lever, pull down on the belt to hold the auxiliary shaft stationary then loosen the bolt.

23 Unscrew the bolt and remove the sprocket from the locating dowel on the auxiliary shaft **(see illustration)**.

8.23 Removing the auxiliary shaft sprocket

8.16 Unscrewing the camshaft sprocket retaining bolts

Inspection

24 Inspect the sprocket for wear and damage and renew it if necessary.

Refitting

25 Refitting is a reversal of removal, but tighten all nuts and bolts to the specified torque. Fit the new timing belt as described in Section 7.

Injection pump sprocket

Removal

26 Remove the timing belt and injection pump drivebelt as described in Section 7.

27 Mark the sprocket in relation to the injection pump flange, then hold the sprocket stationary using a suitable tool engaged with the sprocket holes.

28 Unscrew the retaining bolts and remove the sprocket from the flange.

Inspection

29 Inspect the sprocket for wear and damage and renew it if necessary.

Refitting

30 Locate the sprocket on the flange making sure that the previously made marks are aligned with each other.

31 Fit the new timing belt (see Section 7).

Standard tensioner (timing belt and injection pump drivebelt)

Removal

32 Remove the timing belt/injection pump drivebelt as described in Section 7.

33 Unscrew the bolt and remove the tensioner pulley and tension spring **(see illustration)**.

Inspection

34 Spin the pulley by hand and check for roughness and resistance. If evident, renew the tensioner.

Refitting

35 Clean the tensioner and the front face of the cylinder head/block.

36 Refit the tensioner and spring and tighten the mounting bolt to the specified torque.

37 Fit the new timing belt/injection pump drivebelt as described in Section 7.

Automatic tensioner

Removal

38 Remove the timing belt as described in Section 7 - there is no need to remove the injection pump drivebelt.

39 Unscrew the bolt from the centre of the adjustment tensioner sprocket and remove the sprocket together with the eccentric.

40 Unscrew the bolts and remove the tensioner idler pulley and tension spring.

Inspection

41 Check the tensioner components for wear and damage and renew as necessary.

Refitting

42 Refit the tensioner sprocket and idler and tighten the bolts to the specified torque.

43 Fit the new timing belt as described in Section 7.

Idler

Removal

44 Remove the timing belt as described in Section 7 - there is no need to remove the injection pump drivebelt.

45 Unbolt and remove the idler.

Inspection

46 Spin the idler pulley by hand and check for roughness and resistance. If evident, renew.

Refitting

47 Refit the idler and tighten the mounting bolt to the specified torque.

48 Fit the new timing belt as described in Section 7.

9 Camshaft oil seal - renewal

1 Remove the camshaft sprocket as described in Section 8.

2 Note the fitted depth of the oil seal before removing it, as a guide to fitting the new one.

3 Using a screwdriver or suitable hooked instrument, pull the oil seal from the cylinder head. If the seal is tight, drill two or three small holes in its outer face, then screw in self-

8.33 Standard timing belt tensioner (A) and idler sprocket (B)

10.3 Auxiliary shaft oil seal housing on the cylinder block

10.6a Auxiliary shaft oil seal retainer with plastic fitting ring

10.6b Tightening the auxiliary shaft oil seal housing bolts

tapping screws. Pull on the screws with a pair of pliers to remove the oil seal.

4 Wipe clean the seating and end of the camshaft.

5 Dip the new seal in oil, then locate it over the camshaft and initially press it in by hand making sure that it enters the cylinder head squarely.

6 Using a piece of metal tubing or a socket, carefully drive the oil seal into the cylinder head to the previously noted depth.

7 Wipe any excess oil from the oil seal and surrounding area.

8 Refit the camshaft sprocket and fit the new timing belt with reference to Section 8.

10 Auxiliary shaft oil seal - renewal

1 Remove the auxiliary shaft sprocket as described in Section 8.

2 Unbolt and remove the timing belt side cover.

3 Unscrew the bolts and remove the oil seal housing from the cylinder block **(see illustration)**. The oil seal is integral with the housing.

4 Clean the cylinder block and end of the auxiliary shaft.

5 Smear fresh engine oil on the auxiliary shaft and on the sealing lips of the new oil seal. Before fitting the new seal, locate the special fitting ring inside the sealing lips.

6 Locate the new oil seal over the end of the auxiliary shaft, then insert the bolts and tighten **(see illustrations)**.

7 Carefully remove the special ring and make sure that the seal lips are located on the shaft correctly.

8 Refit the timing belt side cover and tighten the bolts.

9 Refit the auxiliary shaft sprocket as described in Section 8.

11 Camshaft and tappets - removal, inspection and refitting

Removal

1 Remove the camshaft sprocket and flange as described in Section 8.

2 Disconnect the crankcase ventilation hose from the right-hand rear of the cylinder head.

3 Disconnect the crankcase ventilation hose from the left-hand front of the cylinder head cover, then unscrew the bolts and remove the cover.

4 Unscrew the nuts and remove the baffle plate.

5 Undo the nuts of bearing caps Nos 2 and 4. Remove these caps and their shells. Keep the shells with their caps if they are to be re-used. Note that the caps are numbered and carry an arrow pointing to the pulley end of the engine **(see illustration)**.

6 Slacken the nuts of bearing caps Nos 1, 3 and 5 one turn at a time, working from end to end so that the camshaft is released gradually. Remove the bearing caps and shells, again keeping the shells with their caps if necessary.

7 Lift out the camshaft with its oil seal. Recover the lower half bearing shells, keeping them in order if necessary.

8 If purchasing new bearing shells, note that either standard or oversize outside diameter shells may have been fitted in production. Oversize shells are identified by a green mark.

9 Obtain eight small, clean containers, and number them 1 to 8 from the timing end. Lift the tappets one by one from the cylinder head keeping the shims with their respective tappets.

Inspection

10 With the camshaft and tappets removed, check for signs of obvious wear (scoring, pitting etc) and for ovality, and renew if necessary.

11 If possible, use a micrometer to measure the outside diameter of each tappet - take measurements at the top and bottom of each tappet, then a second set at right-angles to the first; if any measurement is significantly different from the others, the tappet is tapered or oval (as applicable) and must be renewed. If the tappets or the cylinder head bores are excessively worn, new tappets and/or a new cylinder head will be required.

12 Visually examine the camshaft lobes for score marks, pitting, and evidence of overheating (blue, discoloured areas). Look for flaking away of the hardened surface layer of each lobe. If any such signs are evident, renew the component concerned.

13 Examine the camshaft bearing journals and the bearing shells for signs of obvious wear or pitting. If any such signs are evident, renew the camshaft and/or obtain a set of bearing shells.

14 To check camshaft endfloat, remove the tappets, clean the bearing surfaces carefully, and refit the camshaft and bearing caps with shells. Tighten the bearing cap nuts to the specified torque wrench setting, then measure the endfloat using a dial gauge mounted on the cylinder head so that its tip bears on the camshaft right-hand end.

15 Tap the camshaft fully towards the gauge, zero the gauge, then tap the camshaft fully away from the gauge, and note the gauge reading. If the endfloat measured is found to be more than the value given in the Specifications, fit a new camshaft and repeat the check; if the clearance is still excessive, the cylinder head must be renewed.

2C

11.5 Camshaft bearing caps - note numbers and arrows

11.17 Fitting a camshaft lower bearing shell

11.18 Fitting the camshaft

11.19a Fitting a camshaft upper bearing shell to its cap

Refitting

16 Commence reassembly by lubricating the cylinder head tappet bores and the tappets with engine oil. Carefully refit the tappets (together with their respective shims - lettering facing downwards) to the cylinder head, ensuring that each tappet is refitted to its original bore. Some care will be required to enter the tappets squarely into their bores.

17 Place the lower half bearing shells (the ones with the oil holes) in position **(see illustration)**. Lubricate the shells.

18 Make sure that all tappets, shims and the vacuum pump plunger are in place. Remove the old oil seal, if not already done, and place the camshaft on the lower half bearings **(see illustration)**. Position the camshaft with the timing setting slot parallel with the head top face and the larger semi-circular segment uppermost.

19 Clean any old sealant from No. 1 bearing cap. Fit the upper bearing shells to their caps and lubricate them. Coat the mating surfaces of with sealant (to Ford spec No. 1 cap SPM-41G-9112 F/G) in the areas shown **(see illustrations)**.

20 Fit bearing caps and shells Nos 1, 3 and 5, making sure that they are the right way round (the arrows point to the timing belt end). Tighten the cap nuts, half a turn at a time, in the sequence No. 3 - No. 1 - No. 5. Carry on until the caps are seated.

21 Fit caps and shells Nos 2 and 4, tapping them down with a mallet if necessary to seat them. Fit their nuts.

22 Tighten all the bearing cap nuts to the specified torque **(see illustration)**.

23 Insert the camshaft setting tool into the slot so that it is a snug fit.

24 Fit a new oil seal to the camshaft nose as described in Section 9.

25 Lubricate the cam lobes liberally with engine oil, or with special cam lube if supplied with a new camshaft.

26 Refit the baffle plate and tighten the nuts.

27 Refit the cylinder head cover together with a new gasket and tighten the bolts to the specified torque.

28 Reconnect the crankcase ventilation hoses, then refit the camshaft sprocket and flange as described in Section 8. Remember the timing belt has to be renewed.

12 Cylinder head - removal, inspection and refitting

Removal

1 Disconnect the battery negative (earth) lead (see Chapter 5A).

2 Apply the handbrake, then jack up the front of the vehicle and support it on axle stands (see *"Jacking and Vehicle Support"*). Remove the engine undershield if fitted.

3 Drain the cooling system as described in Chapter 1B. Save the coolant in a clean container if it is fit for re-use.

4 Remove the timing belt as described in Section 7. There is no need to remove the injection pump drivebelt.

5 If a support bar was used to support the engine in paragraph 4, locate a trolley jack and block of wood beneath the sump then remove the support bar.

6 Remove the camshaft sprocket and timing belt tensioner with reference to Section 8.

7 Disconnect the crankcase ventilation hose from the right-hand rear end of the cylinder head.

8 Loosen the clips and remove the air inlet duct from the inlet manifold and air cleaner.

9 Unscrew the bolts and remove the upper inlet manifold from the lower manifold. Seal the lower manifold using cloth rags or masking tape.

10 Loosen the clips and disconnect the coolant hoses from the thermostat housing.

11 Disconnect the wiring from the glow plugs, engine coolant temperature sensor, temperature gauge sender, and oil pressure switch.

12 Disconnect the brake servo vacuum line at the front left-hand side of the engine.

13 Disconnect the fuel feed line at the top of the filter.

14 Disconnect the fuel line to the fuel heater at the left-hand side of the engine.

15 Disconnect the fuel heater wiring.

16 Disconnect the vacuum hose and the wiring from the exhaust gas recirculation valve.

17 Disconnect the coolant hose from the fuel heater.

18 Disconnect the fuel leak-off pipes from the injectors.

19 Unscrew the union nuts and remove the injection pipes from the injectors and injection pump. Be prepared for some loss of fuel.

20 Unbolt the glow plug wiring bracket, then unbolt the oil dipstick tube bracket.

21 Unscrew the nuts securing the catalytic converter to the exhaust manifold.

22 Disconnect the crankcase ventilation hose from the front of the cylinder head cover. Unscrew the bolts and remove the cylinder head cover and gasket.

23 Remove the oil baffle plate.

24 Remove the injectors and heat shields as described in Chapter 4B.

25 Set No 1 piston to TDC as described in Section 3.

11.19b Camshaft No 1 bearing cap - coat shaded area with sealant

11.22 Tightening the camshaft bearing cap nuts

12.27 Removing the cylinder head

12.28 Cylinder head gasket thickness is indicated by the number of teeth (arrowed)

12.37a Lowering the cylinder head onto the cylinder block - note the injectors protected against dirt

26 Unscrew the cylinder head bolts in the reverse order to tightening (see illustration 12.37b). As new bolts will be required when refitting the cylinder head, note that the bolts have an M12 thread and a Torx T70 head.

27 With the help of an assistant, lift the cylinder head from the block together with the manifolds (see illustration).

28 Remove the cylinder head gasket, but retain it for comparison with the new gasket. Three possible thicknesses of gasket are available according to the piston protrusion, the details of which are given in the Specifications for the cylinder head at the start of this Chapter (see illustration).

Inspection

29 The mating faces of the cylinder head and block must be perfectly clean before refitting the head. Use a scraper to remove all traces of gasket and carbon, and also clean the tops of the pistons. Take particular care with the aluminium cylinder head, as the soft metal is damaged easily. Also, make sure that debris is not allowed to enter the oil and water channels - this is particularly important for the oil circuit, as carbon could block the oil supply to the camshaft or crankshaft bearings. Using adhesive tape and paper, seal the water, oil and bolt holes in the cylinder block. Clean the piston crowns in the same way.

> **HAYNES HiNT** *To prevent carbon entering the gap between the pistons and bores, smear a little grease in the gap. After cleaning the piston, rotate the crankshaft so that the piston moves down the bore, then wipe out the grease and carbon with a cloth rag.*

30 Check the block and head for nicks, deep scratches and other damage. If slight, they may be removed carefully with a file. More serious damage may be repaired by machining, but this is a specialist job.

31 If warpage of the cylinder head is suspected, use a straight-edge to check it for distortion. Refer to Chapter 2D if necessary.

32 Clean out the bolt holes in the block using

a pipe cleaner, or a rag and screwdriver. Make sure that all oil is removed, otherwise there is a possibility of the block being cracked by hydraulic pressure when the bolts are tightened.

33 Examine the bolt threads and the threads in the cylinder block for damage. If necessary, use the correct-size tap to chase out the threads in the block.

34 If necessary, the valve clearances may be checked and adjusted with the cylinder head on the bench. Refer to Section 4.

Refitting

35 Before fitting the cylinder head, make sure that the groove on the camshaft rear eccentric is parallel with the upper surface of the cylinder head, and the larger segment is uppermost. Also make sure that the crankshaft is at TDC.

36 Fit the new selected gasket and use new cylinder head bolts. Make sure that the centralising dowel sleeves are located at bolt holes 8 and 10, and the word TOP/OBEN is visible.

37 Fit the cylinder head, screw in the new bolts (do not oil the bolts), and tighten in the stages indicated in the Specifications and in the sequence shown (see illustrations).

38 Refit the injectors and heat shields as described in Chapter 4B.

39 Refit the oil baffle plate and tighten the nuts.

40 Refit the cylinder head cover together with a new gasket, and tighten the bolts.

41 Reconnect the crankcase ventilation hose.

42 Refit the catalytic converter to the exhaust manifold, then tighten the retaining nuts.

43 Refit the oil dipstick tube bracket and tighten the bolt.

44 Refit the glow plug wiring bracket.

45 Refit the injection pipes and tighten the union nuts. Reconnect the leak-off pipes.

46 Reconnect the coolant hose to the fuel heater.

47 Reconnect the exhaust gas recirculation vacuum valve hose and wiring.

48 Reconnect the fuel heater wiring and fuel line.

49 Reconnect the fuel feed line to the top of the filter, then reconnect the brake servo vacuum line.

50 Reconnect the wiring to the oil pressure switch, temperature gauge sender, engine coolant temperature sensor, and glow plugs.

51 Reconnect the hoses to the thermostat housing and tighten the clips.

52 Remove the cloth rags or masking tape, then refit the upper inlet manifold to the lower manifold and tighten the bolts.

53 Refit the air inlet duct between the inlet manifold and air cleaner and tighten the clips.

54 Reconnect the crankcase ventilation hose to the right-hand rear end of the cylinder head.

55 Refit the timing belt tensioner and camshaft sprocket as described in Section 8.

2C

12.37b Cylinder head bolt tightening sequence. Arrow points to timing end of the engine

13.9 Removing the sump gasket from the crankcase

13.12 Apply suitable sealant to the cylinder block/sump mating surfaces at the points arrowed

56 Where applicable, attach the support bar to the engine and remove the trolley jack.
57 Fit a new timing belt with reference to Section 7.
58 Refill the cooling system as described in Chapter 1B.
59 Refit the engine undershield, then lower the vehicle to the ground.
60 Reconnect the battery earth lead (see Chapter 5A).
61 The fuel system can now be primed, with reference to Chapter 4B.
62 Start the engine and run it to normal operating temperature. Check for leaks of oil and coolant.

13 Sump -
removal and refitting

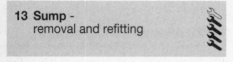

Removal

1 Note that the crankshaft rear oil seal housing is bolted directly onto the sump and cylinder block, making it necessary to remove the flywheel in order to unbolt the rear oil seal housing.
2 Apply the handbrake, then jack up the front of the vehicle and support it on axle stands (see *"Jacking and Vehicle Support"*).
3 Drain the engine oil, then check the sealing washer and renew if necessary. Clean and refit the engine oil drain plug together with the washer, and tighten it to the specified torque wrench setting. Although not strictly necessary

as part of the dismantling procedure, owners are advised to remove and discard the oil filter, so that it can be renewed with the oil (see Chapter 1B).
4 Remove the transmission as described in Chapter 7A. Make sure the engine is adequately and safely supported.
5 Remove the flywheel as described in Section 16.
6 Unbolt the rear oil seal housing and withdraw it over the end of the crankshaft (refer to Section 15).
7 If necessary, remove the crankshaft position sensor and unbolt its bracket from the sump.
8 Progressively unscrew the sump retaining bolts, then lower the sump from the crankcase and withdraw it from under the vehicle.
9 Recover the sump gasket (see illustration).
10 While the sump is removed, take the opportunity to remove the oil pump pick-up/strainer pipe and clean it with reference to Section 14.

Refitting

11 Thoroughly clean the contact surfaces of the sump and crankcase. If necessary, use a cloth rag to clean the interior of the sump and crankcase. If the oil pump pick-up/strainer pipe was removed, fit a new O-ring and refit the pipe with reference to Section 14.
12 Apply suitable sealant (Ford recommend SPM-4G-9112-F/G) to the joint (on each side) between the front timing housing and crankcase (see illustration).

13 Locate the gasket on the sump, then offer the sump onto the crankcase and insert the retaining bolts finger-tight.
14 Before tightening the bolts, the sump must be accurately aligned with the end face of the cylinder block using a straight-edge.
15 Once the sump is correctly aligned, progressively tighten the sump-to-crankcase bolts to the specified torque.
16 If removed, refit the crankshaft position sensor and bracket.
17 Refit the crankshaft rear oil seal housing and tighten the bolts to the specified torque (refer to Section 15).
18 Refit the flywheel with reference to Section 16.
19 Refit the transmission as described in Chapter 7A.
20 Lower the vehicle to the ground, then fit a new oil filter (if necessary) and refill the engine with oil with reference to Chapter 1B.
21 Finally start the engine and check for signs of oil or coolant leaks.

14 Oil pump -
removal, inspection and refitting

Note: *The following procedure includes removal of the oil filter, and it is recommended that the filter be renewed rather than refitting the old unit. The engine oil should also be changed at the same time.*

Removal

1 Apply the handbrake, then jack up the front of the vehicle and support it on axle stands (see *"Jacking and Vehicle Support"*).
2 Where necessary, drain the engine oil with reference to Chapter 1B.
3 Place a suitable container beneath the rear of the engine, then unscrew and remove the oil filter (see Chapter 1B).
4 Unscrew the mounting bolts and remove the oil pump from the cylinder block. Recover the gasket (see illustrations).

Inspection

5 Unscrew the crosshead screws and remove the cover from the oil pump.

14.4a Unscrew the mounting bolts . . .

14.4b . . . remove the oil pump from the cylinder block . . .

14.4c . . . and recover the gasket

14.7a Removing the oil pump pick-up tube from the crankcase - note the O-ring which must be renewed

6 Clean all parts and inspect them for wear or damage. Using a feeler blade, measure the inner to outer rotor clearance. If the clearance exceeds that specified then the pump must be renewed as pump components are not available individually. It is wise to renew the pump on a precautionary basis at time of major overhaul, especially if there is evidence of oil starvation elsewhere.

7 If there are any signs of metallic debris inside the oil pump, it is recommended that the sump be removed and the pick-up pipe and strainer cleaned thoroughly. Renew the pick-up tube O-ring and the sump gasket on refitting and tighten the bolts to the specified torque **(see illustrations)**.

Refitting

8 Before refitting the oil pump, pour approximately 10 cc of engine oil into the pump to prime it, and oil the pump drive gear and driven gear.

9 Clean the mating faces of the pump and cylinder block, then refit the oil pump together with a new gasket, and tighten the mounting bolts progressively to the specified torque.

10 Fit a new oil filter and fill the engine with fresh oil as described in Chapter 1B.

11 Lower the vehicle to the ground.

15 Crankshaft oil seals - renewal

Front (timing belt) oil seal

1 Remove the crankshaft sprockets as described in Section 8.

2 Note the fitted depth of the oil seal in the engine front plate.

3 Using a screwdriver or other suitable instrument, prise the oil seal from the engine front plate. An alternative method is to drill two small holes in the oil seal, then screw in self-tapping screws and use grips to pull out the oil seal. If this method is used, make sure that all swarf is removed.

4 Inspect the seal rubbing surface on the inner crankshaft sprocket, and if necessary, renew the sprocket.

14.7b Tightening the oil pump pick-up tube mounting bolts

5 Wipe clean the oil seal seating in the front plate.

6 Note that the new oil seal is supplied with a support ring which must remain in position until just before the inner crankshaft sprocket is fitted. The oil seal must be fitted dry.

7 Using a length of metal tube or a socket, drive the new oil seal into the front plate to the previously noted depth. Leave the support ring in place at this stage.

8 Refit the crankshaft sprockets and timing belt with reference to Section 8.

Rear (flywheel end) oil seal

9 Remove the flywheel as described in Section 16.

10 Unbolt the rear oil seal housing from the sump and cylinder block and withdraw it over the end of the crankshaft. Note that the housing incorporates an integral rear oil seal and a vulcanised gasket.

11 Wipe clean the mating faces of the sump and cylinder block. Also wipe all oil from the rear end of the crankshaft. Note that the oil seal must be fitted dry.

12 Make sure that the support ring is located inside the oil seal, then locate the housing over the crankshaft. Screw in the retaining bolts finger-tight.

13 Make sure that the oil seal is centred on the end of the crankshaft, then progressively tighten the mounting bolts to the specified torque **(see illustration)**.

14 Carefully remove the support ring so that the lips of the oil seal rest on the crankshaft. If the ring is tight, it is likely that the rear faces

15.13 Tightening the rear oil seal mounting bolts

of the sump and cylinder block are not accurately aligned with each other. To rectify this situation, loosen all of the sump bolts, reposition the sump, and retighten the bolts to the specified torque.

15 With the housing bolts tightened, refit the flywheel and transmission with reference to Section 16.

16 Flywheel - removal, inspection and refitting

Removal

1 Remove the transmission as described in Chapter 7A.

2 Remove the clutch components with reference to Chapter 6.

3 Make alignment marks on the flywheel and crankshaft to ensure correct refitting.

4 Hold the flywheel stationary using a locking tool engaged with the starter ring gear. A suitable home-made tool bolted to one of the transmission mounting bolt holes and engaged with the ring gear can be fabricated out of metal bar.

5 Unscrew the mounting bolts and lift the flywheel from the rear of the crankshaft. Take care not to drop the flywheel as it is very heavy. Discard the bolts and obtain new ones for the refitting procedure.

Inspection

6 Examine the clutch mating surface of the flywheel for scoring or cracks. Light grooving or scoring may be ignored. Surface cracks or deep grooving can sometimes be removed by specialist machining, provided not too much metal is taken off; otherwise the flywheel must be renewed.

7 Inspect the starter ring gear for damaged or missing teeth. A damaged ring gear can be renewed separately. The average DIY mechanic may prefer to leave the job to a Ford dealer or other competent workshop; for the enthusiast the procedure is as follows.

8 Drill two adjacent holes, 7 or 8 mm in diameter, through the ring gear. Take care not to drill into the flywheel.

9 Knock the ring gear off the flywheel with a hammer. Use light blows, evenly spaced around the ring.

10 Heat the new ring gear evenly to between 260° and 280°C (500° and 536°F). This is just about within the capability of most domestic ovens. Take care not to overheat the ring gear or its temper will be lost.

11 Using tongs or asbestos gloves, place the ring gear on the flywheel and tap it into place. Allow it to cool naturally. If the teeth have a bevelled lead-in for the starter motor pinion, make sure this is facing outwards (ie towards the clutch face).

12 If renewing the flywheel, transfer the clutch locating dowels to the new unit.

2C

16.14 Angle-tightening the flywheel bolts

Refitting

13 Commence refitting by placing the flywheel on the end of the crankshaft. Observe the alignment marks if refitting the original unit.

14 Insert the new bolts, and tighten them to the torque and angles given in the Specifications **(see illustration)**.

15 Refit the clutch components with reference to Chapter 6.

16 Refit the transmission with reference to Chapter 7A.

17 Engine/transmission mountings - inspection and renewal

Inspection

1 The engine/transmission mountings seldom require attention, but broken or deteriorated mountings should be renewed immediately, or the added strain placed on the driveline components may cause damage or wear.

2 During the check, the engine/transmission must be raised slightly, to remove its weight from the mountings.

3 Apply the handbrake, then jack up the front of the vehicle and support it on axle stands (see *"Jacking and Vehicle Support"*). Remove the engine undershield where fitted. Position a jack under the sump, with a large block of wood between the jack head and the sump, then carefully raise the engine/transmission just enough to take the weight off the mountings.

4 Check the mountings to see if the rubber is cracked, hardened or separated from the metal components. Sometimes, the rubber will split right down the centre.

5 Check for relative movement between each mounting's brackets and the engine/transmission or body (use a large screwdriver or lever to attempt to move the mountings). If movement is noted, lower the engine and check the mounting nuts and bolts for tightness.

Renewal

6 The engine mountings can be removed if the weight of the engine/transmission is supported by one of the following alternative methods.

7 Either support the weight of the assembly from underneath using a jack and a suitable piece of wood between the jack and the sump (to prevent damage), or from above by attaching a hoist to the engine. A third method is to use a suitable support bar with end pieces which will engage in the water channel each side of the bonnet lid aperture. Using an adjustable hook and chain connected to the engine, the weight of the engine and transmission can then be taken from the mountings.

8 Once the weight of the engine and transmission is suitably supported, any of the mountings can be unbolted and removed.

9 To remove the right-hand engine mounting, first unbolt the reinforcement bracket then unscrew the nuts and remove the upper bracket. Unscrew the bolts and remove the lower bracket from the cylinder head. Unbolt the insulator from the right-hand side of the engine compartment.

10 To remove the left-hand mounting first remove the battery and battery tray as described in Chapter 5A, then loosen the clips and remove the air inlet duct from between the air mass air flow sensor on the air cleaner and the throttle housing. Unscrew the mounting nuts from the left-hand engine mounting, then unscrew the bolts and remove the upper bracket. Unscrew the bolts and remove the insulator from the left-hand side of the engine compartment.

11 To remove the rear engine mounting/link, apply the handbrake, then jack up the front of the vehicle and support it on axle stands (see *"Jacking and Vehicle Support"*). Unscrew the through-bolts and remove the rear engine mounting link from the bracket on the transmission and from the bracket on the underbody. Hold the engine stationary while the bolts are being removed since the link will be under tension.

12 Refitting of all mountings is a reversal of the removal procedure. Do not fully tighten the mounting nuts/bolts until all of the mountings are in position. Check that the mounting rubbers do not twist or distort as the mounting bolts and nuts are tightened to their specified torques.

Chapter 2 Part D:
Engine removal and overhaul procedures

Contents

Degrees of difficulty

Easy, suitable for novice with little experience   **Fairly easy,** suitable for beginner with some experience   **Fairly difficult,** suitable for competent DIY mechanic   **Difficult,** suitable for experienced DIY mechanic   **Very difficult,** suitable for expert DIY or professional

Specifications

Torque wrench settings
Refer to Specifications in Chapter 2A, 2B or 2C.

2D

1 General information

Included in this part of Chapter 2 are the general overhaul procedures for the cylinder head, cylinder block/crankcase and internal engine components.

The information ranges from advice concerning preparation for an overhaul and the purchase of replacement parts, to detailed step-by-step procedures covering removal, inspection, renovation and refitting of internal engine parts.

The following Sections have been compiled based on the assumption that the engine has been removed from the car. For information concerning in-car engine repair, as well as the removal and refitting of the external components necessary for the overhaul, refer to Part A (Endura-E petrol engine), Part B (Zetec-SE petrol engine), or Part C (Endura-DE diesel engine) of this Chapter, and to Section 7 of this Part.

2 Engine overhaul - general information

It is not always easy to determine when, or if, an engine should be completely overhauled, as a number of factors must be considered.

High mileage is not necessarily an indication that an overhaul is needed, while low mileage does not preclude the need for an overhaul. Frequency of servicing is probably the most important consideration. An engine which has had regular and frequent oil and filter changes, as well as other required maintenance, will most likely give many thousands of miles of reliable service. Conversely, a neglected engine may require an overhaul very early in its life.

Excessive oil consumption is an indication that piston rings, valve stem oil seals and/or valves and valve guides are in need of attention. Make sure that oil leaks are not responsible before deciding that the rings and/or guides are bad. Perform a cylinder compression check to determine the extent of the work required.

Check the oil pressure with a gauge fitted in place of the oil pressure sender, and compare it with the value given in the Specifications. If it is extremely low, the main and big-end bearings and/or the oil pump are probably worn out.

Loss of power, rough running, knocking or metallic engine noises, excessive valve gear noise and high fuel consumption may also point to the need for an overhaul, especially if they are all present at the same time. If a complete tune-up does not remedy the situation, major mechanical work is the only solution.

An engine overhaul involves restoring the internal parts to the specifications of a new engine. During an overhaul, the pistons and rings are renewed, and the cylinder bores are reconditioned. New main bearings, connecting rod bearings and camshaft bearings are generally fitted, and if necessary, the crankshaft may be reground to restore the journals (note however that some of this work is not possible on the Zetec-SE engine due to the manufacturing processes used). The valves are also serviced as well, since they are usually in less-than-perfect condition at this point. While the engine is being overhauled, other components, such as the starter and alternator, can be overhauled as well. The end result should be a like-new engine that will give many trouble-free miles. **Note:** *Critical cooling system components such as the hoses, drivebelts, thermostat and water pump MUST be renewed when an engine is overhauled. The radiator should be checked carefully, to ensure that it is not clogged or leaking. Also, it is a good idea to renew the oil pump whenever the engine is overhauled.*

Before beginning the engine overhaul, read through the entire procedure to familiarise yourself with the scope and requirements of the job. Overhauling an engine is not difficult if you follow all of the instructions carefully, have the necessary tools and equipment, and pay close attention to all specifications; however, it can be time-consuming. Plan on the vehicle being tied up for a minimum of two weeks, especially if parts must be taken to an engineering works for repair or reconditioning. Check on the availability of parts, and make sure that any necessary special tools and equipment are obtained in advance. Most work can be done with typical hand tools, although a number of precision measuring tools are required for inspecting parts to determine if they must be renewed. Often the engineering works will handle the inspection of parts, and offer advice concerning reconditioning and renewal. **Note:** *Always wait until the engine has been completely dismantled, and all components, especially the engine block, have been inspected before deciding what service and repair operations must be performed by an engineering works. Since the condition of the block will be the major factor to consider when determining whether to overhaul the original engine or buy a reconditioned unit, do not purchase parts or have overhaul work done on other components until the block has been thoroughly inspected.* As a general rule, time is the primary cost of an overhaul, so it does not pay to fit worn or substandard parts.

As a final note, to ensure maximum life and minimum trouble from a reconditioned engine, everything must be assembled with care, and in a spotlessly-clean environment.

3 Engine removal - methods and precautions

If you have decided that an engine must be removed for overhaul or major repair work, several preliminary steps should be taken.

Locating a suitable place to work is extremely important. Adequate work space, along with storage space for the vehicle, will be needed. If a garage is not available, at the very least a flat, level, clean work surface is required.

Cleaning the engine compartment and engine before beginning the removal procedure will help keep tools clean and organised.

An engine hoist or A-frame will also be necessary. Make sure the equipment is rated in excess of the combined weight of the engine and transmission. Safety is of primary importance, considering the potential hazards involved in lifting the engine out of the vehicle.

If the engine is being removed by a novice, an assistant should be available. Advice and aid from someone more experienced would also be helpful. There are many instances when one person cannot simultaneously perform all of the operations required when removing the engine from the vehicle.

Plan the operation ahead of time. Arrange for, or obtain, all of the tools and equipment you will need, prior to beginning the job. Some of the equipment necessary to perform engine removal and installation safely and with relative ease are (in addition to an engine hoist) a heavy-duty floor jack, complete sets of spanners and sockets as described at the end of this manual, wooden blocks, and plenty of rags and cleaning solvent for mopping up spilled oil, coolant and fuel. If the hoist must be hired, make sure that you arrange for it in advance, and perform all of the operations possible without it beforehand. This will save you money and time.

Plan for the vehicle to be out of use for quite a while. An engineering works will be required to perform some of the work which the do-it-yourselfer cannot accomplish without special equipment. These places often have a busy schedule, so it would be a good idea to consult them before removing the engine, in order to accurately estimate the amount of time required to rebuild or repair components that may need work.

Always be extremely careful when removing and refitting the engine. Serious injury can result from careless actions. Plan ahead, take your time, and you will find that a job of this nature, although major, can be accomplished successfully.

4 Petrol engine and manual transmission - removal, separation and refitting

Note: *The engine and manual transmission is lowered from the engine compartment, then separated on the bench.*

Removal

1 Apply the handbrake, then jack up the front of the vehicle and support it on axle stands (see *"Jacking and Vehicle Support"*). Where applicable, remove the engine undershield.
2 Depressurise the fuel system with reference to Chapter 4A.
3 Disconnect the battery negative (earth) lead (see Chapter 5A).
4 Drain the cooling system as described in Chapter 1A.
5 Drain the manual transmission with reference to Chapter 7A.

6 If necessary, drain the engine oil with reference to Chapter 1A.
7 Disconnect the wiring for the electric cooling fan on the rear of the radiator. To prevent damage to the radiator it is recommended that it be removed completely as described in Chapter 3.
8 Loosen the clips and disconnect the air inlet duct from the throttle body housing and air flow meter on the air cleaner.
9 Remove the battery and battery box as described in Chapter 5A.
10 Trace the wiring back from the oxygen sensor on the top of the exhaust manifold to the connector, then disconnect the wiring.
11 Disconnect the accelerator cable from the throttle body housing and release it from the supports. Position it to one side.
12 Loosen the clip and disconnect the top hose from the thermostat housing. Release the engine wiring loom from the clips on the top hose.
13 Unclip the HT leads and position them to one side.
14 Disconnect the wiring from the alternator.
15 Disconnect the heater hose on the bulkhead by releasing the quick release fitting.
16 Disconnect the hose from the top right-hand side of the radiator.
17 Disconnect the engine wiring loom at the two connectors on the bulkhead, and unclip the wiring support bracket.
18 Disconnect the brake servo vacuum line at the inlet manifold.
19 Disconnect the evaporative canister purge vacuum line from the solenoid valve on the bulkhead.
20 Disconnect the wiring from the engine coolant temperature sensor on the right-hand rear of the engine.
21 Remove the oil filler cap and disconnect the crankcase ventilation hose from it, then refit the cap.
22 At the left-hand rear of the engine, disconnect the starter motor wiring and release the main cable from the support clip. Unscrew the nut and disconnect the main cable from the starter motor.
23 Unbolt the earth lead from the transmission. Also disconnect the wiring and detach it from the support on the transmission **(see illustrations).**

4.23a Disconnect the wiring from the transmission . . .

4.23b ... and detach it from the support

4.24 Disconnecting the speedometer cable from the rear of the transmission

4.27 Removing the auxiliary drivebelt tensioner from the cylinder block

24 Disconnect the speedometer cable from the rear of the transmission **(see illustration)**.
25 Disconnect the vehicle speed sensor wiring at the bulkhead.
26 Remove the cover from the auxiliary drivebelt by unscrewing the bolts at the front right-hand side of the engine.
27 Using a spanner, turn the tensioner pulley clockwise to release the tension, then slip the auxiliary drivebelt from the pulleys and remove it from the engine compartment. If necessary, the tensioner may be unbolted from the cylinder block **(see illustration)**.
28 Using a socket bar through the holes in the power steering pump pulley (where fitted), unscrew and remove the pump front mounting bolts. At the rear of the pump, unscrew the mounting bolt then lift the pump from its bracket and tie it to one side.

4.37 Gearchange rod and clamp on the rear of the transmission

29 Working beneath the vehicle, unbolt the lower cover from the crankshaft pulley.
30 Loosen the clip and disconnect the bottom hose from the coolant pump.
31 Unbolt the radiator shroud.
32 Where applicable, unbolt the air conditioning condenser from the top of the radiator. Do not remove the condenser.
33 Loosen the clips and disconnect the two hoses from the bottom right of the radiator.
34 Support the radiator, then unbolt the lower crossmember and remove it together with the radiator and fan. Where applicable, tie the air conditioning condenser to one side.
35 Where applicable, disconnect the air conditioning compressor wiring plug then unbolt the compressor and tie it to one side.
36 Under the vehicle, remove the exhaust downpipe and catalytic converter with reference to Chapter 4A.
37 Mark the position of the gearchange clamp on the transmission selector rod, then unscrew the clamp bolt and remove the gearchange rod. Tie the rod to one side **(see illustration)**.
38 Unbolt the stabiliser bar from the transmission and tie it to one side **(see illustration)**.
39 Unscrew the though-bolts and remove the rear engine mounting link. Note the link will be under tension, so support the engine until the link is removed.
40 Remove the left- and right-hand driveshafts from the transmission with reference to Chapter 8. Carefully swivel the

driveshafts forward and tie them to the subframe leaving sufficient room to lower the engine and transmission assembly.
41 Place cloth rags beneath the fuel feed and return lines on the fuel rail, then squeeze the quick release tags and disconnect the fittings.
42 Fit a hose clamp to the clutch hydraulic hose leading to the slave cylinder. Alternatively tighten the fluid reservoir cap onto a piece of polythene - this will prevent excessive loss of hydraulic fluid.
43 Pull out the clip and disconnect the hydraulic hose quick release connector from the clutch slave cylinder. Plug the hose and slave cylinder to prevent dust and dirt entering the system. Release the hydraulic hose from the support bracket.
44 Attach a suitable hoist to the engine and transmission and take the weight of the assembly **(see illustration)**. Make sure there is sufficient height beneath the front of the vehicle to withdraw the assembly.
45 Unscrew the nuts from the left-hand engine/transmission mounting.
46 Unscrew the nuts and remove the right-hand engine mounting upper bracket.
47 With the help of an assistant, carefully lower the assembly from the engine compartment making sure that it clears the surrounding components and bodywork **(see illustration)**.
48 If the engine is to be overhauled, remove the wiring loom from the engine noting its location and routing.

2D

4.38 Unbolting the stabiliser bar from the transmission. Note the location of the washer

4.44 Attaching a hoist to the engine and transmission assembly

4.47 Lowering the engine/transmission assembly to the ground

4.53 Separating the transmission from the rear of the engine

Separation

49 To separate the transmission from the engine, first remove the starter motor with reference to Chapter 5A.

50 Unscrew and remove the bolts securing the right-hand rear of the transmission to the engine.

51 Move the cable guide to one side, then unscrew the bolts securing the top of the transmission to the engine and withdraw the adapter plate.

52 At the front of the transmission, unscrew and remove the bolts securing the transmission to the engine. Note the location of the TDC sensor cover retained by two of the bolts.

53 With the help of an assistant withdraw the transmission directly from the engine making sure that its weight is not allowed to bear on the clutch friction disc **(see illustration)**.

Refitting

54 Refitting is a reversal of removal, noting the following additional points.
a) Make sure that all mating faces are clean.
b) Apply a smear of high-melting-point grease to the splines of the transmission input shaft. Do not apply too much, otherwise there is the possibility of the grease contaminating the clutch friction disc.
c) Make sure that the clutch release bearing is correctly located in the slave cylinder inside the transmission bellhousing.
d) On the Endura-E engine, ensure that the engine adapter plate is correctly seated on the locating dowels on the engine.

5.12 Disconnecting the wiring from the engine coolant temperature sensor on the left-hand side of the cylinder head

e) Fit new circlips to the grooves in the inner end of each driveshaft CV joint, and ensure that they fully engage as they are fitted into the transmission.
f) Refit and adjust the engine mountings as described in Chapter 2A.
g) Check and if necessary adjust the gearchange as described in Chapter 7A.
h) Replenish the transmission oil, and check the level with reference to Chapter 1A.
i) Top up and bleed the clutch hydraulic system as described in Chapter 6.
j) Refill the cooling system as described in Chapter 1A.
k) Tighten all nuts and bolts to the specified torque setting.

5 Petrol engine and automatic transmission - removal, separation and refitting

Note: *The engine and automatic transmission is lowered from the engine compartment, then separated on the bench.*

Removal

1 Apply the handbrake, then jack up the front of the vehicle and support it on axle stands (see *"Jacking and Vehicle Support"*). Where applicable, remove the engine undershield.

2 Depressurise the fuel system with reference to Chapter 4A.

3 Disconnect the battery negative (earth) lead (see Chapter 5A).

4 Drain the cooling system as described in Chapter 1A.

5 Drain the automatic transmission fluid with reference to Chapter 7B.

6 If necessary, drain the engine oil with reference to Chapter 1A.

7 Remove the battery and battery box as described in Chapter 5A.

8 Loosen the clips and disconnect the air inlet duct from the throttle body housing and air flow meter on the air cleaner.

9 Lift the flap from the front of the cylinder head cover then disconnect the crankcase ventilation hose.

10 Disconnect the accelerator cable from the throttle body housing and release it from the supports. Position it to one side.

11 Remove the oil filler cap, then unscrew the retaining screws and remove the plastic cover from the top of the cylinder head cover. Refit the oil filler cap.

12 Disconnect the wiring from the following **(see illustration)**:
a) Throttle position switch
b) DIS ignition coil
c) Engine coolant temperature sensor
d) Engine wiring loom plug at the left-hand side of the cylinder head
e) Vehicle speed sensor on the rear of the transmission
f) Camshaft position sensor
g) Oxygen sensor
h) Injectors

i) Idle air control valve
j) Alternator

13 Disconnect the hoses from the exhaust gas recirculation valve.

14 Disconnect the vacuum hoses from the throttle body housing, inlet manifold and cylinder block.

15 Loosen the clips and disconnect the heater hose, expansion tank hose and thermostat housing hose at the left-hand side of the cylinder head. Also disconnect the expansion tank hose from the top of the radiator.

16 Disconnect the cooling fan wiring from the radiator.

17 Unbolt the radiator shroud.

18 Position a suitable container beneath the transmission, then unscrew the union nuts and disconnect the cooler pipes.

19 Loosen the clips and disconnect the bottom hose and heater hoses from the radiator and coolant pump.

20 Support the radiator, then unbolt the lower crossmember and remove it together with the radiator and fan.

21 Disconnect the solenoid and battery cables from the starter motor.

22 Remove the cover from the auxiliary drivebelt by unscrewing the bolts at the front right-hand side of the engine.

23 Using a spanner, turn the tensioner pulley clockwise to release the tension, then slip the auxiliary drivebelt from the pulleys and remove it from the engine compartment.

24 Unbolt the power steering pump and bracket from the cylinder block and tie it to one side. Note that one of the mounting bolts secures the pipe support.

25 Release the clip and disconnect the selector cable end fitting from the lever on the transmission, then withdraw the cable from the bracket.

26 Disconnect the speedometer cable from the rear of the transmission. Also disconnect the wiring from the reversing light switch.

27 Remove the left- and right-hand driveshafts from the transmission with reference to Chapter 8. Carefully swivel the driveshafts forward and tie them to the subframe leaving sufficient room to lower the engine and transmission assembly.

28 Unscrew the flange nuts and separate the exhaust downpipe from the intermediate section.

29 Unscrew the though-bolts and remove the rear engine mounting link. Note the link will be under tension, so support the engine until the link is removed.

30 Place cloth rags beneath the fuel feed and return lines on the fuel rail, then squeeze the quick release tags and disconnect the fittings. Unclip the lines from the supports.

31 Attach a suitable hoist to the engine and transmission and take the weight of the assembly. Make sure there is sufficient height beneath the front of the vehicle to withdraw the assembly.

32 Unscrew the nuts from the left-hand engine/transmission mounting.

33 Unscrew the nuts and remove the right-hand engine mounting upper bracket.

34 With the help of an assistant, carefully lower the assembly from the engine compartment making sure that it clears the surrounding components and bodywork.

35 If the engine is to be overhauled, remove the wiring loom from the engine noting its location and routing.

Separation

36 To separate the transmission from the engine, first remove the starter motor with reference to Chapter 5A.

37 Unscrew the upper mounting bolts securing the transmission to the engine, noting the location of the wiring support brackets and earth lead.

38 Unclip the vehicle speed sensor and disconnect the wiring plug.

39 Disconnect the wiring from the lock switch on the lower rear of the transmission.

40 Undo the remaining transmission flange bolts and carefully withdraw the transmission from the engine noting the location of the wiring support brackets. Do not allow the weight of the transmission to bear on the input shaft and vibration damper.

41 If necessary, mark the torsional vibration damper in relation to the flywheel then unscrew the mounting bolts and withdraw the damper. Use a wide-bladed screwdriver engaged with the starter ring gear to hold the flywheel stationary. Examine the damper for wear and damage and renew it if necessary.

Refitting

42 Refitting is a reversal of removal, noting the following additional points.
   a) *Fit new circlips to the grooves in the inner end of each driveshaft CV joint, and ensure that they fully engage as they are fitted into the transmission.*
   b) *Refit and adjust the engine mountings as described in Chapter 2A.*
   c) *Replenish the transmission fluid, and check the level with reference to Chapter 1A.*
   d) *Tighten all nuts and bolts to the specified torque settings.*
   e) *Check and if necessary adjust the selector cable (Chapter 7B, Section 2) and accelerator cable (Chapter 4A).*
   f) *Refill the cooling system as described in Chapter 1A.*
   g) *Tighten all nuts and bolts to the specified torque setting.*

---

6 Diesel engine and manual transmission - removal, separation and refitting

Note: *The engine and manual transmission is lowered from the engine compartment, then separated on the bench.*

Removal

1 Apply the handbrake, then jack up the front of the vehicle and support it on axle stands (see "*Jacking and Vehicle Support*"). Where applicable, remove the engine undershield.

2 Depressurise the fuel system with reference to Chapter 4A.

3 Disconnect the battery negative (earth) lead (see Chapter 5A).

4 Drain the cooling system as described in Chapter 1B.

5 Drain the manual transmission with reference to Chapter 7A.

6 If necessary, drain the engine oil with reference to Chapter 1B.

7 Loosen the clips and disconnect the air inlet duct from the inlet manifold and air cleaner housing. Release the duct from the support clip and disconnect the resonator hose.

8 Loosen the clip and disconnect the top hose from the thermostat housing.

9 Loosen the clip and disconnect the vent hose from the expansion tank.

10 Identify the heater hoses on the bulkhead, then loosen the clips and disconnect them.

11 Loosen the clip and disconnect the vent hose from the top of the radiator.

12 Disconnect the following wiring:
   a) *Injection pump wiring loom*
   b) *Glow plug wiring*
   c) *Temperature gauge sender unit*
   d) *Engine coolant temperature sensor*
   e) *Oil pressure switch on the left-hand side of the cylinder head*
   f) *Diesel fuel heater on the left-hand side of the cylinder head*
   g) *Exhaust gas recirculation valve*

13 Pull out the clip and disconnect the outer accelerator cable from the bracket on the injection pump. Disconnect the inner cable from the lever.

14 Disconnect the fuel return line from the injection pump, and the fuel feed line from the filter.

15 Unbolt and remove the earth lead from the transmission.

16 Fit a hose clamp to the clutch hydraulic hose leading to the slave cylinder. Alternatively tighten the fluid reservoir cap onto a piece of polythene - this will prevent excessive loss of hydraulic fluid.

17 Pull out the clip and disconnect the hydraulic hose quick release connector from the clutch slave cylinder. Plug the hose and slave cylinder to prevent dust and dirt entering the system. Release the hydraulic hose from the support bracket.

18 Unbolt the cover from the power steering pump.

19 Loosen the power steering pump pulley bolts and hexagon socket-headed bolt of the tensioner pulley. Release the tension and remove the belt from the pulleys.

20 Unscrew the bolts and remove the power steering pump belt pulley.

21 Unscrew the bolt from the power steering fluid hose support bracket.

22 Unbolt and remove the power steering pump with reference to Chapter 10. Tie the pump to one side without disconnecting the hoses.

23 Unbolt the auxiliary drivebelt tensioner.

24 Unscrew the bolts and remove the reinforcement bracket from the top of the right-hand engine mounting.

25 Remove the battery and battery box as described in Chapter 5A.

26 Loosen the clips and disconnect the bottom hoses from the radiator.

27 Where applicable, disconnect the air conditioning compressor wiring at the connector and release the wiring from the cable tie.

28 Disconnect the wiring plugs at the bottom left-hand side of the radiator.

29 Unscrew the air conditioning condenser lower mounting bolts and tie the condenser to one side. **Do not** disconnect the refrigerant lines.

30 Support the radiator, then unbolt the lower crossmember and remove it downwards together with the radiator and fan.

31 Where applicable, unbolt the air conditioning compressor and tie it to one side.

32 Disconnect the wiring from the starter motor.

33 Disconnect the wiring from the multi-function switch on the front of the transmission.

34 Mark the position of the gearchange clamp on the transmission selector rod, then unscrew the clamp bolt and remove the gearchange rod. Tie the rod to one side.

35 Unbolt the stabiliser bar from the transmission and tie it to one side.

36 Unscrew the flange nuts and separate the exhaust downpipe from the intermediate section.

37 Disconnect the wiring from the alternator.

38 Disconnect the wiring from the crankshaft position sensor.

39 Disconnect the speedometer cable from the rear of the transmission.

40 Remove the left-hand driveshaft from the transmission with reference to Chapter 8, then carefully swivel the driveshaft forward and tie it to the subframe.

41 Remove the right-hand driveshaft completely as described in Chapter 8.

42 Unscrew the though-bolts and remove the rear engine mounting link. Note the link will be under tension, so support the engine until the link is removed.

43 Attach a suitable hoist to the engine and transmission and take the weight of the assembly. Make sure there is sufficient height beneath the front of the vehicle to withdraw the assembly.

44 Unscrew the nuts from the left-hand engine/transmission mounting.

45 Unscrew the nuts and remove the right-hand engine mounting upper bracket.

46 With the help of an assistant, carefully lower the assembly from the engine compartment making sure that it clears the surrounding components and bodywork.

47 If the engine is to be overhauled, remove the wiring loom from the engine noting its location and routing.

2D

Separation

48 To separate the transmission from the engine, first remove the starter motor with reference to Chapter 5A.

49 Unbolt the air inlet resonator from the transmission.

50 At the front of the transmission, unscrew and remove the bolts securing the transmission to the engine.

51 Unscrew and remove the remaining bolts securing the transmission to the engine.

52 With the help of an assistant withdraw the transmission directly from the engine making sure that its weight is not allowed to bear on the clutch friction disc. Remove the adapter plate from the dowels on the cylinder block.

Refitting

53 Refitting is a reversal of removal, noting the following additional points.

a) *Make sure that all mating faces are clean.*

b) *Apply a smear of high-melting-point grease to the splines of the transmission input shaft. Do not apply too much, otherwise there is the possibility of the grease contaminating the clutch friction disc.*

c) *Make sure that the clutch release bearing is correctly located in the slave cylinder inside the transmission bellhousing.*

d) *Ensure that the engine adapter plate is correctly seated on the locating dowels on the engine.*

e) *Fit new circlips to the grooves in the inner end of each driveshaft CV joint, and ensure that they fully engage as they are fitted into the transmission.*

f) *Refit and adjust the engine mountings as described in Chapter 2D.*

g) *Check and if necessary adjust the gearchange as described in Chapter 7A.*

h) *Replenish the transmission oil, and check the level with reference to Chapter 1B.*

i) *Top up and bleed the clutch hydraulic system as described in Chapter 6.*

j) *Refill the cooling system as described in Chapter 1B.*

k) *Tighten all nuts and bolts to the specified torque setting.*

7 Engine overhaul - dismantling sequence

1 It is much easier to disassemble and work on the engine if it is mounted on a portable engine stand. These stands can often be hired from a tool hire shop. Before the engine is mounted on a stand, the flywheel/driveplate should be removed from the engine, so that the engine stand bolts can be tightened into the end of the cylinder block.

2 If a stand is not available, it is possible to disassemble the engine with it blocked up on a sturdy workbench or on the floor. Be extra-careful not to tip or drop the engine when working without a stand.

3 If you are going to obtain a reconditioned engine, all the external components must come off first, in order to be transferred to the replacement engine (just as they will if you are doing a complete engine overhaul yourself). Check with the engine supplier for details. Normally these components include:

Petrol engine models

a) *Alternator and brackets.*

b) *DIS ignition coil, HT leads and spark plugs.*

c) *Thermostat and cover.*

d) *Fuel injection equipment.*

e) *Inlet and exhaust manifolds.*

f) *Oil filter.*

g) *Engine mountings and lifting brackets.*

h) *Ancillary (power steering pump, air conditioning compressor) brackets.*

i) *Oil filler tube and dipstick.*

j) *Coolant pipes and hoses.*

k) *Flywheel/driveplate.*

Diesel engine models

a) *Alternator mounting bracket.*

b) *Fuel injection pump and mounting bracket, and fuel injectors and glow plugs (see Chapter 4B).*

c) *Thermostat and cover.*

d) *Inlet and exhaust manifolds.*

e) *Oil cooler.*

f) *Engine lifting brackets, hose brackets and wiring brackets.*

g) *Ancillary (power steering pump, air conditioning compressor) brackets.*

h) *Oil pressure warning light switch and oil level sensor (where applicable) (see Chapter 5A).*

i) *Coolant temperature sensors (see Chapter 3).*

j) *Wiring harnesses and brackets.*

k) *Coolant pipes and hoses.*

l) *Oil filler tube and dipstick.*

m) *Clutch (Chapter 6).*

n) *Flywheel*

Note: *When removing the external components from the engine, pay close attention to details that may be helpful or important during refitting. Note the fitted position of gaskets, seals, spacers, pins, washers, bolts and other small items.*

4 If you are obtaining a 'short' motor (which, when available, consists of the engine cylinder

8.2 Unbolting the engine lifting eyes from the cylinder head

block, crankshaft, pistons and connecting rods all assembled), then the cylinder head, sump, oil pump, and timing belt (where applicable) will have to be removed also.

5 If you are planning a complete overhaul, the engine can be disassembled and the internal components removed in the following order:

a) *Engine external components (including inlet and exhaust manifolds).*

b) *Timing sprockets and chain/belt.*

c) *Cylinder head.*

d) *Flywheel/driveplate.*

e) *Sump.*

f) *Oil pump.*

g) *Pistons and connecting rods.*

h) *Crankshaft and main bearings.*

i) *Tappets and camshaft (Endura-E engine).*

6 Before beginning the disassembly and overhaul procedures, make sure that you have all of the correct tools necessary. Refer to the reference section at the end of this manual for further information.

8 Cylinder head - dismantling

Note: *New and reconditioned cylinder heads are available from the manufacturers and from engine overhaul specialists. Due to the fact that some specialist tools are required for the dismantling and inspection procedures, and new components may not be readily available, it may be more practical and economical for the home mechanic to purchase a reconditioned head rather than dismantle, inspect and recondition the original head.*

1 Remove the cylinder head as described in Part A, B or C of this Chapter (as applicable).

2 If not already done, remove the inlet and exhaust manifolds with reference to the relevant Part of Chapter 4. Also remove all external brackets and elbows **(see illustration)**.

3 Proceed as follows according to engine type.

Endura-E petrol engine

4 Valve removal should commence with No 1 valve (nearest the timing chain end).

5 To remove the valve springs and valves from the cylinder head, a standard valve spring compressor will be required. Fit the spring compressor to the first valve and spring to be removed. Assuming that all of the valves and springs are to be removed, start by compressing the No 1 valve (nearest the timing cover end) spring. Take care not to damage the valve stem with the compressor, and do not over-compress the spring, or the valve stem may bend. When tightening the compressor, it may be found that the spring retainer does not release and the collets are then difficult to remove. In this instance, remove the compressor, then press a piece of tube (or a socket of suitable diameter) so that it does not interfere with the removal of the

8.6 Compress the valve spring to remove the collets

8.7a Remove the valve spring retainer and spring . . .

8.7b . . . followed by the valve

collets, against the retainer's outer rim. Tap the tube (or socket) with a hammer to unsettle the components.

6 Refit the compressor, and wind it in to enable the collets to be extracted **(see illustration)**.

7 Loosen off the compressor, and remove the retainer and spring. Withdraw the valve from the cylinder head **(see illustrations)**.

8 Pull the valve stem seals from the valve guides using a pair of pliers **(see illustration)**.

9 Repeat the removal procedure with each of the remaining seven valve assemblies in turn. As they are removed, keep the individual valves and their components together, and in their respective order of fitting, by placing them in a separate labelled bag **(see illustration)**.

Zetec-SE petrol engine and Endura-DE diesel engine

10 Remove the camshafts and tappets as described in Part B or C of this Chapter, being careful to store the components as described.

11 Using a valve spring compressor, compress each valve spring in turn until the split collets can be removed. A special valve spring compressor will be required, to reach into the deep wells in the cylinder head without risk of damaging the tappet bores; such compressors are now widely available from most good motor accessory shops. Release the compressor, and lift off the spring upper seat and spring **(see illustration)**.

12 If, when the valve spring compressor is

screwed down, the spring upper seat refuses to free and expose the split collets, gently tap the top of the tool, directly over the upper seat, with a light hammer. This will free the seat.

13 Withdraw the valve through the combustion chamber. If it binds in the guide (won't pull through), push it back in, and de-burr the area around the collet groove with a fine file; take care not to mark the tappet bores.

14 Pull the valve stem seals from the valve guides using a pair of pliers. Note on the Zetec-SE engine, the inlet seals are coloured green and the exhaust seals are coloured brown.

15 It is essential that the valves are kept together with their collets, spring seats and springs, and in their correct sequence (unless they are so badly worn that they are to be renewed). If they are going to be kept and used again, place them in a labelled polythene bag or similar small container **(see illustration 8.9)**. Note that No 1 valve is nearest to the timing belt end of the engine.

9 Cylinder head and valves - cleaning, inspection and renovation

1 Thorough cleaning of the cylinder head and valve components, followed by a detailed inspection, will enable you to decide how much valve service work must be carried out during the engine overhaul.

Cleaning

2 Scrape away all traces of old gasket material and sealing compound from the cylinder head. Take care not to damage the cylinder head surfaces.

3 Scrape away the carbon from the combustion chambers and ports, then wash the cylinder head thoroughly with paraffin or a suitable solvent.

4 Scrape off any heavy carbon deposits that may have formed on the valves, then use a power-operated wire brush to remove deposits from the valve heads and stems.

5 On the Endura-DE diesel engine, the swirl chambers may be removed from their locations using a soft metal drift inserted through the injector holes (if this is done, mark the swirl chambers so that they can be refitted in their original locations). Before removing the swirl chambers use feeler blades and a straight-edge to measure their projection, and compare with the information given in the Specifications (see Chapter 2C). Alternatively, use a dial test indicator to make the check. Zero the dial test indicator on the gasket surface of the cylinder head, then measure the protrusion of the swirl chamber.

6 If the head is extremely dirty, it should be steam cleaned. On completion, make sure that all oil holes and oil galleries are cleaned.

Inspection and renovation

Note: *Be sure to perform all the following inspection procedures before concluding that the services of an engine overhaul specialist are required. Make a list of all items that require attention.*

2D

8.8 Using pliers to pull the valve stem seals from the valve guides

8.9 Use a labelled plastic bag to store and identify valve components

8.11 Removing the valve spring and upper seat

9.14 Measuring the diameter of a valve stem

9.16 Grinding-in a valve seat

9.17 Checking the valve spring free length

Cylinder head

7 Inspect the head very carefully for cracks, evidence of coolant leakage and other damage. If cracks are found, a new cylinder head should be obtained.

8 Use a straight-edge and feeler blade to check that the cylinder head surface is not distorted. On the Endura-DE diesel engine, do not position the straight-edge over the swirl chambers, as these may be proud of the cylinder head face. If the specified distortion limit is exceeded, machining of the gasket face is not recommended by the manufacturers, so the only course of action is to renew the cylinder head.

9 Examine the valve seats in each of the combustion chambers. If they are severely pitted, cracked or burned, then they will need to be renewed or recut by an engine overhaul specialist. If they are only slightly pitted, this can be removed by grinding the valve heads and seats together with coarse, then fine, grinding paste as described below.

10 If the valve guides are worn, indicated by a side-to-side motion of the valve in the guide, new guides must be fitted. If necessary, insert a new valve in the guides to determine if the wear is on the guide or valve. If new guides are to be fitted, the valves must be renewed as a matter of course. Valve guides may be renewed using a press and a suitable mandrel, however, the work is best carried out by an engine overhaul specialist, since if it is not done skilfully, there is a risk of damaging the cylinder head.

11 On the Endura-DE diesel engine, inspect the swirl chambers for burning or cracks and renew the chambers if necessary.

12 On the Zetec-SE and Endura-DE engines, check the tappet bores in the cylinder head for wear. If excessive wear is evident, the cylinder head must be renewed.

13 Except on the Endura-E engine, examine the camshaft bearing surfaces in the cylinder head as described in Chapter 2B or 2C.

Valves

14 Examine the head of each valve for pitting, burning, cracks and general wear, and check the valve stem for scoring and wear ridges. Rotate the valve, and check for any obvious indication that it is bent. Look for pits and excessive wear on the end of each valve stem. If the valve appears satisfactory at this stage,

measure the valve stem diameter at several points using a micrometer **(see illustration)**. Any significant difference in the readings obtained indicates wear of the valve stem. Should any of these conditions be apparent, the valve(s) must be renewed. If the valves are in satisfactory condition, or if new valves are being fitted, they should be ground (lapped) into their respective seats to ensure a smooth gas-tight seal.

15 Valve grinding is carried out as follows. Place the cylinder head upside-down on a bench, with a block of wood at each end to give clearance for the valve stems.

16 Smear a trace of coarse carborundum paste on the seat face, and press a suction grinding tool onto the valve head. With a semi-rotary action, grind the valve head to its seat, lifting the valve occasionally to redistribute the grinding paste **(see illustration)**. When a dull-matt even surface is produced on both the valve seat and the valve, wipe off the paste and repeat the process with fine carborundum paste. A light spring placed under the valve head will greatly ease this operation. When a smooth unbroken ring of light grey matt finish is produced on both the valve and seat, the grinding operation is complete. Be sure to remove all traces of grinding paste, using paraffin or a suitable solvent, before reassembly of the cylinder head.

Valve components

17 Examine the valve springs for signs of damage and discoloration, and also measure their free length using vernier calipers or a steel rule **(see illustration)** or by comparing the existing spring with a new component.

10.2a Fitting a valve stem oil seal (Endura-E engine)

18 Stand each spring on a flat surface, and check it for squareness. If any of the springs are damaged, distorted or have lost their tension, obtain a complete new set of springs. It is normal to renew the springs as a matter of course during a major overhaul.

19 On Zetec-SE petrol and Endura-DE diesel engines, inspect the tappet buckets and their shims for scoring, pitting (especially on the shims), and wear ridges. Renew any components as necessary. Note that some scuffing is to be expected, and is acceptable provided that the tappets are not scored.

Rocker arm components on the Endura-E engine

20 Check the rocker arm contact surfaces for pits, wear, score marks or any indication that the surface-hardening has worn through. Dismantle the rocker shaft and check the components as described in Chapter 2A.

Valve stem oil seals

21 The valve stem oil seals should be renewed as a matter of course.

10 Cylinder head - reassembly

1 On the Endura-DE diesel engine, if the swirl chambers have been removed, refit them to their original locations. Check the projection of the swirl chambers as described in Section 9.

2 Lubricate the valve stem oil seals with clean engine oil, then fit them by pushing into position in the cylinder head using a suitable socket or special tool **(see illustrations)**.

10.2b Using a special tool to fit the valve stem oil seals

10.3a Oil the valve stems . . .

10.3b . . . then insert the valves in their guides

10.5a Apply a small dab of grease to each collet before installation - it will hold them in place on the valve stem

Ensure that the seals are fully engaged with the valve guide. Note on the Zetec-SE engine, the inlet valve stem seals are coloured green and the exhaust valve stem seals are coloured brown.

3 Lubricate the valve stems then insert the valves into their original locations. If new valves are being fitted, insert them into the locations to which they have been ground. Take care not to damage the valve stem oil seal as each valve is fitted (see illustrations).

4 Locate the spring seat over the guide where applicable (on the Zetec-SE engine the seat is incorporated in the valve stem seal). Fit the spring and cap.

5 Compress the valve spring and locate the split collets in the recess in the valve stem (see illustrations). Release the compressor, then repeat the procedure on the remaining valves.

HAYNES HiNT *Use a little grease to hold the collets in place.*

6 With all the valves installed, place the cylinder head flat on the bench and, using a hammer and interposed block of wood, tap the end of each valve stem to settle the components.

7 The previously removed components can now be refitted with reference to Section 8 (see illustration).

11 Auxiliary shaft (Endura-DE diesel engine) - removal, inspection and refitting

Note: *A new auxiliary shaft oil seal, housing gasket (or suitable sealant, as applicable), and oil pump drivegear cover plate O-ring will be required on refitting.*

Removal

1 With the engine removed from the vehicle, proceed as follows.

2 Remove the auxiliary shaft sprocket and the oil pump as described in Chapter 2C.

3 Unbolt and remove the timing belt side cover.

10.5b A dab of grease on a screwdriver will help to fit the collets

4 Unscrew the bolts and remove the oil seal housing from the cylinder block. The oil seal is integral with the housing.

5 Unscrew the bolts securing the thrust plate to the cylinder block, then carefully withdraw the auxiliary shaft taking care not to allow the oil pump gear to snag on the shaft bearing. Remove the thrust plate from the shaft noting that the oilways are facing outwards (see illustrations).

Inspection

6 Examine the auxiliary shaft and oil pump drivegear for pitting, scoring or wear ridges on the bearing journals, and for chipping or wear of the gear teeth. Renew as necessary. Check the auxiliary shaft bearings in the cylinder block for wear and, if worn, have these renewed by your Ford dealer or suitably-

10.7 Fit a new gasket when refitting the outlet elbow to the left-hand end of the cylinder head

equipped engineering works. Wipe them clean if they are still serviceable.

7 Temporarily fit the thrustplate to its position on the auxiliary shaft, and check for excessive wear. If possible, compare the shaft and thrustplate with new components to indicate the amount of wear, and renew them if necessary.

Refitting

8 Lubricate the bearing journals of the auxiliary shaft and the bearings in the cylinder block with fresh engine oil.

9 Lubricate the thrust plate then locate it on the shaft with the oilways facing outwards (ie towards the sprocket position). Insert the shaft and thrust plate into the cylinder block, then refit the bolts and tighten to the specified torque.

2D

11.5a Withdraw the auxiliary shaft a little, then remove the thrust plate

11.5b Removing the auxiliary shaft

12.3 Checking the camshaft endfloat

12.4 Removing the camshaft thrust plate

12.5 Removing the camshaft from the front end of the engine

10 Clean the cylinder block and end of the auxiliary shaft.

11 Smear fresh engine oil on the auxiliary shaft and on the sealing lips of the new oil seal. Before fitting the new seal, locate the special fitting ring inside the sealing lips.

12 Locate the new oil seal housing over the end of the auxiliary shaft, then insert the bolts and tighten.

13 Carefully remove the special ring and make sure that the seal lips are located on the shaft correctly.

14 Refit the timing belt side cover and tighten the bolts.

15 Refit the auxiliary shaft sprocket as described in Chapter 2C.

12 Camshaft and tappets (Endura-E petrol engine) - removal, inspection and refitting

Removal

1 Refer to the relevant Sections in Chapter 2A and remove the cylinder head, timing chain and camshaft sprocket, and the sump.

2 Invert the engine so that it is supported on its cylinder head face (on a clean work area). This is necessary to make all of the tappets slide to the top of their stroke, thus allowing the camshaft to be withdrawn. Rotate the camshaft through a full turn, to ensure that all of the tappets slide up their bores, clear of the camshaft.

3 Before removing the camshaft, check its endfloat using a dial gauge mounted on the front face of the engine or feeler blades. Pull the camshaft fully towards the front (timing chain) end of the engine, then insert feeler blades between the camshaft sprocket flange and the camshaft thrust plate to assess the endfloat clearance **(see illustration)**. The camshaft endfloat must be as specified (see Chapter 2A Specifications).

4 Undo the two retaining bolts, and remove the camshaft thrust plate **(see illustration)**.

5 Carefully withdraw the camshaft from the front end of the engine **(see illustration)**.

6 Extract each tappet in turn. Keep them in order of fitting by inserting them in a card with eight holes in it, numbered 1 to 8 (from the

timing chain end of the engine). A valve grinding suction tool will be found to be useful for the removal of tappets **(see illustration)**.

Inspection

7 Examine the camshaft bearing journals and lobes for damage or excessive wear. If evident, the camshaft must be renewed.

8 Examine the camshaft bearing internal surfaces for signs of damage or excessive wear. If evident, the bearings must be renewed by a Ford dealer.

9 If not carried out on removal, check the camshaft endfloat as described in paragraph 3. If the endfloat exceeds the specified tolerance, renew the thrust plate.

10 It is seldom that the tappets wear excessively in their bores, but it is likely that after a high mileage, the cam lobe contact surfaces will show signs of depression or grooving.

11 Where this condition is evident, renew the tappets. Grinding out the grooves and wear marks will reduce the thickness of the surface hardening, and will accelerate further wear.

Refitting

12 To refit the tappets and the camshaft, it is essential that the crankcase is inverted.

13 Lubricate the tappets and their bores. Insert each tappet fully into its original bore in the cylinder block.

14 Lubricate the camshaft bearings, camshaft and thrust plate, then insert the camshaft into the crankcase from the timing case end.

13.2 The big-end caps and connecting rods are normally marked with their relevant cylinder number

12.6 Removing the tappets, using a valve grinding tool suction cup

15 Fit the thrust plate and tighten the retaining bolts to the specified torque setting. Check that the camshaft is able to rotate freely, and that the endfloat is as specified (see Chapter 2A Specifications).

13 Piston/connecting rod assemblies - removal

1 With the cylinder head, sump, oil pump pick-up tube and baffle plate (Zetec-SE and Endura-DE engines) removed (see Chapter 2A, 2B or 2C), proceed as follows.

2 Rotate the crankshaft so that No 1 big-end cap (timing end of the engine) is at the lowest point of its travel. If the big-end cap and rod are not already numbered, mark them with a marker pen or centre-punch **(see illustration)**. Mark both cap and rod to identify the cylinder they operate in.

3 Unscrew and remove the big-end bearing cap bolts, and withdraw the cap complete with shell bearing from the connecting rod. Make sure that the shell remains in the cap and if necessary identify it for position. On the Endura-DE engine a Torx socket will be required to unscrew the bolts **(see illustrations)**.

4 If only the bearing shells are being attended to, push the connecting rod up and off the crankpin, and remove the upper bearing shell. Keep the bearing shells and cap together in their correct sequence if they are to be refitted.

13.3a Removing the bolts . . .

13.3b . . . and big-end bearing caps on the Zetec-SE petrol engine

13.3c No 12 Torx socket and big-end bearing cap bolt on the Endura-DE diesel engine

5 If the piston is being removed, push the connecting rod up and remove the piston and rod from the top of the bore. Note that if there is a pronounced wear ridge at the top of the bore, there is a risk of damaging the piston as the rings foul the ridge. However, it is reasonable to assume that a rebore and new pistons will be required in any case if the ridge is so pronounced.

6 Repeat the procedure for the remaining piston/connecting rod assemblies. Ensure that the caps and rods are marked before removal, as described previously, and keep all components in order.

14 Crankshaft (except Zetec-SE engine) - removal

Caution: Do not attempt to remove the crankshaft or main bearing cap/ladder on the Zetec-SE engine, as it is not possible to refit it accurately using conventional tooling. The manufacturers do not supply torque settings for the main bearing cap/ladder retaining bolts. If the crankshaft is worn excessively on the Zetec-SE engine, it will be necessary to obtain a new short motor comprising the cylinder block together with the pistons and crankshaft.

1 Remove the timing belt or chain (as applicable), crankshaft sprocket, engine front plate (Endura-DE diesel engine), sump, oil pick-up tube, flywheel/driveplate and rear oil seal housing. The pistons/connecting rods must be free of the crankshaft journals, however it is not essential to remove them completely from the cylinder block.

2 Before the crankshaft is removed, check the endfloat. Mount a dial gauge with the probe in line with the crankshaft and just touching the crankshaft **(see illustration)**.

3 Push the crankshaft fully away from the gauge, and zero it. Next, lever the crankshaft towards the gauge as far as possible, and check the reading obtained. The distance that the crankshaft moved is its endfloat; if it is greater than specified, new thrust washers will be required Chapter 2A or 2C Specifications).

4 If no dial gauge is available, feeler blades can be used. Gently lever or push the crankshaft in one direction, then insert feeler blades between the crankshaft web and the main bearing incorporating the thrustwashers to determine the clearance.

5 Check that the main bearing caps have marks to indicate their respective fitted positions in the block. They also have arrow marks pointing towards the timing end of the engine to indicate correct orientation **(see illustration)**.

6 Unscrew the retaining bolts, and remove the main bearing caps. If the caps are reluctant to separate from the block face, lightly tap them free using a plastic- or copper-faced hammer. If the bearing shells are likely to be used again, keep them with their bearing caps for safekeeping. However, unless the engine is known to be of low mileage, it is recommended that they be renewed.

7 Lift the crankshaft out from the crankcase, then extract the upper bearing shells and side thrustwashers. Keep them with their respective caps for correct repositioning if they are to be used again.

15 Cylinder block/crankcase and bores - cleaning and inspection

Cleaning

Caution: If cleaning the cylinder block (with fitted crankshaft) on the Zetec-SE engine, it is recommended that only the external surfaces are cleaned, as otherwise the internal oilways and channels may become contaminated leading to premature wear of the crankshaft and main bearings.

2D

14.2 Checking the crankshaft endfloat with a dial gauge

14.5 Connecting rod big-end bearing cap and main bearing cap markings

15.1a The core plugs should be removed with a puller - if they are driven into the block, they may be impossible to remove

15.1b Unbolting the right-hand driveshaft centre bearing bracket from the rear of the cylinder block

15.1c Unscrew the bolts . . .

1 For complete cleaning, the core plugs should be removed. Drill a small hole in them, then insert a self-tapping screw and pull out the plugs using a pair of grips or a slide-hammer. Also remove all external components and senders (if not already done), noting their locations **(see illustrations)**. Where applicable, remove the oil sprayers from the bottom of each bore.

2 Scrape all traces of gasket or sealant from the cylinder block, taking care not to damage the head and sump mating faces.

3 If the block is extremely dirty, it should be steam-cleaned.

4 After the block has been steam-cleaned, clean all oil holes and oil galleries one more time. Flush all internal passages with warm water until the water runs clear, dry the block thoroughly and wipe all machined surfaces with a light rust-preventative oil. If you have access to compressed air, use it to speed up the drying process and to blow out all the oil holes and galleries.

 Warning: Wear eye protection when using compressed air!

5 If the block is not very dirty, you can do an adequate cleaning job with hot soapy water and a stiff brush. Take plenty of time, and do a thorough job. Regardless of the cleaning method used, be sure to clean all oil holes and galleries very thoroughly, dry the block completely and coat all machined surfaces with light oil.

6 The threaded holes in the block must be clean to ensure accurate torque wrench

readings during reassembly. Run the proper-size tap into each of the holes to remove rust, corrosion, thread sealant or sludge, and to restore damaged threads **(see illustration)**. If possible, use compressed air to clear the holes of debris produced by this operation. Now is a good time to clean the threads on the head bolts and the main bearing cap bolts as well.

7 Where applicable, refit the main bearing caps, and tighten the bolts finger-tight.

8 After coating the mating surfaces of the new core plugs with suitable sealant, refit them in the cylinder block. Make sure that they are driven in straight and seated properly, or leakage could result. Special tools are available for this purpose, but a large socket, with an outside diameter that will just slip into the core plug, will work just as well.

9 On the Endura-DE diesel engine, remove the oil jets from their locations in the crankcase and clean them. After cleaning the cylinder block, refit the jets.

10 If the engine is not going to be reass-embled right away, cover it with a large plastic bag to keep it clean and prevent it rusting.

Inspection

11 Visually check the block for cracks, rust and corrosion. Look for stripped threads in the threaded holes. If there has been any history of internal water leakage, it may be worthwhile having an engine overhaul specialist check the block with special equipment. If defects are found, have the block repaired, if possible, or renewed.

15.1d . . . and remove the oil trap and gasket from the front of the cylinder block (Zetec-SE engine)

12 Check the cylinder bores for scuffing and scoring. Normally, bore wear will be evident in the form of a wear ridge at the top of the bore. This ridge marks the limit of piston travel.

13 Measure the diameter of each cylinder at the top (just under the ridge area), centre and bottom of the cylinder bore, parallel to the crankshaft axis **(see illustration)**.

14 Next measure each cylinder's diameter at the same three locations across the crankshaft axis. If the difference between any of the measurements is greater than 0.20 mm, indicating that the cylinder is excessively out-of-round or tapered, then remedial action must be considered.

15 Repeat this procedure for the remaining cylinders, then measure the diameter of each piston at right-angles to the gudgeon pin axis, and compare the result with the information given in the Specifications **(see illustration)**.

15.6 All bolt holes in the block should be cleaned and restored with a tap

15.13 Measure the diameter of each cylinder just under the wear ridge (A), at the centre (B) and at the bottom (C)

15.15 Measure the piston skirt diameter at right-angles to the gudgeon pin axis, just above the base of the skirt

15.19a When refitting the oil pressure switch, apply suitable sealant to the threads . . .

15.19b . . . then insert it in the cylinder block and tighten to the specified torque

By comparing the piston diameters with the bore diameters, an idea can be obtained of the clearances.

16 If the cylinder walls are badly scuffed or scored, or if they are excessively out-of-round or tapered, have the cylinder block rebored (where possible) by an engine overhaul specialist. New pistons (oversize in the case of a rebore) will also be required.

17 If the cylinders are in reasonably good condition, then it may only be necessary to renew the piston rings.

18 If this is the case, the bores should be honed in order to allow the new rings to bed in correctly and provide the best possible seal. The conventional type of hone has spring-loaded stones, and is used with a power drill. You will also need some paraffin or honing oil and rags. The hone should be moved up and down the cylinder to produce a crosshatch pattern, and plenty of honing oil should be used. Ideally, the crosshatch lines should intersect at approximately a 60° angle. Do not take off more material than is necessary to produce the required finish. If new pistons are being fitted, the piston manufacturers may specify a finish with a different angle, so their instructions should be followed. Do not withdraw the hone from the cylinder while it is still being turned, but stop it first. After honing a cylinder, wipe out all traces of the honing oil. If equipment of this type is not available, or if you are not sure whether you are competent to undertake the task yourself, an engine overhaul specialist will carry out the work at a moderate cost.

16.2 Using feeler blades to remove piston rings

19 Refit all external components and senders in their correct locations, as noted before removal **(see illustrations)**.

16 Piston/connecting rod assemblies - inspection and reassembly

Inspection

1 Before the inspection process can begin, the piston/connecting rod assemblies must be cleaned, and the original piston rings removed from the pistons.

2 Carefully expand the old rings over the top of the pistons. The use of two or three old feeler blades will be helpful in preventing the rings dropping into empty grooves **(see illustration)**. Note that the oil control scraper ring is in two sections.

3 Scrape away all traces of carbon from the top of the piston. A hand-held wire brush or a piece of fine emery cloth can be used once the majority of the deposits have been scraped away.

4 Remove the carbon from the ring grooves in the piston by cleaning them using an old ring. Break the ring in half to do this. Be very careful to remove only the carbon deposits; do not remove any metal, or scratch the sides of the ring grooves. Protect your fingers - piston rings are sharp.

5 Once the deposits have been removed, clean the piston/connecting rod assembly with paraffin or a suitable solvent, and dry thoroughly. Make sure the oil return holes in the ring grooves are clear.

6 If the pistons and cylinder bores are not damaged or worn excessively, and if the cylinder block does not need to be rebored, the original pistons can be re-used. Normal piston wear appears as even vertical wear on the piston thrust surfaces, and slight looseness of the top ring in its groove. New piston rings, however, should always be used when the engine is reassembled.

7 Carefully inspect each piston for cracks around the skirt, at the gudgeon pin bosses, and at the piston ring lands (between the piston ring grooves).

8 Look for scoring and scuffing on the sides of the skirt, holes in the piston crown, and burned areas at the edge of the crown. If the skirt is scored or scuffed, the engine may have been suffering from overheating and/or abnormal combustion, which caused excessively-high operating temperatures. The cooling and lubricating systems should be checked thoroughly. Scorch marks on the sides of the pistons show that blow-by has occurred and the rings are not sealing correctly. A hole in the piston crown is an indication that abnormal combustion (pre-ignition, knocking or detonation) has been occurring. If any of the above problems exist, the causes must be corrected, or the damage will occur again. On petrol engines, the causes may include inlet air leaks, incorrect fuel/air mixture or incorrect ignition timing. On diesel engines, incorrect injection pump timing or a faulty injector may be the cause.

9 Corrosion of the piston, in the form of small pits, indicates that coolant is leaking into the combustion chamber and/or the crankcase. Again, the cause must be corrected, or the problem may persist in the rebuilt engine.

10 If new rings are being fitted to old pistons, measure the piston ring-to-groove clearance by placing a new piston ring in each ring groove and measuring the clearance with a feeler blade. Check the clearance at three or four places around each groove. Where no values are specified, if the measured clearance is excessive - say greater than 0.10 mm - new pistons will be required. If the new ring is excessively tight, the most likely cause is dirt remaining in the groove.

11 Check the piston-to-bore clearance by measuring the cylinder bore (see Section 15) and the piston diameter. Measure the piston across the skirt, at a 90° angle to the gudgeon pin, approximately half way down the skirt. Subtract the piston diameter from the bore diameter to obtain the clearance. If this is greater than the figures given in the Specifications, the block will have to be rebored and new pistons and rings fitted.

12 Check the fit of the gudgeon pin by twisting the piston and connecting rod in opposite directions. Any noticeable play indicates excessive wear, which must be corrected. If the pistons or connecting rods are to be renewed, the work should be carried out by a Ford garage or engine overhaul specialist. Note in the case of the Endura-DE diesel engine, the gudgeon pins are secured by circlips, so the pistons and connecting rods can be separated without difficulty. Note the position of the piston relative to the rod before dismantling, and use new circlips on reassembly.

13 Before refitting the rings to the pistons, check their end gaps by inserting each of them in their cylinder bores. Use the piston to make sure that they are square. Using feeler blades, check that the gaps are within the tolerances given in the Specifications. Genuine rings are supplied pre-gapped; no attempt should be made to adjust the gaps by filing.

2D

16.14 Look for etched markings identifying the piston ring top surface

Reassembly

14 Install the new rings by fitting them over the top of the piston, starting with the oil control scraper ring sections. Use feeler blades in the same way as when removing the old rings. New rings generally have their top surfaces identified, and must be fitted the correct way round **(see illustration)**. Note that the first and second compression rings have different sections. Be careful when handling the compression rings; they will break if they are handled roughly or expanded too far. With all the rings in position, space the ring gaps at 120° to each other. The oil control scraper ring expander must also be positioned opposite to the actual ring.

17 Crankshaft (except Zetec-SE engine) - inspection

1 Clean the crankshaft and dry it with compressed air if available.

 Warning: Wear eye protection when using compressed air! Be sure to clean the oil holes with a pipe cleaner or similar probe.

18.2 Typical bearing failures

(Labels in illustration:)
CRATERS OR POCKETS — FATIGUE FAILURE
BRIGHT (POLISHED) SECTIONS — IMPROPER SEATING
SCRATCHES / DIRT IMBEDDED INTO BEARING MATERIAL — SCRATCHED BY DIRT
OVERLAY WIPED OUT — LACK OF OIL
OVERLAY GONE FROM ENTIRE SURFACE — EXCESSIVE WEAR
RADIUS RIDE — TAPERED JOURNAL

17.4 Measure the diameter of each crankshaft journal at several points, to detect taper and out-of round conditions

2 Check the main and big-end bearing journals for uneven wear, scoring, pitting and cracking.

3 If the crankshaft has been reground, check for burrs around the crankshaft oil holes (the holes are usually chamfered, so burrs should not be a problem unless regrinding has been carried out carelessly). Remove any burrs with a fine file or scraper, and thoroughly clean the oil holes as described previously.

4 Using a micrometer, measure the diameter of the main bearing and connecting rod journals, and compare the results with the Specifications **(see illustration)**. By measuring the diameter at a number of points around each journal's circumference, you will be able to determine whether or not the journal is out-of-round. Take the measurement at each end of the journal, near the webs, to determine if the journal is tapered. If any of the measurements vary by more than 0.025 mm, the crankshaft will have to be reground, and undersize bearings fitted.

5 Check the oil seal contact surfaces at each end of the crankshaft for wear and damage. If an excessive groove is evident in the surface of the crankshaft, consult an engine overhaul specialist who will be able to advise whether a repair is possible or if a new crankshaft is necessary.

18 Main and big-end bearings - inspection

1 Even though the main and big-end bearings should be renewed during the engine overhaul, the old bearings should be retained for close examination, as they may reveal valuable information about the condition of the engine. The size of the bearing shells is stamped on the back metal, and this information should be given to the supplier of the new shells.

2 Bearing failure occurs because of lack of lubrication, the presence of dirt or other foreign particles, overloading the engine, and corrosion. Regardless of the cause of bearing failure, it must be corrected before the engine is reassembled, to prevent it from happening again **(see illustration)**.

3 When examining the bearings, remove them from the engine block, the main bearing caps, the connecting rods and the rod caps, and lay them out on a clean surface in the same general position as their location in the engine. This will enable you to match any bearing problems with the corresponding crankshaft journal.

4 Dirt and other foreign particles get into the engine in a variety of ways. Dirt may be left in the engine during assembly, or it may pass through filters or the crankcase ventilation system. It may get into the oil, and from there into the bearings. Metal chips from machining operations and normal engine wear are often present. Abrasives are sometimes left in engine components after reconditioning, especially when parts are not thoroughly cleaned using the proper cleaning methods. Whatever the source, these foreign objects often end up embedded in the soft bearing material, and are easily recognised. Large particles will not embed in the bearing, and will score or gouge the bearing and journal. The best prevention for this cause of bearing failure is to clean all parts thoroughly, and keep everything spotlessly-clean during engine assembly. Frequent and regular engine oil and filter changes are also recommended.

5 Lack of lubrication (or lubrication breakdown) has a number of interrelated causes. Excessive heat (which thins the oil), overloading (which squeezes the oil from the bearing face) and oil leakage (from excessive bearing clearances, worn oil pump or high engine speeds) all contribute to lubrication breakdown. Blocked oil passages, which usually are the result of misaligned oil holes in a bearing shell, will also oil-starve a bearing and destroy it. When lack of lubrication is the cause of bearing failure, the bearing material is wiped or extruded from the steel backing of the bearing. Temperatures may increase to the point where the steel backing turns blue from overheating.

6 Driving habits can have a definite effect on bearing life. Full-throttle, low-speed operation (labouring the engine) puts very high loads on bearings, which tends to squeeze out the oil film. These loads cause the bearings to flex, which produces fine cracks in the bearing face (fatigue failure). Eventually, the bearing material will loosen in pieces and tear away from the steel backing. Short-trip driving leads to corrosion of bearings, because insufficient engine heat is produced to drive off the condensed water and corrosive gases. These products collect in the engine oil, forming acid and sludge. As the oil is carried to the engine bearings, the acid attacks and corrodes the bearing material.

7 Incorrect bearing installation during engine assembly will lead to bearing failure as well. Tight-fitting bearings leave insufficient bearing oil clearance, and will result in oil starvation. Dirt or foreign particles trapped behind a bearing shell result in high spots on the bearing which lead to failure.

20.4a Fit the bearing shells to their locations in the crankcase

20.4b The tab on each bearing shell must engage with the notch in the cylinder block or cap, and the oil holes in the upper shells must align with the block oilways

8 If new bearings are to be fitted, the bearing running clearances should be measured before the engine is finally reassembled, to ensure that the correct bearing shells have been obtained (see Sections 20 and 21). If the crankshaft has been reground, the engineering works which carried out the work will advise on the correct size bearing shells to suit the work carried out.

19 Engine overhaul - reassembly sequence

1 Before reassembly begins ensure that all new parts have been obtained and that all necessary tools are available. Read through the entire procedure to familiarise yourself with the work involved, and to ensure that all items necessary for reassembly of the engine are at hand. In addition to all normal tools and materials, jointing and thread locking compound will be needed during engine reassembly. *Do not* use any kind of silicone-based sealant on any part of the fuel system or inlet manifold, and *never* use exhaust sealants upstream of the catalytic converter.
2 In order to save time and avoid problems,

20.6 Place the crankshaft thrustwashers into position in the crankcase so that their oil grooves are facing outwards

engine reassembly can be carried out in the following order.
a) *Tappets and camshaft (Endura-E engine).*
b) *Crankshaft and main bearings.*
c) *Pistons and connecting rods.*
d) *Oil pump.*
e) *Sump.*
f) *Flywheel/driveplate.*
g) *Cylinder head.*
h) *Timing sprockets and chain/belt.*
i) *Engine external components (including inlet and exhaust manifolds).*
3 Ensure that everything is clean prior to reassembly. As mentioned previously, dirt and metal particles can quickly destroy bearings and result in major engine damage. Use clean engine oil to lubricate during reassembly.

20 Crankshaft (not Zetec-SE engine) - main bearing running clearance check and refitting

1 It is assumed at this point that the cylinder block/crankcase and crankshaft have been cleaned and repaired or reconditioned as necessary. Position the engine upside-down.
2 Remove the main bearing cap bolts, and lift out the caps. Lay the caps out in the proper order, to ensure correct installation.
3 If they're still in place, remove the old bearing shells from the block and the main bearing caps. Wipe the bearing recesses of the block and caps with a clean, lint-free cloth. They must be kept spotlessly-clean!

Main bearing clearance check

4 Wipe clean the main bearing shell seats in the crankcase, and clean the backs of the bearing shells. Insert the respective upper shells (dry) into position in the crankcase. Note that the upper shells have grooves in them (the lower shells are plain, and have a wider location lug). Note also that the No 1 lower shell on the Endura-DE diesel engine

has a groove. Where the old main bearings are being refitted, ensure that they are located in their original positions. Make sure that the tab on each bearing shell fits into the notch in the block or cap **(see illustrations)**.
Caution: Don't hammer the shells into place, and don't damage the bearing faces. No lubrication should be used at this time.
5 Before the crankshaft can be permanently installed, the main bearing running clearance should be checked; this can be done in either of two ways. One method is to fit the main bearing caps to the cylinder block, with the bearing shells in place. With the cap retaining bolts tightened to the specified torque, measure the internal diameter of each assembled pair of bearing shells using a vernier dial indicator or internal micrometer. If the diameter of each corresponding crankshaft journal is measured and then subtracted from the bearing internal diameter, the result will be the main bearing running clearance. The second (and more accurate) method is to use a product known as 'Plastigauge'. This consists of a fine thread of perfectly-round plastic which is compressed between the bearing cap and the journal. When the cap is removed, the deformation of the plastic thread is measured with a special card gauge supplied with the kit. The running clearance is determined from this gauge. The procedure for using Plastigauge is as follows.
6 Place the crankshaft thrustwashers into position in the crankcase, so that their oil grooves are facing outwards (away from the central web) **(see illustration)**. Hold them in position with a little grease. Clean the bearing surfaces of the shells in the block, and the crankshaft main bearing journals with a clean, lint-free cloth.
7 With the crankshaft clean, carefully lay it in position in the main bearings **(see illustration)**. Do not use any lubricant; the crankshaft journals and bearing shells must be perfectly clean and dry.

2D

20.7 Lowering the crankshaft in the main bearings

20.8 Lay the Plastigauge strips on the main bearing journals, parallel to the crankshaft centre-line

8 Cut several pieces of the appropriate-size Plastigauge (they should be slightly shorter than the width of the main bearings), and place one piece on each crankshaft journal axis **(see illustration)**.

9 With the bearing shells in position in the caps, fit the caps to their numbered or previously-noted locations **(see illustration)**. Take care not to disturb the Plastigauge.

10 Starting with the centre main bearing and working outward, tighten the main bearing cap bolts progressively to their specified torque setting. Don't rotate the crankshaft at any time during this operation.

11 Remove the bolts and carefully lift off the main bearing caps, keeping them in order. Don't disturb the Plastigauge or rotate the crankshaft. If any of the bearing caps are difficult to remove, tap them from side-to-side with a soft-faced mallet.

12 Compare the width of the crushed Plastigauge on each journal to the scale printed on the gauge to obtain the main bearing running clearance **(see illustration)**.

13 If the clearance is not as specified, the bearing shells may be the wrong size (or excessively-worn if the original shells are being re-used). Before deciding that different size shells are needed, make sure that no dirt

or oil was trapped between the bearing shells and the caps or block when the clearance was measured. If the Plastigauge was wider at one end than at the other, the journal may be tapered.

14 Carefully scrape away all traces of the Plastigauge material from the crankshaft and bearing shells, using a fingernail or something similar which is unlikely to score the shells.

Final crankshaft refitting

15 Carefully lift the crankshaft out of the engine. Clean the bearing surfaces of the shells in the block, then apply a thin layer of clean engine oil to each shell. Coat the thrustwasher bearing surfaces as well.

16 Make sure the crankshaft journals are clean, then lay the crankshaft back in place in the block. Clean the bearing surfaces of the shells in the caps, then lubricate them with oil. Install the caps in their respective positions, with the arrows pointing to the timing belt/chain end of the engine.

17 Working on one cap at a time, from the centre main bearing outwards (and ensuring that each cap is tightened down squarely and evenly onto the block), tighten the main bearing cap bolts to the specified torque wrench setting. On the Endura-DE diesel engine,

angle-tighten the bolts in the same sequence using an angle-tightening adapter on a socket.

18 Rotate the crankshaft a number of times by hand, to check for any obvious binding.

19 Check the crankshaft endfloat (refer to Section 14).

20 Refit the crankshaft rear oil seal housing as described in Chapters 2A or 2C (as applicable). On the Endura-E petrol engine, also fit a new oil seal - the oil seal is integral in the housing on the Endura-DE diesel engine.

21 Refit the components removed in Section 14.

21 Piston/connecting rod assemblies - big-end bearing running clearance check and refitting

1 Clean the backs of the big-end bearing shells and the recesses in the connecting rods and big-end caps. If new shells are being fitted, ensure that all traces of the protective grease are cleaned off using paraffin. Wipe the shells and connecting rods dry with a lint-free cloth.

2 Press the big-end bearing shells into the connecting rods and caps in their correct positions. On the Endura-E petrol engine and the Endura-DE diesel engine, make sure that the location tabs are engaged with the cut-outs in the connecting rods **(see illustration)**. On the Zetec-SE engine, make sure that the shells are located centrally and aligned with the split faces of the connecting rod and cap - the shells are finally held in position when the big-end cap bolts are tightened to the specified torque (see later in this Section) **(see illustration)**.

Big-end bearing running clearance check

3 Lubricate No 1 piston and piston rings, and check that the ring gaps are spaced at 120° intervals to each other.

20.9 The crankshaft main bearing cap arrows point to the timing belt end of the engine (A), and the bearing numbers (B) are consecutive from the timing belt end

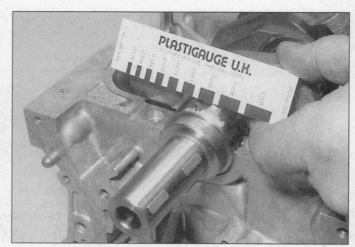

20.12 Compare the width of the crushed Plastigauge to the scale on the envelope to determine the main bearing running clearance

21.2a The location tab on each big-end bearing shell must engage with the notch in the connecting rod or cap

21.2b On the Zetec-SE engine, make sure that the shells are located centrally and aligned with the split faces of the connecting rod and cap

21.4a With the compressor fitted, use the handle of a hammer to gently drive the piston into the cylinder

4 Fit a ring compressor to No 1 piston, then insert the piston and connecting rod into No 1 cylinder. Make sure that the arrow on the piston crown is facing the timing end of the engine. With No 1 crankpin at its lowest point, drive the piston carefully into the cylinder with the wooden handle of a hammer, at the same time guiding the connecting rod onto the crankpin **(see illustrations)**.

5 To measure the big-end bearing running clearance, refer to the information contained in Section 20; the same general procedures apply, however note that there are no specifications for the Zetec-SE petrol engine. If the Plastigauge method is being used, ensure that the crankpin journal and the big-end bearing shells are clean and dry, then engage the connecting rod with the crankpin. Place the Plastigauge strip on the crankpin, fit the bearing cap in its previously-noted position, then tighten the bolts to the specified torque. Do not rotate the crankshaft during this operation. Remove the cap and check the running clearance by measuring the Plastigauge as previously described.

6 Repeat the above procedures on the remaining piston/connecting rod assemblies.

Final refitting

7 Having checked the running clearance of all the crankpin journals and taken any corrective action necessary, clean off all traces of Plastigauge from the bearing shells and crankpin.

8 Liberally lubricate the crankpin journals and big-end bearing shells. Refit the bearing caps once more, ensuring correct positioning as previously described. Tighten the bearing cap bolts to the specified torque and angles , and turn the crankshaft each time to make sure that it is free before moving on to the next assembly **(see illustrations)**.

9 On completion, refit the oil pump pick-up tube and baffle plate (Zetec-SE engine), sump and cylinder head as described in Chapter 2A, 2B or 2C.

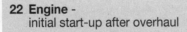

22 Engine - initial start-up after overhaul

1 With the engine refitted in the vehicle, double-check the engine oil and coolant levels (see "Weekly Checks"). Make a final check that everything has been reconnected, and that there are no tools or rags left in the engine compartment.

Petrol engine models

2 With the spark plugs removed and the ignition and fuel injection systems disabled by disconnecting the low tension wires from the coil (Chapter 5B) and depressurising the fuel system by removing the fuel pump relay (Chapter 4A), crank the engine on the starter motor until the oil pressure light goes out.

3 Refit the spark plugs and connect the low tension wires. Refit the fuel pump relay.

4 Start the engine, noting that this may take a little longer than usual, due to the fuel pump being empty.

5 While the engine is idling, check for fuel, water and oil leaks. Where applicable, check the power steering pipe/hose unions for leakage. Do not be alarmed if there are some odd smells and smoke from parts getting hot and burning off oil deposits.

6 Keep the engine idling until hot water is felt circulating through the top hose, then switch it off.

7 After a few minutes, recheck the oil and coolant levels, and top-up as necessary (see "Weekly Checks").

8 There is no requirement to retighten the cylinder head bolts.

9 If new pistons, rings or crankshaft bearings have been fitted, the engine must be run-in for the first 500 miles (800 km). Do not operate the engine at full-throttle, nor allow it to labour in any gear during this period. It is recommended that the oil and filter be changed at the end of this period.

Diesel engine

10 Prime the fuel system as described in Chapter 4B.

11 Fully depress the accelerator pedal, turn the ignition key and wait for the preheating warning light to go out.

2D

21.4b Make sure that the arrow on the piston crown is facing the timing end of the engine

21.8a Angle-tightening the big-end bearing cap bolts

21.8b Torx big-end bolts fitted to the Zetec-SE engine

12 Start the engine. Additional cranking may be necessary to completely bleed the fuel system before the engine starts.

13 Once started, keep the engine running at fast tickover. Check that the oil pressure light goes out, then check that there are no leaks of oil, fuel and coolant. Where applicable, check the power steering pipe/hose unions for leakage. Do not be alarmed if there are some odd smells and smoke from parts getting hot and burning off oil deposits.

14 Keep the engine idling until hot coolant is felt circulating through the radiator top hose, indicating that the engine is at normal operating temperature, then stop the engine and allow it to cool.

15 Recheck the oil and coolant levels and top up if necessary (see "*Weekly Checks*").

16 Check the idle speed (Chapter 4B).

17 If new pistons, rings or bearings have been fitted, the engine must be run-in at reduced speeds and loads for the first 500 miles (800 km) or so. Do not operate the engine at full throttle, or allow it to labour in any gear during this period. It is recommended that the engine oil and filter be changed at the end of this period.

Chapter 3
Cooling, heating and air conditioning systems

Contents

Degrees of difficulty

Easy, suitable for novice with little experience	Fairly easy, suitable for beginner with some experience	Fairly difficult, suitable for competent DIY mechanic	Difficult, suitable for experienced DIY mechanic	Very difficult, suitable for expert DIY or professional

Specifications

Torque wrench settings	Nm	lbf ft
Coolant pump securing bolts:		
Petrol engines	10	7
Diesel engines	33	24
Thermostat housing securing bolts	18	13
Coolant pump pulley securing bolts	11	8
Coolant temperature sensor	12	9

3

1 General information and precautions

General information

The cooling system is of pressurised type, comprising a pump driven by the auxiliary drivebelt (petrol engines) or the timing belt (diesel engines), an aluminium crossflow radiator, electric cooling fan, and a thermostat. The system functions as follows. Cold coolant from the radiator passes through the hose to the coolant pump, where it is pumped around the cylinder block and head passages. After cooling the cylinder bores, combustion surfaces and valve seats, the coolant reaches the underside of the thermostat, which is initially closed. The coolant passes through the heater, and is returned via the cylinder block to the coolant pump.

When the engine is cold, the coolant circulates only through the cylinder block, cylinder head and heater. When the coolant reaches a predetermined temperature, the thermostat opens and the coolant passes through to the radiator. As the coolant circulates through the radiator, it is cooled by the inrush of air when the car is in forward motion. Airflow is supplemented by the action of the electric cooling fan when necessary. Once the coolant has passed through the radiator, and has cooled, the cycle is repeated.

The electric cooling fan, mounted on the rear of the radiator, is controlled by a thermostatic switch. At a predetermined coolant temperature, the switch actuates the fan.

An expansion tank is fitted to allow for the expansion of the coolant when hot. The expansion tank is connected to the top of the radiator.

Refer to Section 10 for information on the air conditioning system.

Precautions

 Warning: Do not attempt to remove the radiator filler cap, or disturb any part of the cooling system, while the engine is hot; there is a high risk of scalding. If the radiator filler cap must be removed before the engine and radiator have fully cooled (even though this is not recommended) the pressure in the cooling system must first be relieved. Cover the cap with a thick layer of cloth, to avoid scalding, and slowly unscrew the filler cap until a hissing sound can be heard. When the hissing has stopped, indicating that the pressure has reduced, slowly unscrew the filler cap until it can be removed; if more hissing sounds are heard, wait until they have stopped before unscrewing the cap completely. At all times, keep well away from the filler cap opening.

 Warning: Do not allow antifreeze to come into contact with skin, or with the painted surfaces of the vehicle. Rinse off spills immediately, with plenty of water. Never leave antifreeze lying around in an open container, or in a puddle on the driveway or garage floor. Children and pets are attracted by its sweet smell, but antifreeze can be fatal if ingested.

 Warning: If the engine is hot, the electric cooling fan may start rotating even if the engine is not running; be careful to keep hands, hair and loose clothing well clear when working in the engine compartment.

Warning: Refer to Section 10 for precautions to be observed when working on models equipped with air conditioning.

2.3 Disconnecting a coolant hose from the coolant reservoir

3.6 Disconnect the wiring plug from the cooling fan motor

3.7 Release the wiring connectors from the radiator support member

2 Cooling system hoses – disconnection and renewal

Note: *Refer to the warnings given in Section 1 of this Chapter before proceeding. Do not attempt to disconnect any hose while the system is still hot.*

1 If the checks described in Chapter 1 reveal a faulty hose, it must be renewed as follows.

2 First drain the cooling system (see Chapter 1A or B). If the coolant is not due for renewal, it may be re-used if it is collected in a clean container.

3 Before disconnecting a hose, first note its routing in the engine compartment, and whether it is secured by any clips or ties. Use a screwdriver to slacken the clips, then move the clips along the hose, clear of the relevant inlet/outlet union. Carefully work the hose free **(see illustration)**.

4 Note that the radiator inlet and outlet unions are fragile; do not use excessive force when attempting to remove the hoses. If a hose proves to be difficult to remove, try to release it by rotating the hose ends before attempting to free it.

HAYNES HINT *If all else fails, cut the coolant hose with a sharp knife, then slit it so that it can be peeled off in two pieces. Although this may prove expensive if the hose is otherwise undamaged, it is preferable to buying a new radiator.*

5 When fitting a hose, first slide the clips onto the hose, then work the hose into position. If clamp-type clips were originally fitted, it is a good idea to replace them with screw-type clips when refitting the hose. If the hose is stiff, use a little soapy water (washing-up liquid is ideal) as a lubricant, or soften the hose by soaking it in hot water.

6 Work the hose into position, checking that it is correctly routed and secured. Slide each clip along the hose until it passes over the flared end of the relevant inlet/outlet union, before tightening the clips securely.

7 Refill the cooling system with reference to Chapter 1A or B.

8 Check thoroughly for leaks as soon as possible after disturbing any part of the cooling system.

3 Radiator – removal, inspection and refitting

Removal

1 Disconnect the battery negative lead with reference to Chapter 5A.

2 Drain the cooling system as described in Chapter 1A or B.

3 Loosen the hose clip, and disconnect the top hose from the radiator. Similarly, where applicable disconnect the expansion tank hose from the top of the radiator.

4 Apply the handbrake, then jack up the front of the vehicle and support securely on axle stands (see *"Jacking and Vehicle Support"*).

5 Where applicable, remove the securing screws and withdraw the shield from under the radiator.

6 Disconnect the cooling fan wiring plug from the fan motor, and unclip the wiring harness from the cooling fan shroud **(see illustration)**.

7 Where applicable, release the wiring connectors from the lower left-hand side of the radiator support member **(see illustration)**.

8 Disconnect the hose(s) from the lower right-hand side of the radiator.

9 On models with automatic transmission, place a suitable container beneath the automatic transmission fluid cooler pipes at the transmission, then unscrew the union nuts, and disconnect the pipes from the transmission. Allow the fluid to drain into the container, then plug or cover the open ends of the transmission and the pipes to prevent dirt entry and further fluid spillage.

10 Support the radiator assembly, then unscrew the four bolts securing the radiator support member to the front of the vehicle **(see illustration)**.

11 Carefully lower the radiator/fan assembly (complete with the automatic transmission fluid cooler pipes, where applicable), and withdraw the assembly from under the front of the vehicle **(see illustration)**.

12 If a new radiator is to be fitted, remove the fan assembly and, where applicable, the automatic transmission fluid cooler pipes, and transfer them to the new radiator.

Inspection

13 If the radiator has been removed due to suspected blockage, reverse-flush it as described in Chapter 1A or B. Clean dirt and debris from the radiator fins, using an air line (in which case, wear eye protection) or a soft brush. Be careful, as the fins are easily damaged, and are sharp.

14 If necessary, a radiator specialist can perform a "flow test" on the radiator, to establish whether an internal blockage exists.

15 A leaking radiator must be referred to a specialist for permanent repair. Do not attempt to weld or solder a leaking radiator, as damage may result.

16 In an emergency, minor leaks from the radiator can be cured by using a suitable radiator sealant (in accordance with its manufacturer's instructions) with the radiator *in situ*.

3.10 Unscrew the radiator support member bolts

3.11 Lower the radiator/cooling fan assembly from under the front of the vehicle

3.17 Inspect the radiator mounting rubbers (arrowed) and renew if necessary

4.5a Unscrew the securing bolts . . .

4.5b . . . then remove the thermostat housing (gasket arrowed) – Zetec-SE engine

17 Inspect the radiator mounting rubbers, and renew them if necessary (see illustration).

Refitting

18 Refitting is a reversal of removal, bearing in mind the following points.
  a) Ensure that the mounting rubbers are correctly located between the radiator and the support member.
  b) Ensure that all hoses are correctly reconnected, and their retaining clips securely tightened.
  c) On completion, refill the cooling system as described in Chapter 1A or B and, on models with automatic transmission, check and if necessary top up the automatic transmission fluid level as described in Chapter 1A or B.

---

4 Thermostat – removal, testing and refitting

Zetec-SE engines

Note: A new thermostat housing gasket and a new thermostat sealing ring will be required on refitting.

Removal

1 Disconnect the battery negative lead with reference to Chapter 5A.
2 Drain the cooling system as described in Chapter 1A or B (as applicable).
3 Loosen the clamps, and disconnect the two coolant hoses from the thermostat housing.

4.6 Removing the thermostat – Zetec-SE engine

4 Remove the alternator as described in Chapter 5A.
5 Unscrew the four securing bolts, and remove the thermostat housing from the cylinder head. Recover the gasket (see illustrations).
6 Lift out the thermostat, and recover the sealing ring (see illustration).

Testing

7 A rough test of the thermostat's operation may be made by suspending it with a piece of string in a container full of water. Heat the water to bring it to the boil - the thermostat must open by the time the water boils. If not, renew it.
8 The opening temperature is usually marked on the thermostat. If a thermometer is available, the precise opening temperature of the thermostat may be determined, and compared with the value marked on the thermostat (see illustration).
9 A thermostat which fails to close as the water cools must also be renewed.

Refitting

10 Thoroughly clean the mating faces of the thermostat housing and the cylinder head.
11 Refit the thermostat, using a new sealing ring. Ensure that the thermostat air bleed valve is uppermost.
12 Refit the thermostat housing, using a new gasket, and tighten the securing bolts to the specified torque.
13 Refit the alternator as described in Chapter 5A.
14 Reconnect the coolant hoses, then fill the cooling system as described in Chapter 1A.
15 On completion, reconnect the battery negative lead.

Endura-E engines

Note: A new thermostat cover gasket and a new thermostat sealing ring will be required on refitting.

Removal

16 Proceed as described in paragraphs 1 and 2.
17 Where applicable, disconnect the wiring from the cooling fan switch mounted in the thermostat housing.

18 Unscrew the securing bolts, and lift off the thermostat housing. Recover the gasket. If necessary, disconnect the coolant hoses from the thermostat housing to enable the housing to be withdrawn.
19 Using pliers, compress the thermostat retaining clip, and remove it from the housing.
20 Lift out the thermostat and recover the sealing ring.

Testing

21 Proceed as described in paragraphs 7 to 9.

Refitting

22 Refitting is a reversal of removal, bearing in mind the following points.
  a) Thoroughly clean the mating faces of the thermostat cover and the cylinder head.
  b) Refit the thermostat using a new sealing ring.
  c) Refit the thermostat housing, using a new gasket.
  d) Refill the cooling system as described in Chapter 1A.

Endura-DE diesel engines

Note: A new thermostat sealing ring will be required on refitting.

Removal

23 Proceed as described in paragraphs 1 and 2.

4.8 Testing the thermostat

3

4.24 Thermostat cover location (arrowed) – Endura-DE diesel engine

24 Unscrew the securing bolts, and lift off the thermostat cover **(see illustration)**.
25 Lift out the thermostat and recover the sealing ring.

Testing

26 Proceed as described in paragraphs 7 to 9.

Refitting

27 Refitting is a reversal of removal, bearing in mind the following points.
  a) *Thoroughly clean the mating faces of the thermostat housing and cover.*
  b) *Refit the thermostat using a new sealing ring.*
  c) *Refill the cooling system as described in Chapter 1B.*

5 Electric cooling fan – testing, removal and refitting

Testing

1 On all models, the cooling fan is controlled by the Powertrain Control Module (PCM - see Chapter 4), using signals provided by the engine coolant temperature sensor.
2 The fan operation can be checked by connecting the fan motor directly to a 12-volt power supply. Disconnect the motor wiring plug, and apply 12-volts across the motor terminals (the black wire is the earth) – take great care not to short out the power supply wires.

5.14 Fan motor securing nuts (arrowed)

3 If the fan fails to operate, the fan motor is almost certainly at fault.
4 Testing of the fan motor control circuit must be entrusted to a Ford dealer, who will have the necessary specialist diagnostic equipment to test the powertrain control system – do not attempt to test the system using conventional test equipment, as the Powertrain Control Module may be damaged.

Removal

5 Using suitable lengths of wire or string, support the radiator by tying it to the engine compartment front panel.
6 Disconnect the battery negative lead with reference to Chapter 5A.
7 Apply the handbrake, then jack up the front of the vehicle and support securely on axle stands (see *"Jacking and Vehicle Support"*).
8 Where applicable, remove the securing screws and withdraw the shield from under the radiator.
9 Disconnect the cooling fan wiring plug from the fan motor, and unclip the wiring harness from the cooling fan shroud.
10 Where applicable, release the wiring plugs from the left-hand side of the radiator support member.
11 Ensure that the radiator assembly is securely suspended from the front panel, then unscrew the four bolts securing the radiator support member to the front of the vehicle.
12 On models with automatic transmission, proceed as follows **(see illustrations)**.
  a) *Slacken the union nuts securing the transmission fluid cooler pipes to the fluid cooler - do not disconnect the pipes.*
  b) *Unclip the fluid cooler pipes from the fan shroud.*
  c) *Working at the bottom of the fluid cooler, unscrew the bolt securing the fluid cooler to the radiator.*
  d) *Pull the bottom of the fluid cooler away from the radiator, then lower the fluid cooler from the side of the radiator, and support it, taking care not to strain the fluid pipes.*
13 Lower the fan shroud assembly from the radiator.
14 If desired, the fan motor can be removed from the shroud after unscrewing the three securing nuts **(see illustration)**.

5.12a Slacken the transmission fluid cooler pipe unions (arrowed)

5.12b Unscrew the bolt (arrowed) securing the fluid cooler to the radiator

Refitting

15 Refitting is a reversal of removal, bearing in mind the following points.
  a) *Ensure that the fan shroud locating lugs are correctly positioned.*
  b) *On automatic transmission models, take care not to strain the fluid cooler pipes, and if any fluid leakage has occurred, check and top up the fluid level as described in Chapter 1A or B.*
  c) *Ensure that the mounting rubbers are correctly located between the radiator and the support member.*

6 Cooling system electrical switches and sensors – testing, removal and refitting

Coolant temperature sensor – Zetec-SE engines

Testing

1 Testing of the coolant temperature sensor circuit must be entrusted to a Ford dealer, who will have the necessary specialist diagnostic equipment to test the powertrain control system – do not attempt to test the system using conventional test equipment, as the Powertrain Control Module may be damaged.

Removal

2 The sensor is located in a housing, beneath the ignition coil, at the left-hand end of the cylinder head.

6.5 Unscrew the securing bolts (arrowed) and remove the HT lead cover – Zetec-SE engines

3 Disconnect the battery negative lead with reference to Chapter 5A.
4 Drain the cooling system as described in Chapter 1A.
5 Unscrew the securing bolts, and remove the HT lead cover from the camshaft cover, then disconnect the HT leads from the ignition coil **(see illustration)**.
6 Disconnect the ignition coil wiring plug.
7 Unscrew the four securing bolts, and remove the ignition coil **(see illustration)**.
8 Disconnect the wiring plug from the coolant temperature sensor **(see illustration)**.
9 Unscrew the coolant temperature sensor from its housing.

Refitting

10 Refitting is a reversal of removal, but refit the camshaft cover with reference to Chapter 2B and on completion, refill the cooling system as described in Chapter 1A.

Coolant temperature sensor – Endura-E engine

Testing

11 Testing of the coolant temperature sensor circuit must be entrusted to a Ford dealer, who will have the necessary specialist diagnostic equipment to test the powertrain control system – do not attempt to test the system using conventional test equipment, as the Powertrain Control Module may be damaged.

Removal

12 The sensor is located at the left-hand bottom corner of the inlet manifold.
13 Disconnect the battery negative lead with reference to Chapter 5A.
14 Drain the cooling system as described in Chapter 1A.
15 Disconnect the wiring plug from the coolant temperature sensor.
16 Unscrew the sensor from the manifold.

Refitting

17 Refitting is a reversal of removal. Refill the cooling system as described in Chapter 1A.

Coolant temperature sensor – Endura-DE diesel engine

Testing

18 Testing of the coolant temperature sensor circuit must be entrusted to a Ford dealer, who will have the necessary specialist diagnostic equipment to test the powertrain control system – do not attempt to test the system using conventional test equipment, as the Powertrain Control Module may be damaged.

Removal

19 The sensor is located in the thermostat housing at the front of the engine **(see illustration)**.
20 Disconnect the battery negative lead with reference to Chapter 5A.

6.7 Unscrew the securing bolts (arrowed) and remove the ignition coil – Zetec-SE engines

21 Drain the cooling system as described in Chapter 1B.
22 Disconnect the wiring plug from the coolant temperature sensor.
23 Unscrew the sensor from the thermostat housing.

Refitting

24 Refitting is a reversal of removal. Refill the cooling system as described in Chapter 1B.

Temperature gauge sender – Zetec-SE engines

Testing

25 The coolant temperature gauge is fed with a stabilised voltage supply from the instrument panel feed (via the ignition switch and a fuse), and its earth is controlled by the sender. The sender contains a thermistor (thermal resistor), an electronic component whose electrical resistance decreases at a predetermined rate as its temperature rises. When the coolant is cold, the sender resistance is high, current flow through the gauge is reduced, and the gauge needle points towards the 'cold' end of the scale. If the sender is faulty, it must be renewed.
26 If the gauge develops a fault, first check the other instruments; if they do not work at all, check the instrument panel electrical feed. If the readings are erratic, there may be a fault in the voltage stabiliser, which will necessitate renewal of the stabiliser. If the fault lies in the temperature gauge alone, check it as follows.

6.19 Coolant sensor location (arrowed) – Endura-DE diesel engine

6.8 Disconnect the coolant temperature sensor wiring plug (arrowed) – Zetec-SE engines

27 If the gauge needle remains at the 'cold' end of the scale, disconnect the sender wire, and earth it to the cylinder head. If the needle then deflects when the ignition is switched on, the sender unit is proved faulty, and should be renewed. If the needle still does not move, remove the instrument panel (Chapter 12) and check the continuity of the wiring between the sender unit and the gauge, and the feed to the gauge unit. If continuity is shown, and the fault still exists, then the gauge is faulty, and the gauge unit should be renewed.
28 If the gauge needle remains at the 'hot' end of the scale, disconnect the sender wire. If the needle then returns to the 'cold' end of the scale when the ignition is switched on, the sender unit is proved faulty, and should be renewed. If the needle still does not move, check the remainder of the circuit as described previously.

Removal and refitting

29 The sensor is located in a housing, beneath the ignition coil, at the left-hand end of the cylinder head.
30 Proceed as described in paragraphs 2 to 8.
31 Release the clamps, and disconnect the two coolant hoses from the sensor/sender housing **(see illustration)**.
32 Disconnect the wiring plug from the temperature sender, then unscrew the bolt securing the exhaust gas recirculation pipe bracket, and release the wiring connector from the bracket **(see illustration)**.

6.31 Disconnect the two coolant hoses (arrowed) from the sensor/sender housing – Zetec-SE engines

3

6.32 Disconnect the wiring plug (arrowed) from the temperature sender – Zetec-SE engines

6.33 Unscrew the sensor/sender housing securing nuts (arrowed) – Zetec-SE engines

6.37 Coolant temperature gauge sender location (arrowed) – Endura-E engines

33 Unscrew the four securing nuts, and withdraw the sensor/sender housing from the engine **(see illustration)**.
34 Unscrew the sender from the housing.
35 Refitting is a reversal of removal, bearing in mind the following points.
a) *Tighten all fixings to the specified torque, where given.*
b) *Thoroughly clean the mating faces of the sensor/sender housing and the cylinder head, and use a new housing gasket.*
c) *On completion, refill the cooling system as described in Chapter 1A.*

Temperature gauge sender – Endura-E engines

Testing

36 Proceed as described in paragraphs 25 to 28.

Removal

37 The sender is located at the rear of the engine **(see illustration)**.
38 Disconnect the battery negative lead with reference to Chapter 5A.
39 Drain the cooling system as described in Chapter 1A.
40 Release the wiring looms from the clips on the bulkhead, then disconnect the wiring plug from the coolant temperature sensor.
41 Unscrew the sensor.

Refitting

42 Refitting is a reversal of removal. Refill the cooling system as described in Chapter 1A.

Temperature gauge sender – diesel engines

Testing

43 Proceed as described in paragraphs 25 to 28.

Removal and refitting

44 The sender is located in the thermostat housing, and the removal and refitting procedure is as described for the coolant temperature sensor in paragraphs 19 to 24.

Cooling fan switch

45 The electric cooling fan is controlled by the Powertrain Control Module, using signals provided by the engine coolant temperature sensor.

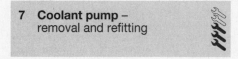

7 Coolant pump – removal and refitting

Zetec-SE engines

Removal

1 Disconnect the battery negative lead with reference to Chapter 5A.
2 Drain the cooling system as described in Chapter 1A.
3 Slacken the four bolts securing the coolant pump pulley **(see illustration)**.
4 Remove the alternator as described in Chapter 5A.

5 Unscrew the securing bolts, and remove the coolant pump pulley.
6 Unscrew the securing bolt, and remove the auxiliary drivebelt idler pulley.
7 Remove the timing belt covers as described in Chapter 2B.
8 Unscrew the six securing bolts, then withdraw the coolant pump **(see illustration)**.

Refitting

9 Commence refitting by thoroughly cleaning the mating faces of the coolant pump and the cylinder block.
10 Refit the coolant pump, using a new gasket, and tighten the securing bolts to the specified torque.
11 Further refitting is a reversal of removal, bearing in mind the following points.
a) *Refit the timing belt covers as described in Chapter 2B.*
b) *Tighten all fixings to the specified torque.*
c) *Refit and tension the auxiliary drivebelt as described in Chapter 1A.*
d) *On completion, refill the cooling system as described in Chapter 1A.*

Endura-E engines

Removal

12 Disconnect the battery negative lead with reference to Chapter 5A.
13 Drain the cooling system as described in Chapter 1A.
14 Slacken the coolant pump pulley securing bolts, then remove the auxiliary drivebelt as described in Chapter 1A.
15 Unscrew the securing bolts, and remove the coolant pump pulley.
16 Slacken the clip, and disconnect the coolant hose from the coolant pump.
17 Unscrew the three securing bolts, and withdraw the coolant pump **(see illustration)**. Recover the gasket.

Refitting

18 Commence refitting by thoroughly cleaning the mating faces of the coolant pump and the cylinder block.
19 Refit the coolant pump, using a new gasket, and tighten the securing bolts to the specified torque.

7.3 Slacken the coolant pump pulley securing bolts (arrowed) – Zetec-SE engines

7.8 Coolant pump securing bolts (arrowed) – Zetec-SE engines

7.17 Coolant pump securing bolts (arrowed) – Endura-E engine

7.24 Remove the two securing bolts (arrowed) and remove the timing belt tensioner pulley – Endura-DE diesel engine

7.26 Engine mounting bracket securing bolts. Loosen bolts (1) and slacken bolt (2) – Endura-DE diesel engine

20 Further refitting is a reversal of removal, bearing in mind the following points.
   a) Tighten all fixings to the specified torque.
   b) Refit and tension the auxiliary drivebelt as described in Chapter 1A.
   c) On completion, refill the cooling system as described in Chapter 1A.

Diesel engines

Removal

21 Disconnect the battery negative lead with reference to Chapter 5A.
22 Drain the cooling system as described in Chapter 1B.
23 Remove the fuel injection pump drivebelt as described in Chapter 4B.
24 Unscrew the two securing bolts, and remove the timing belt tensioner pulley **(see illustration)**. Recover the tensioner spring.
25 Accurately mark the position of the engine mounting on the body, then unscrew the four securing bolts, and remove the mounting from the vehicle body.
26 Unscrew the four bolts securing the right-hand engine mounting bracket to the engine. Note that the bracket is slotted around the lower front bolt location, so this bolt need only be loosened to remove the bracket **(see illustration)**. If necessary, raise the engine to give sufficient clearance to remove the mounting bracket bolts (the lower front bolt can be left in place), and withdraw the bracket.
27 Unscrew the securing bolt, and remove the timing belt idler sprocket.
28 Loosen the clamp, and disconnect the coolant hose from the elbow on the coolant pump.
29 Unscrew the remaining coolant pump securing bolts, then raise the engine until the coolant pump can be manipulated out from the engine compartment **(see illustration)**. Recover the gasket.

Refitting

30 Refitting is a reversal of removal, bearing in mind the following points.
   a) Tighten all fixings to the specified torque.
   b) Ensure that the engine mounting is aligned with the marks made before removal.
   c) Fit a new fuel injection pump drivebelt as described in Chapter 4B.

   d) On completion, refill the cooling system as described in Chapter 1B.

8 Heating and ventilation system – general information

The heater/ventilation system consists of a four-speed blower motor (housed behind the facia), face-level vents in the centre and at each end of the facia, and air ducts to the front footwells.

The control unit is located in the facia, and the controls operate flap valves and a coolant valve, to deflect and mix the air flowing through the various parts of the heater/ventilation system. The flap valves are contained in the air distribution housing, which acts as a central distribution unit, passing air to the various ducts and vents.

Cold air enters the system through the grille at the rear of the engine compartment.

The air (boosted by the blower fan if required) then flows through the various ducts, according to the settings of the controls. Stale air is expelled through ducts at the rear of the vehicle. If warm air is required, the cold air is passed through the heater matrix, which is heated by the engine coolant.

A recirculation switch enables the outside air supply to be closed off, while the air inside the vehicle is recirculated. This can be useful to prevent unpleasant odours entering from outside the vehicle, but should only be used

7.29 Unscrew the remaining coolant pump securing bolts (arrowed) – Endura-DE diesel engine

briefly, as the recirculated air inside the vehicle will soon deteriorate.

9 Heater/ventilation system components – removal and refitting

Heater/ventilation control unit

Removal

1 Disconnect the battery negative lead with reference to Chapter 5A.
2 Remove the radio/cassette player as described in Chapter 12.
3 Working at the top of the heater/ventilation control unit, unscrew the two securing screws **(see illustration)**.
4 Release the two securing clips at the sides of the panel, then pull the control panel forwards from the facia.
5 Disconnect the wiring plugs from the rear of the unit.
6 Disconnect the air distribution control cable end fitting from the rear of the control unit, then withdraw the unit **(see illustration)**.

Refitting

7 Refitting is a reversal of removal, but ensure that the air distribution control cable end fitting engages correctly with the gear at the rear of the control unit (turn the control knob as necessary), and check the operation of the heater/ventilation controls before finally refitting the unit to the facia.

9.3 Unscrew the heater/ventilation control unit securing screws

3

9.6 Disconnecting the air distribution control cable from the heater/ventilation control unit

9.9a Remove the securing screw . . .

9.9b . . . and release the heater blower motor switch

Heater blower motor switch

Removal

8 Remove the heater/ventilation control unit as described previously in this Section.

9 Working at the rear of the control unit, remove the blower motor switch securing screw, then turn the switch clockwise, and release if from the control unit **(see illustrations)**.

Refitting

10 Refer to paragraph 7.

Heater blower motor

> ⚠ **Warning: On left-hand-drive models with air conditioning, read the precautions given in Section 10, and have the system discharged by a Ford dealer or an air conditioning specialist. Do not carry out**

the following work unless the system had been discharged.

Removal

11 Disconnect the battery negative lead with reference to Chapter 5A.

12 Drain the cooling system as described in Chapter 1A or B (as applicable).

13 Remove the scuttle cover panel as described in Chapter 11.

14 Remove the two securing screws and withdraw the pollen filter housing **(see illustrations)**. Lift the housing over the mounting brackets as it is withdrawn.

15 Remove the two securing screws, and withdraw the blower motor cover **(see illustrations)**.

16 Working in the scuttle, unscrew the two screws securing the blower motor to the heater housing **(see illustration)**.

17 Working in the passenger's footwell, disconnect the blower motor wiring plug **(see illustration)**.

18 Pull the wiring grommet from the motor housing, then withdraw the blower motor from the scuttle, pulling the wiring and plug, through the bulkhead **(see illustrations)**.

Refitting

19 Refitting is a reversal of removal, bearing in mind the following points.

a) Make sure that the motor wiring grommet is securely located in the bulkhead.

b) Refill the cooling system as described in Chapter 1A or B (as applicable).

c) Where applicable, have the air conditioning system re-charged by a Ford dealer or an air conditioning specialist, then check the operation of the air conditioning system.

9.14a Remove the two securing screws (arrowed) . . .

9.14b . . . and withdraw the pollen filter housing

9.15a Remove the securing screws . . .

9.15b . . . and withdraw the blower motor cover

9.16 Remove the blower motor securing screws

9.17 Disconnect the blower motor wiring plug (arrowed)

9.18a Pull out the wiring grommet . . .

9.18b . . . then withdraw the blower motor

9.23 Heater blower motor resistor (1) and
securing screw (2)

Heater blower motor resistor

Removal

20 The resistor is located in the passenger's side footwell.

21 Disconnect the battery negative lead with reference to Chapter 5A.

22 Disconnect the resistor wiring plug.

23 Unscrew the securing screw, and withdraw the resistor (see illustration).

Refitting

24 Refitting is a reversal of removal.

Air recirculation control valve motor

Removal

25 Remove the complete facia assembly as described in Chapter 11.

26 Disconnect the control motor wiring plug.

27 Unscrew the three securing screws, and withdraw the motor from the heater assembly (see illustration).

Refitting

28 Refitting is a reversal of removal.

Heater matrix

 Warning: On models with air conditioning, read the precautions given in Section 10, and have the system discharged by a Ford dealer or an air conditioning specialist. Do not carry out the following work unless the system had been discharged.

Note: On models with air conditioning, Ford special tool No 34-001 will be required to

release the refrigerant line connectors from the evaporator.

Removal

29 Disconnect the battery negative lead with reference to Chapter 5A.

30 Drain the cooling system as described in Chapter 1A or B (as applicable).

31 Remove the scuttle cover panel as described in Chapter 11.

32 On models with air conditioning, disconnect the refrigerant lines from the evaporator, accessible in the scuttle - do not do this unless the air conditioning system has been discharged. Plug or cover the open ends of the refrigerant lines and the evaporator.

33 Disconnect the wiring plug from the heater coolant valve, and the windscreen wiper motor, then unclip the wiring harness, and move it clear of the heater matrix housing (see illustration).

34 Slacken the hose clips, and disconnect the heater coolant hoses from the top of the heater matrix pipes (see illustration).

35 Slide the coolant valve from the top of the heater matrix housing (see illustration).

36 Remove the four securing screws, and withdraw the heater matrix housing cover from the scuttle (see illustrations).

37 On models with air conditioning, pull the evaporator from the heater housing.

38 Carefully pull the heater matrix from the heater housing, taking care not to damage the matrix fins on the plastic lugs in front of the matrix (see illustration).

3

9.27 Air recirculation control valve motor
mounting details

1 Wiring plug   2 Securing screws

9.33 Unclip the wiring harness and move it
clear of the matrix housing

9.34 Disconnect the coolant hoses from
the heater matrix pipes

9.35 Slide the coolant valve from the
heater matrix housing

9.36a Remove the four securing
screws . . .

9.36b . . . and withdraw the heater matrix housing cover

9.38 Pull out the heater matrix

9.42 Disconnecting the coolant valve wiring plug

Refitting

39 Refitting is a reversal of removal, bearing in mind the following points.
a) Refill the cooling system as described in Chapter 1A or B (as applicable).
b) Where applicable, have the air conditioning system re-charged by a Ford dealer or an air conditioning specialist, then check the operation of the air conditioning system.

Coolant valve

Removal

40 Disconnect the battery negative lead with reference to Chapter 5A.
41 Remove the scuttle cover panel as described in Chapter 11.
42 Disconnect the wiring plug from the now-exposed coolant valve **(see illustration)**.
43 Slacken the hose clips, and disconnect the four coolant hoses from the coolant valve (be prepared for some coolant spillage), then slide the valve from the heater matrix housing. Note the locations of the hoses, to ensure correct refitting. Clamp or plug the open ends of the hoses to prevent further coolant spillage.

Refitting

44 Refitting is a reversal of removal, bearing in mind the following points.
a) Ensure that the coolant hoses are correctly reconnected to the valve as noted before removal.

b) On completion check the coolant level and top up if necessary, then check the operation of the heater.

Heater assembly

 Warning: On models with air conditioning, read the precautions given in Section 10, and have the system discharged by a Ford dealer or an air conditioning specialist. Do not carry out the following work unless the system had been discharged.

Removal

45 Disconnect the battery negative lead with reference to Chapter 5A.
46 Drain the cooling system as described in Chapter 1A or B (as applicable).
47 Remove the complete facia assembly as described in Chapter 11.
48 Remove the scuttle cover panel as described in Chapter 11.
49 On models with air conditioning, disconnect the refrigerant lines from the evaporator, accessible in the scuttle - **do not** do this unless the air conditioning system has been discharged. Plug or cover the open ends of the refrigerant lines and the evaporator.
50 Disconnect the wiring plug from the heater coolant valve.
51 Slacken the hose clips, and disconnect the coolant hoses from the top of the heater matrix pipes **(see illustration 9.34)**.

52 Working inside the vehicle, disconnect the wiring plugs from the following components **(see illustration)**.
a) Heater blower motor
b) Air recirculation valve control motor
c) Blower motor resistor
53 On models with air conditioning, disconnect the drain hose from the condenser.
54 Unscrew the three nuts securing the heater assembly to the bulkhead, then lift the assembly from the bulkhead, and withdraw it from the vehicle **(see illustration)**.

Refitting

55 Refitting is a reversal of removal, bearing in mind the following points.
a) Refit the facia as described in Chapter 11.
b) Refill the cooling system as described in Chapter 1A or B (as applicable).
c) Where applicable, have the air conditioning system re-charged by a Ford dealer or an air conditioning specialist, then check the operation of the air conditioning system.

10 Air conditioning system –
general information and precautions

General information

1 Air conditioning is available on certain models. It enables the temperature of incoming air to be lowered, and also dehumidifies the air, which makes for rapid demisting and increased comfort.
2 The cooling side of the system works in the same way as a domestic refrigerator. Refrigerant gas is drawn into a belt-driven compressor, and passes into a condenser mounted in front of the radiator, where it loses heat and becomes liquid. The liquid passes through an expansion valve to an evaporator, where it changes from liquid under high pressure to gas under low pressure. This change is accompanied by a drop in temperature, which cools the evaporator. The refrigerant returns to the compressor, and the cycle begins again.
3 Air blown through the evaporator passes to the heater assembly, where it is mixed with

9.52 Disconnect the heater wiring plugs

1 Blower motor wiring plug
2 Air recirculation control valve wiring plug
3 Blower motor resistor wiring plug

9.54 Heater assembly securing nuts (arrowed)

hot air blown through the heater matrix, to achieve the desired temperature in the passenger compartment.

4 The heating side of the system works in the same way as on models without air conditioning (see Section 8).

5 The operation of the system is controlled electronically. Any problems with the system should be referred to a Ford dealer or an air conditioning specialist.

Precautions

6 It is necessary to observe special precautions whenever dealing with any part of the system, its associated components, and any items which necessitate disconnection of the system.

 Warning: The refrigeration circuit contains a liquid refrigerant (Freon). This refrigerant is potentially dangerous, and should only be handled by qualified persons. If it is splashed onto the skin, it can cause frostbite. It is not itself poisonous, but in the presence of a naked flame it forms a poisonous gas; inhalation of the vapour through a lighted cigarette could prove fatal. Uncontrolled discharging of the refrigerant is dangerous, and potentially damaging to the environment. It is therefore dangerous to disconnect any part of the system without specialised knowledge and equipment. If for any reason the system must be disconnected, entrust this task to an authorised dealer or an air conditioning specialist.

7 Do not operate the air conditioning system if it is known to be short of refrigerant, as this may damage the compressor.

11 Air conditioning system components – removal and refitting

Compressor

 Warning: Read the precautions given in Section 10, and have the system discharged by a Ford dealer or an air conditioning specialist. Do not carry out the following work unless the system had been discharged.

Removal

1 Disconnect the battery negative lead with reference to Chapter 5A.

2 Apply the handbrake, then jack up the front of the vehicle and support securely on axle stands (see *"Jacking and Vehicle Support"*).

3 Remove the auxiliary drivebelt as described in Chapter 1A or B (as applicable).

4 Slacken the union bolt which secures the refrigerant line connector block to the compressor. **Do not** slacken the bolt unless the air conditioning system has been discharged **(see illustration)**.

11.4 Slacken the union bolt (arrowed) securing the connector block to the compressor

5 Disconnect the compressor wiring plug.

6 Support the compressor, then unscrew the four compressor mounting bolts **(see illustration)**.

7 Remove the union bolt, and disconnect the refrigerant line connector block from the compressor, then lower the compressor and withdraw it from under the vehicle. Plug the openings in the connector block and the compressor to prevent dirt entry.

Refitting

8 Refitting is a reversal of removal, but refit and tension the auxiliary drivebelt as described in Chapter 1A or B (as applicable). On completion, have the air conditioning system re-charged by a Ford dealer or an air conditioning specialist, then check the operation of the air conditioning system.

Evaporator

9 Removal and refitting of the evaporator is described as part of the heater matrix removal and refitting procedure in Section 9.

Condenser

 Warning: Read the precautions given in Section 10, and have the system discharged by a Ford dealer or an air conditioning specialist. Do not carry out the following work unless the system had been discharged.

Note: *Ford special tool No 34-001 will be required to release the refrigerant line connectors.*

11.13 Use the special tool to disconnect the refrigerant line at the condenser

11.6 Air conditioning compressor securing bolts (arrowed)

Removal

10 The condenser is located in front of the radiator.

11 Disconnect the battery negative lead with reference to Chapter 5A.

12 Remove the right-hand headlight as described in Chapter 12.

13 Using the special tool, disconnect the refrigerant line connecting the evaporator to the condenser, at the condenser **(see illustration)**. Plug the open ends of the pipes to prevent dirt entry. **Do not** disconnect the line unless the air conditioning system has been discharged.

14 Apply the handbrake, then jack up the front of the vehicle and support securely on axle stands (see *"Jacking and Vehicle Support"*).

15 Working under the front of the vehicle, again using the special tool, disconnect the refrigerant line connecting the dehydrator to the condenser, at the condenser. Plug the open ends of the pipes to prevent dirt entry. Again, **do not** disconnect the line unless the air conditioning system has been discharged.

16 Remove the securing screws, and withdraw the undershield from under the radiator/condenser assembly.

17 Unscrew the two bolts securing the condenser to the radiator support member **(see illustration)**.

18 Using suitable lengths of wire or string, support the radiator by tying it to the engine compartment front panel.

3

11.17 Unscrew the two bolts (arrowed) securing the condenser to the radiator support member

11.26 Dehydrator upper securing bolt (arrowed)

11.29 Dehydrator lower securing bolts (arrowed)

19 Where applicable, unclip the wiring plug from the lower left-hand side of the radiator support member.

20 Ensure that the radiator assembly is securely suspended from the front panel, then unscrew the four bolts securing the radiator support member to the front of the vehicle, and withdraw the support member.

21 Unhook the top end of the condenser from its supports, then withdraw the condenser from under the front of the vehicle.

Refitting

22 Refitting is a reversal of removal, bearing in mind the following points.

 a) Use new O-rings when reconnecting the refrigerant lines.

 b) Refit the headlight with reference to Chapter 12 if necessary.

 c) On completion, have the air conditioning system re-charged by a Ford dealer or an air conditioning specialist, then check the operation of the air conditioning system.

Dehydrator

 Warning: Read the precautions given in Section 10, and have the system discharged by a Ford dealer or an air conditioning specialist. Do not carry out the following work unless the system had been discharged.
Note: *Ford special tool No 34-003 will be required to release the refrigerant line connectors.*

Removal

23 The dehydrator is located at the right-hand front corner of the engine compartment.

24 Disconnect the battery negative lead with reference to Chapter 5A.

25 Using the special tool, disconnect the refrigerant lines from the dehydrator. **Do not** disconnect the lines unless the air conditioning system has been discharged.

26 Unscrew the dehydrator upper securing bolt **(see illustration)**.

27 Apply the handbrake, then jack up the front of the vehicle and support securely on axle stands (see *"Jacking and Vehicle Support"*).

28 Working under the wheel arch, unscrew the four securing screws, and carefully pull the wheel arch liner back to expose the two dehydrator lower securing bolts.

29 Unscrew the two lower securing bolts, and withdraw the dehydrator downwards from under the front of the vehicle **(see illustration)**.

Refitting

30 Refitting is a reversal of removal, but use new O-rings when reconnecting the refrigerant lines. On completion, have the air conditioning system re-charged by a Ford dealer or an air conditioning specialist, then check the operation of the air conditioning system.

Chapter 4 Part A:
Fuel and exhaust systems - petrol engine models

Contents

Degrees of difficulty

Easy, suitable for novice with little experience	**Fairly easy,** suitable for beginner with some experience	**Fairly difficult,** suitable for competent DIY mechanic 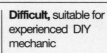	**Difficult,** suitable for experienced DIY mechanic	**Very difficult,** suitable for expert DIY or professional

Specifications

General
System type .... Sequential Electronic Fuel injection (SEFi)
Application .... 1.25 litre DHA Zetec-SE, 1.3 litre JJA and J4C Endura-E, and 1.4 litre FHA Zetec-SE engines

Fuel grade
Fuel octane requirement .... 95 RON unleaded

Fuel system data
Regulated fuel pressure:
  Pressure regulator vacuum hose disconnected .... 2.7 ± 0.2 bar
  With engine running and pressure regulator vacuum hose connected . 2.1 ± 0.2 bar
Hold pressure - engine stopped after five minutes .... 1.8 bars minimum

Torque wrench settings

	Nm	lbf ft
Fuel rail-to- cylinder head (Zetec-SE engine)	23	17
Fuel rail-to-inlet manifold bolts (Endura-E engine)	18	13
Fuel pressure regulator screws (Endura-E engine)	10	7
Fuel injector bolts	6	4
Idle air control valve:		
Endura-E engine	8	6
Zetec-SE engine	10	7
Fuel pressure regulator screws	6	4
Shrader valve retaining bolts	10	7
Fuel supply pipe retaining plate bolts	10	7
Inlet manifold	18	13
Engine coolant temperature sensor	12	9
Camshaft position sensor	10	7
Crankshaft position sensor	7	5
Exhaust manifold	53	39
Exhaust downpipe to manifold nuts:		
Stage 1	30	22
Stage 2	38	28
Exhaust flange bolts/nuts	47	35

1 General information and precautions

General information

The fuel system consists of a fuel tank (mounted under the body, beneath the rear seats), fuel hoses, an electric fuel pump mounted in the fuel tank, and a sequential electronic fuel injection system controlled by a EEC V engine management control module (Powertrain Control Module).

The electric fuel pump supplies fuel under pressure to the fuel rail, which distributes fuel to the injectors. A pressure regulator controls the system pressure in relation to inlet tract depression. From the fuel rail, fuel is injected into the inlet ports, just above the inlet valves, by four fuel injectors. On the Endura-E engine a plastic moulded fuel rail is fitted, whereas on the Zetec-SE engine the fuel rail is of aluminium alloy. The Endura-E fuel rail is mounted on the inlet manifold, whereas the Zetec-SE fuel rail is mounted in the cylinder head.

The amount of fuel supplied by the injectors is precisely controlled by the Powertrain Control Module (PCM). The module uses the signals from the crankshaft position sensor and the camshaft position sensor, to trigger each injector separately in cylinder firing order (sequential injection), with benefits in terms of better fuel economy and leaner exhaust emissions.

The Powertrain Control Module is the heart of the entire engine management system, controlling the fuel injection, ignition and emissions control systems. The module receives information from various sensors which is then computed and compared with pre-set values stored in it's memory, to determine the required period of injection.

Information on crankshaft position and engine speed is generated by a crankshaft position sensor. The inductive head of the sensor runs just above the engine flywheel and scans a series of 36 protrusions on the flywheel periphery. As the crankshaft rotates, the sensor transmits a pulse to the system's ignition module every time a protrusion passes it. There is one missing protrusion in the flywheel periphery at a point corresponding to 90° BTDC. The ignition module recognises the absence of a pulse from the crankshaft position sensor at this point to establish a reference mark for crankshaft position. Similarly, the time interval between absent pulses is used to determine engine speed. This information is then fed to the Powertrain Control Module for further processing.

On the Zetec-SE engine, the camshaft position sensor is located in the cylinder head so that it registers with a lobe on the camshaft. On the Endura-E engine, it is located on the timing cover and registers with

a plate located beneath the camshaft sprocket retaining bolts. The camshaft position sensor functions in the same way as the crankshaft position sensor, producing a series of pulses; this gives the Powertrain Control Module a reference point, to enable it to determine the firing order, and operate the injectors in the appropriate sequence.

The mass air flow sensor is based on a "hot-wire" system, sending the Powertrain Control Module a constantly-varying (analogue) voltage signal corresponding to the mass of air passing into the engine. Since air mass varies with temperature (cold air being denser than warm), measuring air mass provides the module with a very accurate means of determining the correct amount of fuel required to achieve the ideal air/fuel mixture ratio.

Engine temperature information is supplied by the coolant temperature sensor. This component is an NTC (Negative Temperature Coefficient) thermistor - that is, a semiconductor whose electrical resistance decreases as its temperature increases. It provides the Powertrain Control Module with a constantly-varying (analogue) voltage signal, corresponding to the temperature of the engine coolant. This is used to refine the calculations made by the module, when determining the correct amount of fuel required to achieve the ideal air/fuel mixture ratio.

Inlet air temperature information is supplied by the inlet air temperature sensor. This component is also an NTC thermistor - see the previous paragraph - providing the module with a signal corresponding to the temperature of air passing into the engine. This is used to refine the calculations made by the module, when determining the correct amount of fuel required to achieve the ideal air/fuel mixture ratio.

A throttle position sensor is mounted on the end of the throttle valve spindle, to provide the Powertrain Control Module with a constantly-varying (analogue) voltage signal corresponding to the throttle opening. This allows the module to register the driver's input when determining the amount of fuel required by the engine.

Road speed is monitored by the vehicle speed sensor. This component is a Hall-effect generator, mounted on the transmission's speedometer drive. It supplies the module with a series of pulses corresponding to the vehicle's road speed, enabling the module to control features such as the fuel shut-off on overrun.

The clutch pedal position is monitored by a switch fitted to the pedal bracket. This sends a signal to the Powertrain Control Module.

Where power steering is fitted, a pressure-operated switch is screwed into the power steering system's high-pressure pipe. The switch sends a signal to the Powertrain Control Module to increase engine speed to maintain idle speed during power steering assistance.

The oxygen sensor in the exhaust system provides the module with constant feedback - "closed-loop" control - which enables it to adjust the mixture to provide the best possible operating conditions for the catalytic converter.

The air inlet side of the system consists of an air cleaner housing, the mass air flow sensor, an inlet hose and duct, and a throttle housing.

The throttle valve inside the throttle housing is controlled by the driver, through the accelerator pedal. As the valve opens, the amount of air that can pass through the system increases. As the throttle valve opens further, the mass air flow sensor signal alters, and the Powertrain Control Module opens each injector for a longer duration, to increase the amount of fuel delivered to the inlet ports.

Both the idle speed and mixture are under the control of the Powertrain Control Module, and cannot be adjusted.

Precautions

 Warning: Many of the procedures in this Chapter require the removal of fuel lines and connections, which may result in some fuel spillage. Before carrying out any operation on the fuel system, refer to the precautions given in "Safety first!" at the beginning of this manual, and follow them implicitly. Petrol is a highly-dangerous and volatile liquid, and the precautions necessary when handling it cannot be overstressed.

Note: *Residual pressure will remain in the fuel lines long after the vehicle was last used. When disconnecting any fuel line, first depressurise the fuel system as described in Section 2.*

2 Fuel system - depressurisation

Note: *Refer to the warning note in Section 1 before proceeding.*

 Warning: The following procedure will merely relieve the pressure in the fuel system - remember that fuel will still be present in the system components, and take precautions accordingly before disconnecting any of them.

1 The fuel system referred to in this Chapter is defined as the fuel tank and tank-mounted fuel pump/fuel gauge sender unit, the fuel filter, the fuel injector, fuel pressure regulator, and the metal pipes and flexible hoses of the fuel lines between these components. All these contain fuel, which will be under pressure while the engine is running and/or while the ignition is switched on.

2 The pressure will remain for some time after the ignition has been switched off, and must be relieved before any of these components is disturbed for servicing work.

3 The simplest depressurisation method is to disconnect the fuel pump electrical supply by removing the fuel pump fuse (No 19) and starting the engine; allow the engine to idle until it dies through lack of fuel. Turn the engine over once or twice on the starter to ensure that all pressure is released, then switch off the ignition; do not forget to refit the fuse when work is complete.

4 If an adapter is available to fit the Schrader-type valve on the fuel rail pressure test/release fitting (identifiable by its blue plastic cap, and located on the union of the fuel feed line and the fuel rail), this may be used to release the fuel pressure. The Ford adapter (tool number 23-033) operates similar to a drain tap - turning the tap clockwise releases the pressure. If the adapter is not available, place cloth rags around the valve, then remove the cap and allow the fuel pressure to dissipate. Refit the cap on completion.

5 Note that, once the fuel system has been depressurised and drained (even partially), it will take significantly longer to restart the engine - perhaps several seconds of cranking - before the system is refilled and pressure restored.

3 Unleaded petrol - general information and usage

The fuel recommended by Ford is given in the Specifications section of this Chapter, followed by the equivalent petrol currently on sale in the UK.

All petrol models are designed to run on fuel with a minimum octane rating of 95 (RON). All models have a catalytic converter, and so must be run on unleaded fuel only. Under no circumstances should leaded fuel (UK "4-star") be used, as this will damage the converter.

Super unleaded petrol (98 octane) can also be used in all models if wished, though there is no advantage in doing so.

4 Fuel lines and fittings - general information

Note: *Refer to the warning note in Section 1 before proceeding.*

Disconnecting and connecting quick-release couplings

1 Quick-release couplings are employed at many of the unions in the fuel feed and return lines.

2 Before disconnecting any fuel system component, relieve the residual pressure in the system (see Section 2), and equalise tank pressure by removing the fuel filler cap.

 Warning: This procedure will merely relieve the increased pressure necessary for the

engine to run - remember that fuel will still be present in the system components, and take precautions accordingly before disconnecting any of them.

3 Release the protruding locking lugs on each union, by squeezing them together and carefully pulling the coupling apart. Use rag to soak up any spilt fuel. Where the unions are colour-coded, the pipes cannot be confused. Where both unions are the same colour, note carefully which pipe is connected to which, and ensure that they are correctly reconnected on refitting.

4 To reconnect one of these couplings, press them together until the locking lugs snap into their groove. Switch the ignition on and off five times to pressurise the system, and check for any sign of fuel leakage around the disturbed coupling before attempting to start the engine.

Checking

5 Checking procedures for the fuel lines are included in Chapter 1A.

Component renewal

6 If any damaged sections are to be renewed, use original-equipment replacement hoses or pipes, constructed from exactly the same material as the section being replaced. Do not install substitutes constructed from inferior or inappropriate material; this could cause a fuel leak or a fire.

7 Before detaching or disconnecting any part of the fuel system, note the routing of all hoses and pipes, and the orientation of all clamps and clips. Replacement sections must be installed in exactly the same manner.

8 Before disconnecting any part of the fuel system, be sure to relieve the fuel system pressure (see Section 2), and equalise tank pressure by removing the fuel filler cap. Also disconnect the battery negative (earth) lead - see Chapter 5A, Section 1. Cover the fitting being disconnected with a rag, to absorb any fuel that may spray out.

5 Air cleaner assembly and air inlet components - removal and refitting

Air cleaner assembly

1 Loosen the clip and disconnect the air inlet duct from the mass air flow sensor on the air cleaner.

2 Disconnect the wiring from the air flow sensor and air intake temperature sensor.

3 Unscrew the screws securing the cover to the air cleaner housing.

4 Withdraw the cover and remove the filter element.

5 Release the retaining strap from the rear of the air cleaner base, then lift the front of the base from the rubber grommets.

6 Disconnect the remaining hose and detach the air cleaner base from the air inlet duct.

Withdraw the assembly from the engine compartment.

7 Check the rubber grommets for deterioration and renew them if necessary.

8 Refitting is the reverse of the removal procedure. Ensure that the base pegs seat fully in their rubber grommets, and that the mass air flow sensor is correctly located.

Air inlet components

9 To remove the air inlet duct between the mass air flow sensor and throttle housing, loosen the retaining clips and carefully ease off the duct.

10 To remove the air inlet duct attached to the air cleaner base, first remove the air cleaner assembly as described in paragraphs 1 to 6. Unbolt the resonator then disconnect it from the duct. If necessary, the silencers may be detached from the duct.

11 Refitting is a reversal of removal.

6 Accelerator cable - removal, refitting and adjustment

Removal

1 Fold back the carpet and insulation in the driver's footwell to gain access to the accelerator pedal.

2 Disconnect the inner cable from the top of the pedal.

3 From within the engine compartment, detach the outer cable from the adjuster/support bracket by removing the metal retaining clip **(see illustration)**.

4 Disconnect the inner cable from the quadrant on the throttle housing by pivoting the quadrant then extracting the retaining clip (manual transmission models) or releasing the end fitting (automatic transmission models).

5 Release the cable from the supports in the engine compartment, and withdraw it from the bulkhead.

Refitting

6 Refitting is a reversal of removal. When the cable is reconnected at each end, adjust the cable as follows.

6.3 Metal retaining clip on the accelerator cable adjuster/support bracket

4A

Adjustment

7 Remove the outer cable metal retaining clip at the adjuster/support bracket and lubricate the cable adjuster grommet with soapy water.
8 Remove any slack by pulling the cable as far as possible out of the adjuster. Have an assistant depress the accelerator pedal fully - the cable outer will move back into the adjuster - and hold it there while the clip is refitted.
9 Check that the throttle quadrant moves smoothly and easily from the fully-closed to the fully-open position and back again as the assistant depresses and releases the accelerator pedal. Re-adjust the cable if required.

---

7 Accelerator pedal - removal and refitting

Removal

1 Peel back the carpet and insulation from the driver's footwell to allow access to the accelerator pedal.
2 Detach the accelerator cable from the pedal (see Section 6), then release the circlip from the pivot shaft and remove the accelerator pedal.

Refitting

3 Refit in the reverse order of removal. On completion, check the action of the pedal and the cable to ensure that the throttle has full unrestricted movement, and fully returns when released.
4 Check and if necessary adjust the accelerator cable as described in Section 6.

---

8 Fuel pump/fuel pressure - checking

Note: *Refer to the warning note in Section 1 before proceeding.*

Fuel pump operation check

1 Switch on the ignition, and listen for the fuel pump (the sound of an electric motor running, audible from beneath the rear seats). Assuming there is sufficient fuel in the tank, the pump should start and run for approximately one or two seconds, then stop, each time the ignition is switched on.
Note: *If the pump runs continuously all the time the ignition is switched on, the electronic control system is running in the backup (or "limp-home") mode referred to by Ford as "Limited Operation Strategy" (LOS). This almost certainly indicates a fault in the EEC V module itself, and the vehicle should therefore be taken to a Ford dealer for a full test of the complete system, using the correct diagnostic equipment; do not waste time or risk damaging the components by*

trying to test the system without such facilities.
2 Listen for fuel return noises from the fuel pressure regulator. It should be possible to feel the fuel pulsing in the regulator and in the feed hose from the fuel filter.
3 If the pump does not run at all, check the fuse, relay and wiring (see Chapter 12). Check also that the fuel cut-off switch has not been activated and if so, reset it.

Fuel pressure check

4 A fuel pressure gauge will be required for this check and should be connected in the fuel line between the fuel filter and the fuel rail, in accordance with the gauge maker's instructions. On Zetec engines, a pressure gauge equipped with an adapter to suit the Schrader-type valve on the fuel rail pressure test/release fitting (identifiable by its blue plastic cap, and located on the union of the fuel feed line and the fuel rail) will be required. If the Ford special tool 29-033 is available, the tool can be attached to the valve, and a conventional-type pressure gauge attached to the tool.
5 If using the service tool, ensure that its tap is turned fully anti-clockwise, then attach it to the valve. Connect the pressure gauge to the service tool. If using a fuel pressure gauge with its own adapter, connect it in accordance with its maker's instructions.
6 Start the engine and allow it to idle. Note the gauge reading as soon as the pressure stabilises, and compare it with the regulated fuel pressure figures listed in the Specifications.
  a) *If the pressure is high, check for a restricted fuel return line. If the line is clear, renew the fuel pressure regulator.*
  b) *If the pressure is low, pinch the fuel return line. If the pressure now goes up, renew the fuel pressure regulator. If the pressure does not increase, check the fuel feed line, the fuel pump and the fuel filter.*
7 Detach the vacuum hose from the fuel pressure regulator; the pressure shown on the gauge should increase. Note the increase in pressure, and compare it with that listed in the *Specifications*. If the pressure increase is not as specified, check the vacuum hose and pressure regulator.

9.9 Disconnecting the fuel supply hose quick-release fitting from the fuel filter

8 Reconnect the regulator vacuum hose, and switch off the engine. Verify that the hold pressure stays at the specified level for five minutes after the engine is turned off.
9 Carefully disconnect the fuel pressure gauge, depressurising the system first as described in Section 2. Be sure to cover the fitting with a rag before slackening it. Mop up any spilt petrol.
10 Run the engine, and check that there are no fuel leaks.

---

9 Fuel tank - removal, inspection and refitting

Note: *Refer to the warning note in Section 1 before proceeding.*

Removal

1 Run the fuel level as low as possible prior to removing the tank.
2 Relieve the residual pressure in the fuel system (see Section 2), and equalise tank pressure by removing the fuel filler cap.
3 Disconnect the battery negative (earth) lead (see Chapter 5A).
4 Where possible, syphon or pump out the remaining fuel from the fuel tank (there is no drain plug). The fuel must be emptied into a suitable container for storage.
5 Chock the front wheels then jack up the rear of the car and support it on axle stands (see *"Jacking and Vehicle Support"*). Remove the rear roadwheels.
6 Unhook the exhaust system mounting rubbers at the front and rear and allow the exhaust system to rest on the rear suspension crossmember. There is no need to disconnect the exhaust from the exhaust manifold.
7 Unscrew the nuts and remove the exhaust heat shields from the underbody.
8 Loosen the clip and disconnect the filler pipe lower vent hose from the rear of the fuel tank.
9 Position a container beneath the fuel filter at the front of the tank, then disconnect the fuel supply hose from the filter inlet by squeezing the locking lugs on the quick-release fitting **(see illustration)**. Be prepared for some loss of fuel. The supply hose remains attached to the fuel pump until the tank is lowered.
10 At the rear of the tank, disconnect the hose leading to the evaporative emission canister from the fuel tank vent valve, then release the valve from the bracket.
11 Support the fuel tank using a jack and block of wood.
12 Unscrew and remove the tank mounting bolts **(see illustration)**.
13 Partially lower the fuel tank and at the same time loosen the clip and disconnect the lower filler pipe from the tank **(see illustration)**.
14 Squeeze the locking lugs on the quick-release fitting and disconnect the fuel return

9.12 Fuel tank mounting bolt

9.13 Lower filler pipe connection to the fuel tank

9.16 Filter location on the fuel tank

pipe. Note the return pipe is identified by a red colour band.

15 Disconnect the wiring from the fuel pump/fuel gauge sender on top of the tank.

16 Lower the fuel tank and withdraw it from under the vehicle. If necessary, disconnect the supply hose from the fuel pump. The filter may also be removed at this time **(see illustration)**.

17 Check the condition of the filler pipe seal and renew it if necessary.

Inspection

18 Whilst removed, the fuel tank can be inspected for damage or deterioration. Removal of the fuel pump/fuel gauge sender unit (see Section 10) will allow a partial inspection of the interior. If the tank is contaminated with sediment or water, swill it out with clean fuel. Do not under any circumstances undertake any repairs on a leaking or damaged fuel tank; this work must be carried out by a professional who has experience in this critical and potentially-dangerous work.

19 Whilst the fuel tank is removed from the vehicle, it should be placed in a safe area where sparks or open flames cannot ignite the fumes coming out of the tank. Be especially careful inside garages where a natural-gas type appliance is located, because the pilot light could cause an explosion.

20 Check the condition of the lower filler pipe and renew it if necessary.

Refitting

21 Refitting is a reversal of the removal procedure. Ensure that all connections are securely fitted. When refitting the quick-release couplings, press them together until the locking lugs snap into their groove. If evidence of contamination was found, do not return any previously-drained fuel to the tank unless it is carefully filtered first.

10 Fuel pump/fuel gauge sender unit - removal and refitting

Note: *Refer to the warning note in Section 1 before proceeding. Ford specify the use of their service tool 23-026 (a large ring spanner with projecting teeth to engage the fuel pump/sender unit retaining ring's slots) for this task. In practice it was found that a long metal bar could be used with success (see text).*

Removal

1 A combined fuel pump and fuel gauge sender unit is located in the top face of the fuel tank. The combined unit can only be detached and withdrawn from the tank after the tank is released and lowered from under the vehicle. Refer to Section 9 and remove the fuel tank, then proceed as follows.

2 With the fuel tank removed, disconnect the fuel supply pipe (if still attached to the tank) from the inlet stub by squeezing the quick release lugs. Note that the fuel supply pipe

connector is identified by a white band.

3 Unscrew and remove the special retaining ring then remove the insert. Ford technicians use a special wrench to unscrew the ring, however a long metal bar may be used with success **(see illustrations)**.

4 Carefully withdraw the fuel pump/sender unit from the fuel tank taking care not to damage the strainer and pump components **(see illustration)**.

5 Remove the rubber seal from the periphery of the pump. The seal must be renewed whenever the pump/sender unit is removed from the tank.

Refitting

6 Refitting is a reversal of removal, but fit a new rubber seal and tighten the retaining ring securely. Refit the fuel tank as described in Section 9.

11 Fuel tank roll-over valve - removal and refitting

Note: *Refer to the warning note in Section 1 before proceeding.*

Removal

1 The roll-over valve is located in a rubber grommet in the top of the fuel tank, in the hose leading rearwards to the carbon canister. Its purpose is to prevent fuel loss if the vehicle becomes inverted in a crash.

 4A

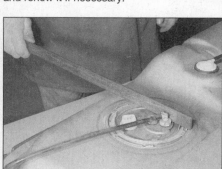

10.3a Using a long metal bar to loosen the special retaining ring from the fuel pump/fuel gauge sender unit

10.3b Removing the retaining ring

10.4 Withdrawing the fuel pump/sender unit from the tank

11.3 Vent hose clip on the top of the fuel tank

2 Remove the fuel tank as described in Section 9.

3 Release the vent hose from the clip on the top of the tank **(see illustration)**.

4 Carefully prise the roll-over valve from the rubber grommet and remove it together with the hose.

5 Check the condition of the rubber grommet and renew it if necessary.

Refitting

6 Refitting is a reversal of removal, but apply a light smear of clean engine oil to the rubber grommet, to ease fitting.

12 Fuel tank filler pipe -
removal and refitting

Note: *Refer to the warning note in Section 1 before proceeding.*

Removal

1 Remove the fuel tank as described in Section 9.

2 With the vehicle still raised, unscrew and remove the filler pipe lower mounting bolt.

3 Open the filler flap, then lift the plastic cover and unscrew the filler pipe upper mounting bolt.

4 Withdraw the filler pipe from under the vehicle.

5 If necessary, loosen the clips and disconnect the lower filler pipe and vent hose from the bottom of the filler pipe.

6 Check the condition of the filler pipe and hose and renew if necessary.

Refitting

7 Refitting is a reversal of removal.

13 Fuel cut-off switch -
removal and refitting

Note: *To reset the switch after an accident, use a coin to remove the plug in the passenger footwell trim, then depress the button on top of the switch.* **Do not** *reset the switch if fuel has escaped from the fuel system.*

Removal

1 The fuel cut-off switch is located behind the front passenger footwell side trim. First disconnect the battery negative (earth) lead (see Chapter 5A).

2 Pull up the weatherstrips from the door apertures and release them from the side trim. Using a sharp instrument, remove the trim clips, then on 5-door models only prise out the cover and remove the rear securing screw. Prise out the front clips and remove the trim.

3 Unscrew and remove the switch securing screws, then disconnect the wiring plug and remove the switch.

Refitting

4 Refitting is a reversal of removal, but make sure that the switch is reset. Start the engine to prove this.

14 Fuel injection system -
checking

Note: *Refer to the warning note in Section 1 before proceeding.*

If a fault appears in the fuel injection system, first ensure that all the system wiring connectors are securely connected and free of corrosion. Ensure that the fault is not due to poor maintenance; ie, check that the air

cleaner filter element is clean, the spark plugs are in good condition and correctly gapped, the valve clearances are correctly adjusted, the cylinder compression pressures are correct, and that the engine breather hoses are clear and undamaged, referring to Chapters 1 and 2 for further information.

If these checks fail to reveal the cause of the problem, the vehicle should be taken to a suitably-equipped Ford dealer for testing. A wiring block connector is incorporated in the engine management circuit, into which a special electronic diagnostic tester can be plugged. The tester will locate the fault quickly and simply, alleviating the need to test all the system components individually, which is a time-consuming operation that also carries a risk of damaging the EEC V engine management module.

15 Fuel injection system components -
removal and refitting

Note: *Refer to the warning note in Section 1 before proceeding.*

Throttle body housing

1 The housing is located on the left-hand side of the inlet manifold. First disconnect the battery negative (earth) lead (see Chapter 5A).

2 Remove the air inlet duct as described in Section 5.

3 Disconnect the accelerator cable from the lever on the throttle body housing.

4 Disconnect the throttle position sensor multi-plug **(see illustration)**.

5 Unscrew and remove the mounting bolts and withdraw the throttle housing from the inlet manifold. On the Zetec-SE engine also unbolt and remove the support bracket. Discard the gasket and obtain a new one **(see illustrations)**.

6 Refitting is a reversal of removal, but clean the mating faces and fit a new gasket, and tighten the mounting bolts securely. Check and if necessary adjust the accelerator cable as described in Section 6.

15.4 Disconnecting the throttle position sensor multi-plug

15.5a On the Zetec-SE engine, unscrew the lower support bracket bolt . . .

15.5b . . . and upper bolt . . .

15.5c . . . then unscrew the mounting bolts . . .

15.5d . . . remove the throttle body housing . . .

15.5e . . . and remove the gasket from the groove in the inlet manifold

Fuel rail and injectors

7 Relieve the residual pressure in the fuel system (see Section 2), and equalise tank pressure by removing the fuel filler cap.

 Warning: This procedure will merely relieve the increased pressure necessary for the engine to run - remember that fuel will still be present in the system components, and take precautions accordingly before disconnecting any of them.

8 Disconnect the battery negative (earth) lead (see Chapter 5A).

Endura-E engine

9 Disconnect the wiring from the idle air control valve. Unscrew the two bolts and remove the idle air control valve.
10 Pull out the accelerator cable adjustment clip, then release the outer cable from the support bracket and disconnect the inner cable from the throttle lever on the throttle housing.
11 Remove the air inlet resonator, then loosen the clips and disconnect the air inlet duct from the air cleaner and throttle housing. Remove the duct from the engine compartment.
12 Disconnect the crankcase ventilation hoses from the inlet manifold.
13 Unscrew the bolt and remove the accelerator cable retaining bracket.
14 Disconnect the HT leads from the spark plugs, then unclip the lead supports and

position the leads to one side. When disconnecting the leads, pull on the end fittings and not the leads.
15 Disconnect the wiring from the throttle position sensor. To do this, depress the locking wire and pull off the plug.
16 Disconnect the wiring from the fuel injectors, then undo the injector wiring loom retaining screws, disconnect the loom multiplug, and position the loom to one side.
17 Pull the vacuum hose from the fuel pressure regulator on the end of the fuel rail.
18 Unscrew and remove the fuel rail mounting bolts.
19 Undo the single screw and remove the fuel supply and return pipe retaining bracket.
20 Disconnect the fuel supply and return pipes from the fuel rail by squeezing the lugs on the special quick release fittings.
21 Carefully pull the injectors from the inlet manifold and withdraw them together with the fuel rail.
22 Remove the clips and carefully pull the injectors from the fuel rail.
23 Using a screwdriver prise the O-rings from the grooves at each end of the injectors. Discard the O-rings and obtain new ones.
24 Refitting is the reverse of the removal procedure, noting the following points:
a) *Lubricate the new O-rings with clean engine oil to aid refitting.*
b) *Ensure that the hoses and wiring are routed correctly, and secured on reconnection by any clips or ties provided.*

c) *Adjust the accelerator cable as described in Section 6.*
d) *On completion, switch the ignition on to activate the fuel pump and pressurise the system, without cranking the engine. Check for signs of fuel leaks around all disturbed unions and joints before attempting to start the engine.*

Zetec-SE engine

25 Lift the cover from the centre of the fuel injector wiring loom holder, and disconnect the vent hose.
26 The wiring loom adapter must now be disconnected from the injectors. To do this, depress two of the injector clips and lift the adapter up a little until release from the injectors. Now depress the remaining two clips and lift the complete adapter from the injectors **(see illustrations)**. Position the adapter to one side.
27 If it is only required to remove the injectors, proceed to paragraph 32.
28 To remove the fuel rail, disconnect the feed and return hoses from the left-hand end of the rail by squeezing together the lugs of the quick release fittings **(see illustration)**.
29 Unscrew the mounting bolts and lift the fuel rail from the cylinder head **(see illustrations)**.
30 Recover the bolt hole adapters from the cylinder head **(see illustration)**.
31 Recover the seals from the inner ends of the fuel rail **(see illustration)**.

4A

15.26a Depress the wire clips on the injectors . . .

15.26b . . . and disconnect the wiring loom adapter

15.28 Disconnecting the quick-release fuel feed and return hoses from the fuel rail

15.29a Unscrew the mounting bolts . . .

15.29b . . . and lift the fuel rail from the cylinder head

15.30 Remove the bolt hole adapters . . .

32 To remove the injectors, unscrew the two retaining bolts from each injector and carefully prise the injectors from the fuel rail **(see illustrations)**. If they are tight, use a soft faced tool inserted from the holes on the inner end of the fuel rail.

33 Remove the O-ring seals from the grooves in the injectors. Discard them and obtain new ones.

34 Refitting is a reversal of removal, but fit new O-ring seals and lubricate them with a little fresh engine oil before inserting the injectors in the fuel rail **(see illustration)**. Tighten the bolts to the specified torque.

Fuel pressure regulator

35 Relieve the residual pressure in the fuel system (see Section 2), and equalise tank pressure by removing the fuel filler cap.

 Warning: This procedure will merely relieve the increased pressure necessary for the engine to run - remember that fuel will still be present in the system components, and take precautions accordingly before disconnecting any of them.

36 Disconnect the battery negative (earth) lead (see Chapter 5A).

Endura-E engine

37 Loosen the clips and disconnect the air inlet duct from the air cleaner and throttle housing.

38 Disconnect the vacuum pipe from the fuel pressure regulator.

39 Undo the single screw and remove the fuel supply and return pipe retaining bracket.

40 Disconnect the fuel return pipe from the

fuel rail by squeezing the lugs on the special quick release fittings.

41 Undo the two screws and remove the fuel pressure regulator from the fuel rail.

42 Using a screwdriver, prise the O-ring from the groove in the fuel pressure regulator. Discard the O-ring and obtain a new one.

43 Refitting is a reversal of removal, but lubricate the new O-ring with clean engine oil to aid installation. Tighten the mounting screws to the specified torque.

Zetec-SE engine

44 Disconnect the vacuum pipe from the fuel pressure regulator.

45 Undo the two screws and remove the fuel pressure regulator from the fuel rail.

46 Using a screwdriver, prise the O-rings from the grooves in the fuel pressure regulator. Discard the O-rings and obtain new ones.

47 Refitting is a reversal of removal, but lubricate the new O-rings with clean engine oil to aid installation. Tighten the mounting screws to the specified torque.

Idle air control (IAC) valve

48 The valve is located on the inlet manifold.

49 Depress the wire clip and disconnect the wiring from the valve **(see illustration)**.

50 Unscrew the mounting bolts and remove the valve from the inlet manifold **(see illustration)**.

51 Recover the O-ring seals from the inlet manifold and discard them **(see illustration)**. Obtain new seals.

15.31 . . . and the fuel rail seals

15.32a Unscrew the bolts . . .

15.32b . . . and remove the injectors from the fuel rail

15.34 Oil the O-ring seals before refitting the injectors

15.49 Disconnect the wiring . . .

15.50 . . . then unbolt and remove the idle air control valve . . .

15.51 . . . and recover the O-ring seals from the inlet manifold

15.54 Disconnecting the wiring from the mass air flow sensor

52 Refitting is a reversal of removal, but note the following points.
  a) *Clean the mating surfaces, and fit new O-ring seals.*
  b) *Once the wiring and battery are reconnected, start the engine and allow it to idle. When it has reached normal operating temperature, check that the idle speed is stable, and that no induction (air) leaks are evident. Switch on all electrical loads (headlights, heated rear window, etc), and check that the idle speed is still satisfactory.*

Mass air flow sensor

53 Loosen the clip and disconnect the air inlet duct from the mass air flow sensor on the air cleaner cover. If necessary, remove the air cleaner cover for improved access.
54 Disconnect the wiring from the sensor **(see illustration)**.

55 Unscrew the crosshead mounting screws and remove the sensor from the air cleaner cover **(see illustration)**.
56 Refitting is a reversal of removal.

Powertrain Control Module

Note: *The module is fragile. Take care not to drop it, or subject it to any other kind of impact. Do not subject it to extremes of temperature, or allow it to get wet.*
57 The Module (engine management module) is located behind the passenger footwell side trim. First disconnect the battery negative (earth) lead (see Chapter 5A).
58 Remove the fuel cut-off switch as described in Section 13.
59 Drill out or cut off the two rivets and remove the security shield from over the module.
60 Release the module from its bracket and withdraw it downwards.

61 Undo the screw and swivel the wiring multiplug away from the module. **Do not** pull on the wiring, only on the multiplug itself.
62 Withdraw the module from inside the vehicle.
63 Refitting is a reversal of removal. Take care when refitting the multiplug, and tighten the retaining bolt by hand first. Use new pop rivets when refitting the security shield.

Crankshaft position sensor

64 The sensor is located on the front left-hand side of the engine. For improved access, apply the handbrake then jack up the front of the vehicle and support it on axle stands (see *"Jacking and Vehicle Support"*).
65 Unbolt (Endura-E) or unclip (Zetec-SE) the cover from the crankshaft position sensor on the front of the engine, then disconnect the wiring.
66 Unscrew the mounting bolt and withdraw the sensor.
67 Refitting is a reversal of removal.

Camshaft position sensor

68 On the Endura-E engine the sensor is located on the timing chain cover. On the Zetec-SE engine it is located on the right-hand rear of the cylinder head.
69 Depress the wire clip and disconnect the wiring from the camshaft position sensor **(see illustrations)**. Where applicable on the Endura-E engine, release the fuel feed and return hoses from their clip.
70 Unscrew the mounting bolt and withdraw the sensor from the cylinder head or timing chain cover (as applicable) **(see illustrations)**.

4A

15.55 One of the mass air flow sensor mounting screws

15.69a Camshaft position sensor located on the right-hand rear of the cylinder head - Zetec-SE engine

15.69b Disconnect the wiring . . .

15.70a . . . then unscrew the mounting bolt . . .

15.70b . . . and withdraw the camshaft position sensor from the cylinder head

15.71 Removing the O-ring from the camshaft position sensor

15.81a Disconnect the wiring . . .

15.81b . . . then remove it from the air cleaner cover

71 Remove the O-ring from the groove in the sensor **(see illustration)**.

72 Refitting is a reversal of removal but fit a new O-ring. Smear a little engine oil on the seal before fitting the sensor.

Engine coolant temperature (ECT) sensor

73 Drain the cooling system (see Chapter 1A).

74 Unbolt the plastic cover from the top of the cylinder head cover.

75 Disconnect the HT leads from the ignition coil, then disconnect the low tension wiring from the coil.

76 Unbolt and remove the ignition coil.

77 Disconnect the wiring from the coolant temperature sensor.

78 Unscrew and remove the sensor.

79 Refitting is a reversal of removal. Clean the threads of the sensor and mounting hole, then refit the sensor and tighten it to the specified torque.

Inlet air temperature sensor

80 The sensor is located in the air cleaner cover. If necessary, remove the air cleaner cover for improved access.

81 Disconnect the wiring from the sensor, then twist the sensor through 90° and remove it **(see illustrations)**.

82 Refitting is a reversal of removal.

Throttle position sensor

83 The sensor is located on the throttle body housing on the left-hand side of the inlet manifold. First disconnect the wiring by depressing the retaining clip.

84 Remove the retaining screws, and withdraw the unit from the throttle housing. *Do not* force the sensor's centre to rotate past its normal operating sweep; the unit will be seriously damaged.

85 Refitting is a reversal of removal, but ensure that the sensor is correctly orientated, by locating its centre on the D-shaped throttle shaft (throttle closed), and aligning the sensor body so that the bolts pass easily into the throttle housing.

Vehicle speed sensor

86 The sensor is mounted on the rear of the transmission at the base of the speedometer drive cable.

87 Undo the retaining nut, and withdraw the speedometer cable from the vehicle speed sensor. Use two spanners to loosen the nut - one to counterhold the sensor, and the other to unscrew the cable nut.

88 Disconnect the wiring from the vehicle speed sensor, then unscrew the sensor from the top of the drive pinion.

89 Refitting is a reversal of removal.

Manual transmission multi-function switch

90 Refer to Chapter 7A.

Clutch pedal position switch

91 Inside the vehicle, reach up under the clutch pedal and disconnect the return spring from the bracket.

92 Disconnect the wiring from the clutch switch, then twist the switch and remove it from the pedal bracket.

93 Refitting is a reversal of removal.

Power steering pressure switch

94 The switch is screwed into the power steering system's high-pressure pipe at the front right-hand side of the engine compartment.

95 Releasing its clip, unplug the switch's electrical connector, then unscrew the switch from the power steering high pressure pipe. Place a wad of rag underneath, to catch any spilt fluid. If a sealing washer is fitted, renew it if it is worn or damaged.

96 Refitting is the reverse of the removal procedure; tighten the switch securely, then

16.12 Disconnecting the carbon canister purge valve vacuum line from the inlet manifold

top-up the fluid reservoir (see *"Weekly Checks"*) to replace any fluid lost from the system, and bleed out any trapped air (see Chapter 10).

Oxygen sensor

97 Refer to Chapter 4C.

16 Manifolds - removal and refitting

Note: *Refer to the warning note in Section 1 before proceeding.*

Inlet manifold

Removal

1 Apply the handbrake, then jack up the front of the vehicle and support it on axle stands (see *"Jacking and Vehicle Support"*).

2 On the Endura-E engine, depressurise the fuel system as described in Section 2.

3 Disconnect the battery negative (earth) lead (see Chapter 5A).

4 Disconnect the wiring from the DIS ignition coil and throttle position sensor.

5 Loosen the clips and disconnect the air intake duct from the air cleaner and throttle body housing. Remove the duct from the engine compartment.

6 On the Endura-E engine, release the spark plug HT lead supports from the inlet manifold and move the leads to one side.

7 Disconnect the accelerator cable from the throttle body housing, then pull out the adjustment clip and detach the cable from the bracket. Release the cable from the further support on the inlet manifold.

8 On the Endura-E engine, remove the oil filler cap from the valve cover, and disconnect the crankcase ventilation hose from the T-piece.

9 On the Zetec-SE engine disconnect the crankcase ventilation hose from the PCV valve.

10 On the Endura-E engine, disconnect the engine wiring loom connectors at the rear of the engine and unclip the wiring bracket.

11 Disconnect the brake servo vacuum hose from the inlet manifold.

12 Disconnect the carbon canister purge valve vacuum line from the inlet manifold **(see illustration)**.

16.22a Unscrew the mounting bolts . . .

16.22b . . . and withdraw the inlet manifold from the cylinder head

16.22c Removing the gasket from the groove in the inlet manifold

13 On the Endura-E engine, disconnect the wiring from the camshaft position (CMP) sensor.
14 Disconnect the wiring from the engine coolant temperature sensor (Endura-E) and oil pressure switch (Endura-E and Zetec-SE).
15 On the Endura-E engine, release the heater hose from the rear of the inlet manifold.
16 Unbolt and remove the engine oil level dipstick tube.

Endura-E engine
17 Identify the positions of the fuel supply and return hoses on the fuel rail, then disconnect them by squeezing the lugs on the quick release fittings. Be prepared for some fuel loss.
18 Unbolt the cover from the crankshaft position sensor on the front of the engine, then disconnect the wiring from the sensor.
19 Unbolt the cable guide from the inlet manifold.
20 Unscrew the three nuts and remove the inlet manifold protection cover.

21 Progressively unscrew the self-locking nuts and remove the inlet manifold from the cylinder head. Recover the gasket.

Zetec-SE engine
22 Progressively unscrew the inlet manifold mounting bolts and withdraw the manifold from the cylinder head. Recover the gasket from the groove in the inlet manifold **(see illustrations)**.

All engines
23 Tape over the inlet ports on the cylinder head to prevent entry of dust and dirt. Alternatively place cloth rags in the ports.

Refitting
24 Refitting is a reversal of removal, but note the following additional points.

a) *Clean the mating faces of the inlet manifold and cylinder head and use a new gasket.*
b) *Tighten the nuts/bolts to the specified torque.*

Exhaust manifold
25 On the Endura-E engine, the exhaust manifold is located on the front of the engine, while on the Zetec-SE engine it is on the rear.
26 Disconnect the wiring from the oxygen sensor located on top of the exhaust manifold. If preferred, remove the sensor completely as described in Chapter 4C.
27 Unbolt and remove the shroud components from the exhaust manifold **(see illustration)**.
28 Unscrew the bolts/nuts securing the exhaust downpipe/catalytic converter to the exhaust manifold.
29 Unscrew the mounting bolts and nuts and withdraw the exhaust manifold from the cylinder head **(see illustrations)**.
30 Remove the gasket from the studs on the cylinder head **(see illustration)**.
31 Check the sealing ring located in the groove in the top of the catalytic converter, and renew it if necessary.
32 Refitting is a reversal of removal, but fit a new gasket and tighten the bolts and nuts to the specified torque.

17 Exhaust system - general information, removal and refitting

4A

General information
1 On new vehicles the exhaust system consists of two sections; the front downpipe and catalytic converter, and the remaining system consisting of a resonator, tailpipe and silencer.

16.27 Removing the shroud from the exhaust manifold

16.29a Unscrew the mounting bolts . . .

16.29b . . . and nuts . . .

16.29c . . . and withdraw the exhaust manifold from the cylinder head

16.30 Recover the gasket from the studs on the cylinder head

17.9 Removing the gasket fitted between the front pipe and intermediate pipe

The front section is attached to the rear section by a flanged joint with a gasket.

2 For service replacements, it is possible to obtain the catalytic converter and front downpipe each separately, however the original pipe must be cut with a hacksaw to accommodate either new item. Similarly, it is possible to obtain the rear silencer separate from the resonator and intermediate pipe. It is not possible to obtain a Ford manufactured intermediate pipe and resonator separate from the tailpipe.

3 The rear section of the exhaust is located above the rear axle, making it necessary to lower the rear axle where the complete rear section is to be renewed.

4 The system is suspended throughout its entire length by rubber mountings.

Removal

5 To remove a part of the system, first jack up the front or rear of the car, and support it on axle stands (see *"Jacking and Vehicle Support"*). Alternatively, position the car over an inspection pit, or on car ramps.

Front downpipe and catalytic converter

6 Disconnect the battery negative (earth) lead (see Chapter 5A).

7 Unbolt and remove the heatshields from the exhaust manifold.

8 Unscrew the nuts securing the downpipe to the exhaust manifold.

9 Unscrew the flange nuts and separate the front pipe from the intermediate section. Recover the gasket **(see illustration)**.

10 Where necessary, unscrew the bolts and move the heatshield away from the catalytic converter.

11 Unscrew the bolts securing the catalytic converter strap to the support bracket **(see illustration)**.

12 Undo the bolt and lower the gearchange stabiliser bar from the transmission.

13 Unscrew the bolt securing the rear engine mounting link to the transmission.

14 Carefully withdraw the front pipe and catalytic converter; it may be necessary to rock the engine slightly in order to provide enough room to remove the catalytic converter. Remove the sealing ring from the top of the catalytic converter **(see illustrations)**.

15 Unscrew the bolt and remove the strap from the catalytic converter. If necessary, unbolt the support bracket from the rear of the cylinder block **(see illustration)**.

16 If a new catalytic converter is to be fitted, cut the original pipe at a point 350 mm (Zetec-SE) or 604 mm (Endura-E) forward of the flange joint face. Ensure the cut is made at 90° to the pipe.

17 Refitting is a reversal of removal, but note the following points.
   a) *Fit a new gasket to the front pipe rear flange.*
   b) *Fit a new sealing ring between the downpipe/catalytic converter and exhaust manifold and fit new nuts.*
   c) *Tighten all nuts/bolts to the specified torque.*
   d) *Delay tightening the clamp bolt until the remaining joints have been tightened.*

Intermediate pipe, resonator and tailpipe (original system)

18 If the complete original rear section is to be renewed, the rear axle must be lowered with reference to Chapter 10 to allow room to withdraw the exhaust. If the rear silencer alone is to be renewed, refer to paragraph 23 onwards.

19 Unscrew the flange nuts and separate the front pipe from the intermediate section. Recover the gasket.

20 With the help of an assistant, disconnect the rubber mountings from the stubs and withdraw the exhaust forwards over the rear axle.

21 Check the condition of the rubber mountings and renew as necessary.

17.11 Bolt securing the catalytic converter strap to the support bracket

22 Refitting is a reversal of removal, but note the following points.
   a) *Fit a new gasket to the front pipe rear flange.*
   b) *Tighten the nuts to the specified torque.*

Tailpipe and silencer

23 If the original rear section is fitted, cut it just forward of the rear silencer at a point 1850 mm (Zetec-SE) or 1830 mm (Endura-E) rearward of the flange joint face. Ensure the cut is made at 90° to the pipe.

24 If a service tailpipe and silencer is fitted, unscrew the nuts and remove the clamp, then separate the tailpipe from the intermediate section.

25 Disconnect the rubber mountings and remove the tailpipe and silencer from under the vehicle.

26 Fit the new tailpipe and silencer using a reversal of the removal procedure. Make sure the intermediate and tailpipe sections are correctly aligned before tightening the clamp nuts.

Heat shield(s)

27 The heat shields are secured to the underside of the body by special nuts. Each shield can be removed separately but note that they overlap making it necessary to loosen another section first. If a shield is being removed to gain access to a component located behind it, it may prove sufficient in some cases to remove the retaining nuts and/or bolts, and simply lower the shield, without disturbing the exhaust system. Otherwise remove the exhaust section as described earlier.

17.14a Removing the front pipe and catalytic converter

17.14b Removing the sealing ring from the top of the catalytic converter

17.15 Catalytic converter support bracket on the rear of the cylinder block

Chapter 4 Part B:
Fuel and exhaust systems - diesel engine models

Contents

Degrees of difficulty

| **Easy,** suitable for novice with little experience | | **Fairly easy,** suitable for beginner with some experience | | **Fairly difficult,** suitable for competent DIY mechanic | | **Difficult,** suitable for experienced DIY mechanic | | **Very difficult,** suitable for expert DIY or professional | |

Specifications

General

System type	Rear mounted fuel tank, combined lift and injection pump, indirect injection
Application	1.8 litre Endura-DE engine
Firing order	1 - 3 - 4 - 2 (No. 1 at timing belt end)
Glow plug type	Champion CH147
Air filter element type	Champion U663
Fuel filter type	Champion L138

Fuel

Fuel type	Commercial diesel fuel for road vehicles (DERV)

Injection pump

Make and type	Bosch VE
Rotation (viewed from crankshaft pulley end)	Clockwise
Drive	By toothed belt from crankshaft

Injectors

Type	Pintle
Needle seat leakage/Injector dribble	Holds 125 bar (1813 lbf/in^2) for 10 seconds

Adjustment data

Idle speed:	
Models without air conditioning	920 ± 50 rpm
Models with air conditioning	950 ± 50 rpm
Injection pump timing	By timing pins, at TDC
Maximum no-load speed:	
Continuous	4800 rpm
Intermittent	5350 ± 50 rpm
Deceleration time (no load at idle)	5 seconds maximum

Torque wrench settings	Nm	lbf ft
Crankshaft pulley/vibration damper	35	26
Engine mounting bracket bolts	50	37
Engine mounting bracket nut (centre)	69	51
Engine mounting bracket nuts (outer)	120	88
Exhaust manifold	24	18
Fuel injector delivery pipe unions	20	15
Fuel injectors	75	55
Glow plugs	28	21
Injection pump drive gear	20	15
Injection pump drivebelt tensioner	50	37
Injection pump mounting bolts	20	15
Injection pump rear support bracket	20	15
Inlet manifold lower section to cylinder head	23	17
Inlet manifold upper section to lower section	23	17
TDC timing pin blanking plug	24	18

1 General information and precautions

General information

The fuel system consists of a fuel tank (mounted under the body, beneath the rear seats), fuel filter, fuel injection pump, injectors, fuel lines and hoses, fuel gauge sender unit mounted in the fuel tank, and EEC V engine management control module (Powertrain control module).

Fuel is drawn from the tank by the transfer pump incorporated in the injection pump. It then passes through the fuel filter, located in the engine bay, where foreign matter and water are removed. The injection pump is belt-driven from the crankshaft and supplies fuel under very high pressure to each injector in turn as it is needed. The engine has two drivebelts, one to drive the injection pump and the other to drive the camshaft, oil pump, auxiliary shaft and water pump. The amount of fuel delivered is determined by the pump governor, which reacts to throttle position and to engine speed. Injection timing is varied automatically to suit the prevailing speed and load.

Rigid pipes connect the pump to the four injectors. Each injector sprays fuel into a pre-combustion or "swirl" chamber as its piston approaches TDC on the compression stroke. This system is known as indirect injection. The injectors only open under very high pressure. Lubrication is provided by allowing a small quantity of fuel to leak back past the injector internal components. The leaked-back fuel is returned to the pump and then to the fuel tank.

Two systems, both automatically controlled by the powertrain control module, assist cold starting. A cold start advance solenoid on the injection pump advances the injection timing during cold starts. The amount of time the solenoid remains energised decreases as the engine temperature increases. The preheater or "glow" plugs fitted to each swirl chamber are electrically heated before, during and immediately after starting and are particularly effective during a cold start. A warning light illuminates when the ignition is switched on, showing that the glow plugs are in operation. When the light goes out, preheating is complete and the engine can be started. The glow plugs are controlled by the powertrain control module, and the amount of time they remain on is dependent on engine temperature.

Except on models with air conditioning, cold start idle speed is controlled by a waxstat system comprising a wax element and cable connected to the idle lever on the injection pump. Models with air conditioning are fitted with an idle speed control motor located beneath the battery tray with a cable connected to the idle lever on the injection pump. The idle speed motor is controlled by the powertrain control module and it is operative with the engine cold or warm.

A light load retard device is fitted, and is controlled by the powertrain control module. Under normal light load conditions, the injection timing is retarded by 3°. During full load conditions with the engine temperature below 50°C and engine speed above 3500 rpm, the device is energised thus effectively advancing the injection timing by 3°.

To stop the engine, a solenoid valve if fitted to the rear of the fuel pump. The valve is of the "fail safe" type, so it must be energised to allow the engine to run. When power is removed from the valve, its plunger moves under spring pressure and interrupts fuel delivery.

The fuel system on diesel engines is normally very reliable. Provided that clean fuel is used and the specified maintenance is conscientiously carried out, no problems should be experienced. The injection pump and injectors may require overhaul after a high mileage has been covered, but this cannot be done on a DIY basis.

Precautions

Warning: It is necessary to take certain precautions when working on the fuel system components. Before carrying out any operations on the fuel system, refer to the precautions given in "Safety first!" at the beginning of this manual, and to any additional warning notes at the start of the relevant Sections.

2 Fuel system - priming and bleeding

Note: *The valve fitted between the filter and the pump on later engines is used at the factory only to fill and bleed the system on production. Check regularly that it is tightly closed.*

1 As this system is intended to be "self-bleeding", no hand-priming pump or separate bleed screws/nipples are fitted.

2 When any part of the system has been disturbed therefore, air must be purged from the system by cranking the engine on the starter motor until it starts. When it has started, keep the engine running for approximately 5 minutes to ensure that all air has been removed from the system. To minimise the strain on the battery and starter motor when trying to start the engine, crank it in 10-second bursts, pausing for 30 seconds each time, until the engine starts.

3 Depending on the work that has been carried out, it may be possible to partially prime the system so as to spare the battery by reducing as much as possible the amount of cranking time required to start the engine. To spare the battery, fill the filter with clean fuel via its vent screw opening, but it is essential that no dirt is introduced into the system and that no diesel fuel is poured over vulnerable components when doing this.

4 If a hand-operated vacuum pump is available, this can be connected to the pump's fuel return union and used to suck fuel through the supply lines and filter. This will obviously save the battery a good deal of work. If a long length of clear plastic tubing is used to connect the vacuum pump to the injection pump union, it will be easier to see when fuel emerges free from air bubbles. Do not forget to energise the fuel shut-off solenoid by switching on the ignition, to position "II" so that fuel can pass through the pump.

5 If air has entered the injector pipes, slacken each union at the injectors and crank the engine until fuel emerges, then tighten securely all unions and mop up the spilt fuel. Start the engine and keep it running for a few minutes to ensure that all air has been expelled.

3 Fuel system - contamination

1 If, at any time, sudden fuel filter blockage, poor starting or otherwise unsatisfactory engine performance should be traced to the appearance of black sludge or slime within the fuel system, this may be due to corrosion caused by the presence of various micro-organisms in the fuel. These can live in the fuel tank if water is allowed to remain there in significant quantities, their waste products causing corrosion of steel and other metallic components of the fuel system.

2 If the fuel system is thought to be contaminated in this way, immediately seek the advice of a Ford dealer or diesel specialist. Thorough treatment is required to cure the problem and to prevent it from occurring again.

3 If you are considering treating the vehicle on a DIY basis proceed as follows. Do not re-use contaminated fuel.

4 First drain and remove the fuel tank, flush it thoroughly with clean diesel fuel and use a torch to examine as much as possible of its interior. If the contamination is severe, the tank must be steam-cleaned internally and then flushed again with clean diesel fuel.

5 Disconnect the fuel feed and return hoses from the injection pump, remove the fuel filter element and flush through the system's feed and return lines with clean diesel fuel.

6 Renew the filter element, refit the fuel tank and reconnect the fuel lines, then fill the tank with clean diesel fuel and bleed the system as described above. Watch carefully for signs of the problem occurring again.

7 While it is unlikely that such contamination will be found beyond the fuel filter, if it is thought to have reached the injection pump, the pump may require cleaning. This is a task only for the local diesel specialist. Do not attempt to disturb any part of the pump (other than the few adjustments detailed in this Manual) or to clean it yourself.

8 The most common cause of excessive quantities of water being in the fuel is condensation from the water vapour in the air. Diesel fuel tanks (whether underground storage tanks or that in the vehicle) are more susceptible to this problem than petrol tanks because of petrol's higher vapour pressure. Water formation in the vehicle's tank can be minimised by keeping the tank as full as possible at all times and by using the vehicle regularly.

9 Note that proprietary additives are available to inhibit the growth of micro-organisms in vehicle fuel tanks or storage tanks.

10 If you buy all your fuel from the same source and suspect that to be the source of the contamination, the owner or operator should be advised. Otherwise, the risk of taking on contaminated fuel can be minimised by using only reputable filling stations which have a good turnover.

4 Air cleaner assembly and air inlet components - removal and refitting

Air cleaner assembly

1 Loosen the clip and disconnect the air inlet tube from the rear of the air cleaner cover.

2 Unscrew the screws securing the cover to the air cleaner housing. Withdraw the cover and remove the filter element.

3 Release the retaining strap from the rear of the air cleaner base, then lift the base from the rubber grommets.

4 Disconnect the inlet duct and withdraw the base from the engine compartment.

5 Check the rubber grommets for deterioration and renew them if necessary.

6 Refitting is the reverse of the removal procedure. Ensure that the base pegs seat fully in their rubber grommets.

Air inlet components

7 To remove the air inlet components between the air cleaner and inlet manifold, first pull the tube from the air cleaner cover. Loosen the clip and disconnect the tube from the flexible tube, then release it from the mounting and withdraw it from the engine compartment. Loosen the clips and disconnect the resonator and connector.

8 To remove the flexible tube, loosen the clips and disconnect the tube from the inlet manifold and rigid tube.

9 To remove the primary inlet ducts first remove the air cleaner base, then unscrew the mounting bolt and lift out the ducts. Separate the resonator and silencer.

10 Refitting is a reversal of removal.

5 Accelerator cable - removal, refitting and adjustment

Removal

1 On the front of the injection pump, pull out the adjustment clip from the ferrule on the outer cable, and pull the outer cable from the support bracket (see illustration).

2 Disconnect the inner cable end fitting from the speed control (throttle) lever on the pump (see illustration).

3 Inside the vehicle, fold back the carpet and insulation in the driver's footwell to gain access to the accelerator pedal.

4 Disconnect the inner cable from the top of the pedal.

5 Release the cable from the supports in the engine compartment, and withdraw it from the bulkhead.

Refitting

6 Refitting is a reversal of removal. When the cable is reconnected at each end, adjust the cable as follows.

4B

5.1 Accelerator cable adjustment clip and ferrule

5.2 Inner accelerator cable fitting to speed control lever on the injection pump

Adjustment

7 Remove the adjustment clip from the outer cable ferrule, and lubricate the cable adjuster grommet with soapy water.

8 Remove any slack by pulling the cable as far as possible out of the adjuster. Have an assistant depress the accelerator pedal fully - the cable outer will move back into the adjuster - and hold it there while the clip is refitted.

9 Check that the speed control (throttle) lever moves smoothly and easily from the fully-closed to the fully-open position and back again as the assistant depresses and releases the accelerator pedal. Re-adjust the cable if required.

6 Accelerator pedal - removal and refitting

Removal

1 Peel back the carpet and insulation from the driver's footwell to allow access to the accelerator pedal.

2 Detach the accelerator cable from the pedal (see Section 5), then release the circlip from the pivot shaft and remove the accelerator pedal.

Refitting

3 Refit in the reverse order of removal. On completion, check the action of the pedal and the cable to ensure that the throttle has full unrestricted movement, and fully returns when released.

4 Check and if necessary adjust the accelerator cable as described in Section 5.

7 Fuel tank - removal, inspection and refitting

Note: *Refer to the warning note in Section 1 before proceeding.*

Removal

1 Run the fuel level as low as possible prior to removing the tank. Remove the fuel filler cap.

2 Disconnect the battery negative (earth) lead (see Chapter 5A).

3 Where possible, syphon or pump out the remaining fuel from the fuel tank (there is no drain plug). The fuel must be emptied into a suitable container for storage.

4 Chock the front wheels then jack up the rear of the vehicle and support it on axle stands (see *"Jacking and Vehicle Support"*). Remove the rear roadwheels.

5 Unhook the exhaust system mounting rubbers at the front, centre and rear and allow the exhaust system to rest on the rear suspension crossmember. There is no need to disconnect the exhaust from the exhaust manifold.

6 Unscrew the nuts and remove the exhaust heat shields from the underbody.

7 Loosen the clip and disconnect the filler pipe lower vent hose from the rear of the fuel tank.

8 Position a container beneath the vent valve at the rear of the fuel tank, then disconnect the hose and remove the valve from its mounting bracket.

9 Support the fuel tank using a trolley jack and block of wood.

10 Unscrew and remove the tank mounting bolts.

11 Partially lower the fuel tank and at the same time disconnect the bottom of the filler pipe from the rubber seal in the tank.

12 Disconnect the wiring from the fuel gauge sender unit on top of the tank.

13 Squeeze the locking lugs on the quick-release fitting and disconnect the fuel return pipe. Note the return pipe is identified by a red colour band.

14 Similarly squeeze the locking lugs and disconnect the fuel supply pipe from the fuel gauge sender unit. Note the supply pipe is identified by a white colour band.

15 Lower the fuel tank and withdraw it from under the vehicle.

16 Check the condition of the filler pipe seal and renew it if necessary.

Inspection

17 Whilst removed, the fuel tank can be inspected for damage or deterioration. Removal of the fuel gauge sender unit (see Section 8) will allow a partial inspection of the interior. If the tank is contaminated with sediment or water, swill it out with clean fuel. Do not under any circumstances undertake any repairs on a leaking or damaged fuel tank; this work must be carried out by a professional who has experience in this critical and potentially-dangerous work.

18 Whilst the fuel tank is removed from the vehicle, it should be placed in a safe area where sparks or open flames cannot ignite the fumes coming out of the tank. Be especially careful inside garages where a natural-gas type appliance is located, because the pilot light could cause an explosion.

19 Check the condition of the filler pipe seal in the fuel tank, and renew it if necessary.

Refitting

20 Refitting is a reversal of the removal procedure. Apply a light smear of clean engine oil to the filler pipe seal, to ease fitting. Ensure that all connections are securely fitted. When refitting the quick-release couplings, press them together until the locking lugs snap into their groove. If evidence of contamination was found, do not return any previously-drained fuel to the tank unless it is carefully filtered first.

8 Fuel gauge sender unit - removal and refitting

Note: *Refer to the warning note in Section 1 before proceeding. Ford specify the use of their tool 23-014 (a box spanner with castellated lugs) to remove the retaining ring for the sender unit. In practice it was found that a long metal bar could be used with success (see text).*

Removal

1 The fuel gauge sender unit is located in the top face of the fuel tank. The unit can only be detached and withdrawn from the tank after the tank is released and lowered from under the vehicle. Refer to Section 7 and remove the fuel tank, then proceed as follows.

2 With the fuel tank removed, disconnect the fuel supply pipe (still attached to the tank) from the inlet stub by squeezing the quick-release lugs. Note that the fuel supply pipe connector is identified by a white band.

3 Unscrew and remove the special retaining ring. Ford technicians use a special wrench to unscrew the ring, however a long metal bar may be used with success.

4 Carefully withdraw the fuel gauge sender unit from the fuel tank.

5 Remove the inlet from the bottom of the sender unit.

Refitting

6 Refitting is a reversal of removal, but tighten the retaining ring securely. Refit the fuel tank as described in Section 7.

9 Fuel tank roll-over valve - removal and refitting

Note: *Refer to the warning note in Section 1 before proceeding.*

Removal

1 The roll-over valve is located in a rubber grommet in the top of the fuel tank, in the hose leading rearwards to the vent valve. Its purpose is to prevent fuel loss if the vehicle becomes inverted in a crash.

2 Remove the fuel tank as described in Section 7.

3 Release the vent hose from the clip on the top of the tank.

4 Carefully prise the roll-over valve from the rubber grommet and remove it together with the hose.

5 Check the condition of the rubber grommet and renew it if necessary.

Refitting

6 Refitting is a reversal of removal, but apply a light smear of clean engine oil to the rubber grommet, to ease fitting.

11.5 Idle speed adjustment screw and locknut

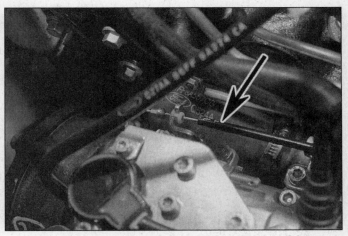

12.1 The cold start cable is located on the rear of the injection pump

10 Fuel tank filler pipe - removal and refitting

Note: *Refer to the warning note in Section 1 before proceeding.*

Removal

1 Remove the fuel tank (see Section 7).
2 With the vehicle still raised, unscrew and remove the filler pipe lower mounting bolt.
3 Open the filler flap, then lift the plastic cover and unscrew the filler pipe upper mounting bolt.
4 Withdraw the filler pipe from under the vehicle.
5 If necessary, loosen the clips and disconnect the lower vent hose from the filler pipe.
6 Check the condition of the filler pipe seal and renew it if necessary.

Refitting

7 Refitting is a reversal of removal, but apply a light smear of clean engine oil to the seal, to ease fitting.

11 Idle speed - checking and adjustment

1 The usual type of tachometer (rev counter), which works from ignition system pulses, cannot be used on diesel engines. If it is not felt that adjusting the idle speed "by ear" is satisfactory, one of the following alternatives must be used:
   a) *Purchase or hire of an appropriate tachometer*
   b) *Delegation of the job to a Ford dealer or other specialist*
   c) *Timing light (strobe) operated by a petrol engine running at the desired speed. If the timing light is pointed at a chalk mark on the diesel engine crankshaft pulley, the mark will appear stationary when the two*

engines are running at the same speed (or multiples of that speed)
   d) *Calculating the mph/rpm relationship for a particular gear and running the engine, in that gear, with the front wheels free. The speedometer accuracy may not be adequate, especially at low speeds. Stringent safety precautions must be observed*

2 The adjustment must be carried out with the engine at normal operating temperature. If necessary, take the vehicle on a short run.
3 On models with air conditioning, mark the position of the idle speed control cable in relation to the clip located on the injection pump, then release it from the clip.
4 Start the engine and allow it to idle, then check that the idle speed is as given in the Specifications. If adjustment is necessary, proceed as follows.
5 Loosen the idle speed adjustment screw locknut then turn the screw as necessary until the engine is idling at the specified speed. Tighten the locknut on completion **(see illustration)**.
6 Increase the engine speed by temporarily moving the idle lever on the injection pump. With the lever released, check that the engine returns to the specified idling speed.
7 On models with air conditioning, refit the idle speed control cable and adjust it as described in Section 13.
8 Disconnect the tachometer (if applicable).

12 Cold start cable - adjustment, removal and refitting

Adjustment

1 The cold start cable is fitted to models without air conditioning only. It is located on the cylinder head side of the injection pump **(see illustration)**. The adjustment must be carried out with the engine cold.
2 Release the clip securing the cold start

cable to the support bracket.
3 Hold the idle lever fully against its stop, then position the outer cable so that there is between 1.0 and 2.0 mm play in the inner cable. With the cable held in this position, refit the clip to the support bracket.

Removal

4 Drain the cooling system (see Chapter 1B).
5 Release the clip securing the cold start cable to the support bracket.
6 Disconnect the inner cable from the idle lever on the injection pump.
7 Unscrew the cold start cable wax element from the thermostat housing and withdraw the cable from the engine compartment. Be prepared for some loss of coolant - place cloth rags beneath the thermostat housing.

Refitting

8 Refitting is a reversal of removal, but adjust the cable as described in paragraphs 1 to 3. Refill the cooling system as described in Chapter 1B.

13 Idle speed control system - adjustment, removal and refitting

Note: *This work requires the use of a tachometer and the FDS 2000 Ford Diagnostic Tester - this Section is included for the benefit of those who have access to these instruments. If necessary, have the work carried out by a Ford dealer.*

Adjustment

1 The idle speed control system is fitted to models with air conditioning only. The system consists of a control motor located beneath the battery tray with a cable connected to the idle lever on the injection pump.
2 Connect the Tester to the diagnostic socket in accordance with the manufacturers instructions. The adjustment is carried out with the ignition switched off.

4B

3 Release the idle speed control cable from the clip on the injection pump.

4 Using the Tester, extend the idle speed control motor plunger.

5 Move the outer cable away from the idle lever until the lever is touching the high idle adjustment screw, then secure the outer cable in this position by refitting the clip. **Note:** *Push the outer cable rather than pull it, as a precaution against stretching it.*

6 Disconnect the Tester then connect a tachometer to the engine.

7 Start the engine and allow it to idle.

8 Move the main speed control (throttle) lever to increase the engine speed above 1400 rpm. Check that the idle speed control cable moves the idle lever against the high idle adjustment screw, then backs it off slightly. If this is not the case, carry out the idle speed control cable adjustment again.

9 Switch off the engine and disconnect the tachometer.

Removal

10 Release the idle speed control cable from the clip on the injection pump.

11 Disconnect the inner cable from the idle lever.

12 Remove the battery and tray as described in Chapter 5A.

13 Disconnect the inner cable from the control motor, and the outer cable from the support.

Refitting

14 Refitting is a reversal of removal, but adjust the cable as described in paragraphs 1 to 9.

14 Maximum speed - checking and adjustment

Caution: The maximum speed adjustment screw is sealed by the manufacturers at the factory, using paint or a locking wire and a lead seal. There is no reason why it should require adjustment. Do not disturb the screw if the vehicle is still within the warranty period, otherwise the warranty will be invalidated.

1 The maximum no load speed may be checked if wished, using one of the methods described in Section 11. Running the engine with the wheels free is not recommended, because of the risk of damage or injury if anything goes wrong.

2 The maximum speed adjusting screw is sealed in production. Adjustment should only be made by a Ford dealer or authorised fuel injection specialist. Unauthorised adjustment may invalidate the warranty.

3 When checking the maximum speed, do not hold the engine at this speed for more than five seconds. Keep well clear of the water pump/alternator drivebelt and pulleys.

4 The engine speed should drop from maximum to idle within the specified time when the throttle is released. If not, check that the throttle linkage is not binding or obstructed. If this is in order, seek specialist advice.

15 Fuel injection pump timing - checking and adjustment

Injection pump timing is carried using the TDC setting method described in Chapter 2C. At the time of writing, no information was available in connection with the internal setting of the injection pump plunger using a dial test indicator. Where necessary, the injection pump should be checked and adjusted by a Ford dealer or diesel engine specialist.

16 Fuel injection pump - removal and refitting

Caution: Be careful not to allow dirt into the injection pump or injector pipes during this procedure. New sealing rings should be used on the fuel pipe banjo unions when refitting.

Removal

1 Disconnect the battery negative (earth) lead (see Chapter 5A).

2 Apply the handbrake, then jack up the front of the vehicle and support it on axle stands (see *"Jacking and Vehicle Support"*). Remove the right-hand front roadwheel.

3 Using a hoist, support the weight of the engine. Alternatively, use a purpose-made support bar across the engine compartment, located in the front wing drain channels.

4 Unscrew and remove the bolts from the right-hand engine mounting bracket and lift off the upper bracket **(see illustration)**. Unscrew the nuts and remove the lower mounting bracket. Make sure the engine is supported adequately.

5 Remove the alternator as described in Chapter 5A.

16.4 Right-hand engine mounting upper bracket (1) and lower bracket (2)

6 Unscrew and remove the bolts securing the crankshaft pulley/vibration damper to the drive gear flange. To do this, have an assistant temporarily engage 4th gear and depress the footbrake pedal in order to hold the crankshaft stationary. Remove the pulley.

7 Unscrew and remove the three lower bolts from the lower timing cover.

8 On models with air conditioning, loosen the power-assisted steering pump drive pulley bolts. Using an Allen key, loosen the PAS pump drivebelt tensioner central screw, then back off the tensioner adjustment bolt until the drivebelt can be removed. Fully remove the bolts and remove the pulley from the PAS pump.

9 Unscrew the remaining bolts and release the clip, then remove the upper, intermediate and lower timing covers from the engine.

10 Using a socket on the crankshaft pulley bolt, turn the engine clockwise until the slot in the injection pump drive gear is at the 11 o'clock position. To make this task easier, remove the glow plugs as described in Chapter 5C.

11 Working under the vehicle, unbolt and remove the alternator bracket.

12 Unscrew the timing pin blank plug from the cylinder block, then screw in the timing pin (refer to Chapter 2C).

13 Slowly turn the crankshaft in its normal direction of rotation, until the crankshaft web just contacts the TDC pin.

Caution: Take care when turning the crankshaft to avoid bending the TDC pin.

14 On engines with a standard timing belt tensioner, insert the camshaft timing pin (refer to Chapter 2C).

15 Insert the injection pump timing pin (refer to Chapter 2C).

16 Remove the timing belt as described in Chapter 2C. Ford recommend that the belt is renewed every time it is removed.

17 Pull out the adjustment clip securing the accelerator cable ferrule to the support on the injection pump, then release the outer cable and disconnect the inner cable from the speed control (throttle) lever.

18 On models without air conditioning release the clip securing the cold start cable to the support bracket, then disconnect the inner cable from the idle lever on the injection pump.

19 On models with air conditioning release the idle speed control cable from the clip on the injection pump, then disconnect the inner cable from the idle lever.

20 Release the wiring loom from the clip, then disconnect the multi-plug.

21 Note the location of the fuel leak-off pipe then disconnect it at the fuel return union.

22 Identify the fuel inlet and return pipes then disconnect the quick-release fittings by squeezing the lugs together. Be prepared for some loss of fuel by placing cloth rags beneath the pipes.

23 Disconnect the fuel injector leak-off pipes from the injectors.

24 Release the fuel supply pipe from the support clips, then unscrew the union nuts at the injector pump and injectors and remove the delivery pipes as an assembly.

25 Loosen the injection pump drivebelt tensioner bolt then lever the tensioner away from the drivebelt and secure it by re-tightening the bolt. Take care not to damage the drivebelt.

26 With the timing pin inserted, loosen the injection pump drive gear bolts. Take care not to bend the timing pin.

27 Slip the drivebelt from the gear teeth. Ford recommend that the drivebelt is renewed after removal.

28 Remove the timing pin, then unscrew the bolts and remove the drive gear from the injection pump.

29 Unscrew the bolts from the injection pump rear support bracket.

30 Support the weight of the injection pump. Unscrew and remove the front mounting bolts from within the timing gear housing and withdraw the injection pump from the engine.

31 Unbolt the rear support bracket from the injection pump.

Refitting

32 Before fitting a new pump, remove the blanking plugs and prime it with clean fuel, poured in through the return port.

33 Commence refitting by fitting the rear support bracket to the injection pump. Do not fully tighten the bolts at this stage.

34 Locate the injection pump on the timing gear housing, insert the bolts and tighten them progressively to the specified torque.

35 Insert the rear bracket-to-cylinder block bolts and tighten to the specified torque.

36 Fully tighten the rear support bracket-to-injection pump bolts.

37 Refit the drive gear and hand-tighten the retaining bolts at this stage. Refit the timing pin.

38 With the timing pins in position, locate a new drivebelt on the crankshaft and injection pump gears.

39 Loosen the tensioner bolt and allow the spring to tension the drivebelt. Tighten the bolt to the specified torque.

40 Tighten the drive gear retaining bolts to the specified torque, making sure that the elongated holes are centralised as the bolts are tightened.

41 Fit a new timing belt with reference to Chapter 2C.

42 Refit the delivery pipes and tighten the union nuts to the specified torque. Locate the fuel supply pipe in the support clips.

43 Reconnect the fuel injector leak-off pipes to the injectors.

44 Reconnect the fuel inlet and return pipes making sure that the quick-release fittings are correctly engaged.

45 Reconnect the fuel leak-off pipe at the fuel return union.

46 Reconnect the multi-plug and refit the wiring loom to the clip.

47 On models with air conditioning refit the idle speed control cable. If necessary, adjust it with reference to Section 13.

48 On models without air conditioning refit the cold start cable. If necessary, adjust it with reference to Section 12.

49 Refit the accelerator cable and adjust it with reference to Section 5.

50 Refit the alternator bracket and tighten the retaining bolts.

51 Refit the lower, intermediate and upper timing covers and tighten the bolts.

52 On models with air conditioning refit the power-assisted steering pump pulley and hand-tighten the bolts, then locate the drivebelt on the pulleys and tension it with reference to Chapter 1B. Tighten the pulley bolts to the specified torque (see Chapter 10), then check and if necessary re-tension the drivebelt.

53 Refit the crankshaft pulley/vibration damper to the drive gear flange and tighten the bolts to the specified torque while holding the crankshaft stationary as described for removal.

54 Refit the alternator as described in Chapter 5A.

55 Refit the right-hand engine mounting lower bracket and tighten the nuts to the specified torque. Refit the upper bracket and tighten the bolts to the specified torque.

56 Disconnect the hoist or support bar from the engine.

57 Refit the right-hand front roadwheel and lower the vehicle to the ground.

58 Reconnect the battery negative (earth) lead (see Chapter 5A).

59 Prime and bleed the fuel system as described in Section 2.

60 Start the engine, and bring it to operating temperature. Check and if necessary adjust the idle speed as described in Section 11.

17 Injection pipes - removal and refitting

Caution: Be careful not to allow dirt into the injection system during this procedure.

Removal

1 The injection pipes should be removed as a set. Individual pipes may then be renewed if necessary after releasing the anti-rattle clips.

2 Disconnect the battery negative (earth) lead (see Chapter 5A). Clean around the pipe unions at the injectors and at the pump.

3 Protect the alternator against fuel spillage, then disconnect the fuel leak-off pipes from the injectors.

4 Release the fuel supply pipe from the clips on numbers 2 and 4 injectors.

5 Counterhold the pump adapters and unscrew the pipe union nuts.

6 Similarly unscrew the injector union nuts, counterholding the injector bodies as the nuts are slackened.

7 Remove the pipe assembly. Plug or cap open unions to keep fuel in and dirt out.

Refitting

8 When refitting, make sure that all the anti-rattle clips are in place. Do not bend or strain the pipes. Blow through the pipes with compressed air (from an air line or a foot pump) to expel any debris.

9 Refit the pipe assembly to both the injectors and injection pump, initially hand-tightening the union nuts. With the assembly in place, fully tighten the nuts to the specified torque.

10 Refit the fuel supply pipe to the clips and reconnect the fuel leak-off pipes to the injectors.

11 Reconnect the battery negative (earth) lead (see Chapter 5A).

12 Prime and bleed the fuel system as described in Section 2.

13 Run the engine and check the disturbed unions for leaks.

18 Fuel injectors - removal, testing and refitting

⚠ Warning: Exercise extreme caution when working on the fuel injectors. Never expose the hands or any part of the body to injector spray, as the high working pressure can cause the fuel to penetrate the skin, with possibly fatal results. You are strongly advised to have any work which involves testing the injectors under pressure carried out by a dealer or fuel injection specialist.

Caution: Be careful not to allow dirt into the injection system during this procedure.

Removal

1 Disconnect the battery negative (earth) lead (see Chapter 5A). Clean around the injectors and the injection pipe unions.

2 Disconnect the fuel return hoses from the injectors **(see illustration)**.

3 Remove the injection pipes as described in Section 17.

18.2 Disconnecting a fuel return hose from an injector

4B

18.4a Removing an injector using a deep socket

18.4b Removing an injector . . .

4 Unscrew and remove the injectors. A 27 mm box spanner or deep socket will be required (see illustrations).

5 Retrieve the heat protection washers from the injector bores. Obtain new washers for reassembly (see illustration).

6 Take care not to drop the injectors, nor allow the needles at their tips to become damaged.

Testing

7 Testing of injectors is quite simple, but requires a special high pressure pump and gauge. Should such equipment be available, use it in accordance with its maker's instructions, referring to the Specifications for the desired values. Do not expose the skin to spray from the injectors - the pressure is high enough to penetrate the skin.

8 Defective injectors should be renewed or professionally repaired. DIY repair is not a practical proposition.

Refitting

9 Commence refitting by inserting new heat protection washers, domed faces downwards, to the injector bores.

10 Insert the injectors and screw them in by hand, then tighten them to the specified torque. No outer sealing washer is used and the injectors are a taper fit in the head.

11 Refit the injection pipes with reference to Section 17.

19 Fuel shut-off solenoid - removal and refitting

Caution: Be careful not to allow dirt into the injection system during this procedure.

1 If the fuel shut-off solenoid is disconnected, the engine will not run. The same applies if the solenoid is defective. If the plunger jams in the raised position, the engine will not stop. A defective solenoid should be removed for inspection or renewal as follows:

2 Disconnect the battery negative (earth) lead (see Chapter 5A).

3 Disconnect the electrical lead from the solenoid (see illustration).

4 Wipe clean the area around the solenoid, then unscrew it from the fuel injection pump using a deep socket or box spanner.

Caution: If the solenoid has recently been energised, it may be hot.

5 A defective solenoid must be renewed.

6 Refit the solenoid and tighten moderately.

7 Reconnect the solenoid lead and the battery earth lead. Run the engine to check for correct operation.

20 Fuel heater - removal and refitting

Removal

1 Obtain a container in which to catch any fuel spillage.

2 Disconnect the battery negative (earth) lead (see Chapter 5A).

3 Disconnect the multiplug from the base of the fuel heater located on the left-hand end of the cylinder head (see illustration).

4 Disconnect the fuel inlet pipe from the inlet pipe by squeezing the lugs on the quick release fitting.

5 Release the fuel outlet pipe from the clip, then disconnect it from the filter by squeezing the lugs on the quick release fitting.

6 Remove the single retaining screw and detach the heater and bracket assembly from the engine.

7 Release the two clips and separate the heater from the bracket.

Refitting

8 Refitting is the reverse of the removal procedure. On completion, prime and bleed the fuel system as described in Section 2.

18.5 . . . followed by the heat protection washer

19.3 Fuel shut-off solenoid electrical connector

20.3 The fuel heater is located on the left-hand end of the cylinder head

21 Manifolds - removal and refitting

Inlet

Removal

1 Loosen the clip and disconnect the air inlet duct from the inlet manifold.

2 Undo the retaining bolts, lift the plastic upper section clear of the inlet manifold and collect the four O-ring seals from the grooves in the mating face **(see illustration)**. If required, the connector can be detached from the upper section by unscrewing the four retaining bolts.

3 Detach the crankcase breather hose and unbolt the EGR valve from the manifold end face. Recover the gasket.

4 Unscrew the retaining bolts and nuts, and withdraw the manifold lower section from the cylinder head. Collect the gasket.

Refitting

5 Refitting is a reversal of the removal procedure. Ensure that the mating faces are clean. Ensure that a new gasket is fitted between the manifold and the cylinder head and tighten the retaining bolts/nuts to the specified torque, working from the centre outwards to avoid warping the manifold. Locate new ring seals into the grooves in the plastic upper section prior to fitting it into position and tightening the bolts. Fit a new gasket to the EGR valve before tightening the bolts.

Exhaust

Removal

6 Apply the handbrake, then jack up the front of the vehicle and support it on axle stands (see *"Jacking and Vehicle Support"*).

7 Unbolt and remove the shroud components from the exhaust manifold and catalytic converter.

8 Unscrew the bolts/nuts securing the exhaust downpipe/catalytic converter to the exhaust manifold.

9 Unbolt the EGR valve tube and recover the gasket.

10 Unscrew the mounting bolts and nuts and withdraw the exhaust manifold from the cylinder head.

11 Remove the gasket from the studs on the cylinder head.

12 Check the sealing ring located in the groove in the top of the catalytic converter, and renew it if necessary.

Refitting

13 Refitting is a reversal of removal, but fit new gaskets and tighten the bolts and nuts to the specified torque.

21.2 Inlet manifold and mounting bolts

22 Exhaust system - general information and component renewal

General information

1 On new vehicles the exhaust system consists of two sections; the front downpipe and catalytic converter, and the remaining system consisting of a resonator, tailpipe and silencer. The front section is attached to the rear section by a flanged joint with a gasket.

2 For service replacements, it is possible to obtain the catalytic converter and front downpipe each separately, however the original pipe must be cut with a hacksaw to accommodate either new item. Similarly, it is possible to obtain the rear silencer separate from the resonator and intermediate pipe. It is not possible to obtain a Ford manufactured intermediate pipe and resonator separate from the tailpipe.

3 The rear section of the exhaust is located above the rear axle, making it necessary to lower the rear axle where the complete rear section is to be renewed.

4 The system is suspended throughout its entire length by rubber mountings.

Removal

5 To remove a part of the system, first jack up the front or rear of the car, and support it on axle stands (see *"Jacking and Vehicle Support"*). Alternatively, position the car over an inspection pit, or on car ramps.

Front downpipe and catalytic converter

6 Disconnect the battery negative (earth) lead (see Chapter 5A).

7 Unbolt and remove the heatshields from the exhaust manifold.

8 Unscrew the nuts securing the downpipe to the exhaust manifold.

9 Unscrew the flange nuts and separate the front pipe from the intermediate section. Recover the gasket.

10 Where necessary, unscrew the bolts and move the heatshield away from the catalytic converter.

11 Unscrew the bolts securing the catalytic converter strap to the support bracket.

12 Undo the bolt and lower the gearchange stabiliser bar from the transmission.

13 Unscrew the bolt securing the rear engine mounting link to the transmission.

14 Carefully withdraw the front pipe and catalytic converter; it may be necessary to rock the engine slightly in order to provide enough room to remove the catalytic converter. Remove the sealing ring from the top of the catalytic converter.

15 Unscrew the bolt and remove the strap from the catalytic converter. If necessary, unbolt the support bracket from the rear of the cylinder block.

16 If a new catalytic converter is to be fitted, cut the original pipe at a point 350 mm forward of the flange joint face. Ensure the cut is made at 90° to the pipe.

17 Refitting is a reversal of removal, but note the following points.
 a) *Fit a new gasket to the front pipe rear flange.*
 b) *Fit a new sealing ring between the downpipe/catalytic converter and exhaust manifold and fit new nuts.*
 c) *Delay tightening the clamp bolt until the remaining joints have been tightened.*

Intermediate pipe, resonator and tailpipe (original system)

18 If the complete original rear section is to be renewed, the rear axle must be lowered with reference to Chapter 10 to allow room to withdraw the exhaust. If the rear silencer alone is to be renewed, refer to paragraph 23 onwards.

19 Unscrew the flange nuts and separate the front pipe from the intermediate section. Recover the gasket.

20 With the help of an assistant, disconnect the rubber mountings from the stubs and withdraw the exhaust forwards over the rear axle.

21 Check the condition of the rubber mountings and renew as necessary.

22 Refitting is a reversal of removal, using a new gasket on the front pipe rear flange.

Tailpipe and silencer

23 If the original rear section is fitted, cut it just forward of the rear silencer at a point 1850 mm rearward of the flange joint face. Ensure the cut is made at 90° to the pipe.

24 If the service tailpipe and silencer is fitted, unscrew the nuts and remove the clamp, then separate the tailpipe from the intermediate section.

25 Disconnect the rubber mountings and remove the tailpipe and silencer from under the vehicle.

26 Fit the new tailpipe and silencer using a reversal of the removal procedure. Make sure the intermediate and tailpipe sections are correctly aligned before tightening the clamp nuts.

4B

Heat shield(s)

27 The heat shields are secured to the underside of the body by special nuts. Each shield can be removed separately but note that they overlap making it necessary to loosen another section first. If a shield is being removed to gain access to a component located behind it, it may prove sufficient in some cases to remove the retaining nuts and/or bolts, and simply lower the shield, without disturbing the exhaust system. Otherwise remove the exhaust section as described earlier.

Chapter 4 Part C:
Emission control systems

Contents

Degrees of difficulty

Easy, suitable for novice with little experience		**Fairly easy,** suitable for beginner with some experience		**Fairly difficult,** suitable for competent DIY mechanic		**Difficult,** suitable for experienced DIY mechanic		**Very difficult,** suitable for expert DIY or professional	

Specifications

Torque wrench settings	Nm	lbf ft
Oxygen (Lambda) sensor (petrol engines)	42	31
Exhaust gas recirculation valve:		
Petrol engines	31	23
Diesel engines	20	15
EGR valve pipe to exhaust manifold (EGR valve union)	55	41
EGR valve pipe to exhaust manifold (exhaust manifold union)	73	54
EGR valve pipe to inlet manifold (support bracket union)	55	41
EGR valve pipe to inlet manifold (inlet manifold retaining bolts)	20	15
EGR valve support bracket	10	7

4C

1 General information and precautions

1 All petrol engines have the ability to use unleaded petrol and also have various other features built into the fuel system to help minimise harmful emissions. In addition, all models are equipped with the crankcase emission-control system described below. All models are also equipped with a closed-loop catalytic converter and an evaporative emission control system. In certain territories, some petrol models may be equipped with an exhaust gas recirculation system.

2 All diesel engine models are also designed to meet strict emission requirements and are also equipped with a crankcase emission control system. In addition to this, all models are fitted with a two-way catalytic converter to reduce harmful exhaust emissions. To further reduce

emissions, an exhaust gas recirculation (EGR) system is fitted.

3 The emission control systems function as follows.

Petrol models

Crankcase emission control

4 To reduce the emission of unburned hydrocarbons from the crankcase into the atmosphere, the engine is sealed and the blow-by gases and oil vapour are drawn from inside the crankcase, through an oil separator and regulating (PCV - positive crankcase ventilation) valve, into the inlet manifold to be burned by the engine during normal combustion **(see illustration)**.

5 Under conditions of high manifold depression (idling, deceleration) the gases will be sucked positively out of the crankcase. Under conditions of low manifold depression (acceleration, full-throttle running) the gases are forced out of the crankcase by the

(relatively) higher crankcase pressure; if the engine is worn, the raised crankcase pressure (due to increased blow-by) will cause some of the flow to return under all manifold conditions.

1.4 The positive crankcase ventilation (PCV) valve is located on the oil separator housing fitted to the front of the cylinder block (Zetec-SE petrol engine)

Exhaust emission control

6 To minimise the amount of pollutants which escape into the atmosphere, all models are fitted with a catalytic converter in the exhaust system. The system is of the closed-loop type, in which an oxygen (Lambda) sensor in the exhaust manifold provides the fuel-injection/ignition system Powertrain Control Module (PCM) with constant feedback, enabling the PCM to adjust the mixture to provide the best possible conditions for the converter to operate.

7 The oxygen sensor has a heating element built-in that is controlled by the PCM through a relay to quickly bring the sensor's tip to an efficient operating temperature. The sensor's tip is sensitive to oxygen and sends the PCM a varying voltage depending on the amount of oxygen in the exhaust gases; if the intake air/fuel mixture is too rich, the exhaust gases are low in oxygen so the sensor sends a low-voltage signal, the voltage rising as the mixture weakens and the amount of oxygen rises in the exhaust gases. Peak conversion efficiency of all major pollutants occurs if the intake air/fuel mixture is maintained at the chemically-correct ratio for the complete combustion of petrol of 14.7 parts (by weight) of air to 1 part of fuel (the 'stoichiometric' ratio). The sensor output voltage alters in a large step at this point, the PCM using the signal change as a reference point and correcting the intake air/fuel mixture accordingly by altering the fuel injector pulse width.

Evaporative emission control

8 To minimise the escape into the atmosphere of unburned hydrocarbons, an evaporative emissions control system is also fitted to all models. The fuel tank filler cap is sealed and a charcoal canister is mounted behind the fuel tank on the underbody. The canister collects the petrol vapours generated in the tank when the car is parked and stores them until they can be cleared from the canister (under the control of the fuel-injection/ignition system PCM) via the purge valve into the inlet tract to be burned by the engine during normal combustion. The purge valve is located on the bulkhead in the engine compartment.

9 To ensure that the engine runs correctly when it is cold and/or idling and to protect the catalytic converter from the effects of an over-rich mixture, the purge control valve is not opened by the PCM until the engine has warmed up, and the engine is under load; the valve solenoid is then modulated on and off to allow the stored vapour to pass into the inlet tract.

Diesel models

Crankcase emission control

10 To reduce the emission of unburned hydrocarbons from the crankcase into the atmosphere, the engine is sealed and the blow-by gases and oil vapour are drawn from inside the crankcase, through a hose located

2.1 Always fit a new gasket if the oil separator housing is removed (Zetec-SE petrol engine)

on the rear of the engine, into the inlet manifold to be burned by the engine during normal combustion. A further hose from the cylinder head cover to the crankcase ensures the blow-by gases are circulated freely. Since the inlet manifold depression does not vary on a diesel engine, there is no regulating valve as fitted to petrol engines.

Exhaust emission control

11 To minimise the level of exhaust pollutants released into the atmosphere, a catalytic converter is fitted in the exhaust system of some models.

12 The catalytic converter consists of a canister containing a fine mesh impregnated with a catalyst material, over which the hot exhaust gases pass. The catalyst speeds up the oxidation of harmful carbon monoxide, unburnt hydrocarbons and soot, effectively reducing the quantity of harmful products released into the atmosphere via the exhaust gases.

Exhaust gas recirculation system

13 This system is designed to recirculate small quantities of exhaust gas into the inlet manifold, and therefore into the combustion process. This process reduces the level of oxides of nitrogen present in the final exhaust gas which is released into the atmosphere.

14 The volume of exhaust gas recirculated is controlled by a regulator supplied with vacuum from the brake servo vacuum pump. The regulator is controlled by the Powertrain Control Module.

2.7 Evaporative emission control system purge valve location on the bulkhead in the engine compartment (Zetec-SE petrol engine)

Catalytic converter - precautions

15 For long life and satisfactory operation of the catalytic converter, certain precautions must be observed. These are as follows.

16 For petrol engines, only use unleaded fuel. Leaded fuel will damage the catalyst and the oxygen sensor.

17 Do not run the engine for long periods if it is misfiring. Unburnt fuel entering the catalytic converter can cause it to overheat, resulting in permanent damage. For the same reason, do not try to start the engine by pushing or towing the car, nor crank it on the starter motor for long periods.

18 Do not strike or drop the catalytic converter. The ceramic honeycomb which forms part of its internal structure may be damaged.

19 Always renew seals and gaskets upstream of the catalytic converter whenever they are disturbed.

2 Petrol engine emission control systems - testing and component renewal

Crankcase emission control

1 The components of this system require no attention other than to check that the hose and PCV valve are clear and undamaged at regular intervals. If the hoses are blocked the oil separator housing should be removed from the front of the cylinder block and cleaned; when refitting the housing, fit a new gasket **(see illustration)**.

Evaporative emission control system

Testing

2 If the system is thought to be faulty, disconnect the hoses from the charcoal canister and purge control valve and check that they are clear by blowing through them. If the purge control valve or charcoal canister are thought to be faulty, they must be renewed.

Charcoal canister - renewal

3 The charcoal canister is located under the rear of the vehicle, behind the fuel tank. First chock the front wheels then jack up the rear of the vehicle and support it on axle stands (see "Jacking and Vehicle Support").

4 Unscrew the mounting bolts and lower the canister cover from the underbody.

5 Disconnect the hoses and remove the canister from under the vehicle.

6 Fit the new canister using a reversal of the removal procedure.

Purge valve - renewal

7 The purge valve is mounted on the left-hand end of the engine compartment bulkhead **(see illustration)**.

8 To renew the purge valve, first disconnect the wiring plug.

9 Disconnect the hoses from the valve noting their locations, then detach the valve from its mounting bracket.

10 Fit the new purge valve using a reversal of the removal procedure.

Exhaust emission control

Testing

11 The performance of the catalytic converter can be checked only by measuring the exhaust gases using a good-quality, carefully-calibrated exhaust gas analyser.

12 If the CO level at the tailpipe is too high, the vehicle should be taken to a Ford dealer so that the complete fuel-injection and ignition systems, including the oxygen sensor, can be thoroughly checked using the special diagnostic equipment. Once these have been checked and are known to be free from faults, the fault must be in the catalytic converter, which must be renewed.

Catalytic converter - renewal

13 Refer to Chapter 4A.

Oxygen (Lambda) sensor - renewal

Note: *The oxygen sensor is delicate and will not work if it is dropped or knocked, if its power supply is disrupted, or if any cleaning materials are used on it.*

14 Trace the wiring back from the oxygen sensor to the connector and disconnect the wiring.

15 Unscrew the sensor and remove it from the exhaust manifold.

16 Clean the threads of the sensor and the threads in the exhaust manifold. If necessary for improved access to the manifold, remove the heat shields.

17 Insert the sensor in the manifold and tighten to the specified torque.

18 Refit the heat shields where removed.

19 Reconnect the wiring making sure that it is in no danger of contacting the exhaust manifold.

3 Diesel engine emission control systems - testing and component renewal

Crankcase emission control

1 The components of this system require no attention other than to check that the hoses are clear and undamaged at regular intervals.

Exhaust emission control

Testing

2 The performance of the catalytic converter can be checked only by measuring the exhaust gases using a good-quality, carefully-calibrated exhaust gas analyser.

3 Before assuming that the catalytic converter is faulty, it is worth checking the problem is not due to a faulty injector. Refer to your Ford dealer for further information.

Catalytic converter - renewal

4 Refer to Chapter 4B.

Exhaust gas recirculation (EGR) system

Testing

5 Testing of the system should be entrusted to a Ford dealer.

Recirculation valve - renewal

6 Loosen the clips and disconnect the air inlet duct from the inlet manifold and air cleaner.

7 Depress the clip and disconnect the wiring from the exhaust gas recirculation valve at the left-hand end of the cylinder head **(see illustration)**.

8 Disconnect the vacuum pipe.

9 Unscrew the mounting bolts and remove the valve from the inlet manifold and transfer tube flange. Recover the gaskets.

10 Tape over or cover with cloth rag the openings in the inlet manifold and EGR transfer tube.

11 Clean the mating faces of the valve and inlet manifold.

12 Using new gaskets fit the new valve to the inlet manifold and transfer tube. Tighten the bolts to the specified torque.

13 Reconnect the vacuum pipe and wiring, then refit the air inlet duct.

4 Catalytic converter - general information and precautions

The catalytic converter is a reliable and simple device which needs no maintenance in itself, but there are some facts of which an owner should be aware if the converter is to function properly for its full service life.

Petrol models

a) *DO NOT use leaded petrol in a car equipped with a catalytic converter - the lead will coat the precious metals,*

3.7 Exhaust gas recirculation valve (Endura-DE diesel engine)

reducing their converting efficiency and will eventually destroy the converter.

b) *Always keep the ignition and fuel systems well-maintained in accordance with the manufacturer's schedule.*

c) *If the engine develops a misfire, do not drive the car at all (or at least as little as possible) until the fault is cured.*

d) *DO NOT push- or tow-start the car - this will soak the catalytic converter in unburned fuel, causing it to overheat when the engine does start.*

e) *DO NOT switch off the ignition at high engine speeds.*

f) *DO NOT use fuel or engine oil additives - these may contain substances harmful to the catalytic converter.*

g) *DO NOT continue to use the car if the engine burns oil to the extent of leaving a visible trail of blue smoke.*

h) *Remember that the catalytic converter operates at very high temperatures. DO NOT, therefore, park the car in dry undergrowth, over long grass or piles of dead leaves after a long run.*

i) *Remember that the catalytic converter is FRAGILE - do not strike it with tools during servicing work.*

j) *In some cases a sulphurous smell (like that of rotten eggs) may be noticed from the exhaust. This is common to many catalytic converter-equipped cars and once the car has covered a few thousand miles the problem should disappear.*

k) *The catalytic converter, used on a well-maintained and well-driven car, should last for between 50 000 and 100 000 miles - if the converter is no longer effective it must be renewed.*

Diesel models

Refer to the information given in parts f, g, h and i of the petrol models information given above.

4C

Chapter 5 Part A:
Starting and charging systems

Contents

Degrees of difficulty

| **Easy,** suitable for novice with little experience | | **Fairly easy,** suitable for beginner with some experience | | **Fairly difficult,** suitable for competent DIY mechanic | | **Difficult,** suitable for experienced DIY mechanic | | **Very difficult,** suitable for expert DIY or professional | |

Specifications

System type .... 12-volt, negative earth

Battery
Type .... Lead-acid, low-maintenance or "maintenance free"
Charge condition:
  Poor .... 12.5 volts
  Normal .... 12.6 volts
  Good .... 12.7 volts

Alternator
Type .... Bosch, Magnetti Marelli or Mitsubishi
Output .... 70 amps
Regulated voltage .... 13.5 to 14.8 volts

Starter motor
Type .... Bosch or Magnetti Marelli

Torque wrench settings	Nm	lbf ft
Alternator mounting bolts:		
Upper and lower	50	37
Rear support	25	19
Starter motor mounting bolts	35	26
Starter motor mounting bracket:		
Bolt	25	19
Nut	6	4

5A

1 General information, precautions and battery disconnection

General information

The engine electrical system consists mainly of the charging and starting systems. Because of their engine-related functions, these components are covered separately from the body electrical devices such as the lights, instruments, etc (which are covered in Chapter 12). Information on the ignition system is covered in Part B of this Chapter.

The electrical system is of 12-volt negative earth type.

The battery is of the low maintenance or "maintenance-free" (sealed for life) type and is charged by the alternator, which is belt-driven from the crankshaft pulley.

The starter motor is of the pre-engaged type incorporating an integral solenoid. On starting, the solenoid moves the drive pinion into engagement with the flywheel ring gear before the starter motor is energised. Once the engine has started, a one-way clutch prevents the motor armature being driven by the engine until the pinion disengages from the flywheel.

Precautions

Further details of the various systems are given in the relevant Sections of this Chapter. While some repair procedures are given, the usual course of action is to renew the component concerned. The owner whose interest extends beyond mere component renewal should obtain a copy of the "Automobile Electrical & Electronic Systems Manual", available from the publishers of this manual.

It is necessary to take extra care when working on the electrical system to avoid damage to semi-conductor devices (diodes and transistors), and to avoid the risk of personal injury. In addition to the precautions given in "Safety First!" at the beginning of this manual, observe the following when working on the system:

Always remove rings, watches, etc before working on the electrical system. Even with the battery disconnected, capacitive discharge could occur if a component's live terminal is earthed through a metal object. This could cause a shock or nasty burn.

Do not reverse the battery connections. Components such as the alternator, electronic control units, or any other components having semi-conductor circuitry could be irreparably damaged.

If the engine is being started using jump leads and a slave battery, connect the batteries positive-to-positive and negative-to-negative (see "Booster battery (jump) starting"). This also applies when connecting a battery charger.

Never disconnect the battery terminals, the alternator, any electrical wiring or any test instruments when the engine is running.

Do not allow the engine to turn the alternator when the alternator is not connected.

Never "test" for alternator output by "flashing" the output lead to earth.

Never use an ohmmeter of the type incorporating a hand-cranked generator for circuit or continuity testing.

Always ensure that the battery negative lead is disconnected when working on the electrical system.

Before using electric-arc welding equipment on the car, disconnect the battery, alternator and components such as the fuel injection/ignition electronic control unit to protect them from the risk of damage.

Battery disconnection

Several systems fitted to the vehicle require battery power to be available at all times, either to ensure their continued operation (such as the clock) or to maintain control unit memories (such as that in the engine management system's ECU) which would be wiped if the battery were to be disconnected. Whenever the battery is to be disconnected therefore, first note the following, to ensure that there are no unforeseen consequences of this action:

a) First, on any vehicle with central locking, it is a wise precaution to remove the key from the ignition, and to keep it with you, so that it does not get locked in, if the central locking should engage accidentally when the battery is reconnected.

b) On cars equipped with an engine management system, the system's ECU will lose the information stored in its memory - referred to by Ford as the "KAM" (Keep-Alive Memory) - when the battery is disconnected. This includes idling and operating values, and any fault codes detected - in the case of the fault codes, if it is thought likely that the system has developed a fault for which the corresponding code has been logged, the vehicle must be taken to a Ford dealer for the codes to be read, using the special diagnostic equipment necessary for this. Whenever the battery is disconnected, the information relating to idle speed control and other operating values will have to be re-programmed into the unit's memory. The ECU does this by itself, but until then, there may be surging, hesitation, erratic idle and a generally inferior level of performance. To allow the ECU to relearn these values, start the engine and run it as close to idle speed as possible until it reaches its normal operating temperature, then run it for approximately two minutes at 1200 rpm. Next, drive the vehicle as far as necessary - approximately 5 miles of varied driving conditions is usually sufficient - to complete the relearning process.

c) If the battery is disconnected while the alarm system is armed or activated, the alarm will remain in the same state when the battery is reconnected. The same applies to the engine immobiliser system (where fitted).

d) If a Ford "Keycode" audio unit is fitted, and the unit and/or the battery is disconnected, the unit will not function again on reconnection until the correct security code is entered. Details of this procedure, which varies according to the unit and model year, are given in the "Ford Audio Systems Operating Guide" supplied with the vehicle when new, with the code itself being given in a "Radio Passport" and/or a "Keycode Label" at the same time. Ensure you have the correct code before you disconnect the battery. For obvious security reasons, the procedure is not given in this manual. If you do not have the code or details of the correct procedure, but can supply proof of ownership and a legitimate reason for wanting this information, the vehicle's selling dealer may be able to help.

Devices known as "memory-savers" (or "code-savers") can be used to avoid some of the above problems. Precise details vary according to the device used. Typically, it is plugged into the cigarette lighter, and is connected by its own wires to a spare battery; the vehicle's own battery is then disconnected from the electrical system, leaving the "memory-saver" to pass sufficient current to maintain audio unit security codes and ECU memory values, and also to run permanently-live circuits such as the clock, all the while isolating the battery in the event of a short-circuit occurring while work is carried out.

⚠️ **Warning:** *Some of these devices allow a considerable amount of current to pass, which can mean that many of the vehicle's systems are still operational when the main battery is disconnected. If a "memory-saver" is used, ensure that the circuit concerned is actually "dead" before carrying out any work on it!*

2 Electrical fault finding - general information

Refer to Chapter 12.

3 Battery - testing and charging

Standard and low maintenance battery - testing

1 If the vehicle covers a small annual mileage it is worthwhile checking the specific gravity of the electrolyte every three months to determine the state of charge of the battery.

Use a hydrometer to make the check and compare the results with the following table. Note that the specific gravity readings assume an electrolyte temperature of 15°C (60°F); for every 10°C (18°F) below 15°C (60°F) subtract 0.007. For every 10°C (18°F) above 15°C (60°F) add 0.007.

Ambient temperature - 25°C (77°F)

	above 25°C	below 25°C
Fully-charged	1.210 to 1.230	1.270 to 1.290
70% charged	1.170 to 1.190	1.230 to 1.250
discharged	1.050 to 1.070	1.110 to 1.130

2 If the battery condition is suspect, first check the specific gravity of electrolyte in each cell. A variation of 0.040 or more between any cells indicates loss of electrolyte or deterioration of the internal plates.
3 If the specific gravity variation is 0.040 or more, the battery should be renewed. If the cell variation is satisfactory but the battery is discharged, it should be charged as described later in this Section.

Maintenance-free battery - testing

4 In cases where a "sealed for life" maintenance-free battery is fitted, topping-up and testing of the electrolyte in each cell is not possible. The condition of the battery can therefore only be tested using a battery condition indicator or a voltmeter.
5 Certain models may be fitted with a "Delco" type maintenance-free battery, with a built-in charge condition indicator. The indicator is located in the top of the battery casing, and indicates the condition of the battery from its colour. If the indicator shows green, then the battery is in a good state of charge. If the indicator turns darker, eventually to black, then the battery requires charging, as described later in this Section. If the indicator shows clear/yellow, then the electrolyte level in the battery is too low to allow further use, and the battery should be renewed. **Do not** attempt to charge, load or jump start a battery when the indicator shows clear/yellow.
6 If testing the battery using a voltmeter, connect the voltmeter across the battery and compare the result with those given in the Specifications under "charge condition". The test is only accurate if the battery has not been subjected to any kind of charge for the previous six hours. If this is not the case, switch on the headlights for 30 seconds, then wait four or five minutes before testing the battery after switching off the headlights. All other electrical circuits must be switched off, so check that the doors and tailgate/bootlid are fully shut when making the test.
7 If the voltage reading is less than 12.2 volts, then the battery is discharged, whilst a reading of 12.2 to 12.4 volts indicates a partially discharged condition.
8 If the battery is to be charged, remove it from the vehicle (Section 4) and charge it as described later in this Section.

Standard and low maintenance battery - charging

Note: *The following is intended as a guide only. Always refer to the manufacturer's recommendations (often printed on a label attached to the battery), and always disconnect both terminal leads before charging a battery.*
9 Charge the battery at a rate of 3.5 to 4 amps and continue to charge the battery at this rate until no further rise in specific gravity is noted over a four hour period.
10 Alternatively, a trickle charger charging at the rate of 1.5 amps can safely be used overnight.
11 Specially rapid 'boost' charges which are claimed to restore the power of the battery in 1 to 2 hours are not recommended, as they can cause serious damage to the battery plates through overheating.
12 While charging the battery, note that the temperature of the electrolyte should never exceed 37.8°C (100°F).

Maintenance-free battery - charging

Note: *The following is intended as a guide only. Always refer to the manufacturer's recommendations (often printed on a label attached to the battery), and always disconnect both terminal leads before charging a battery.*
13 This battery type takes considerably longer to fully recharge than the standard type, the time taken being dependent on the extent of discharge, but it can take anything up to three days.
14 A constant voltage type charger is required, to be set, when connected, to 13.9 to 14.9 volts with a charger current below 25 amps. Using this method, the battery should be usable within three hours, giving a voltage reading of 12.5 volts, but this is for a partially discharged battery and, as mentioned, full charging can take considerably longer.
15 If the battery is to be charged from a fully discharged state (condition reading less than 12.2 volts), have it recharged by your Ford dealer or local automotive electrician, as the charge rate is higher and constant supervision during charging is necessary.

4.1 The battery location in the Endura-DE diesel engine compartment

4 Battery - removal and refitting

Note: *Refer to the warnings given in "Safety First!" and in Section 1 of this Chapter before starting work.*

Removal

1 The battery is located on the left-hand side of the engine compartment, on a platform on the vehicle structure above the transmission **(see illustration)**.
2 Loosen the clamp nut, then detach the earth lead from the battery negative (earth) terminal post. This is the terminal to disconnect before working on, or disconnecting, any electrical component on the vehicle. Position the lead away from the battery.
3 Pivot up the plastic cover from the positive terminal, then loosen the positive lead clamp nut. Detach the positive lead from the terminal and position it away from the battery.
4 Unscrew the nuts and remove the clamp bar from the top of the battery **(see illustration)**. Lift the battery from its location, keeping it in an upright position to avoid the possibility of corrosive electrolyte spilling onto the paintwork.
5 If necessary, unbolt the battery box from the platform and detach the wiring supports.
6 Clean the battery terminal posts, clamps and the battery casing. If the platform is rusted as a result of battery acid spilling onto it, clean it thoroughly and re-paint.
7 If you are renewing the battery, make sure that you get the correct one as given in the Specifications. Dispose of the old battery in a responsible fashion. Most local authorities have facilities for the collection and disposal of such items.

Refitting

8 Refitting is a reversal of removal. Smear the battery terminals with a petroleum-based jelly prior to reconnecting. Always connect the positive terminal clamp first and the negative terminal clamp last.

5A

4.4 Removing the clamp bar from the top of the battery

7.2 Disengaging the auxiliary drivebelt from the alternator pulley

7.3 Disconnecting the battery positive cable from the alternator terminal

7.4 Disconnecting the field winding wiring

5 Charging system - testing

Note: *Refer to the warnings given in "Safety First!" and in Section 1 of this Chapter before starting work.*

1 If the ignition warning light fails to illuminate when the ignition is switched on, first check the alternator wiring connections for security. If satisfactory, check that the warning light bulb has not blown, and that the bulbholder is secure in its location in the instrument panel. If the light still fails to illuminate, check the continuity of the warning light feed wire from the alternator to the bulbholder. If all is satisfactory, the alternator is at fault and should be renewed or taken to an auto-electrician for testing and repair.

2 If the ignition warning light illuminates when

7.5 Alternator lower mounting bolt

the engine is running, stop the engine and check that the drivebelt is intact and correctly tensioned (see Chapter 1A or B) and that the alternator connections are secure. If all is so far satisfactory, have the alternator checked by an auto-electrician for testing and repair.

3 If the alternator output is suspect even though the warning light functions correctly, the regulated voltage may be checked as follows.

4 Connect a voltmeter across the battery terminals and start the engine.

5 Increase the engine speed until the voltmeter reading remains steady; the reading should be approximately 12 to 13 volts, and no more than 14 volts.

6 Switch on as many electrical accessories (eg, the headlights, heated rear window and heater blower) as possible, and check that the alternator maintains the regulated voltage at around 13 to 14 volts.

7 If the regulated voltage is not as stated, the fault may be due to worn brushes, weak brush springs, a faulty voltage regulator, a faulty diode, a severed phase winding or worn or damaged slip rings. The alternator should be renewed or taken to an auto-electrician for testing and repair.

6 Alternator drivebelt - removal, refitting and tensioning

Refer to the procedure given for the auxiliary drivebelt in Chapter 1A or B.

7 Alternator - removal and refitting

Note: *Refer to the warnings given in "Safety First!" and in Section 1 of this Chapter before starting work.*

Removal

1 Loosen the clamp nut, then detach the earth lead from the battery negative (earth) terminal post. Position the lead well away from the battery.

Zetec-SE engine models

2 Fit a ring spanner on the auxiliary drivebelt tensioner, and rotate it clockwise to release the tension. Note the routing of the drivebelt, then disengage it from the pulleys and remove it **(see illustration)**.

3 Unscrew the nut and disconnect the battery positive cable from the terminal on top of the alternator **(see illustration)**. A socket will be required as the plastic terminal cover is brittle and easily broken with a ring spanner.

4 Depress the wire clip and disconnect the field winding wiring from the top of the alternator **(see illustration)**.

5 Unscrew and remove the lower mounting bolt **(see illustration)**.

6 Unscrew and remove the bolt securing the rear of the alternator to the cylinder block **(see illustration)**.

7 Support the alternator then unscrew and remove the upper mounting bolt and remove the alternator **(see illustrations)**.

7.6 Bolt securing the rear of the alternator to the cylinder block

7.7a Unscrew and remove the upper mounting bolt . . .

7.7b . . . then remove the alternator from the engine

Endura-E engine models with power steering and/or air conditioning

8 Apply the handbrake, then jack up the front of the vehicle and support on axle stands (see "Jacking and Vehicle Support"). Remove the right-hand front roadwheel.
9 Remove the catalytic converter as described in Chapter 4A.
10 Unscrew the bolts from the crankshaft pulley lower cover then unclip it from the coolant hose.
11 Fit a ring spanner on the auxiliary drivebelt tensioner, and rotate it clockwise to release the tension. Note the routing of the drivebelt, then disengage it from the pulleys and remove it.
12 On models with air conditioning, unbolt the compressor and support it to one side with wire or string (refer to Chapter 3).
13 Disconnect the wiring from the rear of the alternator.
14 Unscrew and remove the rear mounting bolts.
15 Support the alternator, then unscrew and remove the front mounting bolts. Withdraw the alternator from the engine compartment.

Endura-DE engine models

16 Apply the handbrake, then jack up the front of the vehicle and support on axle stands (see "Jacking and Vehicle Support"). Remove the right-hand front roadwheel.
17 As fitted, remove the power-assisted steering pump (see Chapter 10) or air conditioning compressor (see Chapter 3). Do not disconnect either unit from the fluid lines but tie it to one side.
18 Loosen the adjustment clamp bolts, then release the drivebelt tension by backing off the adjustment bolt. Note the routing of the drivebelt, then withdraw it downwards from the pulleys.
19 On models with air conditioning, unbolt the compressor and support it to one side with wire or string (refer to Chapter 3).
20 Unbolt and remove the drivebelt tensioner.
21 Disconnect the wiring from the alternator.
22 Support the alternator, then unscrew and remove the mounting bolts and withdraw the alternator downwards from the engine compartment.

Refitting

23 Refitting is a reversal of removal, but refer to Chapter 1A or B for details of refitting the auxiliary drivebelt.

8 Alternator - testing and overhaul

If the alternator is thought to be suspect, it should be removed from the vehicle and taken to an auto-electrician for testing. Most auto-electricians will be able to supply and fit brushes at a reasonable cost. However, check on the cost of repairs before proceeding as it may prove more economical to obtain a new or exchange alternator.

9 Starting system - testing

Note: Refer to the precautions given in "Safety First!" and in Section 1 of this Chapter before starting work.

1 If the starter motor fails to operate when the ignition key is turned to the appropriate position, the following possible causes may be to blame.
a) The battery is faulty.
b) The electrical connections between the switch, solenoid, battery and starter motor are somewhere failing to pass the necessary current from the battery through the starter to earth.
c) The solenoid is faulty.
d) The starter motor is mechanically or electrically defective.
2 To check the battery, switch on the headlights. If they dim after a few seconds, this indicates that the battery is discharged - recharge (see Section 3) or renew the battery. If the headlights glow brightly, operate the ignition switch and observe the lights. If they dim, then this indicates that current is reaching the starter motor, therefore the fault must lie in the starter motor. If the lights continue to glow brightly (and no clicking sound can be heard from the starter motor solenoid), this indicates that there is a fault in the circuit or solenoid - see following paragraphs. If the starter motor turns slowly when operated, but the battery is in good condition, then this indicates that either the starter motor is faulty, or there is considerable resistance somewhere in the circuit.
3 If a fault in the circuit is suspected, disconnect the battery leads (including the earth connection to the body), the starter/solenoid wiring and the engine/transmission earth strap. Thoroughly clean the connections, and reconnect the leads and wiring, then use a voltmeter or test lamp to check that full battery voltage is available at the battery positive lead connection to the solenoid, and that the earth is sound. Smear petroleum jelly around the battery terminals to prevent corrosion - corroded connections are amongst the most frequent causes of electrical system faults.
4 If the battery and all connections are in good condition, check the circuit by disconnecting the wire from the solenoid terminal. Connect a voltmeter or test lamp between the wire end and a good earth (such as the battery negative terminal), and check that the wire is live when the ignition switch is turned to the `start' position. If it is, then the circuit is sound - if not, the circuit wiring can be checked as described in Chapter 12.
5 The solenoid contacts can be checked by connecting a voltmeter or test lamp between the battery positive feed connection on the starter side of the solenoid, and earth. When the ignition switch is turned to the 'start' position, there should be a reading or lighted bulb, as applicable. If there is no reading or lighted bulb, the solenoid is faulty and should be renewed.
6 If the circuit and solenoid are proved sound, the fault must lie in the starter motor. In this event, it may be possible to have the starter motor overhauled by a specialist, but check on the cost of spares before proceeding, as it may prove more economical to obtain a new or exchange motor.

10 Starter motor - removal and refitting

Note: Refer to the warnings given in "Safety First!" and in Section 1 of this Chapter before starting work.

Removal

1 Loosen the clamp nut, then detach the earth lead from the battery negative (earth) terminal. Position the lead away from the battery.

Zetec-SE engine models

2 Apply the handbrake, then jack up the front of the vehicle and support on axle stands (see "Jacking and Vehicle Support").
3 Working beneath the front of the engine, unscrew the two nuts and disconnect the wiring from the starter motor.
4 Unscrew and remove the lower then upper starter mounting bolts from the transmission bellhousing, noting that the upper bolts secure the throttle body housing support bracket (see illustrations).

10.4a Removing the starter motor lower mounting bolt

10.4b The starter motor upper mounting bolts also secure the throttle body housing support bracket

5A

10.5a Unscrew and remove the rear support bolt . . .

10.5b . . . then withdraw the starter motor

5 Support the starter motor, then unscrew and remove the rear support bolt and withdraw the unit to the right from the transmission bellhousing and downwards from the engine compartment. As there is limited working room, take care not to damage the wiring or terminals, or the surrounding pipes and dipstick tube **(see illustrations)**.

Endura-E engine models with power steering and/or air conditioning

6 Apply the handbrake, then jack up the front of the vehicle and support on axle stands (see *"Jacking and Vehicle Support"*).

7 Unclip and remove the air duct leading from the air cleaner to the throttle housing.

8 Working beneath the vehicle, disconnect the wiring at the connector above the starter motor.

9 Unscrew and remove the starter motor upper mounting bolts.

10 Unscrew and remove the lower mounting bolt, then withdraw the starter motor and lower it for access to the wiring. Unscrew the nuts and disconnect the wiring, then withdraw the starter motor from the engine compartment.

Endura-DE engine models

11 Apply the handbrake, then jack up the front of the vehicle and support on axle stands (see *"Jacking and Vehicle Support"*).

12 Working beneath the vehicle, unscrew the nuts and disconnect the wiring from the starter motor.

13 Unscrew the nuts and bolt, and remove the starter motor rear support bracket.

14 Unscrew the mounting bolts and withdraw the starter motor from the transmission **(see illustration)**.

Refitting

15 Refitting is a reversal of removal, but tighten the mounting bolts to the specified torque.

11 Starter motor - testing and overhaul

If the starter motor is thought to be suspect, it should be removed from the vehicle and taken to an auto-electrician for testing. Most auto-electricians will be able to supply and fit brushes at a reasonable cost. However, check on the cost of repairs before proceeding as it may prove more economical to obtain a new or exchange motor.

12 Oil pressure warning light switch - removal and refitting

Removal

1 On petrol engines, the oil pressure switch is located on the front of the cylinder block. On diesel engines, it is located on the left-hand end of the cylinder head **(see illustration)**.

2 On petrol engine models, apply the handbrake then jack up the front of the vehicle and support on axle stands (see *"Jacking and Vehicle Support"*).

3 Disconnect the wiring from the oil pressure warning light switch.

4 Unscrew the switch and remove it from the cylinder block/head. Be prepared for some loss of oil.

Refitting

5 Clean the threads of the switch and the threads in the cylinder block/head. Also wipe away any oil which may have escaped from the switch hole.

6 Apply suitable sealant to the threads, then insert the switch and tighten securely.

7 Reconnect the wiring and where necessary lower the vehicle to the ground.

8 Check and if necessary top-up the engine oil as described in *"Weekly checks"*.

10.14 Starter motor on the Endura-DE diesel engine

12.1 Oil pressure switch location on the Endura-DE diesel engine

Chapter 5 Part B:
Ignition system - petrol engine models

Contents

Degrees of difficulty

Easy, suitable for novice with little experience	**Fairly easy,** suitable for beginner with some experience	**Fairly difficult,** suitable for competent DIY mechanic	**Difficult,** suitable for experienced DIY mechanic	**Very difficult,** suitable for expert DIY or professional

Specifications

General

System type	Electronic distributorless ignition system (DIS) with ignition module controlled by EEC V engine management module (Powertrain control module)

Firing order:
1.25 and 1.4 Zetec SE engines	1-3-4-2
1.3 Endura E engine	1-2-4-3
Location of No 1 cylinder	Crankshaft pulley end

Ignition system data

Ignition timing	Controlled by the Powertrain Control Module (PCM)

Electronic Ignition (EI) coil resistances:
Primary windings	0.4 to 0.6 ohms
Secondary windings	10 500 to 16 500 ohms

Torque wrench settings

	Nm	lbf ft
Ignition coil	6	4

5B

1 Ignition system - general information and precautions

General information

The ignition system is integrated with the fuel injection system to form a combined engine management system under the control of the Powertrain control module (PCM) (see Chapter 4A for further information). The main ignition system components include the ignition switch, the battery, the crankshaft speed/position sensor, the ignition coil, and the spark plugs.

A Distributorless Ignition System (DIS) is fitted where the main functions of the conventional distributor are replaced by a computerised module within the Powertrain Control Module. The remote ignition coil unit combines a double-ended pair of coils - each time a coil receives an ignition signal, two sparks are produced , at each end of the secondary windings. One spark goes to a cylinder on compression stroke and the other goes to the corresponding cylinder on its exhaust stroke. The first will give the correct power stroke, but the second spark will have no effect (a 'wasted spark'), occurring as it does during exhaust conditions.

The information contained in this Chapter concentrates on the ignition-related components of the engine management system. Information covering the fuel, exhaust and emission control components can be found in the applicable Parts of Chapter 4.

Precautions

The following precautions must be observed, to prevent damage to the ignition system components and to reduce risk of personal injury.

a) Do not keep the ignition on for more than 10 seconds if the engine will not start.
b) Ensure that the ignition is switched off before disconnecting any of the ignition wiring.
c) Ensure that the ignition is switched off before connecting or disconnecting any ignition test equipment, such as a timing light.
d) Do not earth the coil primary or secondary circuits.

 Warning: Voltages produced by an electronic ignition system are considerably higher than those produced by conventional ignition systems. Extreme care must be taken when working on the system with the ignition switched on. Persons with surgically-implanted cardiac pacemaker devices should keep well clear of the ignition circuits, components and test equipment.

2 Ignition system -
testing

1 If the engine either will not turn over at all, or only turns very slowly, check the battery and starter motor as described in Chapter 5A.
2 If the engine turns over at normal speed but will not start, check the HT circuit by connecting a timing light (following the manufacturer's instructions) and turning the engine over on the starter motor; if the light flashes, voltage is reaching the spark plugs, so these should be checked first. If the light does not flash, check the HT leads themselves using the information given in Chapter 1A.
3 If there is still no spark, check the coil's primary and secondary winding resistance as described in Section 3; renew the coil if faulty, but be careful to check carefully the wiring connections themselves before doing so, to ensure that the fault is not due to dirty or poorly-fastened connectors.
4 If these checks fail to reveal the cause of the problem the vehicle should be taken to a suitably equipped Ford dealer for testing. A wiring block connector is incorporated in the engine management circuit into which a special electronic diagnostic tester can be plugged. The tester will locate the fault quickly and simply, alleviating the need to test all the system components individually which is a time consuming operation that carries a high risk of damaging the PCM. If necessary, the system wiring and wiring connectors can be checked as described in Chapter 12.
5 If the engine runs but has an irregular misfire, check the low tension wiring on the

4.2 Unhook the metal cover . . .

4.3 . . . then disconnect the wiring

3.4 Ignition coil bolted to the top of the coolant outlet elbow on the left-hand end of the cylinder head (showing removal together with the elbow during engine overhaul)

ignition coil ensuring that all connections are clean and securely fastened.
6 Check that the coil HT leads are clean and dry. Check the leads themselves and the spark plugs (by substitution, if necessary).
7 Regular misfiring is probably due to a fault in the HT leads or spark plugs. Use a timing light (as described above) to check whether HT voltage is present at all leads.
8 If HT voltage is not present on any particular lead, the fault will be in that lead or in the ignition coil. If HT is present on all leads, the fault will be in the spark plugs; check and renew them if there is any doubt about their condition.
9 If no HT is present, check the coil; its secondary windings may be breaking down under load.

3 Electronic ignition HT coil -
removal, testing and refitting

Removal

1 On the Endura-E engine the ignition coil is bolted to the right-hand rear of the engine. On the Zetec-SE engine the ignition coil is bolted to the coolant outlet elbow on the left-hand end of the cylinder head.
2 Make sure the ignition is switched off, then disconnect the low tension wiring from the coil.
3 Identify the HT leads for position then carefully pull them from the terminals on the coil.
4 Unscrew the mounting bolts and remove the ignition coil from the engine compartment **(see illustration)**.

4.4a Unscrew the bolt . . .

Testing

5 Using an ohmmeter, measure the resistances of the ignition coil's primary and secondary windings and compare with the information given in the Specifications. Renew the coil if necessary.

Refitting

6 Refitting is a reversal of removal.

4 Crankshaft position sensor -
removal and refitting

Removal

1 The crankshaft position sensor is located on the front left-hand end of the cylinder block. For improved access apply the handbrake, then jack up the front of the vehicle and support it on axle stands (see "Jacking and Vehicle Support").
2 Unhook the metal cover from the sensor **(see illustration)**.
3 Depress the wire clip and disconnect the wiring from the sensor **(see illustration)**.
4 Unscrew the bolt and withdraw the sensor from the engine rear flange **(see illustrations)**.

Refitting

5 Refitting is a reversal of removal.

5 Ignition timing -
checking and adjustment

Due to the nature of the ignition system, the ignition timing is constantly being monitored and adjusted by the engine management PCM, and nominal values cannot be given. Therefore, it is not possible for the home mechanic to check the ignition timing.

The only way in which the ignition timing can be checked is using special electronic test equipment, connected to the engine management system diagnostic connector (refer to Chapter 4A). No adjustment of the ignition timing is possible. Should the ignition timing be incorrect, then a fault must be present in the engine management system.

4.4b . . . and withdraw the crankshaft position sensor

Chapter 5 Part C:
Pre-heating system - diesel engine models

Contents

Degrees of difficulty

Easy, suitable for novice with little experience	Fairly easy, suitable for beginner with some experience	Fairly difficult, suitable for competent DIY mechanic	Difficult, suitable for experienced DIY mechanic	Very difficult, suitable for expert DIY or professional

Specifications

Glow plugs

Type . . . . Champion CH 147

Torque wrench settings	Nm	lbf ft
Glow plugs	28	21

1 Pre-heating system - description and testing

Description

1 Each swirl chamber has a heater plug (commonly called a glow plug) screwed into it. The plugs are electrically operated before, during, and a short time after start-up when the engine is cold. Electrical feed to the glow plugs and glow plug indicator lamp are controlled by the Powertrain Control Module (PCM).

2 The glow plugs are energised when the ignition is switched on, and they remain on together with the indicator lamp for a period varying between 1 and 10 seconds, depending on the temperature of the engine coolant. After the indicator lamp is extinguished, the glow plugs remain energised for a period up to 3 seconds, however if the engine is started in this period the glow plugs will remain on for a period up to 40 seconds depending on the engine coolant temperature. With the coolant at 80°C the period is 0 seconds and with the coolant at -40°C the period is 40 seconds.

3 A warning light in the instrument panel tells the driver that pre-heating is taking place.

When the light goes out, the engine is ready to be started. If no attempt is made to start, the timer then cuts off the supply in order to avoid draining the battery and overheating of the glow plugs.

Testing

4 If the system malfunctions, testing is ultimately by substitution of known good units, but some preliminary checks may be made as follows.

5 Connect a voltmeter or 12 volt test lamp between the glow plug supply cable and earth (engine or vehicle metal). Make sure that the live connection is kept clear of the engine and bodywork.

6 Have an assistant switch on the ignition and check that voltage is applied to the glow plugs. Note the time for which the warning light is lit and the total time for which voltage is applied before the system cuts out. Switch off the ignition.

7 If the results of the check do not come within the periods indicated in paragraph 2, refer to Chapters 4B and 12 and check the relevant temperature sensor and power supply.

8 If an ammeter of suitable range (0 to 50 amp approx) is available, connect it between the glow plug feed wire and the bus bar. During the preheating period the ammeter

should show a current draw of approximately 8 amps per working plug, ie. 32 amps if all four plugs are working. If one or more plugs appear not to be drawing current, remove the bus bar and check each plug separately with a continuity tester or self-powered test lamp.

9 If there is no supply at all to the glow plugs, the associated wiring is at fault.

10 To locate a defective glow plug, disconnect the main supply cable and the interconnecting wire or strap from the top of the glow plugs. Be careful not to drop the nuts and washers.

11 Use a continuity tester, or a 12 volt test lamp connected to the battery positive terminal, to check for continuity between each glow plug terminal and earth. The resistance of a glow plug in good condition is very low (less than 1 ohm), so if the test lamp does not light or the continuity tester shows a high resistance the glow plug is certainly defective.

12 If an ammeter is available, the current draw of each glow plug can be checked. After an initial surge of around 15 to 20 amps, each plug should draw around 10 amps. Any plug which draws much more or less than this is probably defective.

13 As a final check the glow plugs can be removed and inspected as described in Section 2.

5C

2.2 Glow plug feed wire connection

2.3 Unscrewing a glow plug terminal nut

2.4 Glow plug removed from cylinder head

2 Glow plugs - removal, inspection and refitting

Removal

Caution: If the pre-heating system has just been energised, or if the engine has been running, the glow plugs may be very hot.

1 Disconnect the battery negative (earth) lead (see Chapter 5A).

2 Disconnect the feed wire from the bus bar **(see illustration)**.

3 Unscrew the terminal nut from each plug to be removed. Remove the nuts, washers and bus bar **(see illustration)**.

4 Clean around the glow plug seats then unscrew and remove them **(see illustration)**.

Inspection

5 Inspect the glow plugs for damage. Burnt or eroded glow plug tips can be caused by a bad injector spray pattern. Have the injectors checked if this sort of damage is found.

6 If the glow plugs are in good physical condition, check them electrically using a 12 volt test lamp or continuity tester as described in the previous Section.

7 The glow plugs can be energised by applying 12 volts to them to verify that they heat up evenly and in the required time. Observe the following precautions:

a) *Support the glow plug by clamping it carefully in a vice or self-locking pliers. Remember it will become red-hot.*

b) *Make sure that the power supply or test lead incorporates a fuse or overload trip to protect against damage from a short-circuit.*

c) *After testing, allow the glow plug to cool for several minutes before attempting to handle it.*

8 A glow plug in good condition will start to glow red at the tip after drawing current for 5 seconds or so. Any plug which takes much longer to start glowing, or which starts glowing in the middle instead of at the tip, is defective.

Refitting

9 When refitting, apply a little anti-seize compound to the glow plug threads. Screw the glow plugs into place and tighten them to the specified torque.

10 Refit the bus bar and washers and secure with the nuts. Make sure that the clamping areas are clean.

11 Reconnect the feed wire and the battery earth lead.

3 Fuel heater - general information, removal and refitting

General information

1 An electrically-operated fuel heater is fitted in the fuel line leading to the fuel filter housing, to prevent the fuel "waxing" at low temperatures **(see illustration)**. The heater is controlled by an internal thermostat. When the fuel is below a predetermined temperature, current to the heater warms the fuel.

Removal

Caution: Be careful not to allow dirt into the fuel system during the following procedure.

2 Obtain a container to catch spilt fuel.

3 Disconnect the battery negative (earth) lead (see Chapter 5A).

4 Disconnect the multiplug from the base of the fuel heater.

5 Depress the tabs on the quick release connector and disconnect the fuel supply pipe from the heater inlet pipe.

6 Release the fuel filter inlet pipe from the support clip.

7 Depress the tabs on the quick release connector and disconnect the inlet pipe from the fuel filter.

8 Unscrew the bolt and remove the fuel heater and bracket from the engine compartment.

9 Release the two clips and remove the heater from the bracket.

Refitting

10 Refitting is the reverse of the removal procedure. On completion, prime the fuel system with reference to Chapter 4B, then carry out leak checks directly after the engine is first started.

3.1 The fuel heater is located on the left-hand end of the cylinder head

Chapter 6
Clutch

Contents

Degrees of difficulty

Easy, suitable for novice with little experience	Fairly easy, suitable for beginner with some experience	Fairly difficult, suitable for competent DIY mechanic	Difficult, suitable for experienced DIY mechanic	Very difficult, suitable for expert DIY or professional 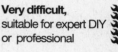

Specifications

General

Clutch type . . . . Single dry plate, diaphragm spring, hydraulically-operated release

Clutch disc

Diameter:
Endura E and Zetec SE petrol engine models . . . . 180 mm
Endura DE diesel engine models . . . . 210.0 mm
Friction material thickness (new) . . . . 8.3 mm (approximate)

Clutch pedal

Pedal travel . . . . 125.0 ± 3.0 mm

Torque wrench settings

	Nm	lbf ft
Clutch slave cylinder	10	7
Clutch slave cylinder pre-loading valve	10	7
Slave cylinder bleed valve	14	10
Pressure plate to flywheel bolts	30	22

---

1 General information

The clutch consists of a friction plate, a pressure plate assembly, a release bearing and hydraulic slave cylinder; all of these components are contained in the large cast-aluminium alloy bellhousing, sandwiched between the engine and the transmission.

The hydraulic master cylinder is located in the pedal bracket on the bulkhead, and the fluid reservoir is shared with the brake reservoir on the top of the brake master cylinder. Inside the reservoir each circuit has its own compartment, so that in the event of fluid loss in the clutch circuit the brake circuit remains fully operational.

The friction plate is fitted between the engine flywheel and the clutch pressure plate, and is allowed to slide on the transmission input shaft splines.

The pressure plate assembly is bolted to the engine flywheel. When the engine is running, drive is transmitted from the crankshaft, via the flywheel, to the friction plate (these components being clamped securely together by the pressure plate assembly) and from the friction plate to the transmission input shaft.

To interrupt the drive, the spring pressure must be relaxed by the hydraulically-operated release mechanism. Depressing the clutch pedal operates the master cylinder which in turn operates the slave cylinder and presses the release bearing against the pressure plate spring fingers. This causes the springs to deform and releases the clamping force on the pressure plate.

When the pedal is released, the diaphragm spring forces the pressure plate into contact with the friction linings on the clutch disc. The disc is now firmly sandwiched between the pressure plate and the flywheel, thus transmitting engine power to the transmission.

A pre-loading valve is fitted on the fluid inlet to the slave cylinder. This valve maintains a pressure of approximately 1.0 bar between the valve and the slave cylinder in order to keep the release bearing constantly pressed against the pressure plate. Upstream of the valve there is no pressure, in order to prevent vibrations being transmitted to the clutch pedal.

Wear of the friction material on the clutch disc is automatically compensated for by the operation of the hydraulic system. As the friction material on the disc wears, the pressure plate moves towards the flywheel causing the clutch diaphragm spring inner fingers to move outwards. When the clutch pedal is released, excess fluid is expelled through the master cylinder into the fluid reservoir.

6

3.1a Hose clamp fitted to the clutch hydraulic pressure hose

3.1b Extract the clip . . .

3.1c . . . and disconnect the line from the pre-loading valve

2 Clutch master cylinder - removal and refitting

Removal

1 Remove the filler cap from the brake master cylinder reservoir on top of the brake master cylinder, and syphon the hydraulic fluid from the reservoir until it is below the outlet to the clutch master cylinder. Alternatively, open the slave cylinder bleed screw, and gently pump the clutch pedal to expel the fluid through a plastic tube connected to the screw; tighten the screw when all the fluid has been removed.

 Warning: Do not syphon the fluid by mouth, as it is poisonous; use a syringe or an old poultry baster

3.2a Remove the protective cap . . .

2 Wipe clean the area around the master cylinder fluid outlets on the engine compartment bulkhead. Remove the clip and disconnect the hydraulic fluid supply hose from the master cylinder inlet stub. Plug the hose to prevent further loss of fluid.
3 Extract the clip from the quick release connection on the master cylinder, then remove the pressure hose and tie it to one side. Plug the end of the hose or tape over the end.
4 Inside the vehicle, reach up under the clutch pedal and disconnect the return spring from the bracket.
5 Extract the retaining clip and withdraw the pin attaching the master cylinder pushrod to the clutch pedal. Use a punch to drive it out.
6 Pull up the clutch pedal to release it from the master cylinder pushrod.
7 Unscrew and remove the bolts securing the master cylinder to the bracket. Note that it will be necessary to depress the brake pedal in order to reach all of the bolts.
8 Withdraw the master cylinder from the bracket together with the sponge rubber padding.
9 If the master cylinder is faulty it must be renewed, as the manufacturers do not supply a repair kit.

Refitting

10 Locate the master cylinder in the bracket together with the sponge padding then insert the mounting bolts. Tighten the bolts securely.
11 Apply a smear of grease to the pushrod pin, then align the pushrod eye with the pedal, insert the pin from the left-hand side of the bracket and fit the retaining clip.

12 Reconnect the return spring to the bracket.
13 In the engine compartment, clean the end of the pressure hose then insert it in the quick release connection on the master cylinder and refit the clip.
14 Fit the supply hose to the top of the master cylinder and retain with the clip.
15 Check and if necessary adjust the pedal travel as described in Section 6.
16 Refill the master cylinder reservoir with fresh fluid, then bleed the hydraulic system as described in Section 5.

3 Clutch slave cylinder - removal and refitting

Removal

1 Remove the transmission as described in Chapter 7A. Note that this procedure includes locating a hose clamp on the hydraulic pressure hose, releasing the pressure line from the support, then disconnecting the line from the pre-loading valve by extracting the clip from the quick release connection (see illustrations).
2 Remove the protective cap from the slave cylinder bleed screw, then unscrew and remove the bleed screw (see illustrations). Be prepared for some loss of fluid by placing a cloth rag around the screw.
3 Unscrew and remove the pre-loading valve from the slave cylinder inlet on the outside of the bellhousing (see illustrations).

3.2b . . . then unscrew and remove the bleed screw

3.3a Unscrew the pre-loading valve . . .

3.3b . . . and remove it from the slave cylinder inlet

3.4a Unscrew the mounting bolts . . .

3.4b . . . and withdraw the slave cylinder over the transmission input shaft

4 Inside the bellhousing, unscrew and remove the mounting bolts, then withdraw the slave cylinder over the transmission input shaft **(see illustrations)**.

5 With the slave cylinder removed, it is recommended that the transmission input shaft oil seal is renewed. Use a suitable tool to hook it out of the transmission casing and over the input shaft. Refer to Chapter 7A if necessary.

6 Remove the release bearing from the slave cylinder by tapping the cylinder on the workbench or against a block of wood.

7 If the slave cylinder is faulty it must be renewed, as the manufacturers do not supply repair kits.

Refitting

8 Locate the release bearing on the slave cylinder making sure it is correctly seated.

9 Locate a new oil seal over the input shaft and into the transmission housing (refer to Chapter 7A), then slide the slave cylinder onto the shaft.

10 Insert the mounting bolts and tighten them progressively to the specified torque. As the bolts are tightened make sure that the oil seal enters the transmission housing correctly.

Caution: Do not exceed the torque wrench setting, otherwise the pre-loading valve may not function correctly.

11 Refit the pre-loading valve to the slave cylinder and tighten to the specified torque.

12 Refit and tighten the bleed screw and fit the protective cap.

13 Refit the transmission as described in

3.4c The clutch slave cylinder on the bench, with the release bearing removed

Chapter 7A and reconnect the pre-loading valve. Refill the master cylinder reservoir with fresh fluid, then bleed the hydraulic system as described in Section 5.

4 Clutch hydraulic hoses - removal and refitting

Caution: Hydraulic fluid can damage vehicle paintwork. Take the necessary precautions to prevent spillage of fluid.

Removal

1 Remove the filler cap from the brake master cylinder reservoir on top of the brake master cylinder, and syphon the hydraulic fluid from the reservoir until it is below the outlet to the clutch master cylinder. Alternatively, open the slave cylinder bleed screw, and gently pump the clutch pedal to expel the fluid through a plastic tube connected to the screw; tighten the screw when all the fluid has been removed.

2 To remove the supply hose, remove the clips then disconnect the hose from the reservoir and master cylinder.

3 To remove the pressure hose, first wipe all traces of dirt from the master cylinder and slave cylinder. Extract the clip from the quick release connections on the master cylinder and slave cylinder, then remove the hose.

Refitting

4 Refitting is a reversal of removal, but on completion bleed the hydraulic system as described in Section 5.

5 Clutch hydraulic system - bleeding

 Warning: Hydraulic fluid is poisonous; wash off immediately and thoroughly in the case of skin contact, and seek immediate medical advice if any fluid is swallowed or gets into the eyes. Certain types of hydraulic fluid are flammable, and may ignite when allowed into contact with hot components; when servicing any

hydraulic system, it is safest to assume that the fluid is flammable, and to take precautions against the risk of fire as though it is petrol that is being handled. Hydraulic fluid is also an effective paint stripper, and will attack plastics; if any is spilt, it should be washed off immediately, using copious quantities of fresh water. Finally, it is hygroscopic (it absorbs moisture from the air) - old fluid may be contaminated and unfit for further use. When topping-up or renewing the fluid, always use the recommended type, and ensure that it comes from a freshly opened sealed container.

1 The correct operation of any hydraulic system is only possible after removing all air from the components and circuit; this is achieved by bleeding the system.

2 During the bleeding procedure, add only clean, unused hydraulic fluid of the recommended type; never re-use fluid that has already been bled from the system. Ensure that sufficient fluid is available before starting work.

3 If there is any possibility of incorrect fluid being already in the system, the hydraulic circuit must be flushed completely with uncontaminated, correct fluid.

4 If hydraulic fluid has been lost from the system, or air has entered because of a leak, ensure that the fault is cured before continuing further.

5 The bleed screw is screwed into the slave cylinder extension which is positioned on the top of the transmission bellhousing.

6 First check that all the hydraulic hoses are securely fitted to the master and slave cylinders. Clean any dirt from around the bleed screw.

7 Unscrew the brake master cylinder fluid reservoir cap, and top up the fluid level to the upper (MAX) level line; refit the cap loosely, and remember to maintain the fluid level at least above the lower (MIN) level line throughout the procedure, or there is a risk of further air entering the system.

8 There are a number of one-man, do-it-yourself bleeding kits currently available from motor accessory shops. It is recommended that one of these kits is used whenever possible, as they greatly simplify the bleeding operation, and reduce the risk of expelled air and fluid being drawn back into the system. If such a kit is not available, the basic (two-man) method must be used, which is described in detail below.

9 If a kit is to be used, prepare the vehicle as described previously, and follow the kit manufacturer's instructions, as the procedure may vary slightly according to the type being used; generally, they are as outlined below in the relevant sub-section.

Bleeding - basic (two-man) method

10 Collect a clean glass jar, a suitable length of plastic or rubber tubing which is a tight fit

6

5.13 Bleeding the clutch hydraulic circuit

over the bleed screw, and a ring spanner to fit the screw. The help of an assistant will also be required.

11 Remove the protective cap from the slave cylinder bleed screw. Fit the spanner and tube to the screw, place the other end of the tube in the jar, and pour in sufficient fluid to cover the end of the tube.

12 Ensure that the fluid level is maintained at least above the lower level line in the reservoir throughout the procedure.

13 Loosen the bleed screw half a turn, then have the assistant slowly depress and release the clutch pedal several times until fluid free of air bubbles emerges **(see illustration)**. On the final stroke have the assistant hold the pedal fully depressed. Note that the pedal must be fully depressed and fully released each time.

14 With the pedal held down, tighten the bleed screw and have the assistant fully release the pedal slowly. Check the reservoir fluid level and top up if necessary, then check the operation of the pedal. After the initial free movement, increased pressure should be felt as the clutch pressure plate diaphragm spring is operated.

15 If the pedal feels spongy, air still remains in the hydraulic system and the bleeding operation must be repeated as described in the previous paragraphs.

16 With the hydraulic system bled, tighten the bleed screw securely then remove the tube and spanner and refit the dust cap. Do not overtighten the bleed screw.

Bleeding - using a one-way valve kit

17 As the name implies, these kits consist of a length of tubing with a one-way valve fitted, to prevent expelled air and fluid being drawn back into the system; some kits include a translucent container, which can be positioned so that the air bubbles can be more easily seen flowing from the end of the tube.

18 The kit is connected to the bleed screw, which is then opened. The user returns to the driver's seat, depresses the clutch pedal with a smooth, steady stroke, and slowly releases it; this is repeated until the expelled fluid is clear of air bubbles.

19 Note that these kits simplify work so much that it is easy to forget the clutch fluid reservoir level; ensure that this is maintained at least above the lower level line at all times.

Bleeding - using a pressure-bleeding kit

20 These kits are usually operated by the reservoir of pressurised air contained in the spare tyre. However, note that it will probably be necessary to reduce the pressure to a lower level than normal; refer to the instructions supplied with the kit.

21 By connecting a pressurised, fluid-filled container to the clutch fluid reservoir, bleeding can be carried out simply by opening the bleed screw and allowing the fluid to flow out until no more air bubbles can be seen in the expelled fluid.

22 This method has the advantage that the large reservoir of fluid provides an additional safeguard against air being drawn into the system during bleeding.

All methods

23 When bleeding is complete, and correct pedal feel is restored, check that the bleed screw is securely tightened and wash off any spilt fluid. Refit the dust cap to the bleed screw.

24 Check the hydraulic fluid level in the master cylinder reservoir, and top-up if necessary.

25 Discard any hydraulic fluid that has been bled from the system; it will not be fit for re-use.

26 If the clutch is not operating correctly after carrying out the bleeding procedure, the master cylinder or slave cylinder may be faulty.

6 Clutch pedal - removal, inspection, refitting and adjustment

Removal

1 Disconnect the battery negative (earth) lead (see Chapter 5A).

2 Inside the vehicle, reach up under the clutch pedal and disconnect the return spring from the bracket.

3 Disconnect the wiring from the clutch switch, then twist the switch and remove it from the pedal bracket.

4 Extract the retaining clip and withdraw the pin attaching the master cylinder pushrod to the clutch pedal. If necessary, use a punch to drive it out. Pull up the clutch pedal to release it from the master cylinder pushrod.

5 Extract the retaining clip from the left-hand end of the pedal pivot shaft, then push the pivot shaft to the right until it clears the clutch pedal.

6 Withdraw the clutch pedal from the pedal bracket.

7 If necessary, prise out the bushes on each side of the pedal.

Inspection

8 Clean the bushes and pedal and inspect them for wear and damage. The bushes may be renewed separately, however if they are worn excessively, the pivot shaft must be checked and if necessary renewed as well. Refer to Chapter 9 for details of removing the brake pedal.

9 Check the return spring and renew it if necessary.

Refitting

10 Refitting is a reversal of removal, but apply multi-purpose grease to the pedal pivot shafts and bushes and make sure that the retaining clips are fully engaged with their grooves.

Adjustment

11 Check that the clutch pedal operates freely and that there is no obstruction or excess matting on the floor. If the pedal is spongy, the hydraulic system must be bled to remove any air as described in Section 5.

12 With the pedal fully released, measure the distance from the floor to the pedal rubber (third groove from bottom) and record.

13 Now fully depress the pedal and measure the distance again. The difference between the two measurements is the pedal travel. If this is not as given in the Specifications, adjust the position of the pedal stop screw by loosening the locknut, repositioning the adjustment screw then tightening the locknut. Note that if the pedal travel is excessive, the master cylinder will be damaged.

7 Clutch assembly - removal, inspection and refitting

⚠️ *Warning: Dust created by clutch wear and deposited on the clutch components may contain asbestos, which is a health hazard. DO NOT blow it out with compressed air, or inhale any of it. DO NOT use petrol or petroleum-based solvents to clean off the dust. Brake system cleaner or methylated spirit should be used to flush the dust into a suitable receptacle. After the clutch components are wiped clean with rags, dispose of the contaminated rags and cleaner in a sealed, marked container.*
Note: *Although some friction materials may no longer contain asbestos, it is safest to assume that they do, and to take precautions accordingly.*

Removal

1 Unless the complete engine/transmission unit is to be removed from the car and separated for major overhaul (see Chapter 2C), the clutch can be reached by removing the transmission as described in Chapter 7A.

2 Before disturbing the clutch, use chalk or a marker pen to mark the relationship of the pressure plate assembly to the flywheel.

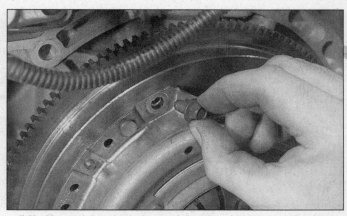

7.3a Home-made tool for holding the flywheel stationary while loosening the clutch pressure plate bolts

7.3b Unscrewing the bolts retaining the clutch pressure plate

3 Working in a diagonal sequence, slacken the pressure plate bolts by half a turn at a time, until spring pressure is released and the bolts can be unscrewed by hand. Hold the flywheel stationary using a suitable tool engaged with the starter ring gear teeth - a piece of metal as shown can be tightened to one of the bolt holes, or alternatively an assistant can use a wide-bladed screwdriver engaged with the teeth **(see illustrations)**.

4 Prise the pressure plate assembly off its locating dowels, and collect the friction disc, noting which way round the disc is fitted.

Inspection

Note: *Due to the amount of work necessary to remove and refit clutch components, it is usually considered good practice to renew the clutch friction disc, pressure plate assembly and release bearing as a matched set, even if only one of these is actually worn enough to require renewal. It is also worth considering the renewal of the clutch components on a preventive basis if the engine and/or transmission have been removed for some other reason.*

5 When cleaning clutch components, read first the warning at the beginning of this Section; remove dust using a clean, dry cloth, and working in a well-ventilated atmosphere.

6 Check the friction disc linings for signs of wear, damage or oil contamination. If the friction material is cracked, burnt, scored or damaged, or if it is contaminated with oil or grease (shown by shiny black patches), the friction disc must be renewed. Check the depth of the rivets below the friction material surface. If any are at or near the surface of the friction material, then the friction disc must be renewed.

7 If the friction material is still serviceable, check that the centre boss splines are unworn, that the torsion springs are in good condition and securely fastened, and that all the rivets are tight. If any wear or damage is found, the friction disc must be renewed.

8 If the friction material is fouled with oil, this must be due to an oil leak from the crankshaft oil seal, from the sump-to-cylinder block joint, or from the transmission input shaft. Renew the seal or repair the joint, as appropriate, as described in Chapter 2 or 7A, before installing the new friction disc.

9 Check the pressure plate assembly for obvious signs of wear or damage; shake it to check for loose rivets or worn or damaged fulcrum rings, and check that the drive straps securing the pressure plate to the cover do not show signs (such as a deep yellow or blue discoloration) of overheating. If the diaphragm spring is worn or damaged, or if its pressure is in any way suspect, the pressure plate assembly should be renewed.

10 Examine the machined bearing surfaces of the pressure plate and of the flywheel; they should be clean, completely flat, and free from scratches or scoring. If either is discoloured from excessive heat, or shows signs of cracks, it should be renewed - although minor damage of this nature can sometimes be polished away using emery paper.

11 Check that the release bearing contact surface rotates smoothly and easily, with no sign of noise or roughness. Also check that the surface itself is smooth and unworn, with no signs of cracks, pitting or scoring. If there is any doubt about its condition, the bearing must be renewed.

Refitting

12 On reassembly, ensure that the disc contact surfaces of the flywheel and pressure plate are completely clean, smooth, and free from oil or grease. Use solvent to remove any protective grease from new components.

13 Fit the friction disc so that its spring hub assembly faces away from the flywheel; there may also be a marking showing which way round the plate is to be refitted. Depending on the type of centralising tool being used, the friction disc may be held in position at this stage **(see illustrations)**.

14 Refit the pressure plate assembly, aligning the marks made on dismantling (if the original pressure plate is re-used), and locating the pressure plate on its locating dowels **(see illustration)**. Fit the pressure plate bolts, but tighten them only finger-tight, so that the friction disc can still be moved.

7.13a 'Flywheel Side' marking on the friction disc hub

7.13b Using the centralising tool to hold the friction disc on the flywheel

7.14 Refitting the pressure plate assembly onto the friction disc

6

7.17 Tightening the clutch pressure plate bolts

8.2 Removing the release bearing from the clutch slave cylinder

15 The friction disc must now be centralised, so that when the transmission is refitted, its input shaft will pass through the splines at the centre of the friction disc.

16 Centralisation can be achieved by passing a screwdriver or other long bar through the friction disc and into the hole in the crankshaft; the friction disc can then be moved around until it is centred on the crankshaft hole. Alternatively, a clutch-aligning -tool can be used to eliminate the guesswork; these can be obtained from most accessory shops. The normal type consists of a spigot bar with several different adapters, but a more recent type consists of a tool which clamps the friction disc to the pressure plate before locating the two items on the flywheel. A home-made aligning tool can be fabricated from a length of metal rod or wooden dowel which fits closely inside the crankshaft hole, and has insulating tape wound around it to match the diameter of the friction disc splined hole.

17 When the friction disc is centralised, tighten the pressure plate bolts evenly and in a diagonal sequence to the specified torque setting (see illustration).

18 Apply a thin smear of molybdenum disulphide grease to the splines of the friction disc and the transmission input shaft.

Caution: Do not apply too much grease as there is a risk that it will contaminate the friction disc material.

19 Refit the transmission as described in Chapter 7A.

8 Clutch release bearing - removal, inspection and refitting

Removal

1 For access to the clutch release bearing, the transmission must be removed as described in Chapter 7A.

2 Withdraw the release bearing from the slave cylinder inside the transmission bellhousing. If necessary, use a screwdriver to carefully prise out the bearing (see illustration).

Inspection

3 Note that it is often considered worthwhile to renew the release bearing as a matter of course regardless of its condition, considering the amount of work necessary to access it. Check that the contact surface rotates smoothly and easily, with no sign of noise or roughness, and that the surface itself is smooth and unworn, with no signs of cracks, pitting or scoring. If there is any doubt about its condition, the bearing must be renewed.

Refitting

4 Align the tag with the cut-out in the slave cylinder, then slide the release bearing fully into position.

5 Refit the transmission with reference to Chapter 7A.

Chapter 7 Part A:
Manual transmission

Contents

Degrees of difficulty

Easy, suitable for novice with little experience	Fairly easy, suitable for beginner with some experience	Fairly difficult, suitable for competent DIY mechanic	Difficult, suitable for experienced DIY mechanic	Very difficult, suitable for expert DIY or professional

Specifications

General

Type .... Manual, five forward speeds and reverse. Synchromesh on all forward speeds

Designation IB5

Note: *Transmission code is stamped on a plate attached to the transmission unit.*

Gear set application

1.3 Endura E Saloon	A (all markets) or B (France only)
1.3 Endura E Courier	A
1.25 Zetec SE Saloon	A
1.4 Zetec SE Saloon and Courier	A
1.8 Endura DE Saloon and Courier	B

Gear set ratio

Gear set A:

1st	3.58 to 1
2nd	2.04 to 1
3rd	1.32 to 1
4th	0.95 to 1
5th	0.76 to 1
Reverse	3.62 to 1

Gear set B:

1st	3.58 to 1
2nd	1.93 to 1
3rd	1.28 to 1
4th	0.95 to 1
5th	0.76 to 1
Reverse	3.62 to 1

Final drive ratio

1.3 Endura E Saloon (gear set A and B)	3.84 to 1
1.3 Endura E Courier (gear set A)	4.06 to 1
1.25 Zetec SE Saloon (gear set A)	4.27 to 1
1.4 Zetec SE Saloon and Courier (gear set A)	4.27 to 1
1.8 Endura DE Saloon and Courier (gear set B)	3.82 to 1

Lubrication

Capacity	2.8 litres
Recommended oil	See end of *"Weekly checks"*

Torque wrench settings

	Nm	lbf ft
Transmission to engine bolts	44	32
Right-hand driveshaft centre bearing bolts	24	18
Steering track rod ends	36	27
Anti-roll bar link to suspension strut	47	35
Left-hand engine mounting nuts	70	52
Right-hand engine mounting	69	51
Rear engine mounting:		
To engine	50	37
To subframe	70	52
Lower suspension arm to hub carrier	52	38
Transmission filler/level plug	35	26
Gearchange clamp bolt	23	17
Transmission earth lead	44	32
Driveshaft nut	270	200
Multi-function switch	6.5	5

1 General information

The transmission is contained in a cast-aluminium alloy casing bolted to the engine's left-hand end, and consists of the gearbox and final drive differential - often called a transaxle. The transmission unit type is stamped on a plate attached to the transmission.

Drive is transmitted from the crankshaft via the clutch to the input shaft, which has a splined extension to accept the clutch friction plate, and rotates in sealed ball-bearings. From the input shaft, drive is transmitted to the output shaft, which rotates in a roller bearing at its left-hand end, and a taper roller bearing at its right-hand end. From the output shaft, the drive is transmitted to the differential crownwheel, which rotates with the differential and planetary gears, thus driving the sun gears and driveshafts. The rotation of the planetary gears on their shaft allows the inner roadwheel to rotate at a slower speed than the outer roadwheel when the car is cornering.

The input and output shafts are arranged side by side, parallel to the crankshaft and driveshafts, so that their gear pinion teeth are in constant mesh. In the neutral position, the output shaft gear pinions rotate freely, so that drive cannot be transmitted to the crownwheel.

Gear selection is via a floor-mounted lever and selector rod mechanism.

The transmission selector rod causes the appropriate selector fork to move its respective synchro-sleeve along the output shaft, to lock the gear pinion to the synchro-hub. Since the synchro-hubs are splined to the output shaft, this locks the pinion to the shaft, so that drive can be transmitted. To ensure that gear-changing can be made quickly and quietly, a synchro-mesh system is fitted to all forward gears, consisting of baulk rings and spring-loaded fingers, as well as the gear pinions and synchro-hubs. The synchro-mesh cones are formed on the mating faces of the baulk rings and gear pinions.

2 Manual transmission - draining and refilling

1 This operation is much quicker and more efficient if the car is first taken on a journey of sufficient length to warm the engine/transmission up to normal operating temperature.

2 Park the car on level ground, switch off the ignition and apply the handbrake firmly. For improved access, jack up the front of the car and support it securely on axle stands (see *"Jacking and Vehicle Support"*). Note that the car must be lowered to the ground and level, to ensure accuracy, when refilling and

checking the oil level.

3 Remove all traces of dirt then unscrew the filler/level plug from the front face of the transmission. Note it is the plug furthest from the engine - do not confuse it with the blanking plug near the bellhousing **(see illustration)**.

4 Position a suitable container under the transmission, then unscrew the drain plug and allow the oil to drain completely into the container. An Allen key will be required to remove the plug **(see illustration)**. If the oil is hot, take precautions against scalding. Clean both the filler/level and the drain plugs, being especially careful to wipe away any metallic particles from the magnet on the drain plug.

5 When the oil has finished draining, clean the drain plug threads and those of the transmission casing and refit the drain plug, tightening it securely. If the car was raised for the draining operation, now lower it to the ground.

6 Refilling the transmission is an awkward operation. Above all, allow plenty of time for the oil level to settle properly before checking it. Note that the car must be parked on flat level ground when checking the oil level.

7 Refill the transmission with the exact amount of the specified type of oil then check the oil level as described in Chapter 1A or B. The level must be between 10 mm and 15 mm below the bottom edge of the filler/level plug hole (use a cranked tool such as an Allen key to check the level). When the level is correct,

2.3 Unscrewing the oil filler/level plug from the front of the transmission

2.4 Unscrewing the transmission drain plug using an Allen key

2.7a Refilling the transmission with oil

2.7b Using an Allen key to check that the oil level is between 10 mm and 15 mm below the bottom edge of the filler/level plug hole

refit the filler level plug and tighten it to the specified torque (see illustrations).
8 Lower the car to the ground.

3 Gearchange linkage - adjustment

1 Firmly apply the handbrake, then jack up the front of the vehicle and support it securely on axle stands (see *"Jacking and Vehicle Support"*).
2 On petrol engine models, unbolt the heatshield(s) from the underbody for access to the bottom of the gear lever. It is not necessary to completely remove the heatshields, only pull down one side of them (see illustration).

3.2 Unscrew the special nuts in order to bend down the underbody heatshields

3.6 Insert a 9 mm drill bit through the special hole

3 Loosen the clamp bolt and disconnect the gearchange rod from the transmission selector shaft.
4 Slide the selector shaft back and forth to find its central position, then turn the selector shaft to the right and left to find the central position in the transverse plane. Hold the selector shaft in the centralised position, then insert a suitable rod (or punch) into the hole in the selector shaft in the transmission, and move it as far forwards as possible.
5 Locate the gearchange rod on the selector shaft, then have an assistant position the gear lever approximately in the 4th position.
6 Using a 9 mm drill bit inserted through the special hole in the bottom of the gear lever housing, lock the gear lever in 4th position. It will be necessary for the assistant to move the gear lever slightly until the drill locates correctly (see illustration).

7 With the gearchange rod and gear lever in 4th, tighten the clamp bolt to the specified torque.
8 Check the adjustment, by moving the gear lever in all positions.
9 Refit the heatshields, then lower the car to the ground.

4 Gearchange linkage and lever - removal, overhaul and refitting

Removal

1 Working inside the vehicle carefully unscrew the knob from the top of the gear lever, then lift the gaiter and frame from the centre console (see illustration).

4.1 Gearchange linkage and lever

1 Assembly	6 Bolt	11 Stabiliser bar	17 Gaiter
2 Gear lever	7 Stabiliser bar	12 Bush	18 Boot
3 Bearing	pivot bolt	13 Washer	19 Rivet
4 Support bracket	8 Bush	14 Nut	20 Knob
5 Housing	9 Boot	15 Insert	21 Collar
	10 Rod and clevis	16 Boot retainer	

7A

4.5 Unscrewing the bolt securing the gearchange stabiliser rod to the transmission

2 Remove the inner gaiter over the gear lever.
3 Apply the handbrake, then jack up the front of the vehicle and support it on axle stands (see *"Jacking and Vehicle Support"*).
4 Unbolt the heatshield(s) from the underbody for access to the bottom of the gear lever.
5 Unscrew the bolt securing the gearchange stabiliser rod to the transmission and tie the rod to one side **(see illustration)**. Note that the washer is located next to the transmission.
6 Mark the position of the gearchange rod clamp on the transmission selector shaft, then unscrew and remove the clamp bolt and disconnect the gearchange rod.
7 Unscrew the gear lever support bracket mounting bolts on the underbody, and withdraw the gearchange linkage from under the car.

Overhaul

8 Unbolt the stabiliser rod from the gear lever housing.
9 Withdraw the noise damping pad over the gear lever, and remove the support bracket from the rear of the housing.
10 Using a screwdriver carefully press out the locking lugs, then withdraw the gear lever from the top of the housing.
11 Mount the inverted gear lever in a vice, then lever off the mounting sleeve using two screwdrivers.
12 Remove the rubber boot from the gearchange rod, then lever off the housing cover and remove the rod.

13 Clean all components and examine them for wear and damage. Obtain new items as necessary.
14 If necessary the bush in the stabiliser rod can be removed by pressing it out using suitable diameter metal tubes and a vice. Press in the new bush using the same method.
15 Reassemble the linkage using a reversal of dismantling, but apply a little grease to the bearing surfaces.

Refitting

16 Refitting is a reversal of removal, but adjust the linkage as described in Section 3.

5 Oil seals - renewal

1 Oil leaks frequently occur due to wear or deterioration of the differential side gear seals and/or the transmission selector shaft oil seal and speedometer drive pinion O-ring. Renewal of these seals is relatively easy, since the repairs can be performed without removing the transmission from the vehicle, however if the input shaft oil seal requires renewal the transmission must be removed.

Differential side gear oil seals

2 The differential side gear oil seals are located at the sides of the transmission, where the driveshafts enter the transmission. If leakage at the seal is suspected, raise the vehicle and support it securely on axle stands (see *"Jacking and Vehicle Support"*). If the seal is leaking, oil will be found on the side of the transmission below the driveshaft.
3 Referring to Chapter 8, disconnect the driveshaft from the transmission. Note that it is not necessary to remove the driveshaft completely, the shaft can be left attached to the hub carrier and slid off from the differential gear splines as the hub assembly is pulled outwards. On the right-hand driveshaft, if the stub has not been removed from the transmission, it will be necessary to remove the left-hand driveshaft then use a screwdriver or similar tool to drive the stub from the right-hand side of the transmission.

Note: *With the driveshaft removed from the transmission, do not allow it to hang down under its own weight as this could damage the constant velocity joints/gaiters.*
4 Wipe clean the old oil seal and note its fitted depth below the casing edge. This is necessary to determine the correct fitted position of the new oil seal. The fitted depth will be approximately 5 mm.
5 Using a large screwdriver or lever, carefully prise the oil seal out of the transmission casing, taking care not to damage the casing **(see illustration)**. If the oil seal is reluctant to move, it is sometimes helpful to carefully drive it *into* the transmission a little way, applying the force at one point only. This will have the effect of swivelling the seal out of the casing, and it can then be pulled out. If the oil seal is particularly difficult to remove, an oil seal removal tool may be obtained from a garage or accessory shop.
6 Wipe clean the oil seal seating in the transmission casing.
7 Dip the new oil seal in clean oil, then press it a little way into the casing by hand, making sure that it is square to its seating with its closed end facing outwards **(see illustration)**.
8 Using suitable tubing or a large socket, carefully drive the oil seal fully into the casing up to its previously-noted fitted depth **(see illustration)**.

> **HAYNES HINT** *Wrap adhesive tape around the socket to indicate the depth to fit the oil seal*

9 Refit the driveshaft with reference to Chapter 8. On the right-hand driveshaft fit the stub first and make sure the circlip is fully engaged with the groove in the differential gears.

Transmission selector shaft oil seal

10 Apply the handbrake, then jack up the front of the vehicle and support it on axle stands (see *"Jacking and Vehicle Support"*).
11 Mark the position of the gearchange rod clamp on the transmission selector shaft.
12 Unscrew and remove the clamp bolt and disconnect the gearchange rod.

5.5 Prising the oil seal from the transmission

5.7 Locating a new oil seal on the transmission aperture

5.8 Driving the new oil seal into the transmission casing. Note the adhesive tape to indicate the fitting depth

13 Remove the rubber boot for access to the oil seal.

14 Using a suitable tool or grips, pull the oil seal out of the transmission casing. Ford technicians use a slide hammer, with an end fitting which locates over the oil seal extension. In the absence of this tool, if the oil seal is particularly tight, drill one or two small holes in the oil seal, and screw in self-tapping screws. The oil seal can then be removed from the casing by pulling on the screws.

15 Wipe clean the oil seal seating in the transmission.

16 Dip the new oil seal in clean oil, then press it a little way into the casing by hand, making sure that it is square to its seating and with its closed end facing outwards.

17 Using suitable tubing or a large socket, carefully drive the oil seal fully into the casing.

18 Locate the rubber boot over the selector shaft.

19 The gearchange linkage rod can now be reconnected and adjusted using the procedure described in Section 3.

Speedometer drive pinion oil seal

20 The procedure is covered in Section 7.

Input shaft oil seal

21 Remove the clutch slave cylinder from the transmission as described in Chapter 6.

22 Hook out the oil seal using a suitable tool, taking care not to damage the input shaft. If it is tight, drill one or two small holes in the oil seal, and screw in self-tapping screws. The oil seal can then be removed from the casing by pulling on the screws.

23 Wipe clean the oil seal seating in the transmission.

24 Dip the new oil seal in clean oil, then locate it over the input shaft and press it a little way into the casing by hand, making sure that it is square to its seating and with its closed end facing outwards.

25 Locate the clutch slave cylinder over the input shaft and refit it with reference to Chapter 6. The action of tightening the mounting bolts evenly, presses the oil seal into the transmission casing.

---

6 Reversing light switch and multi-function switch - testing, removal and refitting

Reversing light switch

Testing

1 The reversing light circuit is controlled by a plunger-type switch that is screwed into the front of the transmission casing, near the bellhousing. If a fault develops in the circuit, first ensure that the circuit fuse has not blown.

2 To test the switch, disconnect the wiring connector, and use a multimeter (set to the resistance function) or a battery-and-bulb test circuit to check that there is continuity between the switch terminals only when reverse gear is selected. If this is not the case, and there are no obvious breaks or other damage to the wires, the switch is faulty, and must be renewed.

Removal

3 Apply the handbrake, then jack up the front of the vehicle and support it on axle stands (see *"Jacking and Vehicle Support"*).

4 Disconnect the wiring from the reversing light switch.

5 Unscrew the switch from the front of the transmission.

Refitting

6 Clean the location in the transmission, and the threads of the switch.

7 Insert the switch and tighten securely.

8 Reconnect the wiring.

9 Check and top-up the transmission oil level if necessary, with reference to Chapter 1A or B.

10 Lower the vehicle to the ground.

Multi-function switch

Testing

11 The multi-function switch is incorporated in the engine management system. Testing should be referred to a Ford dealer.

Removal

12 Apply the handbrake, then jack up the

front of the vehicle and support it on axle stands (see *"Jacking and Vehicle Support"*).

13 Disconnect the wiring from the multi-function switch.

14 Unbolt the retaining bracket and remove the switch from the transmission.

Refitting

15 Refitting is a reversal of removal.

---

7 Speedometer drive - removal and refitting

Removal

1 Disconnect the battery negative (earth) lead (see Chapter 5A).

2 Undo the retaining nut, and withdraw the speedometer cable from the vehicle speed sensor in the top face of the transmission. Use two spanners to loosen the nut - one to counterhold the sensor, and the other to unscrew the cable nut.

3 Disconnect the wiring from the vehicle speed sensor, then unscrew the sensor from the top of the drive pinion **(see illustration)**.

4 Grip the drive pinion retaining pin with self-locking grips or pliers, and withdraw it from the drive pinion housing.

5 Pull the drive pinion and bearing out of the housing, but take care not to tilt it, because the pinion and bearing are not secured and can easily be separated if the pinion is snagged **(see illustration)**.

6 Using a small screwdriver, prise the O-ring from the groove in the bearing; obtain a new one for reassembly.

7 Wipe clean the drive pinion and bearing, also the seating bore in the transmission casing.

Refitting

8 Refitting is a reversal of the removal procedure, but lightly oil the new O-ring before inserting the assembly in the transmission casing. Drive in the retaining roll pin using a hammer **(see illustration)**.

7A

7.3 Vehicle speed sensor on the rear of the transmission

7.5 Speedometer drive pinion (A) pinion bearing (B) and drive cable (C)

7.8 Insert the speedometer drive pinion/bearing (A) and secure with a new retaining pin (B)

8.9 Support bar across the engine compartment supporting the engine

8.12a Removing the left-hand suspension strut and driveshaft complete

8.12b Tie the brake caliper to the inner wing panel using wire

8 Manual transmission - removal and refitting

Zetec SE engine models

Removal

1 The manual transmission is removed downwards from the engine compartment, after disconnecting it from the engine. Due to the weight of the unit, it will be necessary to have a suitable method of supporting the transmission as it is lowered during removal and subsequently raised during its refitting. A trolley jack fitted with a suitable saddle to support the transmission as it is removed will be ideal, but failing this, an engine lift hoist and sling will suffice. The weight of the engine will also need to be supported whilst the transmission is detached from it - an engine support bar fitted in the front wing drain channel each side is ideal for this purpose, but care must be taken not to damage the wings or their paintwork. If this type of tool is not available (or cannot be fabricated), the engine can be supported by blocks or a second jack from underneath.

2 Disconnect and remove the battery as described in Chapter 5A.

3 Unscrew the bolts securing the battery tray to the body. Cut the plastic cable tie and remove the tray.

4 Loosen the clips and remove the air inlet duct from between the air mass air flow sensor on the air cleaner and the throttle housing.

5 Apply the handbrake, then jack up the front of the vehicle and support it on axle stands (see *"Jacking and Vehicle Support"*). Remove both front roadwheels, then unbolt the plastic cover from under the crankshaft pulley.

6 Position a container beneath the transmission, then unscrew the drain plug and drain the oil. On completion clean the drain plug and refit it. Tighten the plug to the specified torque.

7 Unscrew the bolt securing the gearchange stabiliser rod to the transmission and tie the rod to one side.

8 Mark the position of the gearchange rod clamp on the transmission shaft, then unscrew and remove the clamp bolt and disconnect the gearchange rod.

9 Using a hoist, support the weight of the engine. Alternatively, use a purpose-made support bar across the engine compartment, located in the front wing drain channels **(see illustration)**.

10 Unbolt and remove the rear engine mounting link (see Chapter 2A). Hold the engine stationary while the bolts are being removed since the link will be under tension.

11 Unscrew and remove the clamp bolts and disconnect the lower suspension arms from the hub carriers on each side as described in Chapter 10.

12 Using a lever, remove the left-hand driveshaft from the transmission while pulling out the suspension strut (refer to Chapter 8). Tie the driveshaft to one side making sure that the joints are not bent more that 18° otherwise they may be damaged. If preferred to give additional working room, remove the left-hand strut complete with driveshaft with reference to Chapter 8. If this course of action is taken, tie up the brake caliper with a piece of wire **(see illustrations)**.

13 Unscrew and remove the two bolts securing the right-hand driveshaft centre bearing to the rear of the engine and temporarily support it.

14 Using a drift entered from the left-hand side of the transmission, carefully drive the inner end of the right-hand driveshaft from the transmission taking care to prevent it from dropping. Tie the driveshaft to one side making sure that the joints are not bent more that 18° otherwise they may be damaged.

15 Disconnect the wiring from the multi-function switch on the front of the transmission **(see illustration)**.

16 Where fitted, unscrew and remove the pivot bolt from the front of the left-hand lower suspension arm, and remove the small bracket from the front of the subframe **(see illustration)**.

17 Unbolt the reinforcement bar, then pull out the transmission breather and unscrew the mounting nuts from the left-hand engine mounting. Note that the arrow on the breather points to the front of the car **(see illustrations)**.

8.15 Disconnecting the wiring from the multi-function switch on the front of the transmission

8.16 Small bracket located on the left-hand front lower suspension arm front pivot bolt

8.17a Unbolt the reinforcement bar . . .

8.17b . . . then pull out the transmission breather . . .

8.17c . . . and unscrew the nuts from the left-hand mounting

8.22 Releasing the clutch hydraulic line from the support

18 Disconnect the vacuum hose from the EGR valve (see Chapter 4C).

19 Lower the engine and transmission until the left-hand engine mounting is clear of the mounting studs.

20 Unbolt the bracket from the throttle housing.

21 Fit a hose clamp to the clutch hydraulic hose leading to the slave cylinder. Alternatively tighten the fluid reservoir cap onto a piece of polythene - this will prevent excessive loss of hydraulic fluid.

22 Pull out the clip and disconnect the hydraulic hose quick release connector from the clutch slave cylinder. Plug the hose and slave cylinder to prevent dust and dirt entering the system. Release the hydraulic line from the support **(see illustration)**.

23 Unscrew the retaining nut and disconnect the speedometer drive cable from the vehicle speed sensor on the transmission **(see illustration)**.

24 Support the transmission on a trolley jack, then unscrew and remove the bolts securing the right-hand rear of the transmission to the engine.

25 Unscrew and remove the remaining bolts securing the transmission to the engine. Note the lower bolts are on the engine sump side, and also note that the uppermost bolt secures the transmission earth lead.

26 With the help of an assistant withdraw the transmission directly from the engine until the input shaft is clear of the clutch pressure plate assembly, then lower it to the ground and remove from under the car **(see illustration)**.

Refitting

27 Refitting is a reversal of removal, but note the following additional points:
 a) Make sure that all mating faces are clean.
 b) Apply a smear of high-melting-point grease to the splines of the transmission input shaft. Do not apply too much, otherwise there is the possibility of the grease contaminating the clutch friction disc.
 c) Ensure that the engine adapter plate is correctly seated on the locating dowels on the engine.
 d) Fit new circlips to the grooves in the inner end of each driveshaft CV joint, and

ensure that they fully engage as they are fitted into the transmission.
 e) Refit and adjust the engine mountings as described in Chapter 2B.
 f) Check and if necessary adjust the gearchange as described in Section 3.
 g) Replenish the transmission oil, and check the level with reference to Chapter 1A or B.
 h) Top up and bleed the clutch hydraulic system as described in Chapter 6.
 i) Tighten all nuts and bolts to the specified torque settings.

Endura E engine models

Removal

28 The manual transmission is removed downwards from the engine compartment, after disconnecting it from the engine. Due to the weight of the unit, it will be necessary to have a suitable method of supporting the transmission as it is lowered during removal and subsequently raised during its refitting. A trolley jack fitted with a suitable saddle to support the transmission as it is removed will be ideal, but failing this, an engine lift hoist and sling will suffice. The weight of the engine will also need to be supported whilst the transmission is detached from it - an engine support bar fitted in the front wing drain channel each side is ideal for this purpose, but care must be taken not to damage the wings or their paintwork. If this type of tool is not available (or cannot be fabricated), the engine can be supported by blocks or a second jack from underneath.

29 Loosen the clips and remove the air inlet duct.

30 Disconnect and remove the battery as described in Chapter 5A.

31 Unscrew the bolts securing the battery tray to the body. Cut the plastic cable tie and remove the tray.

32 Apply the handbrake, then jack up the front of the vehicle and support it on axle stands (see "Jacking and Vehicle Support"). Remove both front roadwheels.

33 Position a container beneath the transmission, then unscrew the drain plug and drain the oil. On completion clean the drain plug and refit it. Tighten the plug to the specified torque.

34 Disconnect the oxygen sensor wiring at the plug.

35 If necessary, disconnect the wiring from the starter motor and release the wiring from the bracket. This is not essential as the starter motor may be left in position while the transmission is being removed.

36 Unbolt the transmission earth lead from the top of the transmission.

37 Unscrew the retaining nut and disconnect the speedometer drive cable from the speed sensor on the transmission.

38 Disconnect the wiring plug leading to the vehicle speed sensor.

39 Place cloth rags beneath the fuel supply and return hoses at the fuel rail, then depress the quick release fittings and disconnect the hoses. Identify each hose for position to aid reassembly.

7A

8.23 Disconnecting the speedometer drive cable from the vehicle speed sensor on the rear of the transmission

8.26 Withdrawing the transmission from the engine

40 Remove the clutch hydraulic pipe with reference to Chapter 6.

41 Using a hoist, support the weight of the engine. Alternatively, use a purpose-made support bar across the engine compartment, located in the front wing drain channels.

42 Pull out the transmission breather then unscrew the nuts retaining the left-hand engine mounting to the transmission. Note that the arrow on the breather points to the front of the car.

43 Unbolt the auxiliary drivebelt lower cover from the underbody.

44 Disconnect the wiring from the multi-function switch on the front of the transmission.

45 Unbolt the exhaust front downpipe from the intermediate pipe with reference to Chapter 4A.

46 Unscrew the bolt securing the gearchange stabiliser rod to the transmission and tie the rod to one side.

47 Mark the position of the gearchange rod clamp on the transmission shaft, then unscrew and remove the clamp bolt and disconnect the gearchange rod.

48 Unbolt and remove the rear engine mounting link (see Chapter 2A). Hold the engine stationary while the bolts are being removed since the link will be under tension.

49 Unbolt the exhaust pipe mounting bracket from the cylinder block.

50 Disconnect the steering track rod end from the left-hand hub carrier as described in Chapter 10.

51 Unscrew and remove the clamp bolts and disconnect the lower suspension arms from the hub carriers on each side as described in Chapter 10.

52 Unscrew the nuts and disconnect the anti-roll bar link from the left-hand front suspension strut (refer to Chapter 10).

53 Using a lever, remove the left-hand driveshaft from the transmission while pulling out the suspension strut (refer to Chapter 8). Tie the driveshaft to one side making sure that the joints are not bent more that 18° otherwise they may be damaged.

54 Unscrew and remove the two bolts securing the right-hand driveshaft centre bearing to the rear of the engine and temporarily support it.

55 Using a drift entered from the left-hand side of the transmission, carefully drive the inner end of the right-hand driveshaft from the transmission taking care to prevent it from dropping. Tie the driveshaft to one side making sure that the joints are not bent more that 18° otherwise they may be damaged.

56 Lower the transmission and engine until there is free access to the transmission from the left-hand side of the car.

57 Unscrew and remove the bolts securing the right-hand rear of the transmission to the engine.

58 Move the cable guide to one side, then unscrew the bolts securing the top of the transmission to the engine and withdraw the adapter plate.

59 At the front of the transmission, unscrew and remove the bolts securing the transmission to the engine. Note the location of the TDC sensor cover retained by two of the bolts.

60 With the help of an assistant withdraw the transmission directly from the engine until the input shaft is clear of the clutch pressure plate assembly, then lower it to the ground and remove from under the car.

Refitting

61 Refitting is a reversal of removal, but note the following additional points:
a) *Make sure that all mating faces are clean.*
b) *Apply a smear of high-melting-point grease to the splines of the transmission input shaft. Do not apply too much, otherwise there is the possibility of the grease contaminating the clutch friction disc.*
c) *Ensure that the engine adapter plate is correctly seated on the locating dowels on the engine.*
d) *Fit new circlips to the grooves in the inner end of each driveshaft CV joint, and ensure that they fully engage as they are fitted into the transmission.*
e) *Refit and adjust the engine mountings as described in Chapter 2A.*
f) *Check and if necessary adjust the gearchange as described in Section 3.*
g) *Replenish the transmission oil, and check the level with reference to Section 2.*
h) *Top up and bleed the clutch hydraulic system as described in Chapter 6.*
i) *Tighten all nuts and bolts to the specified torque setting.*

Endura DE engine models

Removal

62 The manual transmission is removed downwards from the engine compartment, after disconnecting it from the engine. Due to the weight of the unit, it will be necessary to have a suitable method of supporting the transmission as it is lowered during removal and subsequently raised during its refitting. A trolley jack fitted with a suitable saddle to support the transmission as it is removed will be ideal, but failing this, an engine lift hoist and sling will suffice. The weight of the engine will also need to be supported whilst the transmission is detached from it - an engine support bar fitted in the front wing drain channel each side is ideal for this purpose, but care must be taken not to damage the wings or their paintwork. If this type of tool is not available (or cannot be fabricated), the engine can be supported by blocks or a second jack from underneath.

63 Disconnect and remove the battery as described in Chapter 5A.

64 Unscrew the bolts securing the battery tray to the body.

65 Loosen the clips securing the air inlet duct to the inlet manifold and resonator. Release the duct from the support clip then withdraw it from the air cleaner.

66 Unscrew the mounting bolts and remove the air inlet resonator.

67 Fit a hose clamp to the clutch hydraulic hose leading to the slave cylinder. Alternatively tighten the fluid reservoir cap onto a piece of polythene - this will prevent excessive loss of hydraulic fluid.

68 Pull out the clip and disconnect the hydraulic hose quick release connector from the clutch slave cylinder. Plug the hose and slave cylinder to prevent dust and dirt entering the system.

69 Unscrew and remove the two upper bolts securing the transmission to the engine, noting the location of the bracket.

70 Using a hoist, support the weight of the engine. Alternatively, use a purpose-made support bar across the engine compartment, located in the front wing drain channels.

71 Pull out the transmission breather, then unscrew the nuts securing the left-hand engine mounting to the transmission. Note that the arrow on the breather points to the front of the car.

72 Unscrew the nuts and remove the right-hand engine mounting bracket.

73 Remove the wheel trim from the right-hand front wheel, then loosen the driveshaft nut using a 32 mm socket and extension bar.

74 Apply the handbrake, then jack up the front of the vehicle and support it on axle stands (see *"Jacking and Vehicle Support"*). Remove both front roadwheels.

75 Position a container beneath the transmission, then unscrew the drain plug and drain the oil (refer to Chapter 1A or B). On completion clean the drain plug and refit it. Tighten the plug to the specified torque.

76 Unscrew the bolt securing the gearchange stabiliser rod to the transmission and tie the rod to one side.

77 Mark the position of the gearchange rod clamp on the transmission shaft, then unscrew and remove the clamp bolt and disconnect the gearchange rod.

78 Unbolt and remove the rear engine mounting link (see Chapter 2A). Hold the engine stationary while the bolts are being removed since the link will be under tension.

79 Disconnect the wiring from the multi-function switch on the front of the transmission.

80 Unscrew the retaining nut and disconnect the speedometer drive cable from the speed sensor on the transmission.

81 Unscrew and remove the clamp bolts and disconnect the lower suspension arms from the hub carriers on each side as described in Chapter 10.

82 Using a lever, remove the left-hand driveshaft from the transmission while pulling out the suspension strut (refer to Chapter 8). Tie the driveshaft to one side making sure that the joints are not bent more that 18¡ otherwise they may be damaged.

83 Unscrew and remove the two bolts securing the right-hand driveshaft centre bearing to the rear of the engine and temporarily support it.

84 Push the right-hand driveshaft from the hub carrier while pulling the carrier outwards. If the driveshaft is tight, use a suitable puller mounted on the wheel studs to force it out. Support the driveshaft on an axle stand.

85 Using a drift entered from the left-hand side of the transmission, carefully drive the inner end of the right-hand driveshaft from the transmission taking care to prevent it from dropping. Remove the driveshaft from under the car.

86 Lower the engine and transmission until the rear engine mounting is clear of the mounting studs.

87 Support the weight of the transmission on a trolley jack, then unscrew and remove the bolt securing the exhaust resonator bracket.

88 Unscrew and remove the bolts securing the transmission to the engine.

89 With the help of an assistant withdraw the transmission directly from the engine until the input shaft is clear of the clutch pressure plate assembly, then lower it to the ground and remove from under the car.

Refitting

90 Refitting is a reversal of removal, but note the following additional points:

a) Make sure that all mating faces are clean.
b) Apply a smear of high-melting-point grease to the splines of the transmission input shaft. Do not apply too much, otherwise there is the possibility of the grease contaminating the clutch friction disc.
c) Ensure that the engine adapter plate is correctly seated on the locating dowels on the engine.
d) Fit new circlips to the grooves in the inner end of each driveshaft CV joint, and ensure that they fully engage as they are fitted into the transmission.
e) Refer to Chapter 8 when refitting the right-hand driveshaft, and if necessary use a suitable puller to draw it into the hub carrier. Fit a new driveshaft nut and tighten it to the specified torque.
f) Refit and adjust the engine mountings as described in Chapter 2B.
g) Check and if necessary adjust the gearchange as described in Section 3.
h) Replenish the transmission oil, and check the level with reference to Section 2.
i) Top up and bleed the clutch hydraulic system as described in Chapter 6.
j) Tighten all nuts and bolts to the specified torque settings.

9 Manual transmission overhaul - general information

1 Overhauling a manual transmission unit is a difficult and involved job for the DIY home mechanic. In addition to dismantling and reassembling many small parts, clearances must be precisely measured and, if necessary, changed by selecting shims and spacers. Internal transmission components are also often difficult to obtain, and in many instances, extremely expensive. Because of this, if the transmission develops a fault or becomes noisy, the best course of action is to have the unit overhauled by a specialist repairer, or to obtain an exchange reconditioned unit.

2 Nevertheless, it is not impossible for the more experienced mechanic to overhaul the transmission, provided the special tools are available, and the job is done in a deliberate step-by-step manner, so that nothing is overlooked.

3 The tools necessary for an overhaul include internal and external circlip pliers, bearing pullers, a slide hammer, a set of pin punches, a dial test indicator, and possibly a hydraulic press. In addition, a large, sturdy workbench and a vice will be required.

4 During dismantling of the transmission, make careful notes of how each component is fitted, to make reassembly easier and more accurate.

5 Before dismantling the transmission, it will help if you have some idea what area is malfunctioning. Certain problems can be closely related to specific areas in the transmission, which can make component examination and replacement easier. Refer to the "Fault finding" Section at the rear of this manual for more information.

7A

Notes

Chapter 7 Part B:
Automatic transmission

Contents

Degrees of difficulty

| Easy, suitable for novice with little experience | | Fairly easy, suitable for beginner with some experience | | Fairly difficult, suitable for competent DIY mechanic | | Difficult, suitable for experienced DIY mechanic | | Very difficult, suitable for expert DIY or professional | 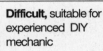 |

Specifications

General
Type . . . . Hydraulically-controlled continuously-variable automatic transmission
Designation . . . . CTX

Lubrication
Capacity . . . . 5.0 litres (at fluid change), 5.6 litres (from dry)
Recommended oil . . . . See end of "Weekly checks"

Torque wrench settings

	Nm	lbf ft
Transmission to engine	44	32
Rear engine mounting to body	56	41
Selector cable bracket to transmission	40	30
Sump	8	6
Oil strainer	8	6
Oil pipe to radiator cooler	20	15
Oil pipe to connector	20	15
Oil filler pipe to transmission	20	15
Drain plug	33	25
Torsional vibration damper	30	22
Radiator support crossmember	25	19

1 General information and precautions

The CTX transmission is an automatic transmission providing continuously-variable drive over the entire speed range. Torque from the engine is transmitted to the transmission via an input shaft and a multi-plate wet clutch (rather than a conventional torque converter employed on most automatic transmissions).

A steel thrust-link drivebelt made of disc-shaped steel elements transmits the torque from the primary cone pulley (driven by the engine) to the secondary cone pulley. The secondary cone pulley is linked by a series of gears to the final drive gear which drives the differential unit and the driveshafts.

The continuous variation in ratio is produced by altering the diameter of the path followed by the drivebelt around the two cone pulleys. This alteration of the drivebelt path is produced by a hydraulic control system which moves one half of each cone pulley in an axial direction. The secondary pulley cone is also spring-loaded, to keep the drivebelt at the required tension needed to transmit the torque. The hydraulic control system is governed by the position of the transmission selector lever, the accelerator pedal and the load resistance encountered (such as up or down gradients), as well as road speed.

The selector lever is connected to the transmission selector shaft by a cable.

A gear-type pump delivers fluid (according to the input speed) to the hydraulic control system. A transmission fluid cooler is attached to the right-hand side of the radiator.

As with conventional automatic transmission systems, the CTX type has a parking mechanism. The parking pawl engages with the teeth on the outside of the secondary pulley. A starter inhibitor switch prevents the engine from being started in selector positions R, D or L.

When accelerating, the engine speed may sound higher than would normally be expected, similar to a slipping clutch on a manual transmission vehicle. The reverse is true when decelerating, with the engine speed dropping faster than the comparable drop in road speed. These are normal characteristics of the CTX transmission.

Precautions

When the vehicle is parked and left with the engine running, or when any checks and/or adjustments are being carried out, the handbrake must be applied and the selector lever moved to the "P" position.

Do not allow the engine speed to rise above the normal idle speed when the vehicle is stationary with the selector lever in the R, D or L position.

7B

2.5 Selector cable fitting to selector lever (A) and selector cable abutment retaining clip arrangement (B)

2.11 Securing the selector cable to the selector lever

The engine must not run at more than 3000 rpm with the selector lever in the R, D or L position when the driving (front) roadwheels are clear of the ground.

It is not permissible to tow a vehicle fitted with the CTX automatic transmission otherwise internal damage will occur to the transmission. The vehicle may be towed with the front wheels lifted clear of the ground, or it may be loaded onto a trailer or breakdown truck.

2 Selector cable - removal, refitting and adjustment

Removal

1 Disconnect the battery negative (earth) lead (see Chapter 5A).
2 Refer to Chapter 11 and remove the centre console.
3 Move the selector lever to position "P" (the lever on the transmission selector shaft should also be in position "P" - the most forward position). This is important for correct subsequent adjustment of the selector cable.
4 Detach the selector gate from the selector lever housing by undoing its two securing screws. Slide it off over the selector lever, having unscrewed the selector lever knob.
5 Using a suitable screwdriver as a lever, prise free the plastic connecting eye of the selector lever from the cable, then prise free the cable retaining clip, and withdraw the cable from the selector housing. If necessary, cut the carpet at the front to allow extra access **(see illustration)**.
6 Chock the rear wheels then jack up the front of the car and support it on axle stands (see "Jacking and Vehicle Support").
7 Working beneath the vehicle, disconnect the cable from the transmission lever by

pulling out the special clip and turning it through 90°.
8 Pull out the outer cable support clip, and withdraw the cable to the rear.
9 Pull free the rubber gaiter from the floor, and then withdraw the selector cable from the vehicle.

Refitting

10 Feed the selector cable up through the floor, refit the rubber gaiter, then lower the vehicle to the ground.
11 Reconnect the selector cable to the lever and housing, ensuring that the annular bead of the cable eye faces the end of the pin. Use a suitable pair of pliers to press the pin in until it is heard to clip into engagement **(see illustration)**.
12 The selector lever must now be moved to the "P" position, and the vehicle then raised and supported at the front end again.
13 Reconnect the cable to the transmission, then adjust the cable as follows before refitting the centre console and selector gate assembly.

Adjustment

14 The vehicle must be raised and supported on axle stands at the front end to make the cable adjustment check (see "Jacking and Vehicle Support").
15 With the selector lever set in the "P" position, the parking pawl engaged and the gears immobilised, check that the lever/selector shaft drilling and the cable yoke are in alignment, and that the connecting pin is an easy fit. If required, draw the gaiter back from the yoke, and screw the yoke in the appropriate direction to reposition it on the cable so that the pin fits freely. Fit the pin and retaining clip, then relocate the bellows.
16 The vehicle can now be lowered to the ground.

3 Gear selector mechanism - removal and refitting

Removal

1 Refer to Section 2, paragraphs 1 to 5 inclusive, to disconnect the cable from the selector housing unit.
2 Pull free the quadrant illumination light bulbholder, then undo the four retaining bolts and remove the selector housing unit **(see illustration)**.
3 To remove the selector lever from the housing, release the clip and extract the lever pivot pin.

Refitting

4 Reassemble and refit in the reverse order of removal.

3.2 Selector lever housing retaining bolts (arrowed), and selector cover illumination bulbholder (A)

4 Speedometer drive pinion - removal and refitting

Removal

1 Disconnect the battery negative (earth) lead (see Chapter 5A).

2 Undo the retaining nut, and withdraw the speedometer cable from the transmission.

3 Grip the drive pinion retaining roll pin with self-locking grips or pliers, and withdraw it from the drive pinion housing.

4 Pull the drive pinion and bearing out of the housing, but take care not to tilt it, because the pinion and bearing are not secured and can easily be separated if the pinion is snagged.

5 Using a small screwdriver, prise the O-ring from the groove in the bearing; obtain a new one for reassembly.

6 Wipe clean the drive pinion and bearing, also the seating bore in the transmission casing.

Refitting

7 Refitting is a reversal of the removal procedure, but lightly oil the new O-ring before inserting the assembly in the transmission. Drive in the retaining roll pin as far as the stop. When fitted, it should protrude by approximately 5.0 mm.

5 Fluid seals - renewal

Differential side gear fluid seals

1 The procedure is the same as described for the oil seals on the manual transmission (refer to Chapter 7A).

Speedometer drive pinion fluid seal

2 The procedure is covered in Section 4 of this Chapter.

6 Automatic transmission - removal and refitting

Removal

1 The automatic transmission is removed downwards from the engine compartment, after disconnecting it from the engine. Due to the weight of the unit, it will be necessary to have a suitable method of supporting the transmission as it is lowered during removal, and subsequently raised during its refitting. A trolley jack fitted with a suitable saddle to support the transmission as it is removed will be ideal, but failing this, an engine lift hoist and sling will suffice. The weight of the engine

will also need to be supported whilst the transmission is detached from it. An engine support bar fitted in the front wing drain channel on each side is ideal for this purpose. If this type of tool is not available (or cannot be fabricated), the engine can be supported by blocks or a second jack from underneath.

2 Remove the battery as described in Chapter 5A.

3 Cut the plastic cable ties, then unbolt and remove the battery tray.

4 Loosen the clips and remove the air inlet duct from between the air cleaner and throttle housing.

5 Disconnect the accelerator cable from the throttle housing with reference to Chapter 4A.

6 Disconnect the hoses from the exhaust gas recirculation (EGR) valve at the left-hand end of the cylinder head.

7 Unscrew the front suspension strut upper mounting nut on each side five turns. The nuts are on top of the front suspension strut turrets.

8 Remove the radiator grille as described in Chapter 11.

9 Unscrew the upper mounting bolts securing the transmission to the engine, noting the location of the wiring support brackets and earth lead.

10 Unclip the vehicle speed sensor and disconnect the wiring plug.

11 Apply the handbrake, then jack up the front of the vehicle and support it on axle stands (see "Jacking and Vehicle Support"). Remove both front roadwheels.

12 Position a container beneath the transmission, then unscrew the drain plug and drain the fluid. On completion, wipe the drain plug clean and refit it, tightening it to the specified torque.

Caution: Make sure the fluid has had time to cool before loosening the drain plug!

13 Undo the screws and remove the radiator lower cover.

14 Disconnect the fluid cooler hoses from the transmission by unscrewing the outer union nut while holding the inner adapter with a further spanner. Be prepared for some fluid loss.

15 Disconnect the electric cooling fan wiring at the connector and unclip it from the radiator.

16 Using plastic cable ties or string, tie the radiator to the bonnet lock plate on the front crossmember. Make sure the radiator is secure.

17 Support the radiator lower support crossmember, then unscrew the mounting bolts and lower it from the underbody and radiator together with the electric cooling fan. Leave the radiator suspended by the cable ties.

18 On models with power-assisted steering remove the auxiliary drivebelt as described in Chapter 1A, then unbolt the pump together with its mounting bracket from the cylinder block and tie it to one side. Refer to Chapter 10 for more information if necessary.

19 Unclip the selector cable from the lever on the transmission, then withdraw the cable from the bracket and tie it to one side.

20 Unscrew the retaining nut and pull the speedometer drive cable from the speed sensor on the rear of the transmission.

21 Remove the brake pipe bracket from the left-hand front suspension strut (refer to Chapter 9).

22 Unscrew the nuts and disconnect the anti-roll bar links from the front suspension struts on each side (refer to Chapter 10).

23 Unclip the ABS sensors on each side (refer to Chapter 9).

24 Disconnect the steering track rod ends from the hub carriers on each side of the car (refer to Chapter 10).

25 Unscrew and remove the clamp bolts and disconnect the lower suspension arms from the hub carriers on each side as described in Chapter 10.

26 Disconnect the wiring from the lock switch on the lower rear of the transmission.

27 Using a lever, remove the left-hand driveshaft from the transmission while pulling out the suspension strut (refer to Chapter 8). Tie the driveshaft to one side making sure that the joints are not bent more that 18° otherwise they may be damaged.

28 Unscrew and remove the two bolts securing the right-hand driveshaft centre bearing to the rear of the engine and temporarily support it.

29 Using a drift entered from the left-hand side of the transmission, carefully drive the inner end of the right-hand driveshaft from the transmission taking care to prevent it from dropping. Tie the driveshaft to one side making sure that the joints are not bent more that 18° otherwise they may be damaged.

30 Remove the starter motor as described in Chapter 5A.

31 Unbolt the exhaust front downpipe from the intermediate pipe with reference to Chapter 4A.

32 Unbolt and remove the rear engine mounting/link (see Chapter 2A or 2B). Hold the engine stationary while the bolts are being removed, since the mounting will be under tension.

33 Using a hoist, support the weight of the engine and transmission. Alternatively, use a purpose-made support bar across the engine compartment, located in the front wing drain channels.

34 Undo the nuts and bolts and remove the left-hand engine mounting bracket from the transmission and insulator.

35 Unscrew the nuts and remove the right-hand engine mounting upper bracket.

36 Lower the engine and transmission until the left-hand engine mounting is clear of the mounting studs and the top of the transmission is level with the crossmember.

37 Support the transmission on a trolley jack, then unscrew and remove the upper rear and lower front bolts (with heads facing the right-hand side) securing the transmission to the engine.

7B

38 At this stage it is advisable to have an assistant at the ready. Undo the remaining transmission bolts and carefully withdraw the transmission from the engine noting the location of the wiring support brackets. Do not allow the weight of the transmission to bear on the input shaft and vibration damper.
39 Lower the jack and remove the transmission from under the car.
40 If necessary, mark the torsional vibration damper in relation to the flywheel then unscrew the mounting bolts and withdraw the damper. Use a wide-bladed screwdriver engaged with the starter ring gear to hold the flywheel stationary. Examine the damper for wear and damage and renew it if necessary.

Refitting

41 If removed, refit the torsional vibration damper to the flywheel and tighten the mounting bolts to the specified torque while holding the flywheel stationary using the method previously described.
42 Do not lubricate the transmission input shaft, as this may contaminate and adversely affect the operation of the torsional vibration damper.
43 Raise the transmission on the jack and align the input shaft with the centre of the torsional vibration damper. Check that the engine adapter plate is correctly fitted, then engage the transmission input shaft with the vibration damper and push the transmission onto the engine.

44 Insert all mounting bolts then progressively tighten them to the specified torque.
45 The remaining refitting procedure is a reversal of removal, but note the following additional points:

a) Fit new circlips to the grooves in the inner end of each driveshaft CV joint, and ensure that they fully engage as they are fitted into the transmission.
b) Refit and adjust the engine mountings as described in Chapter 2A or 2B.
c) Replenish the transmission fluid, and check the level with reference to Chapter 1A.
d) Tighten all nuts and bolts to the specified torque settings.
e) Check and if necessary adjust the selector cable (Section 2) and accelerator cable (Chapter 4A).

7 Automatic transmission overhaul - general

In the event of a fault occurring on the transmission, it is first necessary to determine whether it is of an electrical, mechanical or hydraulic nature, and to do this, special test equipment is required. It is therefore essential to have the work carried out by a Ford dealer if a transmission fault is suspected.

Do not remove the transmission from the car for possible repair before professional fault diagnosis has been carried out, since most tests require the transmission to be in the vehicle.

8 Reversing light/inhibitor switch - removal and refitting

1 Disconnect the battery negative (earth) lead (see Chapter 5A).
2 The switch is located on the rear of the transmission, and prevents the engine from being started with the selector lever in any position except "P" or "N". Access to the switch is gained after raising and supporting the vehicle at the front end on axle stands (see "Jacking and Vehicle Support").
3 Detach the switch multi-plug, then unscrew and remove the switch from the transmission, together with its O-ring. As the switch is removed, catch any fluid spillage in a suitable container, and plug the switch aperture in the transmission to prevent any further loss.
4 Refitting is a reversal of the removal procedure. Use a new O-ring, and tighten the switch securely. Ensure that the wiring connection is securely made. On completion, check and if necessary top-up the automatic transmission fluid (see Chapter 1A) then check that the engine only starts when the selector is in the "P" or "N" position.

Chapter 8
Driveshafts

Contents

Degrees of difficulty

Easy, suitable for novice with little experience	**Fairly easy,** suitable for beginner with some experience	**Fairly difficult,** suitable for competent DIY mechanic	**Difficult,** suitable for experienced DIY mechanic	**Very difficult,** suitable for expert DIY or professional

Specifications

General

Driveshaft type . . . . Solid steel shafts with inner and outer constant velocity (CV) joints, both outer joints are of the ball-and-cage type and the inner joints of the tripod type. Right-hand driveshaft is fitted with a support bearing.

Lubricant:
  Type/specification . . . . Special grease (Ford specification WSD-M1C230-A) supplied in sachets with gaiter kits - joints are otherwise pre-packed with grease and sealed

  Quantity (per joint):
    Inner joint . . . . 125 g
    Outer joint:
      Petrol engine models . . . . 30 g
      Diesel engine models . . . . 40 g

Torque wrench settings

	Nm	lbf ft
Front hub nut	270	200
Right-hand driveshaft support bearing plate nuts	24	18

1 General information

Drive is transmitted from the differential to the front wheels by means of two, unequal-length driveshafts.

Each driveshaft is fitted with an inner and outer constant velocity (CV) joint. The inner constant velocity joint is of the spider-and-yoke type and the outer joint is of the ball-and-cage type. Each outer joint is splined to engage with the wheel hub, and is threaded so that it can be fastened to the hub by a large nut. The inner joint is also splined to engage with the differential sunwheel (left-hand side) or the intermediate shaft (right-hand side).

On the right-hand driveshaft, the inner constant velocity (CV) joint is located approximately halfway along the shaft length, and the joint outer member is supported by the rear of the cylinder block via a support bearing and bracket.

2 Driveshaft - removal and refitting

Removal

Note: *A new front hub nut will be required on refitting. If work is being carried out on the left-hand driveshaft, a new circlip will be required on refitting, and on the right-hand driveshaft new dust cover retaining clips will be required. Where applicable, Nyloc-type self-locking nuts must be renewed on refitting.*
Note: *The driveshaft outer joint splines may be a tight fit in the hub and it is possible that a puller/extractor will be required to draw the hub assembly off of the driveshaft during removal.*

1 Remove the relevant wheel trim, or the wheel centre plate (alloy wheels) for access to the front hub nut.
2 Ensure that the handbrake is applied, then relieve the staking on the front hub nut, using a suitable punch. Slacken the hub nut using a suitable socket and extension bar. Do not remove the hub nut at this stage **(see illustration).**
Caution: Take care, as the hub nut is tightened to a very high torque.
3 Working in the engine compartment, remove the plastic cover, and slacken the

2.2 Relieve the staking on the front hub nut

8

2.3 Slackening the suspension strut top mounting nut

2.6 Slacken the track-rod end balljoint nut, . . .

2.7 . . . then disconnect the track-rod end balljoint from the hub carrier using a balljoint separator tool

relevant suspension strut top mounting nut, using a ring spanner. Counterhold the strut piston rod using a suitable Allen key or hexagon bit **(see illustration)**. **Do not** remove the nut.

4 Slacken the relevant front wheel nuts, then jack up the front of the vehicle, and support securely on axle stands (see *"Jacking and Vehicle Support"*). Remove the roadwheel.

5 Where applicable, unscrew the retaining screws and remove the undershield from beneath the engine/transmission unit.

6 Slacken the track-rod end balljoint nut, and unscrew it as far as the ends of the threads. Counterhold the balljoint pin using a suitable Allen key or hexagon bit **(see illustration)**.

7 Disconnect the track-rod end balljoint from the hub carrier using a balljoint separator tool (leave the nut fitted to protect the threads), taking care not to damage the balljoint rubber

2.8 Unscrew the pinch-nut and bolt securing the hub carrier to the lower arm balljoint

seal **(see illustration)**. Once the balljoint has been released, remove the balljoint nut.

8 Unscrew the pinch-nut and bolt securing the hub carrier to the lower arm balljoint **(see illustration)**. Push the end of the lower arm down to free the balljoint from the hub carrier. If the balljoint is very tight, it may be necessary to lever down using a large screwdriver, or similar tool, but take care not to damage the balljoint rubber seal.

9 Unscrew the nut securing the anti-roll bar drop link to the suspension strut. If necessary, counterhold the drop link pin using a spanner on the flats provided **(see illustration)**.

10 Proceed as follows, according to which driveshaft is being removed.

Left-hand driveshaft

11 Drain the transmission oil as described in Chapter 7A.

12 The hub must now be freed from the end of the driveshaft. It should be possible to pull the hub off the driveshaft, but if the end of the driveshaft is tight in the hub, temporarily refit the hub nut to protect the driveshaft threads, then tap the end of the driveshaft with a soft-faced hammer, or use a suitable puller to free it. Support the driveshaft using wire or string – **do not** allow the driveshaft to hang down under its own weight, as this may result in damage to the constant velocity joints.

 Warning: When freeing the driveshaft from the hub, make sure that the driveshaft does not disengage from the inner constant velocity joint.

13 Insert a lever between the inner driveshaft joint and the transmission housing, positioning a thin piece of wood between the lever and housing to protect it. Carefully lever the driveshaft inner joint out of the differential, taking great care not to damage the transmission housing **(see illustration)**. Manoeuvre the driveshaft out of position, ensuring that the constant velocity joints are not placed under excessive strain, and remove the driveshaft from underneath the vehicle. Whilst the driveshaft is removed, plug the differential aperture with a clean, lint-free cloth to prevent dirt entry.

 Warning: The manufacturers recommend that the inner driveshaft joints are not bent at an angle of more than 18º.

Right-hand driveshaft

14 Release the larger retaining clip securing the dust cover in position on the driveshaft intermediate shaft in the transmission, and slide the cover along the driveshaft **(see illustration)**.

15 Slacken and remove the nuts securing the intermediate support bearing plate to its mounting bracket **(see illustration)**.

16 Free the outer constant velocity joint from the hub as described in paragraph 12. Release the inner end of the driveshaft from the intermediate shaft, and remove the driveshaft assembly from underneath the vehicle, taking care not to place any strain on the constant velocity joints **(see illustration)**.

2.9 Unscrew the nuts securing the anti-roll bar drop link to the suspension strut

2.13 Levering the driveshaft inner joint out of the differential

2.14 Release the retaining clip securing the dust cover to the intermediate shaft

2.15 Remove the nuts (arrowed) securing the intermediate support bearing plate to its mounting bracket

Warning: The manufacturers recommend that the inner driveshaft joints are not bent at an angle of more than 18°.

Refitting

Left-hand driveshaft

17 Before installing the driveshaft, examine the driveshaft oil seal in the transmission for signs of damage or deterioration and, if necessary, renew it, referring to Chapter 7 for further information. (Having got this far it is worth renewing the seal as a matter of course.)
18 Remove the circlip from the end of the driveshaft inner joint splines and discard it. Fit a new circlip, making sure it is correctly located in the groove **(see illustration)**.
19 Thoroughly clean the driveshaft splines, and the apertures in the transmission and hub assembly. Apply a thin film of grease to the oil seal lips, and to the driveshaft splines and shoulders. Check that all gaiter clips are securely fastened.
20 Offer up the driveshaft, and locate the joint splines with those of the differential sun gear, taking great care not to damage the oil seal. Push the joint fully into position, then check that the circlip is correctly located and securely holds the joint in position.
21 Align the outer constant velocity joint splines with those of the hub, and slide the joint back into position in the hub.
22 Fit a new hub nut, and use it to draw the outer joint fully into position in the hub.
23 Locate the lower arm balljoint in the hub carrier and refit the pinch-bolt and nut, tightening to the specified torque (see Chapter 10 Specifications).
24 Reconnect the track-rod end balljoint to the hub carrier, and tighten a new retaining nut to the specified torque (Chapter 10 specifications). Counterhold the balljoint pin as during removal.
25 Reconnect the anti-roll bar drop link to the strut and tighten its retaining nut to the specified torque (Chapter 10 specifications). Again, if necessary, counterhold the drop link pin.
26 The remainder of the refitting procedure is a reversal of removal, bearing in mind the following points.

2.16 Release the inner end of the driveshaft from the intermediate shaft

a) Renew any Nyloc-type self-locking nuts on refitting.
b) Do not fully tighten the hub nut until the vehicle is resting on its wheels.
c) Do not forget to tighten the suspension strut top mounting nut.
d) Tighten all fixings to the specified torque.
e) On completion, refill the transmission with the specified type and amount of oil, and check the level using the information given in Chapter 1A or B.

Right-hand driveshaft

27 Prior to refitting, check the driveshaft support bearing for signs of freeplay or roughness. If necessary, renew the bearing as described in Section 5.
28 Ensure the driveshaft splines are clean and dry, then slide the inner dust cover onto the shaft.
29 Manoeuvre the driveshaft into position, aligning its splines with those of the intermediate shaft and engaging the support bearing plate with its mounting bracket on the rear of the cylinder block. Refit the support bearing plate nuts, tightening them lightly only at this stage.
30 Thoroughly clean the driveshaft splines, and the apertures in the hub assembly, then locate the outer constant velocity joint splines with those of the hub, and slide the joint back into position in the hub.
31 Slide the inner dust cover into position over the driveshaft/intermediate shaft, and secure it in position with new retaining clips.
32 Carry out the operations described in paragraphs 22 to 26, but ignore the reference to refilling the transmission with oil and, on completion, tighten the intermediate support bearing plate mounting nuts to the specified torque before refitting the undershield (where applicable).

3 Driveshaft inner joint gaiter – renewal

1 The inner joint gaiter can be renewed either with the driveshaft removed from the vehicle, or with it *in situ*. If it is wished to fully remove the driveshaft, refer to Section 2 first. Note that if both the inner and outer gaiters are

2.18 Removing the circlip from the left-hand driveshaft inner joint

being renewed at the same time, the outer gaiter can be removed from the inner end of the driveshaft.

Renewal without removing the driveshaft

2 Remove the relevant wheel trim or the wheel centre plate (alloy wheels), then slacken the relevant front wheel nuts. Apply the handbrake, then jack up the front of the vehicle, and support securely on axle stands (see "*Jacking and Vehicle Support*"). Remove the roadwheel.
3 Where applicable, undo the retaining screws and remove the undershield from beneath the engine/transmission unit.
4 Slacken the track-rod end balljoint nut, and unscrew it as far as the ends of the threads. Counterhold the balljoint pin using a suitable Allen key or hexagon bit.
5 Disconnect the track-rod end balljoint from the hub carrier using a balljoint separator tool (leave the nut fitted to protect the threads), taking care not to damage the balljoint rubber seal. Once the balljoint has been released, remove the balljoint nut.
6 Unscrew the nut securing the anti-roll bar drop link to the suspension strut. If necessary, counterhold the drop link pin using a spanner on the flats provided.
7 Unscrew the pinch-nut and bolt securing the hub carrier to the lower arm balljoint.
8 Mark the driveshaft in relation to the joint outer member to ensure correct refitting.
9 Note the fitted location of both of the inner joint gaiter retaining clips. Release the clips from the gaiter, and slide the gaiter back along the driveshaft to expose the inner joint.
10 Push the end of the lower arm down to free the balljoint from the hub carrier. If the balljoint is very tight, it may be necessary to lever down using a large screwdriver, or similar tool, but take care not to damage the balljoint rubber seal.
11 Pull the front suspension strut/hub carrier assembly outwards, while guiding the tripod joint out of the outer member. As the joint tripod is being withdrawn from the outer member, take precautions to prevent the bearing rollers falling off. Wipe away all excess grease and, if necessary, wrap tape around the tripod joint to secure the rollers in position.

8

3.12a Make alignment marks between the tripod joint and the driveshaft

3.12b . . . then prise the circlip from the end of the driveshaft

12 Using a punch, paint or a suitable marker pen, make alignment marks between the tripod joint and driveshaft. Prise the circlip from the end of the driveshaft, then remove the tripod joint assembly **(see illustrations)**. If the joint is a tight fit, it maybe necessary to use a puller to draw it off the shaft - if a puller is used, take great care not to damage the rollers.

13 Slide the gaiter off the end of the driveshaft. If necessary, the outer gaiter can now be renewed with reference to Section 4.

14 Where applicable, remove the tape from the joint, and thoroughly clean the constant velocity joint components using paraffin, or a suitable solvent, and dry the components thoroughly. Carry out a visual inspection of all the components.

15 Check the spider, rollers and outer member for signs of wear, pitting or scuffing on their bearing surfaces. Also check that the spider rollers rotate smoothly and easily, with no traces of roughness.

16 If on inspection, the spider, rollers or outer member reveals signs of wear or damage, it will be necessary to renew the complete driveshaft as an assembly, since no components are available separately. If the joint components are in satisfactory condition, obtain a repair kit from your Ford dealer, consisting of a new gaiter, retaining clips, tripod circlip and the correct type and quantity of grease.

17 Clean the driveshaft, and tape over the splines on its inner end to protect the new gaiter as it is fitted.

18 Slide the new gaiter onto the driveshaft then remove the tape from the driveshaft end.

19 If necessary, again wind tape around the tripod to retain the rollers, then push the tripod onto the driveshaft splines, if necessary using a soft-faced mallet to drive it fully onto the splines. Note that the tripod assembly must be fitted with the chamfered edge leading (towards the driveshaft), and with the previously-made marks on the tripod and driveshaft aligned. Secure the tripod in position using the new circlip, making sure that the circlip locates correctly in the driveshaft groove.

20 Where applicable, remove the tape from around the tripod, then work the grease supplied with the repair kit fully into the roller bearings. Fill the joint outer member with any excess grease.

21 Guide the tripod joint back into the outer member, making sure that the previously-made marks are aligned.

22 Slide the gaiter along the driveshaft, and locate it in the recesses on the driveshaft and joint outer member.

23 Ensure that the gaiter is not twisted or distorted, then carefully lift the lip of the gaiter at the outer member end to equalise air pressure in the gaiter.

24 Fit the large metal retaining clip to the gaiter. Remove any slack in the gaiter retaining clip by carefully compressing the raised section of the clip. In the absence of the special tool, a pair of side cutters may be used. Secure the small retaining clip using the same procedure.

25 Locate the lower arm balljoint in the hub carrier, then refit the pinch-bolt and nut and tighten to the specified torque setting (see Chapter 10 Specifications).

26 Reconnect the track-rod balljoint to the hub carrier, and tighten a new retaining nut to the specified torque (see Chapter 10 Specifications). Counterhold the balljoint pin as during removal.

27 Reconnect the anti-roll bar drop link to the strut and tighten its retaining nut to the specified torque (see Chapter 10 Specifications). Again, if necessary, counterhold the drop link pin.

28 Where applicable, refit the engine undershield and the roadwheel, then lower the vehicle to the ground and tighten the wheel nuts to the specified torque.

Renewal with the driveshaft on the bench

29 Mount the driveshaft in a vice and remove all traces of dirt from the outside of the inner joint.

30 Mark the driveshaft in relation to the joint outer member, to ensure correct refitting.

31 Note the fitted location of both of the inner joint gaiter retaining clips, then release both the large and small retaining clips from the gaiter.

32 Slide the gaiter along the driveshaft and lift off the outer member. As the outer member

is being removed, take precautions to prevent the bearing rollers falling off the tripod. Wipe away all excess grease and wrap tape around the tripod joint to secure the rollers in position.

33 Carry out the operations described in paragraphs 12 to 24.

34 Check that the constant velocity joint moves freely in all directions, then refit the driveshaft to the car as described in Section 2.

4 Driveshaft outer joint gaiter – renewal

1 The outer joint gaiter can be renewed either with the driveshaft removed from the vehicle, or with it *in situ*. If it is wished to fully remove the driveshaft, refer to Section 2 first. Note that if both the outer and inner gaiters are being renewed at the same time, the inner gaiter can also be removed from the outer end of the driveshaft or alternatively both gaiters can be removed from the inner end of the driveshaft (see Section 3).

Renewal without removing the driveshaft

2 Carry out the operations described in paragraphs 2 to 7 of Section 3.

3 Note the fitted location of both of the outer joint gaiter retaining clips. Release both clips and slide the gaiter back along the driveshaft to expose the inner joint.

4 Scoop away all excess grease from the joint assembly to reveal the outer joint circlip.

5 Push the end of the lower arm down to free the balljoint from the hub carrier. If the balljoint is very tight, it may be necessary to lever down using a large screwdriver, or similar tool, but take care not to damage the balljoint rubber seal.

6 With the aid of an assistant expand the driveshaft outer joint circlip while at the same time pulling the hub assembly outwards **(see illustration)**. Free the hub and joint assembly from the end of the driveshaft, taking care not to place any excess strain on the inner joint, then slide off the gaiter.

4.6 Expand the driveshaft outer joint circlip whilst pulling the hub assembly outwards

7 Thoroughly clean the constant velocity joint components using paraffin, or a suitable solvent, and dry them thoroughly. Carry out a visual inspection of the joint components.

8 Move the inner splined driving member from side to side, to expose each ball in turn at the top of its track. Examine the balls for cracks, flat spots, or signs of surface pitting.

9 Inspect the ball tracks on the inner and outer members. If the tracks have widened, the balls will no longer be a tight fit. At the same time, check the ball cage windows for wear or cracking between the windows.

10 If on inspection, any of the constant velocity joint components are found to be worn or damaged, it will be necessary to renew the complete joint assembly (where available), or even the complete driveshaft. Refer to your Ford dealer for further information on parts availability. If the joint is in satisfactory condition, obtain a repair kit consisting of a new gaiter, circlip, retaining clips, and the correct type and quantity of grease.

11 Where necessary, renew the inner gaiter using the information described in Section 3.

12 Clean the driveshaft and tape over the splines on its outer end to prevent damage to the new gaiter as it is fitted.

13 Slide the new gaiter onto the driveshaft, then remove the tape from the driveshaft end.

14 Remove the circlip from the joint inner member and install the new one supplied with the repair kit, making sure it is correctly located in the groove **(see illustration)**.

15 Work the grease supplied with the repair kit fully into the joint assembly and fill the gaiter with any excess grease **(see illustration)**.

16 Align the driveshaft splines with those of the outer joint inner member. Slide the joint onto the driveshaft until its circlip clicks into the driveshaft groove **(see illustration)**.

17 Slide the gaiter along the driveshaft, and locate it in the recesses on the driveshaft and joint outer member.

4.14 Fit a new circlip (arrowed) to the joint outer member

18 Ensure that the gaiter is not twisted or distorted, then carefully lift the lip of the gaiter at the outer member end to equalise air pressure in the gaiter.

19 Fit the large metal retaining clip to the gaiter and remove any slack in the clip by carefully compressing its raised section. In the absence of the special tool, a pair of side cutters may be used. Secure the small retaining clip using the same procedure.

20 Locate the lower arm balljoint in the hub carrier, then refit the pinch-bolt and nut and tighten to the specified torque setting (see Chapter 10 Specifications).

21 Reconnect the track-rod end balljoint to the hub carrier, and tighten its retaining nut to the specified torque (see Chapter 10 Specifications). Counterhold the balljoint pin as during removal.

22 Reconnect the anti-roll bar drop link to the strut and tighten its retaining nut to the specified torque (see Chapter 10 Specifications). Again, if necessary, counterhold the drop link pin.

23 Where applicable, refit the engine undershield and the roadwheel, then lower the vehicle to the ground and tighten the wheel nuts to the specified torque.

Renewal with the driveshaft on the bench

24 Mount the driveshaft in a vice and remove all traces of dirt from the outside of the inner joint.

25 Note the fitted location of both of the retaining clips, then release both the large and small retaining clips from the gaiter.

26 Slide the gaiter along the driveshaft and wipe away all excess grease from the outer joint.

27 Using circlip pliers, expand the circlip, then remove the outer joint from the end of the driveshaft. The gaiter can then be slid off the driveshaft end.

28 Carry out the operations described in paragraphs 7 to 19.

29 Check that the constant velocity joint moves freely in all directions, then refit the driveshaft to the vehicle as described in Section 2.

5 Right-hand driveshaft intermediate bearing – inspection and renewal

Note: *A suitable bearing puller will be required to draw the bearing off the driveshaft.*

1 With the driveshaft removed as described in Section 2, proceed as follows.

2 If not already done, slide the dust cover from the inner end of the driveshaft.

3 Check that the bearing outer race rotates smoothly and easily, without any signs of roughness or undue free play between the inner and outer races. If necessary, renew the bearing as follows.

4 Using a long-reach universal bearing puller, carefully draw the bearing off the driveshaft inner end.

5 Apply a smear of grease to the inner race of the new bearing, then fit the bearing over the end of the driveshaft. Using a soft-faced

4.15 Work the grease into the joint assembly

4.16 Slide the joint into the driveshaft until the circlip (A) engages with the driveshaft groove (B)

8

hammer, and a suitable piece of tubing which bears only on the bearing inner race, tap the new bearing into position on the driveshaft, until it abuts the constant velocity joint outer member.

6 Check that the bearing rotates freely, then refit the driveshaft as described in Section 2.

6 Driveshaft overhaul – general information

1 If any of the checks described in Chapter 1 reveal wear in any driveshaft joint, first remove the wheel trim or centre cap (alloy wheels).

2 If the hub nut staking is still effective, the driveshaft nut should be correctly tightened - if in doubt, relieve the staking using a suitable punch, then tighten the nut to the specified torque and re-stake the nut (ideally, a new nut should be fitted). Refit the wheel trim or centre cap (as applicable), and repeat the check on the remaining front hub nut.

3 Road test the vehicle, and listen for a metallic clicking from the front as the vehicle is driven slowly in a circle on full-lock. If a clicking noise is heard, this indicates wear in the outer constant velocity joint. This means that the joint must be renewed; reconditioning is not possible.

4 If vibration, consistent with road speed, is felt through the car when accelerating, there is a possibility of wear in the inner constant velocity joints.

5 To check the joints for wear, remove the driveshafts, then dismantle them as described in Section 3 and 4 - if any wear or free play is found, the affected joint must be renewed. In the case of the inner joints (and on some models, the outer joints), this means that the complete driveshaft assembly must be renewed, as the joints are not available separately. Refer to your Ford dealer for information on the availability of driveshaft components.

Chapter 9
Braking system

Contents

Degrees of difficulty

Easy, suitable for novice with little experience	Fairly easy, suitable for beginner with some experience	Fairly difficult, suitable for competent DIY mechanic	Difficult, suitable for experienced DIY mechanic	Very difficult, suitable for expert DIY or professional

Specifications

Front brakes
Disc thickness:
Models with solid discs:
New . . . 12.0 mm
Minimum . . . 8.0 mm
Models with ventilated discs:
New . . . 20.0 mm
Minimum . . . 18.0 mm
Maximum disc run-out . . . 0.1 mm
Brake pad friction material minimum thickness . . . 1.5 mm

Rear brakes
Drum internal diameter:
Hatchback and Van models not fitted with ABS:
New . . . 180 mm
Maximum diameter after machining . . . 181 mm
Courier/Combi models, and Hatchback and Van models with ABS:
New . . . 203 mm
Maximum diameter after machining . . . 204 mm
Brake shoe friction material minimum thickness . . . 1.0 mm

Torque wrench settings

	Nm	lbf ft
ABS wheel sensor retaining bolt	10	7
Front brake caliper:		
Guide pin bolts	25	18
Mounting bolts	58	43
Handbrake cable adjusting nut	4	3
Handbrake lever retaining nuts	24	18
Hydraulic hose union	13	11
Hydraulic pipe union nut	13	10
Master cylinder retaining nuts	24	18
Rear hub nut	235	173
Vacuum pump mounting bolts - diesel engine	20	15
Vacuum servo unit mounting nuts	25	18

9

1 General information

The braking system is of the servo-assisted, dual-circuit hydraulic type. The arrangement of the hydraulic system is such that each circuit operates one front and one rear brake from a tandem master cylinder. Under normal circumstances, both circuits operate in unison. However, in the event of hydraulic failure in one circuit, full braking force will still be available at two wheels.

All models are fitted with front disc brakes and rear drum brakes. The front disc brakes are actuated by single-piston sliding type calipers, which ensure that equal pressure is applied to each disc pad. The rear drum brakes incorporate leading and trailing shoes, which are actuated by twin-piston wheel cylinders. A self-adjust mechanism is incorporated, to automatically compensate for brake shoe wear. As the brake shoe linings wear, the footbrake operation automatically operates the adjuster mechanism, which effectively lengthens the shoe strut and repositions the brake shoes, to remove the lining-to-drum clearance.

On models not fitted with an anti-lock braking system (ABS) a pressure-regulating valve is situated in the hydraulic circuit to each rear brake. The valves regulate the hydraulic pressure applied to the rear brakes and so help to prevent rear wheel lock-up during emergency braking. Refer to Section 20 for further information on the ABS system.

The handbrake provides an independent mechanical means of rear brake application.

On diesel engine models, since there is no throttling on the inlet manifold, the manifold is not a suitable source of vacuum to operate the vacuum servo unit. The servo unit is therefore connected to a separate vacuum pump which is bolted onto the front of the cylinder head and operated by an eccentric on the camshaft.

 Warning: When servicing any part of the system, work carefully and methodically; also observe scrupulous cleanliness when overhauling any part of

2.14 Removing a brake caliper bleed screw dust cap (right-hand brake shown)

the hydraulic system. Always renew components (in axle sets, where applicable) if in doubt about their condition, and use only genuine Ford replacement parts, or at least those of known good quality. Note the warnings given in "Safety first" and at relevant points in this Chapter concerning the dangers of asbestos dust and hydraulic fluid.

2 Hydraulic system – bleeding

 Warning: Hydraulic fluid is poisonous; wash off immediately and thoroughly in the case of skin contact, and seek immediate medical advice if any fluid is swallowed or gets into the eyes. Certain types of hydraulic fluid are inflammable, and may ignite when allowed into contact with hot components; when servicing any hydraulic system, it is safest to assume that the fluid is inflammable, and to take precautions against the risk of fire as though it is petrol that is being handled. Hydraulic fluid is also an effective paint stripper, and will attack plastics; if any is spilt, it should be washed off immediately, using copious quantities of fresh water. Finally, it is hygroscopic (it absorbs moisture from the air) - old fluid may be contaminated and unfit for further use. When topping-up or renewing the fluid, always use the recommended type, and ensure that it comes from a freshly-opened sealed container.

General

1 The correct operation of any hydraulic system is only possible after removing all air from the components and circuit; this is achieved by bleeding the system.
2 During the bleeding procedure, add only clean, unused hydraulic fluid of the recommended type; never re-use fluid that has already been bled from the system. Ensure that sufficient fluid is available before starting work.
3 If there is any possibility of incorrect fluid being already in the system, the brake components and circuit must be flushed completely with uncontaminated, correct fluid, and new seals should be fitted to the various components.
4 If hydraulic fluid has been lost from the system, or air has entered because of a leak, ensure that the fault is cured before proceeding further.
5 Park the vehicle on level ground, switch off the engine and select first or reverse gear then chock the wheels and release the handbrake.
6 Check that all pipes and hoses are secure, unions tight and bleed screws closed. Clean any dirt from around the bleed screws.

7 Unscrew the master cylinder reservoir cap, and top the master cylinder reservoir up to the "MAX" level line; refit the cap loosely, and remember to maintain the fluid level at least above the "MIN" level line throughout the procedure, or there is a risk of further air entering the system.
8 There are a number of one-man, do-it-yourself brake bleeding kits currently available from motor accessory shops. It is recommended that one of these kits is used whenever possible, as they greatly simplify the bleeding operation, and also reduce the risk of expelled air and fluid being drawn back into the system. If such a kit is not available, the basic (two-man) method must be used, which is described in detail below.
9 If a kit is to be used, prepare the vehicle as described previously, and follow the kit manufacturer's instructions, as the procedure may vary slightly according to the type being used; generally, they are as outlined below in the relevant sub-section.
10 Whichever method is used, the same sequence must be followed (paragraphs 11 and 12) to ensure that the removal of all air from the system.

Bleeding sequence

11 If the system has been only partially disconnected, and suitable precautions were taken to minimise fluid loss, it should be necessary only to bleed that part of the system (ie the primary or secondary circuit).
12 If the complete system is to be bled, then it should be done working in the following sequence:
  a) Left-hand front brake.
  b) Right-hand front brake.
  c) Right-hand rear brake.
  d) Left-hand rear brake.

Bleeding - basic (two-man) method

13 Collect together a clean glass jar, a suitable length of plastic or rubber tubing which is a tight fit over the bleed screw, and a ring spanner to fit the screw. The help of an assistant will also be required.
14 Remove the dust cap from the first bleed screw in the sequence (see illustration). Fit the spanner and tube to the screw, place the other end of the tube in the jar, and pour in sufficient fluid to cover the end of the tube.
15 Ensure that the master cylinder reservoir fluid level is maintained at least above the "MIN" level line throughout the procedure.
16 Have the assistant fully depress the brake pedal several times to build up pressure, then maintain it on the final downstroke.
17 While pedal pressure is maintained, unscrew the bleed screw (approximately one turn) and allow the compressed fluid and air to flow into the jar. The assistant should maintain pedal pressure, following it down to the floor if necessary, and should not release it until instructed to do so. When the flow stops, tighten the bleed screw again, have the

assistant release the pedal slowly, and recheck the reservoir fluid level.

18 Repeat the steps given in paragraphs 16 and 17 until the fluid emerging from the bleed screw is free from air bubbles. If the master cylinder has been drained and refilled, and air is being bled from the first screw in the sequence, allow approximately five seconds between cycles for the master cylinder passages to refill.

19 When no more air bubbles appear, securely tighten the bleed screw, remove the tube and spanner, and refit the dust cap. Do not overtighten the bleed screw.

20 Repeat the procedure on the remaining screws in the sequence, until all air is removed from the system and the brake pedal feels firm again.

Bleeding - using a one-way valve kit

21 As their name implies, these kits consist of a length of tubing with a one-way valve fitted, to prevent expelled air and fluid being drawn back into the system; some kits include a translucent container, which can be positioned so that the air bubbles can be more easily seen flowing from the end of the tube.

22 The kit is connected to the bleed screw, which is then opened **(see illustration)**. The user returns to the driver's seat, depresses the brake pedal with a smooth, steady stroke, and slowly releases it; this is repeated until the expelled fluid is clear of air bubbles.

23 Note that these kits simplify work so much that it is easy to forget the master cylinder reservoir fluid level; ensure that this is maintained at least above the "MIN" level line at all times.

Bleeding - using a pressure-bleeding kit

24 These kits are usually operated by the reservoir of pressurised air contained in the spare tyre. However, note that it will probably be necessary to reduce the pressure to a lower level than normal; refer to the instructions supplied with the kit.

25 By connecting a pressurised, fluid-filled container to the master cylinder reservoir, bleeding can be carried out simply by opening each screw in turn (in the specified sequence), and allowing the fluid to flow out until no more air bubbles can be seen in the expelled fluid.

26 This method has the advantage that the large reservoir of fluid provides an additional safeguard against air being drawn into the system during bleeding.

27 Pressure-bleeding is particularly effective when bleeding "difficult" systems, or when bleeding the complete system at the time of routine fluid renewal.

All methods

28 When bleeding is complete, and firm pedal feel is restored, wash off any spilt fluid, securely tighten the bleed screws, and refit their dust caps.

29 Check the hydraulic fluid level in the master cylinder reservoir, and top-up if necessary (see "Weekly checks").

30 Discard any hydraulic fluid that has been bled from the system; it will not be fit for re-use.

31 Check the feel of the brake pedal. If it feels at all spongy, air must still be present in the system, and further bleeding is required. Failure to bleed satisfactorily after a reasonable repetition of the bleeding procedure may be due to worn master cylinder seals. **Note:** If difficulty is experienced in bleeding the braking circuit on models with ABS, this maybe due to air being trapped in the ABS hydraulic unit. If this is the case then the vehicle should be taken to a Ford dealer so that the system can be bled using special electronic test equipment.

3 Hydraulic pipes and hoses – renewal

Caution: On models equipped with ABS, disconnect the battery before disconnecting any braking system hydraulic union and do not reconnect the battery until after the hydraulic system has been bled. Failure to do this could lead to air entering the ABS hydraulic unit requiring the unit to be bled using special Ford test equipment (see Section 2).

Note: Before starting work, refer to the note at the beginning of Section 2 concerning the dangers of hydraulic fluid.

1 If any pipe or hose is to be renewed, minimise fluid loss by first removing the master cylinder reservoir cap, then tightening it down onto a piece of polythene to obtain an airtight seal. Alternatively, flexible hoses can be sealed, if required, using a proprietary brake hose clamp; metal brake pipe unions can be plugged (if care is taken not to allow dirt into the system) or capped immediately they are disconnected. Place a wad of rag under any union that is to be disconnected, to catch any spilt fluid.

2 If a flexible hose is to be disconnected, unscrew the brake pipe union nut before removing the spring clip which secures the hose to its mounting bracket **(see illustration)**.

3.2 Unscrew the brake pipe union nut (1) before removing the spring clip (2)

2.22 Bleeding the hydraulic system using a one-way valve kit

3 To unscrew the union nuts, it is preferable to obtain a brake pipe spanner of the correct size; these are available from most large motor accessory shops. Failing this, a close-fitting open-ended spanner will be required, though if the nuts are tight or corroded, their flats may be rounded-off if the spanner slips. In such a case, a self-locking wrench is often the only way to unscrew a stubborn union, but it follows that the pipe and the damaged nuts must be renewed on reassembly. Always clean a union and surrounding area before disconnecting it. If disconnecting a component with more than one union, make a careful note of the connections before disturbing any of them.

4 If a brake pipe is to be renewed, it can be obtained, cut to length and with the union nuts and end flares in place, from Ford dealers. All that is then necessary is to bend it to shape, following the line of the original, before fitting it to the car. Alternatively, most motor accessory shops can make up brake pipes from kits, but this requires very careful measurement of the original, to ensure that the replacement is of the correct length. The safest answer is usually to take the original to the shop as a pattern.

5 On refitting, do not overtighten the union nuts. It is not necessary to exercise brute force to obtain a sound joint.

6 Ensure that the pipes and hoses are correctly routed, with no kinks, and that they are secured in the clips or brackets provided. After fitting, remove the polythene from the reservoir, and bleed the hydraulic system as described in Section 2. Wash off any spilt fluid, and check carefully for fluid leaks.

4 Front brake pads – renewal

Warning: Renew both sets of front brake pads at the same time - never renew the pads on only one wheel, as uneven braking may result. Note that the dust created by wear of the pads may contain asbestos, which is a health hazard. Never blow it out with compressed air, and don't inhale any of it. An approved filtering mask

9

4.2 Prising the pad spring from the caliper

4.3 Prise out the plastic covers . . .

and pick out any large embedded particles of dirt or debris. Carefully clean the pad locations in the caliper and piston.

8 Brush the dust and dirt from the caliper and piston, but **do not** inhale it, as it is injurious to health. Inspect the dust seal around the piston for damage, and the piston for evidence of fluid leaks, corrosion or damage. If attention is necessary, refer to Section 8.

9 Prior to fitting the pads, check that the guide pin bolts are a reasonably tight-fit in the caliper bushes. If there is any sign of freeplay between either bush and bolt, both the bushes and bolts should be renewed - the bushes are a push-fit in the caliper body.

10 If new brake pads are to be fitted, the caliper piston must be pushed back into the cylinder to make room for them. Either use a G-clamp or similar tool, or use suitable pieces of wood as levers. Provided that the master cylinder reservoir has not been overfilled with hydraulic fluid, there should be no spillage, but keep a careful watch on the fluid level while retracting the piston. If the fluid level rises above the "MAX" level line at any time, the surplus should be siphoned off, or ejected via a plastic tube connected to one of the bleed screws (see Section 2). **Note:** *Do not syphon the fluid by mouth, as it is poisonous; use a syringe or an old poultry baster.*

11 Fit the outer pad to the caliper mounting bracket, ensuring that the pad friction material is against the brake disc, then clip the inner pad into position in the caliper piston.

12 Slide the caliper into position over the brake disc, and install the guide pin bolts.

should be worn when working on the brakes. DO NOT use petrol or petroleum-based solvents to clean brake parts; use brake cleaner or methylated spirit only.

1 Chock the rear wheels, apply the handbrake, then jack up the front of the vehicle and support it on axle stands (see *"Jacking and Vehicle Support"*). Remove the front roadwheels.

2 Using a flat-bladed screwdriver, carefully prise the pad spring out from the caliper noting its correct fitted position **(see illustration)**.

3 Remove the plastic covers from the ends of the guide bushes to gain access to the caliper guide pin bolts **(see illustration)**.

4 Slacken and remove the guide pin bolts, then lift the caliper assembly away from the disc **(see illustrations)**. Suspend the caliper from suspension strut coil spring using a suitable piece of wire or string; do not allow

the caliper to hang down by the hose.

5 Remove the outer pad from the caliper mounting bracket, then unclip the inner pad from the caliper piston **(see illustrations)**.

6 Measure the thickness of the friction material on each brake pad **(see illustration)**. If either pad is worn at any point to the specified minimum thickness or less, all four pads must be renewed. Also, the pads should be renewed if any are fouled with oil or grease; there is no satisfactory way of degreasing friction material, once contaminated. If any of the brake pads are worn unevenly, or are fouled with oil or grease, trace and rectify the cause before reassembly.

7 If the brake pads are still serviceable, carefully clean them using a clean, fine wire brush or similar, paying particular attention to the sides and back of the metal backing plate. Clean out the grooves in the friction material,

4.4a . . . then slacken, . .

4.4b . . . and remove the guide pin bolts . . .

4.4c . . . and lift the caliper from the disc

4.5a Remove the outer pad from the caliper mounting bracket . . .

4.5b . . . then unclip the inner pad from the caliper piston

4.6 Measure the thickness of the brake pad friction material

Tighten both guide pin bolts to the specified torque setting, then refit the plastic caps to the ends of the guide bushes.

13 Engage the pad spring with the outer pad, then engage the spring ends correctly in the caliper body holes, as noted before removal.

14 Depress the brake pedal repeatedly until the pads are pressed into firm contact with the brake disc, and normal (non-assisted) pedal pressure is restored.

15 Repeat the procedure to inspect or remove the pads on the remaining front brake caliper.

16 Refit the roadwheels, then lower the vehicle to the ground and tighten the roadwheel nuts to the specified torque setting (see Chapter 10 Specifications).

17 Check the hydraulic fluid level as described in "*Weekly checks*".

 HAYNES HINT *New pads will not give full braking efficiency until they have bedded in. Be prepared for this, and avoid hard braking as far as possible for the first hundred miles or so after pad renewal.*

5 Rear brake shoes – renewal

⚠ *Warning: Brake shoes must be renewed on both rear wheels at the same time - never renew the shoes on only one wheel, as uneven braking may result. Also, the dust created by wear of the shoes may contain asbestos, which is a health hazard. Never blow it out with compressed air, and don't inhale any of it. An approved filtering mask should be worn when working on the brakes. DO NOT use petrol or petroleum-based solvents to clean brake parts; use brake cleaner or methylated spirit only.*

5.8 Remove the shoe retaining springs and the pins

1 Remove the brake drum as described in Section 7.

2 Working carefully, and taking the necessary precautions to avoid inhalation of dust, remove all traces of brake dust from the brake drum, backplate and shoes.

3 Measure the thickness of the friction material of each brake shoe at several points; if either shoe is worn at any point to the specified minimum thickness or less, all four shoes must be renewed as a set. The shoes should also be renewed if any are fouled with oil or grease; there is no satisfactory way of degreasing friction material, once contaminated.

4 If either of the brake shoes are worn unevenly, or fouled with oil or grease, trace and rectify the cause before reassembly.

5 To renew the brake shoes, proceed as follows. If all the components are in good condition, refit the brake drum as described in Section 7.

6 If desired, to improve access to the brake components, proceed as follows.

a) *Where applicable, unscrew the securing bolt, and move the ABS wheel sensor clear of the working area to avoid possible damage.*

b) *Unscrew the four securing bolts, and remove the rear stub axle (or stub*

5.9 Disconnect the lower return spring from both shoes

axle/hub assembly on Courier and Combi models) from the trailing arm.

7 Note the position of each shoe, and the location of each of the springs. Also make a note of the self-adjuster component locations, to aid refitting later.

8 Using a pair of pliers, remove the shoe retainer springs by depressing and sliding them downwards, then withdraw the retainer pins from the brake backplate **(see illustration)**.

9 Ease the shoes out one at a time from the lower anchor point, to release the tension of the return spring, then disconnect the lower return spring from both shoes, using pliers if necessary **(see illustration)**.

10 Ease the upper end of both shoes out from the wheel cylinder pistons, taking care not to damage the wheel cylinder seals, and disconnect the handbrake cable from the lever on the trailing shoe. The brake shoe and adjuster strut assembly can then be manoeuvred out of position and away from the backplate. Do not depress the brake pedal until the brakes are reassembled; wrap a strong elastic band around the wheel cylinder pistons to retain them **(see illustrations)**.

11 With the shoe and adjuster strut assembly on the bench, make a note of the correct fitted positions of the springs and adjuster strut, to use as a guide on reassembly. Unhook and

5.10a Disconnecting the handbrake cable from the lever on the trailing shoe

5.10b Wrap a strong elastic band around the wheel cylinder pistons to retain them

9

5.14a Adjuster strut components correctly assembled for refitting

5.14b Fit the adjuster strut retaining spring

5.15 Engage the adjuster strut with the leading shoe

remove the upper return spring then detach the leading shoe from the trailing shoe and strut assembly. Unhook the adjuster strut from the trailing shoe, and remove its spring noting which way around it is fitted.

12 Carefully examine the adjuster strut assembly for signs of wear or damage, paying particular attention to the self-adjust ratchet mechanism, and renew if necessary.

13 Depending on the type of brake shoes being installed, it may be necessary to remove the handbrake lever from the original trailing shoe, and install it on the new shoe. Secure the lever in position with a new retaining clip. All return springs should be renewed, regardless of their apparent condition; spring kits are available from Ford dealers.

14 Fit the adjuster strut retaining spring to the trailing shoe, ensuring that the shorter hook of the spring is engaged with the shoe **(see illustrations)**.

15 Fully extend the adjuster strut ratchet, then engage the adjuster strut with the leading shoe, and fully release the ratchet **(see illustration)**.

16 Attach the adjuster strut to the retaining spring on the trailing shoe, then ease the strut into position in its slot in the trailing shoe **(see illustration)**.

17 Hook the leading shoe onto the return spring, then manipulate the shoes until the return spring can be connected to the trailing shoe **(see illustration)**.

18 Remove the elastic band fitted to the wheel cylinder. Peel back the rubber

protective caps, and check the wheel cylinder for fluid leaks or other damage. Also check that both cylinder pistons are free to move easily. Refer to Section 9, if necessary, for information on wheel cylinder renewal.

19 Prior to installation, clean the backplate and apply a thin smear of high-temperature brake grease or anti-seize compound to all those surfaces of the backplate which bear on the shoes, particularly the wheel cylinder pistons and lower anchor point. Do not use too much lubricant, and don't allow the lubricant to foul the friction material.

20 Ensure that the adjuster strut self-adjust mechanism is fully released then manoeuvre the shoe and strut assembly into position and attach the handbrake cable to the lever on the trailing shoe. Engage the upper ends of both shoes with the wheel cylinder pistons, then fit the lower return spring to both shoes and ease the shoes into position on the lower anchor point **(see illustration)**.

21 Centralise the shoes relative to the backplate by tapping them. Refit the shoe retainer pins and secure them in position with the springs.

22 Where applicable, refit the rear stub axle (or stub axle/hub assembly on Courier and Combi models), and tighten the securing bolts to the specified torque.

23 Where applicable, refit the ABS wheel sensor, and tighten the securing bolt to the specified torque.

24 Refit the brake drum as described in Section 7.

25 Repeat the procedure to inspect or renew the shoes on the remaining rear brake.

26 Once the brake drums have been refitted, adjust the lining-to-drum clearance by repeatedly depressing the brake pedal. Whilst doing this, have an assistant listen to the rear drums, to check that the adjuster strut is functioning correctly - a clicking sound should be emitted by the strut as the pedal is operated.

27 Adjust the handbrake as described in Section 14 then check the brake fluid level as described in "Weekly checks".

HAYNES HiNT *New shoes will not give full braking efficiency until they have bedded-in. Be prepared for this, and avoid hard braking as far as possible for the first hundred miles or so after shoe renewal.*

6 Front brake disc – inspection, removal and refitting

Note: *Before starting work, refer to the note at the beginning of Section 4 concerning the dangers of asbestos dust.*

Inspection

Note: *If either disc requires renewal, BOTH should be renewed at the same time, to ensure even and consistent braking. New brake pads should also be fitted.*

5.16 Ease the strut into position in its slot in the trailing shoe

5.17 Fitting the upper shoe return spring

5.20 Fit the lower return spring and ease the shoes into position over the lower anchor point

1 Apply the handbrake, then jack up the front of the car and support it on axle stands (see *"Jacking and Vehicle Support"*). Remove the appropriate front roadwheel.

2 Slowly rotate the disc so that the full area of both sides can be checked. Remove the brake pads if better access is required to the inboard surface. Light scoring is normal in the area swept by the brake pads, but if heavy scoring or cracks are found, the disc must be renewed.

3 It is normal to find a lip of rust and brake dust around the disc's perimeter - this can be scraped off if required. If, however, a lip has formed due to excessive wear of the brake pad swept area, then the disc's thickness must be measured using a micrometer. Take measurements at several places around the disc, at the inside and outside of the pad swept area. If the disc has worn at any point to the specified minimum thickness or less, the disc must be renewed.

4 If the disc is thought to be warped, it can be checked for run-out. Using spacers, refit at least two wheel nuts and tighten them securely to seat the disc in position. Either use a dial gauge mounted on any convenient fixed point, while the disc is slowly rotated, or use feeler blades to measure (several points around the disc) the clearance between the disc and a fixed point, such as the caliper mounting bracket **(see illustration)**. If the measurements obtained are at the specified maximum or beyond, the disc is excessively warped, and must be renewed, however, it is worth checking first that the hub bearing is in good condition (see Chapter 1A or B and/or 10). Remove the nuts and spacers.

5 Check the disc for cracks, especially around the wheel stud holes, and any other wear or damage, and renew if necessary.

Removal

6 With the front of the vehicle raised and the wheel removed, slacken and remove the two bolts securing the brake caliper mounting bracket to the hub carrier. Slide the caliper assembly (complete with the brake pads) off of the disc, and suspend the assembly from the suspension strut coil spring, using a piece of wire or string, to avoid placing any strain on the hydraulic brake hose.

6.4 Checking brake disc run-out using a dial gauge

7 Use chalk or paint to mark the relationship of the disc to the hub then, where applicable, remove the retaining clip(s) from wheel studs, and remove the disc. If the disc is tight, lightly tap its rear face with a hide or plastic mallet.

Refitting

8 Refitting is the reverse of the removal procedure, noting the following points:

 a) *Ensure that the mating surfaces of the disc and hub are clean and flat.*
 b) *If a new disc has been fitted, use a suitable solvent to wipe any preservative coating from the disc, before refitting the caliper.*
 c) *Slide the caliper into position, making sure the pads pass either side of the disc, and tighten the caliper bracket bolts to the specified torque setting.*
 d) *Refit the roadwheel then lower the vehicle to the ground and tighten the wheel nuts to the specified torque. Apply the footbrake several times to force the pads back into contact with the disc before driving the vehicle.*

7	Rear brake drum – removal, inspection and refitting

Note: *Before starting work, refer to the note at the beginning of Section 5 concerning the dangers of asbestos dust.*
Note: *The manufacturer's procedure for removal of the brake drum is to undo the four bolts that hold the hub/brake drum assembly*

to the rear axle flange. However, in our experience, as the vehicle gets older so the bolts become covered in road dirt which results in them being increasingly difficult to remove due to corrosion. It is for this reason that we offer the following alternative method.

Hatchback and Van models

Removal

1 An integral hub/brake drum assembly is used, incorporating the rear wheel bearings.

2 Working at the handbrake lever inside the car, back off the handbrake cable adjustment, as described in Section 14.

3 Remove the relevant wheel trim or the wheel centre plate (alloy wheels), then slacken the relevant wheel nuts. Chock the front wheels, and select 1st gear (manual transmission) or "P" (automatic transmission), then jack up the rear of the vehicle, and support securely on axle stands (see *"Jacking and Vehicle Support"*). Remove the rear roadwheel.

4 Using a screwdriver, prise the dust cap from the centre of the hub/brake drum, then unscrew the hub nut **(see illustration)**.

5 Withdraw the hub/brake drum from the stub axle **(see illustration)**. If the drum is tight (this should not be the case if the handbrake cable has been backed off), this may be due to the tightness of the hub bearing on the stub axle, or due to the brake shoes binding on the inner circumference of the drum. If the bearing is tight, tap the periphery of the hub/brake drum using a hide or plastic mallet, or use a universal puller, secured to the hub/brake drum with the wheel nuts, to pull it off. If the brake shoes are binding, proceed as follows.

6 Referring to Section 14, fully slacken the handbrake cable adjuster nut to obtain maximum freeplay in the cable. If this still fails to release the drum, remove the small rubber grommet from the rear of the backplate. Insert a screwdriver through the hole and release the handbrake operating lever by pushing the lever until the stop lug can pass over the surface of the shoe, allowing the brake shoes to retract fully **(see illustration)**. The hub/brake drum should then be free to be removed.

7.4 Unscrew the rear hub nut . . .

7.5 . . . and withdraw the hub/brake drum – Hatchback and Van models

7.6 Insert a screwdriver through the hole (arrowed) to release the handbrake operating lever – Hatchback and Van models

9

7.19 Brake backplate rubber grommet location (arrowed) – Courier and Combi models

Inspection

7 Working carefully, remove all traces of brake dust from the drum, but *avoid inhaling the dust, as it is injurious to health.*

8 Scrub clean the outside of the drum, and check it for obvious signs of wear or damage such as cracks around the roadwheel bolt holes; renew the drum if necessary.

9 Examine carefully the inside of the drum. Light scoring of the friction surface is normal, but if heavy scoring is found, the drum must be renewed. It is usual to find a lip on the drum's inboard edge which consists of a mixture of rust and brake dust; this should be scraped away to leave a smooth surface which can be polished with fine (120 to 150 grade) emery paper. If the lip is due to the friction surface being recessed by wear, then the drum must be refinished (within the specified limits) or renewed.

10 If the drum is thought to be excessively worn or oval, its internal diameter must be measured at several points using an internal micrometer. Take measurements in pairs, the second at right-angles to the first, and compare the two to check for signs of ovality. Minor ovality can be corrected by machining; otherwise, renew the hub/brake drum.

Refitting

11 If a new hub/brake drum is to be installed, use a suitable solvent to remove any preservative coating that may have been applied to its interior.

12 Apply a smear of gear oil to the stub axle,

8.5 Unscrewing a caliper guide pin bolt

and slide on the hub/brake drum, being careful not to get oil onto the brake shoes or the friction surface of the drum.

13 Fit the rear hub nut, tightening it to the specified torque setting, and tap the dust cap securely into position in the centre of the hub/brake drum.

14 Depress the footbrake several times to operate the self-adjusting mechanism until normal, non-assisted pedal action returns. Refit the roadwheel then lower the vehicle to the ground and tighten the wheel nuts to the specified torque.

15 On completion, adjust the handbrake as described in Section 14.

Courier and Combi models

Removal

16 Working at the handbrake lever inside the car, back off the handbrake cable adjustment, as described in Section 14.

17 Remove the relevant wheel trim or the wheel centre plate (alloy wheels), then slacken the relevant wheel nuts. Chock the front wheels, and select 1st gear (manual transmission) or "P" (automatic transmission), then jack up the rear of the vehicle, and support securely on axle stands (see *"Jacking and Vehicle Support"*). Remove the rear roadwheel.

18 Prise off the retaining clip, located on one of the wheel studs, and withdraw the drum from the hub. If the drum is tight (this should not be the case if the handbrake cable has been backed off), this may be due to the brake shoes binding on the inner circumference of the drum. If the brake shoes are binding, proceed as follows.

19 Referring to Section 14, fully slacken the handbrake cable adjuster nut to obtain maximum freeplay in the cable. If this still fails to release the drum, remove the small rubber grommet from the rear of the backplate. Insert a screwdriver through the hole and release the adjuster strut self-adjust mechanism by moving the strut quadrant, allowing the brake shoes to retract fully **(see illustration)**. The drum should then be free to be removed.

Inspection

20 Proceed as described in paragraphs 7 to 10 inclusive.

8.6 Lift the caliper away from the disc

Refitting

21 If a new drum is to be installed, use a suitable solvent to remove any preservative coating that may have been applied to its interior.

22 Ensure that the mating faces of the hub and drum are clean, then slide the drum into position on the hub, and refit the retaining clip to the wheel stud.

23 Depress the footbrake several times to operate the self-adjusting mechanism until normal, non-assisted pedal action returns. Refit the roadwheel then lower the vehicle to the ground and tighten the wheel nuts to the specified torque.

24 On completion, adjust the handbrake as described in Section 14.

---

8 Front brake caliper –
   removal, overhaul and refitting

Caution: On models equipped with ABS, disconnect the battery before disconnecting any braking system hydraulic union and do not reconnect the battery until after the hydraulic system has been bled. Failure to do this could lead to air entering the ABS hydraulic unit requiring the unit to be bled using special Ford test equipment (see Section 2).

Note: *Before starting work, refer to the note at the beginning of Section 2 concerning the dangers of hydraulic fluid, and to the warning at the beginning of Section 4 concerning the dangers of asbestos dust.*

Removal

1 Apply the handbrake, then jack up the front of the vehicle and support it on axle stands (see *"Jacking and Vehicle Support"*). Remove the appropriate roadwheel.

2 Minimise fluid loss by first removing the master cylinder reservoir cap, and then tightening it down onto a piece of polythene, to obtain an airtight seal. Alternatively, use a brake hose clamp, a G-clamp or a similar tool to clamp the flexible hose running to the caliper.

3 Clean the area around the caliper hose union, then loosen the union nut.

4 Using a flat-bladed screwdriver, carefully prise the pad spring out from the caliper noting its correct fitted position.

5 Remove the plastic covers from the ends of the guide bushes to gain access to the caliper guide pin bolts, then slacken and remove the guide pin bolts **(see illustration)**.

6 Lift the caliper assembly away from the disc and unclip the inner pad from the caliper piston **(see illustration)**. Unscrew the caliper from the end of the brake hose and remove it from the vehicle. Plug or cover the end of the hose to minimise fluid loss and to prevent dirt entry.

Overhaul

7 With the caliper on the bench, wipe away all traces of dust and dirt, but *avoid inhaling the dust, as it is injurious to health.*
8 Withdraw the partially ejected piston from the caliper body (see illustration).

> **HAYNES HINT** *If the piston cannot be withdrawn by hand, it can be pushed out by applying compressed air to the brake hose union hole. Only low pressure should be required, such as is generated by a foot pump. As the piston is expelled take great care not to trap your fingers between the piston and caliper.*

9 Using a small screwdriver, prise the dust seal from the piston, then extract the piston hydraulic seal from the caliper bore, taking great care not to damage the bore.
10 Thoroughly clean all components, using only methylated spirit, isopropyl alcohol or clean hydraulic fluid as a cleaning medium. Never use mineral-based solvents such as petrol or paraffin, as they will attack the hydraulic system rubber components. Dry the components immediately, using compressed air or a clean, lint-free cloth. Use compressed air to blow clear the fluid passages.
11 Check all components, and renew any that are worn or damaged. Check particularly the cylinder bore and piston - these should be renewed (note that this means the renewal of the complete caliper body assembly) if they are scratched, worn or corroded in any way. Similarly, check the condition of the guide pin bolts and their bushes - both bolts should be undamaged and (when cleaned) a reasonably tight sliding fit in their bushes. If there is any doubt about the condition of any component, renew it.
12 If the assembly is fit for further use, obtain the appropriate repair kit; the components are available from Ford dealers in various combinations. All rubber seals should be renewed as a matter of course; these should never be re-used.
13 Before commencing reassembly, ensure that all components are clean and dry.
14 Soak the piston and the new piston (fluid) seal in clean hydraulic fluid. Smear clean fluid on the cylinder bore surface.
15 Fit the new piston (fluid) seal, using only your fingers (no tools) to manipulate it into the cylinder bore groove.
16 Fit the new dust seal to the piston groove, then carefully ease the piston squarely into the cylinder bore using a twisting motion. Press the piston fully into position then seat the outer lip of the dust seal on the caliper body.

Refitting

17 Screw the caliper body fully onto the flexible hose union.
18 Ensure that the outer brake pad is still correctly fitted in the caliper mounting bracket, and clip the inner pad into position in the caliper piston.

8.8 Brake caliper components

A *Dust cover*   C *Piston*
B *Piston seal*   D *Caliper body*

19 Slide the caliper over the disc, making sure that the pads remain correctly positioned, and fit the guide pin bolts. Tighten both guide pin bolts to the specified torque, then refit the plastic covers to the bushes.
20 Engage the pad spring with the outer pad and engage the spring ends correctly in the caliper body holes, as noted before removal.
21 Tighten the brake hose union, then remove the brake hose clamp or polythene (where fitted).
22 Bleed the hydraulic system as described in Section 2. Note that, provided precautions were taken to minimise brake fluid loss, it should only be necessary to bleed the relevant front brake.
23 Refit the roadwheel, then lower the vehicle to the ground and tighten the roadwheel nuts to the specified torque.

---

9 Rear wheel cylinder –
removal, overhaul and refitting

Caution: On models equipped with ABS, disconnect the battery before disconnecting any braking system hydraulic union and do not reconnect the battery until after the hydraulic system has been bled. Failure to do this could lead to air entering the ABS hydraulic unit requiring the unit to be bled using special Ford test equipment (see Section 2).

9.3 Unhook the brake shoe upper return spring (arrowed) – Hatchback model shown

Note: *Before starting work, refer to the note at the beginning of Section 2 concerning the dangers of hydraulic fluid, and to the warning at the beginning of Section 5 concerning the dangers of asbestos dust.*

Removal

1 Remove the brake drum as described in Section 7.
2 Minimise fluid loss by first removing the master cylinder reservoir cap, and then tightening it down onto a piece of polythene, to obtain an airtight seal. Alternatively, use a brake hose clamp, a G-clamp or a similar tool to clamp the flexible hose at the nearest convenient point to the wheel cylinder.
3 Carefully unhook the brake shoe upper return spring, and remove it from both brake shoes (see illustration). Pull the upper ends of the shoes away from the wheel cylinder to disengage them from the pistons.
4 Wipe away all traces of dirt around the brake pipe union at the rear of the wheel cylinder, and unscrew the union nut. Carefully ease the pipe out of the wheel cylinder, and plug or tape over its end to prevent dirt entry. Wipe off any spilt fluid immediately.
5 Unscrew the two wheel cylinder retaining bolts from the rear of the backplate, and remove the cylinder, taking great care not to allow surplus hydraulic fluid to contaminate the brake shoe linings (see illustration).

Overhaul

6 It is not possible to overhaul the cylinder, since no components are available separately. If faulty, the complete wheel cylinder assembly must be renewed.

Refitting

7 Ensure that the backplate and wheel cylinder mating surfaces are clean and dry then spread the brake shoes and manoeuvre the wheel cylinder into position. Engage the brake pipe, and screw in the union nut two or three turns to ensure that the thread has started.
8 Insert the two wheel cylinder retaining bolts, tightening them securely, then tighten the brake pipe union nut to the specified torque.
9 Remove the clamp from the flexible brake hose, or the polythene from the master cylinder reservoir (as applicable).

9.5 Rear wheel cylinder securing bolts (arrowed) – Courier model shown

10.4 Disconnect the clutch master cylinder hose (arrowed) from the brake fluid reservoir – manual transmission models

10 Ensure that the brake shoes are correctly located in the cylinder pistons, then carefully refit the brake shoe return spring, ensuring it is correctly located in both shoes. Also check that the adjuster strut components are correctly located on the shoes.

11 Refit the brake drum as described in Section 7.

12 Bleed the brake hydraulic system as described in Section 2. Providing suitable precautions were taken to minimise loss of fluid, it should only be necessary to bleed the relevant rear brake.

10 Master cylinder – removal, overhaul and refitting

Caution: On models equipped with ABS, disconnect the battery before disconnecting any braking system hydraulic union and do not reconnect the battery until after the hydraulic system has been bled. Failure to do this could lead to air entering the ABS hydraulic unit requiring the unit to be bled using special Ford test equipment (see Section 2).
Note: Before starting work, refer to the warning at the beginning of Section 2 concerning the dangers of hydraulic fluid.

Removal

1 Exhaust the vacuum present in the brake servo unit by repeatedly depressing the brake pedal.

10.5 Unscrewing a master cylinder brake pipe union nut

2 Remove the master cylinder reservoir cap and syphon the hydraulic fluid from the reservoir. **Note:** *Do not syphon the fluid by mouth, as it is poisonous; use a syringe or an old poultry baster.* Alternatively, open any convenient bleed screw in the system, and gently pump the brake pedal to expel the fluid through a plastic tube connected to the bleed screw (see Section 2). Disconnect the wiring connector from the brake fluid level sender unit in the reservoir cap.

3 On diesel engine models, if desired, to improve access, slacken the retaining clamps and remove the air intake ducting from behind the reservoir.

4 On manual transmission models, release the retaining clip and disconnect the clutch master cylinder fluid supply hose from the side of the reservoir **(see illustration)**. Be prepared for fluid spillage.

5 On models not fitted with ABS, wipe clean the area around the brake pipe unions on the side of the master cylinder, and place absorbent rags beneath the pipe unions to catch any surplus fluid. Make a note of the correct fitted positions of the unions, then unscrew the union nuts and carefully withdraw the pipes **(see illustration)**. Plug or tape over the pipe ends and master cylinder orifices, to minimise the loss of brake fluid, and to prevent the entry of dirt into the system. Wash off any spilt fluid immediately with cold water.

6 On models with ABS, wipe clean the area around the brake pipe unions on both the master cylinder and ABS hydraulic unit, and place absorbent rags beneath the pipe unions to catch any surplus fluid. Unscrew the union nuts securing each pipe to both the master cylinder and hydraulic unit and remove the pipes from the engine compartment. Plug or tape over the master cylinder and hydraulic unit orifices, to minimise the loss of brake fluid, and to prevent the entry of dirt into the system. Wash off any spilt fluid immediately with cold water.

7 Slacken and remove the nuts securing the master cylinder to the vacuum servo unit **(see illustration)**. Note the locations of any brackets secured by the nuts. Remove the master cylinder from the engine compartment along with its sealing ring - discard the sealing ring a new one must be used on refitting.

10.7 Master cylinder securing nut (arrowed)

Overhaul

8 The master cylinder can be overhauled after obtaining the relevant repair kit from a Ford dealer. Ensure that the correct repair kit is obtained for the master cylinder being worked on. Note the locations of all components to ensure correct refitting, and lubricate the new seals using clean brake fluid. Follow the assembly instructions supplied with the repair kit.

Refitting

9 Ensure the mating surfaces are clean and dry then fit the new sealing ring to the rear of the master cylinder.

10 Carefully fit the master cylinder to the servo unit, ensuring that the servo unit pushrod enters the master cylinder bore centrally. Fit the retaining nuts and tighten them to the specified torque setting. Where applicable, make sure that any brackets secured by the master cylinder retaining nuts are in position as noted before removal.

11 Reconnect the brake pipes to the master cylinder and, on models with ABS, the hydraulic unit and tighten the union nuts securely. Make sure that the pipes are correctly reconnected as noted before removal.

12 On manual transmission models securely reconnect the clutch fluid hose to the side of the reservoir, and secure with the clip.

13 On diesel engine models, refit the air intake ducting, and tighten the retaining clamps.

14 Refill the master cylinder reservoir with new fluid, then bleed the complete hydraulic system as described in Section 2. Thoroughly check the operation of the braking system before using the vehicle on the road.

11 Brake pedal – removal and refitting

Removal

1 Remove the stop-light switch as described in Section 18.

2 On manual transmission models, using pliers, carefully unhook the return spring from the clutch pedal.

3 Remove the retaining clip from the left-hand end of the pedal pivot shaft and push the shaft slightly towards the brake pedal.

4 Remove the retaining clip from the right-hand end of the pivot shaft then slide the shaft sufficiently to the left until the pedal can be lowered from its mounting bracket.

5 Insert a screwdriver into the groove in the plastic retaining clip, then use the screwdriver to spread the clip, and release it from the groove in the pushrod **(see illustration)**. Disconnect the servo unit/linkage pushrod from the pedal.

6 Remove the pivot bushes from either side of the pedal **(see illustration)**.

7 Inspect the pedal for signs of wear or damage, paying particular attention to the pivot bushes, and renew worn components as necessary.

Refitting

8 Apply some multi-purpose grease to the bearing surfaces of the pedal, pivot shaft and bushes. Fit the bushes to the pedal.
9 Manoeuvre the pedal assembly into position under the facia, ensuring that the servo/linkage unit pushrod engages correctly with the pedal, then slide the pivot shaft fully into position.
10 Refit the right-hand retaining clip to the pivot shaft groove, then secure the shaft in position by refitting the left-hand clip to the groove.
11 Secure the servo/linkage pushrod in position with the retaining clip (make sure that the clip engages with the groove in the pushrod end fitting), then refit the stop-light switch as described in Section 18.
12 On manual transmission models, hook the return spring back onto the clutch pedal.
13 Check the operation of the brake pedal before using the vehicle on the road.

12 Vacuum servo unit –
testing, removal and refitting

Testing

1 To test the operation of the servo unit, depress the footbrake several times to exhaust the vacuum, then start the engine whilst keeping the pedal firmly depressed. As the engine starts, there should be a noticeable "give" in the brake pedal as the vacuum builds up. Allow the engine to run for at least two minutes, then switch it off. If the brake pedal is now depressed it should feel normal, but further applications should result in the pedal feeling firmer, with the pedal stroke decreasing with each application.
2 If the servo does not operate as described, first inspect the servo unit check valve as described in Section 13.

11.5 Removing the pushrod-to-brake pedal retaining clip

3 If the servo unit still fails to operate satisfactorily, the fault lies within the unit itself. Repairs to the unit are not possible - if faulty, the servo unit must be renewed.

Removal

4 Remove the master cylinder as described in Section 10.
5 Carefully ease the vacuum hose end fitting out from the servo unit, taking great care not to displace the rubber grommet.
6 Where applicable, disconnect the wiring connectors from the emission control system components mounted on the bracket, situated directly above the servo unit. Slacken and remove the retaining screw then unclip the bracket assembly and remove it from the engine compartment.
7 On models equipped with ABS, disconnect the wiring connector from the ABS hydraulic unit **(see illustration)**.
8 On left-hand-drive models, reach up behind the facia, then prise off the retaining clip securing the servo unit pushrod to the brake pedal (see Section 11). Slacken and remove the four nuts securing the servo unit to its mounting bracket, then manoeuvre the unit forwards and out of the engine compartment.
9 On right-hand-drive models, slacken and remove the four nuts securing the servo unit to its mounting brackets. Pull the servo unit gently forwards until access to the pushrod clevis pin can be gained. Slide out the retaining clip, then withdraw the clevis pin and manoeuvre the servo unit out from the engine compartment **(see illustrations)**.

11.6 Remove the pivot bushes from the brake pedal

10 If the servo unit is faulty it must be renewed - overhaul of the unit is not possible.

Refitting

11 On left-hand-drive models, carefully manoeuvre the servo unit into position, making sure that the pushrod engages correctly with the brake pedal locating piece. Ensure that the pushrod is correctly located, then refit the servo unit securing nuts and tighten them to the specified torque. Secure the pushrod to the pedal with the retaining clip.
12 On right-hand-drive models, apply a smear of multi-purpose grease to the servo unit clevis and clevis pin. Manoeuvre the unit into position, aligning it with the cross-linkage, then refit the clevis pin and secure it in position with the retaining clip. Seat the unit on the bracket and tighten its mounting nuts to the specified torque.
13 Where applicable, refit the emission control system component bracket and securely tighten its retaining screw, then reconnect the wiring connectors to the emission control system components. Where necessary, also reconnect the ABS hydraulic unit wiring connector.
14 Ensure that the rubber grommet is correctly located in the servo unit, then ease the vacuum hose end fitting back into position.
15 Refit the master cylinder as described in Section 10 and bleed the complete hydraulic system as described in Section 2.

12.7 On models with ABS, disconnect the ABS hydraulic unit wiring connector (arrowed)

12.9a Unscrew the four servo securing nuts (arrowed) . . .

12.9b . . . then remove the clevis pin and retaining clip (arrowed)

9

13.1 Vacuum servo unit check valve location (arrowed)

13 Vacuum servo unit check valve – removal, testing and refitting

Removal

1 The valve is integral with the servo vacuum hose **(see illustration)**.
2 Carefully ease the vacuum hose end fitting out from its rubber grommet on the front of the servo unit **(see illustration)**.
3 Work back along the vacuum hose, freeing it from any relevant retaining clips, then unscrew the union nut securing the hose to the manifold/pump (as applicable) and remove the hose assembly from the vehicle. The check valve and hose cannot be separated.

Testing

4 Examine the check valve and hose for signs of damage, and renew if necessary. The valve may be tested by blowing through the hose in both directions. Air should flow through the valve in one direction only - when blown through from the servo unit end of the hose. Renew the valve and hose assembly if this is not the case.
5 Examine the servo unit rubber sealing grommet for signs of damage or deterioration, and renew as necessary.

Refitting

6 Manoeuvre the hose assembly into position and connect the engine end of the hose to the manifold/pump (as applicable), tightening its union nut securely.

14.3 Slackening the handbrake adjuster nut

13.2 Ease the vacuum hose end fitting from the servo unit

7 Ensure the hose is correctly routed and fit the sealing grommet into position in the servo unit. Ease the hose end fitting into position in the servo, taking care not to displace or damage the grommet.
8 On completion, start the engine and check that there are no air leaks.

14 Handbrake – adjustment

Caution: If the handbrake is incorrectly adjusted, the rear brake automatic adjustment mechanism will not be able to function correctly. This will lead to the brake shoe-to-drum clearance becoming excessive as the shoe linings wear, resulting in excessive brake pedal travel.

1 Fully release the handbrake then apply the footbrake firmly several times to ensure that the self-adjust mechanism is fully adjusted.
2 Unclip the handbrake lever gaiter to gain access to the adjuster nut on the side of the lever.
3 From the fully-released position, pull the handbrake lever up noting the number of clicks emitted from the handbrake ratchet mechanism. Position the handbrake lever on the sixth notch of mechanism then slacken the adjusting nut until it rotates freely. Adjust the handbrake by tightening the adjuster nut to the specified torque then clip the gaiter back into position **(see illustration)**.

15.4 Handbrake lever securing nuts (arrowed)

15 Handbrake lever – removal and refitting

Removal

1 Disconnect the battery negative lead (see Chapter 5A).
2 Chock the wheels to prevent the vehicle rolling whilst the handbrake is released.
3 From inside the vehicle, unclip the handbrake lever gaiter and remove it from the lever.
4 Slacken and remove the cable adjusting nut from the side of the lever, then unscrew the two lever retaining nuts **(see illustration)**. Manoeuvre the lever assembly out of position, disconnecting the warning light switch wiring connector as it becomes accessible.

Refitting

5 Refitting is a reversal of removal, tightening the lever retaining nuts to the specified torque. Prior to refitting the gaiter, adjust the handbrake cable as described in Section 14.

16 Handbrake cables – removal and refitting

Removal

1 The handbrake cable consists of three sections, a short front section which connects the lever to the equalizer plate and the left- and right-hand rear sections which link the equalizer plate to the rear brakes. Each section can be removed individually as follows.

Front cable

2 Remove the handbrake lever as described in Section 15.
3 Firmly chock the front wheels, then jack up the rear of the vehicle and support it on axle stands (see *"Jacking and Vehicle Support"*).
4 To gain access to the equalizer plate mechanism which links the handbrake cables, undo the retaining nuts and remove the exhaust system centre heatshield **(see illustration)**. **Note:** *On some models it may*

16.4 Remove the exhaust heatshield for access to the handbrake equalizer plate mechanism (arrowed)

16.10 Unbolt the handbrake cable bracket (arrowed) from the vehicle floor

prove necessary to free the rear of the exhaust system from its mounting rubbers and lower the system slightly to gain the necessary clearance required to remove the heatshield (see Chapter 4).

5 Detach the front cable from the equalizer plate, then free the cable grommet from the body and remove the cable from the vehicle.

Rear cable

6 Carry out the operations described in paragraphs 3 and 4.
7 Undo the retaining nuts and remove the exhaust system centre heatshield from the vehicle.
8 Remove the relevant set of rear brake shoes as described in Section 5.
9 Release the securing clip, then free the handbrake outer cable from the brake backplate.
10 Work back along the cable, noting its correct routing whilst freeing it from any clips or ties. Where necessary, unbolt the handbrake cable brackets from the vehicle floor **(see illustration)**.
11 Detach the front end of the inner cable from the handbrake lever equalizer plate, then remove the outer cable retaining clip from the bracket on the floor, and remove the cable from the vehicle **(see illustration)**.

Refitting

12 Refitting is a reversal of the removal procedure, bearing in mind the following points.
 a) Ensure that the cable is correctly routed and retained by all the relevant clips and ties.
 b) Refit the rear brake shoes with reference to Section 5.
 c) Prior to refitting the gaiter, adjust the handbrake as described in Section 14.

17 Rear brake pressure-regulating valve – testing, removal and refitting

Hatchback and Van models

Testing

1 On models not equipped with ABS, a pressure regulating valve is fitted into the hydraulic circuit to each rear brake. The valves are screwed into the rear brake outlet ports of the master cylinder **(see illustration)**. The valves regulate the hydraulic pressure being applied to the rear brakes to help prevent rear wheels locking up under hard braking.
2 Specialist equipment is required to check the performance of the valves, therefore if the valves are thought to be faulty the car should be taken to a suitably-equipped Ford dealer for testing. Repairs are not possible and, if faulty, the valves must be renewed.

Removal

Note: Before starting work, refer to the warning at the beginning of Section 2 concerning the dangers of hydraulic fluid.
3 Exhaust the vacuum present in the servo unit by repeatedly depressing the brake pedal.
4 Remove the master cylinder reservoir cap and syphon the hydraulic fluid from the reservoir. **Note:** Do not syphon the fluid by

mouth, as it is poisonous; use a syringe or an old poultry baster. Alternatively, open any convenient bleed screw in the system, and gently pump the brake pedal to expel the fluid through a plastic tube connected to the screw (see Section 2).
5 Wipe clean the area around the relevant valve and place absorbent rags beneath the pipe unions to catch any surplus fluid.
6 Slacken the union nut and disconnect the brake pipe from the valve, then unscrew the valve and remove it from the master cylinder. Plug or tape over the pipe end and master cylinder orifice, to minimise the loss of brake fluid, and to prevent the entry of dirt into the system. Wash off any spilt fluid immediately with cold water.

Refitting

7 Ensure that the threads of the valve and master cylinder are clean and dry and fit the valve, tightening it securely. Reconnect the brake pipe and tighten its union nut securely.
8 Refill the master cylinder reservoir, and bleed the complete hydraulic system as described in Section 2.

Courier and Combi models

Testing

9 Specialist equipment is required to check the performance of the valves, therefore if the valves are thought to be faulty the car should be taken to a suitably-equipped Ford dealer for testing. Repairs are not possible and, if faulty, the valves must be renewed.

Removal

Note: Before starting work, refer to the warning at the beginning of Section 2 concerning the dangers of hydraulic fluid.
10 For this operation, the vehicle must be raised for access underneath at the rear, but must still be resting on its wheels. Suitable ramps (or an inspection pit) will therefore be required. If positioning the vehicle on a pair of ramps, chock the front roadwheels.

16.11 Detach the front end of the inner cable (1) from the equalizer plate (2)

17.1 Brake pressure regulating valve (arrowed) screwed into master cylinder – Hatchback model

17.12 Rear brake pressure regulating valve components – Courier and Combi models

1 Valve   3 Operating lever
2 Operating spring   4 Mounting bracket

18.1 Stop-light switch location (arrowed) – viewed through fusebox aperture in facia with fuse/relay box removed

11 Minimise fluid loss by first removing the master cylinder reservoir cap, and then tightening it down onto a piece of polythene, to obtain an airtight seal.

12 Disconnect the four brake pipes from the valve, and drain any escaping fluid into a suitable container for disposal **(see illustration)**. Due to its location, care will be needed not to spill the fluid onto the hands - wear suitable protective gloves. Plug or cap the disconnected pipes and valve openings, to prevent dirt entry and further fluid loss.

13 Unbolt the valve from its mounting bracket, unhook the linkage from the rear axle, then withdraw the valve. The intermediate bracket may be unbolted if required.

Refitting

14 Refitting is the reverse of the removal procedure, but have the valve adjusted at the earliest opportunity, and bleed the complete hydraulic system as described in Section 2. Check the operation of the brakes before taking the vehicle out on the road.

18 Stop-light switch – removal, refitting and adjustment

Removal

1 The stop-light switch is located on the pedal bracket behind the facia **(see illustration)**.

2 Disconnect the battery negative lead (see Chapter 5A).

3 To remove the switch, reach up behind the facia, disconnect the wiring connector, then rotate the switch slightly anti-clockwise and remove it from the bracket.

Refitting and adjustment

4 On left-hand-drive models, insert the switch into position aligning its locating tabs with the bracket cut-out. Pull the brake pedal fully upwards then push the switch fully downwards, to ensure the plunger is fully depressed, and secure the switch in position by rotating it clockwise. This procedure will automatically set the switch adjustment.

5 On right-hand-drive models, insert the switch into position aligning its locating tabs with the bracket cut-out. Hold the brake pedal in the at-rest position then push the switch fully downwards, to ensure the plunger is fully depressed, and secure the switch in position by rotating it clockwise. This procedure will automatically set the switch adjustment.

6 Reconnect the wiring connector, then reconnect the battery negative lead, and check the stop-light operation before using the vehicle on the road.

19.1 Handbrake "on" warning light switch location (arrowed)

19 Handbrake "on" warning light switch – removal and refitting

Removal

1 Remove the handbrake lever assembly as described in Section 15 **(see illustration)**.

2 Remove the securing screw, and withdraw the switch.

Refitting

3 Refitting is a reversal of removal, but on completion, adjust the handbrake cable as described in Section 14.

20 Anti-lock braking system (ABS) – general information

Note: *On models equipped with traction control, the ABS hydraulic unit is a dual-function unit and controls both the anti-lock braking system and the traction control system.*

1 ABS is available as an option on most models. The system comprises the hydraulic unit and the four roadwheel sensors. The hydraulic unit contains the electronic control unit (ECU), the hydraulic solenoid valves (one set for each brake) and the electrically-driven pump. The purpose of the system is to prevent the wheel(s) locking during heavy braking. This is achieved by automatic release of the brake on the relevant wheel, followed by re-application of the brake.

2 The solenoid valves are controlled by the ECU, which itself receives signals from the four wheel sensors (which are fitted to the wheel hubs), which monitor the speed of rotation of each wheel. By comparing these signals, the ECU can determine the speed at which the vehicle is travelling. It can then use this speed to determine when a wheel is decelerating at an abnormal rate, compared to the speed of the vehicle, and therefore predicts when a wheel is about to lock. During normal operation, the system functions in the same way as a non-ABS braking system.

3 If the ECU senses that a wheel is about to lock, it operates the relevant solenoid valve(s) in the hydraulic unit, which then isolates from the master cylinder the relevant brake(s) on the wheel(s) which is/are about to lock, effectively sealing-in the hydraulic pressure.

4 If the speed of rotation of the wheel continues to decrease at an abnormal rate, the ECU operates the electrically-driven pump which pumps the hydraulic fluid back into the master cylinder, releasing the brake. Once the speed of rotation of the wheel returns to an acceptable rate, the pump stops, and the solenoid valves switch again, allowing the hydraulic master cylinder pressure to return to the caliper/wheel cylinder (as applicable), which then re-applies the brake. This cycle can be carried out many-times-a-second.

5 The action of the solenoid valves and return pump creates pulses in the hydraulic circuit. When the ABS system is functioning, these pulses can be felt through the brake pedal.

6 The ABS also incorporates a low-speed traction control system. The hydraulic unit incorporates an additional set of solenoid valves which operate the traction control system. The system operates at speeds up to approximately 30 mph (60 km/h) using the signals supplied by the wheel sensors (see paragraph 2). If the ECU senses that a driving wheel is about to lose traction, it prevents this by momentarily applying the relevant front brake.

7 The operation of the ABS and the traction control system is entirely dependent on electrical signals. To prevent the system

responding to any inaccurate signals, a built-in safety circuit monitors all signals received by the ECU. If an inaccurate signal or low battery voltage is detected, the system is automatically shut down, and the warning light(s) on the instrument panel is/are illuminated, to inform the driver that the system is not operational. Normal braking should still be available, however.

8 If a fault does develop in the ABS/traction control system, the vehicle must be taken to a Ford dealer for fault diagnosis and repair.

21 Anti-lock braking system components – removal and refitting

Hydraulic unit

1 Removal and refitting of the hydraulic unit should be entrusted to a Ford dealer since special electronic test equipment will be required to bleed the hydraulic system on refitting. The electronic test equipment allows the hydraulic unit to be switched into a special mode which purges the unit of all trapped air - it is not possible to remove trapped air from the unit by bleeding the system conventionally.

Wheel sensor

Removal

2 Disconnect the battery negative lead (see Chapter 5A).

3 Apply the handbrake or chock the front wheels, as applicable, then jack up the relevant end of the vehicle and support securely on axle stands (see "Jacking and Vehicle Support"). To improve access, remove the roadwheel.

4 Trace the wiring back from the sensor, releasing it from all the relevant clips and ties whilst noting its correct routing, and disconnect the wiring connector.

5 Slacken and remove the retaining bolt and withdraw the sensor from its housing.

Refitting

6 Ensure that the mating faces of the sensor and the housing are clean, and apply a little multi-purpose grease to the housing bore before refitting.

7 Make sure the sensor tip is clean, then ease the sensor into position in the housing. Refit the retaining bolt and tighten it to the specified torque.

8 Work along the sensor wiring, making sure it is correctly routed, securing it in position with all the relevant clips and ties.

9 Reconnect the sensor wiring connector, then refit the roadwheel, lower the vehicle, and tighten the wheel nuts to the specified torque.

22 Vacuum pump (diesel engine models) – removal and refitting

Removal

1 Disconnect the battery negative lead (see Chapter 5A).

2 Remove the camshaft cover as described in Chapter 2.

3 Using a suitable socket or spanner on the crankshaft pulley bolt, turn the crankshaft until the vacuum pump pushrod (operated by the lobe on the end of the camshaft) is fully retracted into the cylinder head (see illustration).

4 Unscrew the union nut and disconnect the vacuum hose from the top of the pump (see illustration).

5 Release the retaining clip and disconnect the oil return hose from the base of the pump (see illustration). Be prepared for some oil spillage as the hose is disconnected and mop up any spilt oil.

22.3 The vacuum pump pushrod (1) must be fully retracted into the cylinder head (the pushrod must be resting on the lowest point of the cam lobe (2)

22.4 Disconnecting the vacuum hose from the vacuum pump

9

6 Unscrew the bolt securing the fuel heater bracket to the side of the cylinder head (see illustration). Move the fuel heater to one side for access to the lower vacuum pump securing bolt.
7 Evenly and progressively slacken the bolts securing the pump to the front of the cylinder head. Note that there is no need to completely remove the lower bolt, as the lower end of the pump is slotted (see illustrations).
8 Remove the pump from the engine compartment, along with its sealing ring. Discard the sealing ring, a new one should be used on refitting (see illustration).

Refitting

9 Ensure the pump and cylinder head mating surfaces are clean and dry and fit the new sealing ring to the pump recess.
10 Manoeuvre the pump into position, ensuring the sealing ring remains correctly seated, and tighten the pump mounting bolts securely.
11 Reconnect the oil return hose to the base of the pump and secure it in position with the retaining clip.
12 Reconnect the vacuum hose to the pump, tightening its union nut securely.
13 Refit the fuel heater bracket and tighten the securing bolt.

22.5 Disconnecting the oil return hose from the vacuum pump

14 Refit the camshaft cover with reference to Chapter 2.

23 Vacuum pump (diesel engine models) – testing and overhaul

Note: *A vacuum gauge will be required for this check.*
1 The operation of the braking system vacuum pump can be checked using a vacuum gauge.
2 Disconnect the vacuum pipe from the

22.6 Unscrew the bolt (arrowed) securing the fuel heater bracket

pump, and connect the gauge to the pump union using a suitable length of hose.
3 Start the engine and allow it to idle, then measure the vacuum created by the pump. As a guide, after one minute, a minimum of approximately 500 mm Hg should be recorded. If the vacuum registered is significantly less than this, it is likely that the pump is faulty. However, seek the advice of a Ford dealer before condemning the pump.
4 Overhaul of the vacuum pump is not possible, since no components are available separately for it. If faulty, the complete pump assembly must be renewed.

22.7a Vacuum pump lower securing bolt location (arrowed)

22.7b Unscrewing the vacuum pump upper securing bolt

22.8 Use a new sealing ring (arrowed) when refitting the vacuum pump

Chapter 10
Suspension and steering

Contents

Degrees of difficulty

Easy, suitable for novice with little experience	**Fairly easy,** suitable for beginner with some experience	**Fairly difficult,** suitable for competent DIY mechanic	**Difficult,** suitable for experienced DIY mechanic	**Very difficult,** suitable for expert DIY or professional

Specifications

Wheel alignment and steering angles

Front wheel castor:
  Hatchback models:
    Manual steering . . . . 2°35' to 0°05'
    Power steering . . . . 3°29' to 0°59'
  Van models:
    Manual steering . . . . 2°33' to 0°03'
    Power steering . . . . 3°28' to 0°58'
  Courier models:
    Manual steering . . . . 1°35' to -0°55'
    Power steering . . . . 2°13' to -0°17'
  Combi models:
    Manual steering . . . . 1°57' to -0°33'
    Power steering . . . . 2°34' to 0°04'
Front wheel camber:
  Hatchback and Van models:
    Manual steering . . . . 0°44' to -2°04'
    Power steering . . . . 0°47' to -2°01'
  Courier models . . . . 0°49' to -1°59'
  Combi models
    Manual steering . . . . 0°43' to -2°00'
    Power steering . . . . 0°47' to -2°01'
Front wheel toe-setting (all models):
  Allowable tolerance . . . . 0°25' (2.5 mm) toe-in to 0°25' (2.5 mm) toe-out
  Setting value after adjustment . . . . 0°00 (0 mm) ± 0°10' (1.0 mm)
Rear wheel camber:
  Hatchback and Van models . . . . -0°30' to -2°00'
  Courier and Combi models . . . . 0°06' to -1°24'
Rear wheel toe-setting:
  Hatchback and Van models . . . . 0°43' (4.3 mm) to 0°03' (0.3 mm) toe-in
  Courier and Combi models . . . . 0°45' (4.5 mm) to 0°05' (0.5 mm) toe-in

10

Torque wrench settings

	Nm	lbf ft
Front suspension		
Lower arm securing nuts and bolts	80	59
Anti-roll bar clamp bolts	23	17
Anti-roll bar drop link nuts	50	37
Front crossmember securing bolts	103	76
Lower arm-to-hub carrier pinch-bolt and nut	51	38
Hub carrier-to-suspension strut pinch-bolt	85	63
Suspension strut top mounting nut	48	35
Suspension strut piston rod nut	59	44
Front hub nut	290	214
Rear suspension – Hatchback and Van models		
Suspension strut top mounting nut	34	25
Rear axle assembly mounting bracket-to-floor bolts	50	37
Suspension strut lower securing bolt	120	89
Rear axle assembly mounting bracket-to-trailing arm bolts	68	50
Stub axle-to-trailing arm bolts	66	49
Rear hub nut	235	173
Steering		
Track-rod end-to-hub carrier nuts	37	27
Track-rod end locknuts	63	46
Steering gear securing nuts and bolts	48	35
Power steering gear fluid pipe unions	31	23
Flexible coupling-to-steering column shaft pinch-bolt	28	21
Flexible coupling-to-steering gear pinion pinch-bolt	26	19
Steering wheel securing bolt	45	33
Steering column securing nuts	12	9
Power steering pump securing bolts	25	18
Power steering pump bracket securing bolts	25	18
Power steering pump high-pressure fluid pipe union nut	65	48
Power steering fluid pressure switch	11	8
Roadwheels		
Wheel nuts	85	63

1 General information

The front suspension is of independent type, with a subframe, MacPherson struts, lower arms, and an anti-roll bar. The struts, which incorporate coil springs and integral shock absorbers, are attached at their upper ends to the reinforced strut mountings on the body shell. The lower end of each strut is bolted to the top of a cast hub carrier, which carries the hub, and the brake disc and caliper. The hubs run within non-adjustable bearings in the hub carriers. The lower end of each hub carrier is attached, via a balljoint, to a pressed-steel lower arm assembly. The balljoints are integral with the lower arms. Each lower arm is attached at its inboard end to the subframe, via flexible rubber bushes, and controls both lateral and fore and aft movement of the front wheels. An anti-roll bar is fitted to all models. The anti-roll bar is mounted on the subframe, and is connected to the suspension struts via vertical drop links.

On Hatchback and Van models, the rear suspension is semi-independent, with an inverted V-section beam welded between tubular trailing arms. This inverted V-section beam allows a limited torsional flexibility, giving each rear wheel a certain degree of independent movement, whilst maintaining optimum track and wheel camber control. This type of arrangement is called a "twist beam" rear axle. The axle is attached to the body via rubber bushes. The rear suspension struts, which are similar to the MacPherson struts used at the front, are attached at their upper ends to the reinforced strut mountings in the luggage compartment. At their lower ends, the struts are attached to the rear of the trailing arms. The rear hubs are integral with the brake drums, and the hub/drums run on stub axles which are bolted to the rear of the trailing arms.

Courier and Combi models are fitted with a modified version of the twist beam rear axle, using four linked torsion bars in place of springs and an anti-roll bar. The ends of the torsion bars are splined to allow adjustment within their mounting brackets.

The steering is of conventional rack-and-pinion type, incorporating a collapsible safety column. The column is joined to the steering gear via a flexible coupling. The steering gear is mounted on the front suspension subframe. The steering gear track-rods are attached via the track-rod ends to the steering arms on the hub carriers.

Certain models are available with power steering. The power steering pump is belt-driven from the crankshaft pulley.

2 Front hub carrier - removal and refitting

Removal

Note: *A balljoint separator tool will be required for this operation. Where applicable, Nyloc-type self-locking nuts must be renewed on refitting. A new hub nut will be required on refitting.*

1 Remove the relevant wheel trim, or the wheel centre plate (alloy wheels) for access to the front hub nut.

2.2 Relieve the staking on the front hub nut

2.3 Lift the plastic cover from the suspension strut top mounting

2.5 Unbolt the brake hose bracket from the suspension strut

2.6 Unscrew the bolts securing the brake caliper mounting bracket to the hub carrier

2 Ensure that the handbrake is applied, then relieve the staking on the front hub nut, using a suitable punch **(see illustration)**. Slacken the hub nut using a suitable socket and extension bar. Do not remove the hub nut at this stage.

Caution: Take care, as the hub nut is tightened to a very high torque.

3 Working in the engine compartment, lift off the plastic cover, then slacken the relevant suspension strut top mounting nut, using a ring spanner **(see illustration)**. Counterhold the strut piston rod using a suitable Allen key or hexagon bit. **Do not** remove the nut.

4 Slacken the relevant front wheel nuts, then jack up the front of the vehicle, and support securely on axle stands (see *"Jacking and Vehicle Support"*). Remove the roadwheel.

5 Working under the wheel arch, unbolt the brake hose bracket from the suspension strut **(see illustration)**.

2.7 Slackening the track-rod end balljoint nut

6 Unscrew the bolts securing the brake caliper mounting bracket to the hub carrier, then slide the caliper/bracket assembly from the hub carrier and brake disc (there is no need to remove the brake pads) **(see illustration)**. Suspend the caliper/bracket assembly from the strut coil spring using wire or string – do not allow the caliper to hang on the brake hose.

7 Slacken the track-rod end balljoint nut, and unscrew it as far as the ends of the threads. Counterhold the balljoint pin using a suitable Allen key or hexagon bit **(see illustration)**.

8 Disconnect the track-rod end balljoint from the hub carrier using a balljoint separator tool (leave the nut fitted to protect the threads), taking care not to damage the balljoint rubber seal. Once the balljoint has been released, remove the balljoint nut.

9 Where applicable, unbolt the ABS wheel sensor from the hub carrier, and suspend it clear of the working area to prevent any possibility of damage during the following procedure.

10 Unscrew the hub nut from the end of the driveshaft, and lift off the washer **(see illustration)**.

11 Where applicable, prise the locating clip from the wheel stud, then lift off the brake disc.

12 Unscrew the pinch-nut and bolt securing the hub carrier to the lower arm balljoint. Push the end of the lower arm down to free the balljoint from the hub carrier **(see illustrations)**. If the balljoint is very tight, it may be necessary to lever down using a large

screwdriver, or similar tool, but take care not to damage the balljoint rubber seal.

13 The hub must now be freed from the end of the driveshaft. It should be possible to pull the hub carrier off the driveshaft, but if the end of the driveshaft is tight in the hub, temporarily refit the hub nut to protect the driveshaft threads, then tap the end of the driveshaft with a soft-faced hammer, or use a suitable puller to free it. Support the driveshaft using wire or string – **do not** allow the driveshaft to hang down under its own weight, as this may result in damage to the constant velocity joints.

 Warning: When freeing the driveshaft from the hub, make sure that the driveshaft does not disengage from the inner constant velocity joint.

14 Unscrew the pinch-bolt securing the hub carrier to the lower end of the suspension strut. Using a suitable lever, or a large screwdriver, spread the slot in the top of the hub carrier, until the hub carrier can be pulled from the end of the strut. If necessary, tap the hub carrier down to free it from the strut, using a soft-faced mallet.

Refitting

15 Refitting is a reversal of removal, bearing in mind the following points.

   a) Renew any Nyloc-type self-locking nuts on refitting.
   b) Use a new hub nut.
   c) Make sure that the slot for the pinch-bolt in the strut aligns with the corresponding holes in the hub carrier.

2.10 Unscrew the hub nut and lift off the washer

2.12a Unscrew the pinch-bolt and nut securing the hub carrier to the lower arm balljoint . . .

2.12b . . . then push the end of the lower arm down to free the balljoint from the hub carrier

10

3.3 Driving the hub from the hub bearing

3.5 Remove the bearing circlip from the inner face of the hub carrier

d) Do not fully tighten the hub nut until the vehicle is resting on its wheels.
e) Do not forget to tighten the suspension strut top mounting nut.
f) Tighten all fixings to the specified torque.

3 Front hub bearings – renewal

Note: A press, a suitable puller, or similar improvised tools will be required for this operation. Obtain a bearing overhaul kit before proceeding. A new bearing retaining circlip should be used on refitting.

1 With the hub carrier removed as described in Section 2, proceed as follows.
2 The hub must now be removed from the bearing/hub carrier assembly. It is preferable to use a press to do this, but it is possible to drive out the hub using a metal tube of suitable diameter. Alternatively a suitable puller can be used.
3 Securely support the hub carrier, on two metal bars for instance, with the inner face uppermost then, using a metal bar or tube of suitable diameter, press or drive the hub from the hub bearing **(see illustration)**. Alternatively, use the puller to separate the hub from the bearing. Note that the part of the bearing inner

race will remain on the hub.
4 Using a suitable puller, pull the half inner bearing race from the hub. Alternatively, support the bearing race on suitably thin metal bars, and press or drive the hub from the bearing race.
5 Remove the bearing retaining circlip from the inner face of the hub carrier – discard the circlip, a new one must be used on refitting **(see illustration)**.
6 Temporarily refit the half inner bearing race to the bearing, making sure that the bearing cage and the seal are in position then, using a puller, pull the bearing from the hub carrier, applying pressure to the inner race. Alternatively, support the hub carrier, and press or drive out the bearing.
7 Before fitting the new bearing, thoroughly clean the bearing location in the hub carrier.
8 Using a press or a suitable puller, fit the new bearing to the hub carrier. The outer face of the bearing should contact the shoulder in the hub carrier. It may be possible to improvise a suitable puller using a socket, nut, washers, and length of threaded bar.
9 Fit a new bearing retaining clip to the inner face of the hub carrier.
10 Press or draw the hub into the bearing. The bearing inner track must be supported during this operation. This can be achieved

using a socket, nut washers, and a length of threaded bar.
11 Refit the hub carrier (see Section 2).

4 Front suspension strut – removal, overhaul and refitting

Removal
Note: Where applicable, Nyloc-type self-locking nuts must be renewed on refitting.
1 Working in the engine compartment, remove the plastic cover, then slacken the relevant suspension strut top mounting nut, using a ring spanner. Counterhold the strut piston rod using a suitable Allen key or hexagon bit **(see illustration)**. **Do not** remove the nut.
2 Slacken the relevant front wheel nuts. Ensure that the handbrake is fully applied, then jack up the front of the vehicle, and support securely on axle stands (see "Jacking and Vehicle Support"). Remove the roadwheel.
3 Working under the wheel arch, unbolt the brake hose bracket from the suspension strut **(see illustration)**.
4 Unscrew the nut securing the anti-roll bar drop link to the suspension strut. If necessary, counterhold the drop link pin using a spanner on the flats provided **(see illustration)**.

4.1 Slackening the suspension strut top mounting nut

4.3 Unbolt the brake hose bracket from the suspension strut

4.4 Unscrew the nut securing the anti-roll bar drop link to the suspension strut

4.5 Unscrew the pinch-bolt securing the hub carrier to the suspension strut

4.8a Lift off the damper weight (A) and recover the top mounting insulator (B)

5 Unscrew the pinch-bolt securing the hub carrier to the lower end of the suspension strut (see illustration). Using a suitable lever, or a large screwdriver, spread the slot in the top of the hub carrier, until the hub carrier can be pulled from the end of the strut. If necessary, tap the hub carrier down to free it from the strut, using a soft-faced mallet.

6 Support the strut from under the wheel arch then, working in the engine compartment, unscrew the suspension strut top mounting nut, using a ring spanner. Again, counterhold the strut piston rod using a suitable Allen key or hexagon bit.

7 Lower the strut assembly from under the wheel arch.

8 Where applicable, lift the damper weight from the suspension turret in the engine compartment. Recover the top mounting insulator, which fits under the damper weight (it may be stuck in position under the wheel arch) (see illustrations).

Overhaul

Note: A spring compressor tool will be required for this operation.

9 With the suspension strut resting on a bench, or clamped in a vice, fit a spring compressor tool, and compress the coil spring to relieve the pressure on the spring seats (see illustration). Ensure that the compressor tool is securely located on the spring, in accordance with the tool manufacturer's instructions.

10 Counterhold the strut piston rod with the Allen key or hexagon bit used during removal, and unscrew the piston rod nut (see illustration).

11 Remove the piston rod nut, followed by the thrust bearing, the upper spring seat, the spring (with compressor tool still fitted), the gaiter, the rubber bump stop, and the dust cover - note that the gaiter clips into the dust cover.

4.8b The top mounting insulator may be stuck in position under the wheel arch

12 With the strut assembly now completely dismantled, examine all the components for wear, damage or deformation, and check the thrust bearing for smoothness of operation. Renew any of the components as necessary.

4.9 Spring compressor tools fitted to suspension strut coil spring

4.10 Counterhold the strut piston rod with the Allen key and unscrew the piston rod nut

10

4.16a Slide on the dust cover . . .

4.16b . . . followed by the bump stop . . .

4.16c . . . and the gaiter

13 Examine the strut for signs of fluid leakage. Check the strut piston for signs of pitting along its entire length, and check the strut body for signs of damage. While holding it in an upright position, test the operation of the strut by moving the piston through a full stroke, and then through short strokes of 50 to 100 mm. In both cases, the resistance felt should be smooth and continuous. If the resistance is jerky or uneven or if there is any visible sign of wear or damage to the strut, renewal is necessary.

14 If any doubt exists as to the condition of the coil spring, carefully remove the spring compressors and check the spring for distortion and signs of cracking. Renew the spring if it is damaged or distorted, or if there is any doubt as to its condition.

15 Inspect all other components for damage or deterioration, and renew any that are suspect.

16 Slide the dust cover, followed by rubber bump stop and the gaiter, onto the strut piston **(see illustrations)**. Clip the gaiter into position on the dust cover.

17 If the spring compressor tool has been removed from the spring, refit it and compress the spring sufficiently to enable it to be refitted to the strut.

18 Slide the spring over the strut, and position it so that the lower end of the spring is resting against the stop on the lower seat **(see illustrations)**.

19 Refit the upper spring seat, and rotate it as necessary to position the stop against the upper end of the spring **(see illustration)**.

20 Refit the thrust bearing, then refit the piston rod nut, and tighten to the specified torque **(see illustrations)**. Counterhold the piston rod using an Allen key or hexagon bit as during removal.

21 Slowly slacken the spring compressor tool to relieve the tension in the spring. Check that the ends of the spring locate correctly against the stops on the spring seats. If

4.18a Slide the spring over the strut . . .

4.18b . . . and position it so that the lower end of the spring is resting against the stop (arrowed)

4.19 Refit the upper spring seat . . .

4.20a . . . followed by the thrust bearing . . .

4.20b . . . and the piston rod nut

4.22 Make sure that the slot (A) for the pinch-bolt in the strut aligns with the holes (B) in the hub carrier

necessary, turn the spring and the upper seat so that the components locate correctly before the compressor tool is removed. Remove the compressor tool when the spring is fully seated.

Refitting

22 Refitting is a reversal of removal, bearing in mind the following points:
- a) *Make sure that the slot for the pinch-bolt in the strut aligns with the corresponding holes in the hub carrier (see illustration).*
- b) *Make sure that the top mounting insulator is correctly seated on the strut mounting in the engine compartment.*
- c) *Renew any Nyloc-type self-locking nuts on refitting.*
- d) *Tighten all fixings to the specified torque.*
- e) *Do not forget to tighten the suspension strut top mounting nut.*

5 Front suspension anti-roll bar - removal and refitting

Removal

Note: *Where applicable, Nyloc-type self-locking nuts must be renewed on refitting.*
1 Remove the front suspension crossmember as described in Section 7.
2 Unscrew the bolts securing the anti-roll bar mounting clamps to the subframe, then carefully manipulate the anti-roll bar assembly out from under the vehicle.
3 If desired, the drop links can be removed from the anti-roll bar after unscrewing the securing nuts. If necessary, counterhold the drop link pins using a spanner on the flats provided.

Refitting

4 Refitting is a reversal of removal, bearing in mind the following points.
- a) *Renew any Nyloc-type self-locking nuts on refitting.*
- b) *Tighten all fixings to the specified torque.*
- c) *Refit the front suspension crossmember as described in Section 7.*

6 Front suspension lower arm - removal and refitting

Removal

Note: *Where applicable, Nyloc-type self-locking nuts must be renewed on refitting.*
1 Remove the wheel trims or the wheel centre plates (alloy wheels), then slacken the front wheel nuts. Apply the handbrake, then jack up the front of the vehicle, and support securely on axle stands (see *"Jacking and Vehicle Support"*). Remove the roadwheels.
2 Unscrew the pinch-nut and bolt securing the hub carrier to the lower arm balljoint. Push the end of the lower arm down to free the balljoint from the hub carrier **(see illustration)**. If the balljoint is very tight, it may be necessary to lever down using a large screwdriver, or a balljoint separator tool, but take care not to damage the balljoint rubber seal.
3 Working on each side of the vehicle in turn, where applicable, unclip the ABS wheel sensor wiring from the anti-roll bar drop link.
4 Again working on both sides of the vehicle, unscrew the nuts securing the anti-roll bar drop links to the suspension struts. If necessary, counterhold the drop link pins using a spanner on the flats provided.
5 If necessary, rotate the anti-roll bar towards the rear of the vehicle to allow improved access to the lower arm. The anti-roll bar clamp bolts can be slackened to allow the anti-roll bar to rotate more easily.
6 Unscrew the nut and bolt (counterhold the bolt as the nut is unscrewed) securing the front of the lower arm to the subframe **(see illustration)**.
7 Unscrew the bolt securing the rear of the lower arm, noting that the bolts also secures the subframe, then manipulate the lower arm out from under the vehicle **(see illustration)**.

Refitting

8 Refitting is a reversal of removal, bearing in mind the following points.
- a) *Renew any Nyloc-type self-locking nuts on refitting.*
- b) *Tighten all fixings to the specified torque.*

6.6 Lower arm front securing bolt (arrowed)

6.2 Push the lower arm down to free the balljoint from the hub carrier

7 Front suspension crossmember - removal and refitting

Removal

Note: *A balljoint separator tool will be required for this operation. Where applicable, Nyloc-type self-locking nuts must be renewed on refitting. Special tools (Ford Tool No 15-097) will be required to align the crossmember with the body when refitting - do not attempt this procedure without these tools, as incorrect front suspension/steering geometry may result. On models with power steering, new power steering fluid pipe sealing rings should be used on refitting.*
1 Disconnect the battery negative lead, with reference to Chapter 5A.
2 Working in the driver's footwell, unscrew the pinch-bolt securing the lower end of the steering column universal joint to the steering gear pinion.
3 Similarly, slacken the pinch-bolt securing the flexible coupling to the steering column shaft.
4 Disconnect the exhaust downpipe/catalytic converter assembly from the manifold, as described in Chapter 4A or 4B, as applicable.
5 Remove the wheel trims or the wheel centre plates (alloy wheels), then slacken the front wheel nuts. Apply the handbrake, then jack up the front of the vehicle, and support securely on axle stands (see *"Jacking and Vehicle Support"*). Remove the roadwheels.

6.7 Lower arm rear securing bolt (arrowed)

10

7.14 Remove the rear engine/transmission mounting link through-bolt

6 On models with manual transmission, disconnect the gearchange linkage from the transmission, as described in Chapter 7A.

7 On models with automatic transmission, disconnect the selector cable from the transmission as described in Chapter 7B.

8 Working on one side of the vehicle, slacken the track-rod end balljoint nut, and unscrew it as far as the ends of the threads. Counterhold the balljoint pin using a suitable Allen key or hexagon bit.

9 Disconnect the track-rod end balljoint from the hub carrier using a balljoint separator tool (leave the nut fitted to protect the threads), taking care not to damage the balljoint rubber seal. Once the balljoint has been released, remove the balljoint nut.

10 Repeat the procedure given in paragraphs 8 and 9 to disconnect the remaining track-rod end.

11 Remove the exhaust downpipe/catalytic converter assembly as described in Chapter 4A or 4B, as applicable.

12 Working on each side of the vehicle in turn, unscrew the pinch-nut and bolt securing the hub carrier to the lower arm balljoint. Push the end of the lower arm down to free the balljoint from the hub carrier. If the balljoint is very tight, it may be necessary to lever down using a large screwdriver, or a balljoint separator tool, but take care not to damage the balljoint rubber seal.

13 Again working on each side of the vehicle in turn, unscrew the nut securing the anti-roll bar drop link to the suspension strut. If

7.25 Using special tool 15-097 to align the crossmember with the body

1 Guide pin   2 Locking plate

7.17 Crossmember securing bolts (arrowed)

necessary, counterhold the drop link pin using a spanner on the flats provided.

14 Unscrew and remove the rear engine/transmission mounting link through-bolt **(see illustration)**.

15 Where applicable, unclip the ABS wheel sensor wires from the clips on each side of the crossmember.

16 Support the crossmember using a trolley jack, with a block of wood between the jack and the crossmember to spread the load.

17 Progressively unscrew and remove the seven crossmember securing bolts, so that the crossmember is supported by the jack **(see illustration)**. Do not lower the crossmember at this stage.

18 On models with power steering, proceed as follows.

a) Lower the crossmember slightly for access to the power steering fluid pipe connections on the steering gear.

b) Place a container beneath the steering gear to catch escaping fluid, then unscrew the union nuts, and allow the fluid to drain into the container. Plug or cover the open ends of the pipes and steering gear to prevent dirt entry and further fluid loss.

c) Release the power steering fluid pipes from the bracket on the crossmember.

19 Where applicable, remove the seal which fits between the steering gear pinion and the bulkhead, then lower the crossmember assembly, and withdraw it from under the vehicle.

20 If desired, the steering gear, anti-roll bar and lower arms can be removed from the crossmember with reference to the relevant Sections of this Chapter.

Refitting

21 Where applicable, commence refitting by refitting the lower arms, anti-roll bar and/or steering gear to the crossmember, with reference to the relevant Sections of this Chapter.

22 Position the crossmember on the jack with the wooden block between the crossmember and the jack, then raise the jack to lift the crossmember into position under the vehicle. Ensure that the crossmember is securely supported, and make sure that the steering gear pinion-to-bulkhead seal is fitted.

23 On models with power steering, reconnect the power steering fluid pipes to the steering gear using new sealing rings, and tighten the union nuts, then refit the seal which fits between the steering gear pinion and the bulkhead.

24 It is now necessary to obtain two special alignment tools (Ford Tool No 15-097) to align the crossmember with the body before refitting the securing bolts.

25 Fit the tools to the alignment holes at the front of the crossmember, then slide the locking plates into the locking grooves, and tighten the alignment tool sleeves **(see illustration)**.

26 Raise the crossmember into position, making sure that the pins on the alignment tools engage with the alignment holes in the body.

27 Refit the crossmember securing bolts, and tighten them to the specified torque, then remove the alignment tools.

28 Further refitting is a reversal of removal, bearing in mind the following points.

a) Make sure that the seal between the steering gear pinion and the bulkhead is correctly located.

b) Renew any Nyloc-type self-locking nuts on refitting.

c) Tighten all fixings to the specified torque.

d) Refit the exhaust downpipe/catalytic converter assembly as described in Chapter 4A or 4B, as applicable.

e) On models with automatic transmission, reconnect the selector cable to the transmission as described in Chapter 7B.

f) On models with manual transmission, reconnect the gearchange linkage to the transmission as described in Chapter 7A.

g) Ensure that the front wheels and the steering wheel are in the straight-ahead position before reconnecting the universal joint to the steering gear pinion and the steering column shaft.

h) On completion, where applicable, refill and bleed the power steering hydraulic system as described in Section 23.

8 Rear hub/brake drum assembly – removal and refitting

Hatchback and Van models

1 An integral hub/brake drum assembly is used, which incorporates the rear wheel bearings.

2 Removal and refitting of the hub/brake drum assembly is described in Chapter 9.

Courier and Combi models

Removal

3 Remove the relevant wheel trim or the wheel centre plate (alloy wheels), then slacken the relevant wheel nuts. Chock the front wheels, and select 1st gear (manual transmission) or

9.3 Prising the grease seal from the inboard hub bore

9.4 Lifting out the outer bearing cone

9.5 Driving out a bearing cup

"P" (automatic transmission), then jack up the rear of the vehicle, and support securely on axle stands (see *"Jacking and Vehicle Support"*). Remove the rear roadwheel.

4 Remove the brake drum as described in Chapter 9.

5 Using a screwdriver, prise the dust cap from the centre of the hub, then unscrew the hub nut.

6 Withdraw the hub from the stub axle.

Refitting

7 Slide the hub onto the stub axle, then fit the hub nut and tighten to the specified torque.

8 Carefully tap the dust cap into position until it is seated on the shoulder in the hub. If the dust cap was damaged during removal, fit a new one.

9 Refit the brake drum (see Chapter 9).

10 Refit the roadwheel, then lower the vehicle to the ground, tighten the wheel nuts to the specified torque, and refit the wheel trim or centre plate, as applicable.

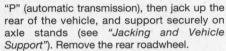

9 Rear hub bearings – renewal

Hatchback and Van models

Note: *Obtain a bearing overhaul kit before proceeding. The kit should contain the bearing components, a grease seal and suitable grease.*

1 With the hub/brake drum removed as described in Section 8, or Chapter 9, as applicable, proceed as follows.

2 On models with ABS, prise the sensor ring from the inboard end of the hub/brake drum using a screwdriver or similar tool. Discard the sensor ring – a new one must be used on refitting.

3 Carefully prise out the grease seal from the inboard hub bore, using a screwdriver **(see illustration)**. Take great care not to damage the bore surface.

4 Lift the inner and outer bearing cones out from the hub bore **(see illustration)**.

5 The bearing cups must now be removed from the hub bore by driving them out with a suitable punch. Drive each cup out from its respective end, by tapping alternately at diagonally opposite points **(see illustration)**.

Do not allow the cups to tilt in the bore, or the surfaces may become burred and prevent the new bearings from seating correctly as they are fitted.

6 Clean the hub bore and the stub axle thoroughly before commencing reassembly.

7 Carefully tap the new bearing cups into position in the hub bore, using a piece of tubing of a slightly smaller diameter than the bearing cups. Make sure that the cups are fitted squarely, and that they abut their respective shoulders in the hub.

8 Pack the inner bearing cone with grease (suitable grease should be supplied with the new bearing kit), then fit the bearing cone to the cup in the hub.

9 Lubricate the inner lip of the new grease seal, then lightly tap the seal into position using a block of wood. Note that the seal lips should face in towards the bearings in the hub.

10 On models with ABS, fit the new sensor ring to the inboard end of the hub/brake drum. Press the sensor ring into position using a tube of suitable diameter. Make sure that the ring seats correctly on the hub shoulder.

Caution: The sensor ring teeth are easily damaged – take great care to avoid damage when fitting. It is not advisable to tap the ring into position, as this may cause damage.

11 Pack the outer bearing cone with grease, then fit it to the bearing cone in the hub.

12 Refit the hub/brake drum as described in Section 8, or Chapter 9, as applicable.

Courier and Combi models

13 The rear wheel bearings are integral with the hubs, and cannot be renewed independently. If a bearing is worn or damaged, the complete hub must be renewed as described in Section 8.

10 Rear strut (Hatchback and Van models) – removal, overhaul and refitting

Removal

Note: *A new strut top mounting nut should be used on refitting.*

1 Remove the relevant rear wheel trim or the wheel centre plate (alloy wheels), then slacken the relevant rear wheel nuts. Chock the front wheels, and select 1st gear (manual transmission) or "P" (automatic transmission), then jack up the rear of the vehicle, and support securely on axle stands (see *"Jacking and Vehicle Support"*). Remove the rear roadwheel.

2 Support the trailing arm using a trolley jack, then unscrew the nut and bolt securing the lower end of the strut assembly to the trailing arm. Counterhold the bolt using a second spanner as the nut is unscrewed **(see illustration)**.

3 Support the strut then, working in the luggage compartment, unscrew the strut top mounting nut **(see illustration)**. If necessary, lower the jack supporting the trailing arm until the strut can be manipulated out from under the vehicle.

10.2 Unscrewing the rear strut lower securing nut and bolt

10.3 Unscrewing the rear strut top mounting nut

10

10.11 Rear suspension strut components

1 Circlip	4 Strut body
2 Top mounting	5 Bump stop
3 Upper spring seat	6 Gaiter
	7 Dust cover

Overhaul

Note: *A spring compressor tool will be required for this operation.*

4 With the suspension strut resting on a bench, or clamped in a vice, fit a spring compressor tool, and compress the coil spring to relieve the pressure on the spring seats. Ensure that the compressor tool is securely located on the spring, in accordance with the tool manufacturer's instructions.

5 Remove the strut top mounting retaining circlip using circlip pliers.

6 Remove the top mounting, followed by the upper spring seat, the spring (with compressor tool still fitted), the gaiter, the rubber bump stop, and the dust cover.

7 With the strut assembly now completely dismantled, examine all the components for wear, damage or deformation. Renew any of the components as necessary.

8 Examine the strut for signs of fluid leakage. Check the strut piston for signs of pitting along its entire length, and check the strut body for signs of damage. While holding it in an upright position, test the operation of the strut by moving the piston through a full stroke, and then through short strokes of 50 to 100 mm. In both cases, the resistance felt should be smooth and continuous. If the resistance is jerky or uneven or if there is any visible sign of wear or damage to the strut, renewal is necessary.

9 If any doubt exists as to the condition of the coil spring, carefully remove the spring compressors and check the spring for distortion and signs of cracking. Renew the spring if it is damaged or distorted, or if there is any doubt as to its condition.

10 Inspect all other components for damage or deterioration, and renew any that are suspect.

11 Slide the dust cover, followed by rubber bump stop and the gaiter, onto the strut piston **(see illustration)**.

12 If the spring compressor tool has been removed from the spring, refit it and compress the spring sufficiently to enable it to be refitted to the strut.

13 Slide the spring over the piston rod, and position it so that the lower end of the spring is resting against the stop on the lower seat.

14 Refit the upper spring seat, and rotate it as necessary to position the stop against the upper end of the spring.

15 Refit the top mounting, then fit a new top mounting retaining circlip

16 Slowly slacken the spring compressor tool to relieve the tension in the spring. Check that the ends of the spring locate correctly against the stops on the spring seats. If necessary, turn the spring and the upper seat so that the components locate correctly before the compressor tool is removed. Remove the compressor tool when the spring is fully seated.

Refitting

17 Refitting is a reversal of removal, but use a new strut top mounting nut, and do not fully tighten the strut mountings until the weight of the vehicle is resting on the wheels.

11 Rear axle assembly (Hatchback and Van models) - removal and refitting

Removal

1 Disconnect the battery negative lead, with reference to Chapter 5A.

2 Working at the handbrake lever inside the car, back off the handbrake cable adjustment, as described in Chapter 9.

3 Remove the rear wheel trims or the wheel centre plates (alloy wheels), then slacken the rear wheel nuts. Chock the front wheels, and select 1st gear (manual transmission) or "P" (automatic transmission), then jack up the rear of the vehicle, and support securely on axle stands (see *"Jacking and Vehicle Support"*). Remove the rear roadwheels.

4 Unhook the rear of the exhaust system from its rubber mountings, then lower the rear of the system and support on a jack or axle stand.

5 Unscrew the securing nuts, and remove the centre section and then the rear section of the exhaust heat shielding from the vehicle floor.

6 Working at the now-exposed handbrake equaliser, disconnect the handbrake cables from the equaliser as follows. If necessary, slacken off the handbrake adjuster to enable the cables to be disconnected (see Chapter 9) **(see illustration)**.

a) *Disconnect the primary (front) cable from the equaliser.*

b) *Prise off the clips securing the secondary (rear) cables to the brackets on the vehicle floor.*

c) *Release the secondary cables from the brackets.*

d) *Disconnect the secondary cables from the equaliser.*

7 Working under the rear of the vehicle, detach the handbrake cables from the clips under the vehicle floor. Where applicable, remove the screws securing the clips to the floor to enable the cables to be released **(see illustration)**.

8 Similarly, where applicable, detach the handbrake cables from the clips on the rear axle assembly.

9 On models with ABS, separate the two halves of the rear wheel sensor wiring connector at the bracket under the vehicle floor, then detach the connector from the bracket.

10 Working on each side of the vehicle in turn, place a container under the brake fluid rigid pipe-to-flexible hose connection at the bracket on the vehicle floor, then unscrew the union nut, and disconnect the brake fluid rigid pipe from the flexible hose **(see illustration)**. Be prepared for fluid spillage, and plug or cover the open ends of the pipe and hose to prevent dirt entry and further fluid loss (the hose can be sealed with a brake hose clamp is desired).

11.6 Heat shield removed to expose handbrake cable equaliser (arrowed)

11.7 Remove the screws (arrowed) securing the handbrake cable clips to the vehicle floor

11 Pull out the retaining clips, and detach the brake fluid flexible hoses from the brackets on the floor.

12 Slacken, but do not remove, the bolts securing the lower ends of the suspension struts to the trailing arms. Counterhold the nuts as the bolts are loosened.

13 Support the rear axle assembly using a jack positioned beneath the axle beam. Use a block of wood between the jack and the axle beam to spread the load.

14 Make a final check to ensure that all relevant cables, wires and hoses have been disconnected to allow removal of the axle assembly.

15 Unscrew the four bolts on each side of the vehicle securing the axle assembly mounting brackets to the vehicle floor (see illustration).

16 Ensure that the axle assembly is securely supported by the jack, then unscrew and remove the bolts securing the lower ends of the suspension struts to the trailing arms.

17 Lower the axle assembly out from under the rear of the vehicle.

18 If desired, the brake assemblies and mounting brackets can be removed from the axle assembly, bearing in mind the following points.

a) Each stub axle assembly is secured to the trailing arm by four bolts.

b) The brake backplates are secured by rivets (accessible with the hub/brake drum removed) which must be renewed on refitting.

c) Mark the hub/brake drum assemblies so that they can be refitted to the correct sides of the axle assembly.

Refitting

19 If the brake assemblies and/or mounting brackets have been removed from the axle assembly, refit them noting the following points, as applicable.

a) Ensure that the hub/brake drum assemblies are refitted to the correct sides of the axle assembly as noted before removal.

b) Use new rivets to secure the brake backplates to the trailing arms.

c) Do not fully tighten the through-bolts and nuts securing the trailing arms to the axle assembly mounting brackets until the weight of the vehicle is resting on its wheels.

20 Refitting of the axle assembly is a reversal of removal, bearing in mind the following points.

a) Do not fully tighten the axle assembly mounting bolts until the weight of the vehicle is resting on its wheels.

b) Tighten all fixings to the specified torque.

c) Bleed the brake hydraulic system as described in Chapter 9.

d) Adjust the handbrake as described in Chapter 9.

11.10 Place a container beneath the brake pipe-to-hose connection (arrowed)

12 Rear axle assembly pivot bushes (Hatchback and Van models) – renewal

1 Remove the rear wheel trims or the wheel centre plates (alloy wheels), then slacken the rear wheel nuts. Chock the front wheels, and select 1st gear (manual transmission) or "P" (automatic transmission), then jack up the rear of the vehicle, and support securely on axle stands (see "Jacking and Vehicle Support"). Remove the rear roadwheels.

2 Support the rear axle assembly using a jack positioned beneath the axle beam. Use a block of wood between the jack and the axle beam to spread the load.

3 Working on each side of the vehicle in turn, release the handbrake cable from the clips on the axle beam and the trailing arms. Where applicable, remove the screws securing the clips trailing arms to enable the cables to be released.

4 Unscrew the through-bolts and nuts (on both sides of the vehicle) securing the trailing arms to the mounting brackets on the vehicle floor.

5 Using the jack, carefully lower the axle assembly until the pivot bushes (in the trailing arms) are clear of the axle mounting brackets and the body side members. Take care not to place the brake fluid lines under strain.

6 Carefully prise the pivot bush outer dust

11.15 Two of the rear axle assembly mounting bracket securing bolts (arrowed)

cover from the relevant trailing arm (see illustration).

7 Make an alignment mark on the bush housing on the trailing arm corresponding to the position of the alignment arrow on the end of the bush (see illustration).

8 Using a metal tube of suitable diameter, flat washers and a long bolt and nut, draw the bush out of its location in the trailing arm.

9 Thoroughly clean the bush housing in the trailing arm.

10 Carefully prise the outer dust cover from the new bush, then mark a line along the side of the bush, corresponding with the alignment arrow on the end of the bush.

11 Lubricate the bush housing, and the new bush, with a soapy solution (eg, washing-up liquid) to aid fitting.

12 Locate the new bush in position against the housing, together with the metal tube, washers, bolt and nut used for removal. Align the line made on the side of the bush with the alignment mark made before removal on the trailing arm, then draw the bush into the housing until it is fully engaged.

13 Fit the outer dust cover to the bush.

14 If desired, repeat the procedure given in paragraphs 6 to 13 for the remaining bush.

15 Further refitting is a reversal of removal, but do not fully tighten the trailing arm-to-mounting bracket through-bolts and nuts to the specified torque until the weight of the vehicle is resting on its wheels.

12.6 Prise the pivot bush dust cover (arrowed) from the trailing arm

12.7 Make an alignment mark on the bush housing corresponding to the alignment arrow on the bush

10

14.3 Rear shock absorber lower mounting bolt (arrowed) – Courier and Combi models

14.4 Rear shock absorber upper mounting nut (arrowed) – Courier and Combi models

15.3 Disconnect the brake fluid hoses from the brackets (arrowed) on the axle beam – Courier and Combi models

13 Rear suspension components (Courier and Combi models) – general

Although it is possible to remove the rear suspension torsion bars and anti-roll bars independently of the complete rear axle assembly, it is essential to have certain special tools available to carry out the work successfully.

Due to the complexity of the tasks, and the requirement for special tools to accurately set the suspension geometry and vehicle ride height on refitting, the removal and refitting of individual rear suspension components is considered to be beyond the scope of DIY work, and should be entrusted to a Ford dealer.

Procedures for removal and refitting of the rear shock absorbers, and the complete rear suspension assembly are given in Sections 14 and 15 respectively.

14 Rear shock absorber (Courier/Combi models) - removal, inspection and refitting

Removal

1 Remove the relevant rear wheel trim or the wheel centre plate (alloy wheels), then slacken the relevant rear wheel nuts. Chock the front wheels, and select 1st gear (manual transmission) or "P" (automatic transmission), then jack up the rear of the vehicle, and support securely on axle stands (see *"Jacking and Vehicle Support"*). Remove the rear roadwheel.

2 Support the rear axle assembly using a jack positioned beneath the axle beam. Use a block of wood between the jack and the axle beam to spread the load.

3 Unscrew the bolt securing the lower end of the shock absorber to the trailing arm **(see illustration)**.

4 Unscrew the nut and bolt securing the top of the shock absorber to the bracket on the body, then withdraw the shock absorber from under the rear of the vehicle **(see illustration)**.

Inspection

5 The shock absorber can be tested by clamping the lower mounting eye in a vice, then fully extending and contracting the shock absorber several times. Any evidence of jerky movement or lack of resistance indicates the need for renewal.

Refitting

6 Refitting is a reversal of removal, but do not finally tighten the shock absorber fixings to the specified torque until the weight of the vehicle is resting on its wheels.

15 Rear suspension assembly (Courier and Combi models) - removal and refitting

Removal

1 Remove the rear wheel trims or the wheel centre plates (alloy wheels), then slacken the rear wheel nuts. Chock the front wheels, and select 1st gear (manual transmission) or "P" (automatic transmission), then jack up the rear of the vehicle, and support securely on axle stands (see *"Jacking and Vehicle Support"*). Remove the rear roadwheels.

2 Working on each side of the vehicle in turn, place a container under the brake fluid rigid pipe-to-flexible hose connection at the bracket on the rear axle beam, then unscrew the union nut, and disconnect the brake fluid rigid pipe from the flexible hose. Be prepared

for fluid spillage, and plug or cover the open ends of the pipe and hose to prevent dirt entry and further fluid loss (the hose can be sealed with a brake hose clamp if desired).

3 Unscrew the union locknuts, and detach the brake fluid flexible hoses from the brackets on the axle beam **(see illustration)**.

4 Working on each side of the vehicle in turn, unscrew the union nuts, and disconnect the brake fluid pipes from the rear brake wheel cylinders, then release the brake pipes from the clips on the rear axle assembly, and remove the brake pipes.

5 Remove the brake drums, with reference to Chapter 9 if necessary.

6 Working on each side of the vehicle in turn, unscrew the four securing bolts on each side securing the hub assemblies to the trailing arms, then remove hub assemblies **(see illustration)**.

7 Release the handbrake cables from the clips on the trailing arms.

8 Drill out the two rivets on each side securing the brake backplates to the trailing arms **(see illustration)**. Suspend the backplates using wire or string to avoid straining the handbrake cables.

9 Unhook the brake pressure regulating valve spring from the bracket on the axle beam.

10 Support the rear axle assembly using a jack positioned beneath the axle beam. Use a block of wood between the jack and the axle beam to spread the load.

11 Remove the bolts securing the lower ends of the shock absorbers to the trailing arms.

15.6 Hub assembly securing bolts (arrowed) – Courier and Combi models

15.8 Drill out the rivets (arrowed) securing the brake backplates – Courier and Combi models

15.12 Unscrew the two bolts (arrowed) on each side securing the axle assembly – Courier and Combi models

12 Ensure that the rear axle assembly is adequately supported, then unscrew the two bolts on each side securing the front of the axle assembly to the vehicle floor **(see illustration)**.
13 Lower the axle assembly out from under the rear of the vehicle.

Refitting

14 Refitting is a reversal of removal, bearing in mind the following points.
  a) *Do not fully tighten the axle assembly securing bolts or the shock absorber-to-trailing arm bolts until the weight of the vehicle is resting on its wheels.*
  b) *Tighten all fixings to the specified torque.*
  c) *Use new rivets to secure the brake backplates to the trailing arms.*
  d) *Refit the brake drums with reference to Chapter 9 if necessary.*
  e) *On completion, bleed the brake hydraulic system as described in Chapter 9.*

16 Rear suspension ride height (Courier and Combi models) – adjustment

Checking and adjustment of the ride height requires the use of Ford special tools to accurately compress the suspension to a pre-determined value. Special tools are also required to reposition the torsion bars.

This operation is considered to be beyond the scope of DIY work, and should be entrusted to a Ford dealer.

17 Steering wheel - removal and refitting

Removal

Note: *Suitable thread-locking compound will be required to coat the threads of the steering wheel securing bolt on refitting.*

1 Disconnect the battery negative lead, with reference to Chapter 5A, then wait at least two minutes before proceeding. If this waiting period is not observed, there is a danger of accidentally activating the air bag(s) and/or seat belt tensioner(s).
2 Remove the steering column shrouds as described in Chapter 11.
3 Remove the air bag unit from the steering wheel as described in Chapter 12.
4 Ensure that the front wheels are pointing in the straight-ahead position, and check that the steering lock is engaged.
5 Where applicable, disconnect the wiring plug and remove the securing screw, then withdraw the anti-theft immobiliser transceiver unit from the ignition switch/steering lock assembly **(see illustration)**.
6 Disconnect the air bag module wiring harness connector, which is located on the right-hand side of the steering column **(see illustration)**.
7 Unscrew and remove the steering wheel securing bolt **(see illustration)**.
8 Turn the ignition key to position "I" and withdraw the steering wheel from the column. Grip the steering wheel on each side, then pull and withdraw it from the splines on the end of the column.
9 Once the steering wheel has been removed, turn the ignition key back to position "0".
10 If a new steering wheel is to be fitted, remove the air bag clockspring assembly from the old wheel, as described in Chapter 12, and fit it to the new steering wheel.

Refitting

11 Where applicable, fit the air bag clockspring assembly, and make sure that the assembly is centralised, as described in Chapter 12.

12 Make sure that the front wheels are pointing in the straight-ahead position, and turn the ignition key to position "I", then fit the steering wheel to the column, making sure that the air bag clockspring tabs engage correctly over the steering lock plunger assembly.
13 Thoroughly clean the threads of the steering wheel securing bolt, then coat the threads with suitable locking compound. Refit the steering wheel securing bolt, and tighten to the specified torque, then turn the ignition key back to position "0".
14 The remainder of the refitting procedure is a reversal of removal, but refit the air bag unit as described in Chapter 12.

18 Steering column - removal and refitting

Removal

Warning: Before proceeding, refer to Chapter 12, and take note of the precautions to be observed when working with an air bag. If the steering wheel is left fitted to the steering column, handle the assembly with care, and note the precautions given for storing an air bag.

Note: *New steering column securing nuts should be used on refitting.*

1 Removal and refitting of the steering column is described here leaving the steering wheel in place on the column.
2 Disconnect the battery negative lead, with reference to Chapter 5A, then wait at least two minutes before proceeding. If this waiting period is not observed, there is a danger of accidentally activating the air bag(s) and/or seat belt tensioner(s).
3 Remove the steering column shrouds as described in Chapter 11.
4 Ensure that the front wheels are pointing in the straight-ahead position, and check that the steering lock is engaged.
5 Working around the steering column, disconnect the following wiring plugs **(see illustrations)**.

17.5 Removing the anti-theft immobiliser transceiver unit securing screw. Transceiver unit arrowed

17.6 Disconnecting the air bag module wiring connector

17.7 Removing the steering wheel securing bolt

10

18.5a Disconnect the air bag module wiring harness connector . . .

18.5b . . . then the anti-theft immobiliser transceiver unit wiring connector . . .

18.5c . . . the steering column stalk switch wiring connectors (wash/wipe switch shown) . . .

18.5d . . . and the ignition switch wiring connector

18.6 Disconnecting the bonnet release cable

18.7 Universal joint-to-steering column shaft pinch-bolt (1) and retaining cage (2)

a) Air bag module wiring harness connector.
b) Anti-theft immobiliser transceiver unit wiring connector.
c) Steering column stalk switch wiring connectors.
d) Ignition switch wiring connector.

Where applicable, release the cable-tie securing the immobiliser wiring to the receiver unit.

6 Disconnect the end of the bonnet release cable from the release lever under the steering column, then release the cable sheath from the steering column lock housing **(see illustration)**.

7 Working in the footwell, unscrew the pinch-bolt securing the universal joint to the lower end of the steering column shaft, then withdraw the retaining cage, and remove the shaft alignment collar **(see illustration)**.

8 Unscrew the two steering column securing nuts, and withdraw the column assembly from inside the vehicle **(see illustration)**.

Refitting

9 Refitting is a reversal of removal, bearing in mind the following points.
a) Use new steering column securing nuts
b) Tighten all fixings to the specified torque.
c) Ensure that the steering column universal joint pinch bolt alignment collar retaining cage is correctly installed.

20 Steering gear -
removal and refitting

Removal

Note: *Any self-locking nuts should be renewed on refitting.*

1 Remove the front suspension crossmember as described in Section 7, noting the following points.
a) There is no need to disconnect the hub carriers from the lower arm balljoints.
b) There is no need to disconnect the anti-roll bar drop links from the suspension struts.
c) Lower the crossmember to give sufficient clearance to allow the steering gear to be

19 Steering gear rubber gaiters
– renewal

1 Remove the relevant track-rod end as described in Section 25.

2 Where applicable, on models with power steering, disconnect the steering gear breather pipe to enable the gaiter to be removed **(see illustration)**.

3 Remove the inboard and outboard securing clips, then slide the gaiter off the end of the track-rod.

4 Thoroughly clean the track-rod, then slide the new gaiter into position.

5 Fit the gaiter securing clips, using new clips if necessary, making sure that the gaiter is not twisted.

6 On models with power steering, reconnect the steering gear breather pipe.

7 Refit the track-rod end as described in Section 25.

18.8 Steering column securing nut (arrowed)

19.2 On models with power steering, disconnect the steering gear breather pipe (1) to enable the gaiter to be removed (2)

20.2 Steering gear securing bolt (arrowed)

withdrawn from under the vehicle – there is no need to remove the crossmember completely.

2 Unscrew the steering gear securing nuts and bolts, then manipulate the steering gear out from under the vehicle **(see illustration)**.

Refitting

3 Refit the steering gear to the crossmember, and tighten the securing nuts and bolts to the specified torque.

4 Raise the crossmember, and refit it to the vehicle as described in Section 7.

21 Power steering pump - removal and refitting

Zetec-SE engine models

Note: *A new power steering pump high pressure pipe sealing ring will be required on refitting.*

Removal

1 Disconnect the battery negative lead, with reference to Chapter 5A.

2 Apply the handbrake, then jack up the front of the vehicle and support securely on axle stands (see *"Jacking and Vehicle Support"*).

3 Remove the auxiliary drivebelt as described in Chapter 1A.

4 Working under the power steering pump, unscrew the bolt securing the high-pressure power steering fluid pipe bracket **(see illustration)**.

5 Place a container beneath the high-pressure pipe union on the pump, then unscrew the union nut, and disconnect the pipe from the pump. Allow the fluid to drain into the container.

6 Slacken the hose clamp, and disconnect the low-pressure fluid hose from the pump.

7 Plug or cover the open ends of the pipe, hose and pump, to prevent dirt entry and further fluid loss.

8 Unscrew the three bolts securing the power steering pump mounting bracket to the engine, then remove the pump/bracket assembly **(see illustration)**.

9 To remove the pump from the mounting bracket, the pump pulley must be removed,

using a suitable puller. The puller legs can be engaged with the holes in the face of the pulley.

10 Once the pulley has been removed, the pump can be removed from the bracket after unscrewing the four securing bolts **(see illustration)**.

Refitting

11 If a new power steering pump is being fitted, remove and discard the fluid pipe unions fitted to the new assembly.

12 Where applicable, refit the pump to the mounting bracket, then refit and tighten the securing bolts. Refit the pulley to the pump using a suitable puller or a press – note that the pulley should be flush with the end of the pump shaft.

13 Further refitting is a reversal of removal, bearing in mind the following points.

 a) *Use a new sealing ring when reconnecting the high-pressure fluid pipe to the pump.*

 b) *Refit the auxiliary drivebelt as described in Chapter 1A.*

 c) *On completion, bleed the power steering hydraulic circuit as described in Section 23.*

Endura-E engine models without air conditioning

Removal

14 Disconnect the battery negative lead, with reference to Chapter 5A.

15 Apply the handbrake and chock the rear wheels then jack up the front of the car and support it on axle stands (see *"Jacking and Vehicle Support"*). Remove the right-hand front roadwheel.

16 Remove the auxiliary drivebelt as described in Chapter 1A.

17 Insert an Allen key into the centre of the pump drive spindle to prevent it from turning, then unscrew and remove the three pump pulley retaining bolts. Withdraw the pulley from the pump.

18 Position a suitable container beneath the power steering pump, then unscrew and detach the fluid high pressure pipe and fluid return hose from the pump. As they are detached from the pump, allow the fluid to drain from the pipe and hose (and the pump)

21.8 Power steering pump mounting bracket bolts (arrowed) – Zetec-SE engine models

21.4 High pressure fluid pipe bracket securing bolt (1), high pressure pipe union (2) and low pressure fluid hose connection (3) – Zetec-SE engine models

into the container. Plug the exposed ends of the pipe, hose and the pump connections, to prevent the ingress of dirt and excessive fluid loss.

19 Unscrew the four retaining bolts (three from the front and one from the rear) and withdraw the pump from the vehicle.

Refitting

20 Refitting is a reversal of removal, bearing in mind the following points.

 a) *Use a new sealing ring when reconnecting the high-pressure fluid pipe to the pump.*

 b) *Refit the auxiliary drivebelt as described in Chapter 1A.*

 c) *On completion, bleed the power steering hydraulic circuit as described in Section 23.*

Endura-E engine models with air conditioning

Removal

21 Disconnect the battery negative lead, with reference to Chapter 5A.

22 Remove the right-hand headlamp, as described in Chapter 12.

23 Unscrew the two securing bolts, and remove the upper auxiliary drivebelt cover.

24 Apply the handbrake, then jack up the front of the vehicle and support securely on axle stands (see *"Jacking and Vehicle Support"*).

21.10 Power steering pump-to-mounting bracket bolts (arrowed) – Zetec-SE engine models

10

21.25 Lower auxiliary drivebelt cover securing bolts (arrowed) – Endura-E engine models with air conditioning

21.30 Power steering pump front securing bolts (1) and rear securing bolt (2) – Endura-E engine models with air conditioning

21.34a High-pressure fluid pipe securing bolts (1), high-pressure pipe union (2) and low-pressure hose connection (3) – Endura-DE diesel engine models

25 Unscrew the two securing bolts and remove the lower auxiliary drivebelt cover **(see illustration)**.
26 Remove the auxiliary drivebelt as described in Chapter 1A, then lower the vehicle to the ground.
27 Place a container beneath the high-pressure pipe union on the pump, then unscrew the union nut, and disconnect the pipe from the pump. Allow the fluid to drain into the container.
28 Slacken the hose clamp, and disconnect the low-pressure fluid hose from the pump.
29 Plug or cover the open ends of the pipe, hose and pump, to prevent dirt entry and further fluid loss.
30 Unscrew the three front securing bolts, and the single rear securing bolt, and withdraw the pump from the engine **(see illustration)**.
31 If desired, the pulley can be removed from the pump using a suitable puller. The puller legs can be engaged with the holes in the face of the pulley.

Refitting

32 Where applicable, refit the pulley to the pump using a suitable puller or a press – note that the pulley should be flush with the end of the pump shaft.
33 Refitting is a reversal of removal, bearing in mind the following points.
  a) *Tighten the three front pump securing bolts before tightening the rear securing bolt.*

b) *Use a new sealing ring when reconnecting the high-pressure fluid pipe to the pump.*
c) *Refit the auxiliary drivebelt as described in Chapter 1A.*
d) *On completion, bleed the power steering hydraulic circuit as described in Section 23.*

Endura-DE diesel engine models

34 Proceed as described previously in paragraphs 1 to 13 for Zetec-SE engine models, noting that the high-pressure power steering fluid pipe is secured by two brackets, and the pump bracket is secured by four bolts **(see illustrations)**.

22 Power steering fluid cooler - removal and refitting

Removal

1 The fluid cooler takes the form of a pipe assembly fitted in front of the radiator.
2 Apply the handbrake, then jack up the front of the vehicle and support securely on axle stands.
3 Remove the securing screws, and withdraw the shield from under the radiator.
4 Where applicable, remove the securing screws, and withdraw the engine undershield.
5 Working under the front of the vehicle, place a container under the fluid pipe unions on the

right-hand side of the vehicle, the unscrew the union nuts, and disconnect the pipes. Allow the fluid to drain into the container, then plug or cover the open ends of the pipes to prevent dirt entry and further fluid loss.
6 Repeat the procedure for the pipe connections on the left-hand side of the vehicle.
7 Unscrew the bolts securing the high-pressure pipe bracket.
8 Unscrew the two securing bolts, and withdraw the fluid cooler pipes from the front of the vehicle **(see illustration)**.

Refitting

9 Refitting is a reversal of removal, but on completion bleed the power steering hydraulic system as described in Section 23.

23 Power steering hydraulic system – bleeding

Note: *Ford recommend that the power steering system is bled using a hand-operated vacuum pump connected to the reservoir filler neck – this should only be necessary if persistent problems are experienced with air in the hydraulic system.*

Conventional bleeding

1 Check the power steering fluid level as described in "Weekly Checks".
2 Turn the steering wheel quickly from lock-to-lock several times, then re-check the fluid level and top-up if necessary.
3 Start the engine and allow it to idle, then *slowly* turn the steering wheel from lock-to-lock several times - do not hold the steering wheel on full lock for more than 15 seconds at a time. Check for air bubbles in the fluid reservoir - if air bubbles are visible, the system requires further bleeding.
4 Stop the engine, then lower the vehicle to the ground, and re-check the fluid level.
5 If air bubbles appear in the reservoir when the system is operated, or if the pump is noisy in operation (not to be confused with a slipping drivebelt), repeat the bleeding procedure.

21.34b Power steering pump mounting bracket securing bolts (arrowed) – Endura-DE diesel engine models

22.8 Power steering fluid cooler securing bolts (arrowed)

24.2 Power steering fluid pressure switch location (arrowed)

Bleeding using a vacuum pump

Note: *During the bleeding procedure, the pressure will drop, so adequate pressure should be maintained using the vacuum pump. If the pressure drops by more than 0.07 bar in 5 minutes, the system should be checked for leaks.*

6 Connect a vacuum pump to the fluid reservoir filler neck using a suitable adapter (Ford Tool No 13-016 is available for this purpose).

7 Start the engine, and slowly turn the steering to the right, just off full-lock.

8 Stop the engine, and apply a vacuum of 0.51 bar, using the vacuum pump, until the air is purged from the system (this will take at least 5 minutes).

9 Depressurise the system using the vacuum pump.

10 Repeat the procedure given in paragraphs 7 to 9 with the steering turned to just off full left lock.

11 Disconnect the vacuum pump from the fluid reservoir, and top up the fluid level if necessary.

12 Start the engine, and turn the steering wheel from lock-to-lock. If the system is excessively noisy in operation, repeat the bleeding procedure.

13 If problems with air in the system persist, leave the vehicle overnight, then repeat the bleeding procedure.

24 Power steering fluid pressure switch – removal and refitting

Removal

1 The power steering fluid pressure switch provides a signal to the engine management electronic control unit, which is used to reduce the engine speed if the power steering fluid pressure becomes too high.

2 The switch is located in the high pressure fluid pipe **(see illustration)**,

3 Disconnect the battery negative lead, with reference to Chapter 5A.

4 Place a container beneath the switch location to catch any escaping fluid.

5 Disconnect the wiring plug from the switch, then unscrew the switch from the fluid pipe.

6 Be prepared for fluid spillage, and plug or cover the orifice in the pipe to prevent dirt entry and further fluid loss.

Refitting

7 Refitting is a reversal of removal, but tighten the switch securely, and on completion bleed the power steering hydraulic circuit as described in Section 23.

25 Track-rod end - removal and refitting

Note: *A balljoint separator tool will be required for this operation. Where applicable, Nyloc-type self-locking nuts must be renewed on refitting.*

Removal

1 Remove the relevant front wheel trim or the wheel centre plate (alloy wheels), then slacken the wheel nuts. Apply the handbrake, then jack up the front of the vehicle, and support securely on axle stands (see *"Jacking and Vehicle Support"*). Remove the roadwheel.

2 Slacken the track-rod end balljoint nut, and unscrew it as far as the ends of the threads. Counterhold the balljoint pin using a suitable Allen key or hexagon bit **(see illustration)**.

3 Disconnect the track-rod end balljoint from the hub carrier using a balljoint separator tool (leave the nut fitted to protect the threads), taking care not to damage the balljoint rubber seal. Once the balljoint has been released, remove the balljoint nut.

4 Slacken the track-rod end locknut, then unscrew the track-rod end from the track-rod, counting the number of turns necessary to remove it.

Refitting

5 Screw the track-rod end onto the track-rod the number of turns noted during removal, then tighten the locknut while holding the balljoint in position.

6 Engage the track-rod end balljoint pin with the hub carrier, then fit a new securing nut. Tighten the nut to the specified torque, while counterholding the balljoint pin as during removal.

25.2 Unscrewing the track-rod end balljoint nut

7 Refit the roadwheel, then lower the vehicle to the ground, and tighten the wheel nuts.

8 Check the front wheel alignment (see Section 26) at the earliest opportunity.

26 Wheel alignment and steering angles - general information

Front wheel alignment

1 Accurate front wheel alignment is essential to good steering and for even tyre wear. Before considering the steering angles, check that the tyres are correctly inflated, that the front wheels are not buckled, the hub bearings are not worn and that the steering linkage is in good order. without slackness or wear at the joints.

2 Wheel alignment consists of four factors:

Camber, is the angle at which the roadwheels are set from the vertical when viewed from the front or rear of the vehicle. Positive camber is the angle (in degrees) that the wheels are tilted outwards at the top from the vertical. The camber angle is given for reference only and cannot be adjusted.

Castor, is the angle between the steering axis and a vertical line when viewed from each side of the vehicle. Positive castor is indicated when the steering axis is inclined towards the rear of the vehicle at its upper end. This angle is not adjustable.

Steering axis inclination (kingpin inclination), is the angle, when viewed from the front or rear of the vehicle, between the vertical and an imaginary line drawn between the upper and lower front suspension strut mountings. This angle is not adjustable.

Toe, is the amount by which the distance between the front inside edges of the roadwheel rim differs from that between the rear inside edges. If the distance between the front edges is less than that at the rear, the wheels are said to toe-in. If the distance between the front inside edges is greater than that at the rear, the wheels toe-out.

3 Owing to the need for precision gauges to measure the small angles of the steering and suspension settings, it is preferable that checking of camber and castor is left to a service station having the necessary equipment. Camber and castor are set during production of the vehicle, and any deviation from the specified angle will be due to accident damage or gross wear in the suspension mountings.

4 To check the front wheel alignment, first make sure that the lengths of both track-rods are equal when the steering is in the straight-ahead position. The track-rod lengths can be adjusted if necessary by releasing the locknuts from the track-rod ends and rotating the track-rods. If necessary, self-locking grips can be used to rotate the track-rods.

10

5 Obtain a tracking gauge. These are available in various forms from accessory stores, or one can be fabricated from a length of steel tubing suitably cranked to clear the sump and transmission, and having a setscrew and locknut at one end.

6 With the gauge, measure the distances between the two wheel inner rims (at hub height) at the rear of the wheel. Push the vehicle forward to rotate the wheel through 180° (half a turn) and measure the distance between the wheel inner rims, again at hub height, at the front of the wheel. This last measurement should differ from the first by the appropriate toe-in which is given in the Specifications. The vehicle must be on level ground.

7 If the toe-in is found to be incorrect, release the track-rod end locknuts and turn both track-rods equally. Only turn them a quarter-of-a-turn at a time before re-checking the alignment. If necessary use self-locking grips to turn the track-rods - **do not** grip the threaded part of the track-rod during adjustment. It is important not to allow the track-rods to become unequal in length during adjustment, otherwise the alignment of the steering wheel will become incorrect and tyre scrubbing will occur on turns.

8 On completion tighten the locknuts without disturbing the setting. Check that the balljoint is at the centre of its arc of travel.

Rear wheel alignment

9 Figures are provided in the Specifications for rear wheel camber and toe-setting for reference only. No adjustment is possible. Refer to paragraph 2 for a description of the settings.

Chapter 11
Bodywork and fittings

Contents

Degrees of difficulty

Easy, suitable for novice with little experience	Fairly easy, suitable for beginner with some experience	Fairly difficult, suitable for competent DIY mechanic	Difficult, suitable for experienced DIY mechanic	Very difficult, suitable for expert DIY or professional

Specifications

Torque wrench settings	Nm	lbf ft
Tailgate hinge bolts	10	7
Front seat mounting bolts	25	18
Front seat belt height adjuster securing bolts	35	26
Front seat belt stalk/tensioner assembly securing bolt	50	37
Seat belt anchor bolts	38	28

1 General information

The bodyshell is of three- or five-door Hatchback configuration, and is made of pressed steel sections. Most components are welded together, but some use is made of structural adhesives. The front wings are bolted on.

The bonnet, doors and some other vulnerable panels are made of zinc-coated metal, and are further protected by being coated with an anti-chip primer prior to being sprayed.

Extensive use is made of plastic materials, mainly in the interior, but also in exterior components. The front and rear bumpers and the front grille are injection-moulded from a synthetic material which is very strong, and yet light. Plastic components such as wheel arch liners are fitted to the underside of the vehicle, to improve the body's resistance to corrosion.

2 Maintenance - bodywork and underframe

The general condition of a vehicle's bodywork is the one thing that significantly affects its value. Maintenance is easy, but needs to be regular. Neglect, particularly after minor damage, can lead quickly to further deterioration and costly repair bills. It is important also to keep watch on those parts of the vehicle not immediately visible, for instance the underside, inside all the wheel arches, and the lower part of the engine compartment.

The basic maintenance routine for the bodywork is washing - preferably with a lot of water, from a hose. This will remove all the loose solids which may have stuck to the vehicle. It is important to flush these off in such a way as to prevent grit from scratching the finish. The wheel arches and underframe need washing in the same way, to remove any accumulated mud which will retain moisture and tend to encourage rust. Paradoxically enough, the best time to clean the underframe and wheel arches is in wet weather, when the mud is thoroughly wet and soft. In very wet weather, the underframe is usually cleaned of large accumulations automatically, and this is a good time for inspection.

Periodically, except on vehicles with a wax-based underbody protective coating, it is a good idea to have the whole of the underframe of the vehicle steam-cleaned, engine compartment included, so that a thorough inspection can be carried out to see what minor repairs and renovations are necessary. Steam-cleaning is available at many garages, and is necessary for the removal of the accumulation of oily grime, which sometimes is allowed to become thick in certain areas. If steam-cleaning facilities are not available, there are one or two excellent grease solvents available, which can be brush-applied; the dirt can then be simply hosed off. Note that these methods should not be used on vehicles with wax-based underbody protective coating, or the coating will be removed. Such vehicles should be inspected annually, preferably just prior to Winter, when the underbody should be washed down, and any damage to the wax coating repaired. Ideally, a completely fresh coat should be applied. It would also be worth considering the use of such wax-based protection for injection into door panels, sills, box sections, etc, as an additional safeguard against rust damage, where such protection is not provided by the vehicle manufacturer.

After washing paintwork, wipe off with a chamois leather to give an unspotted clear finish. A coat of clear protective wax polish will give added protection against chemical pollutants in the air. If the paintwork sheen has dulled or oxidised, use a cleaner/polisher combination to restore the brilliance of the shine. This requires a little effort, but such dulling is usually caused because regular washing has been neglected. Care needs to be taken with metallic paintwork, as special non-abrasive cleaner/polisher is required to avoid damage to the finish. Always check that the door and ventilator opening drain holes and pipes are completely clear, so that water can be drained out. Brightwork should be treated in the same way as paintwork. Windscreens and windows can be kept clear of the smeary film which often appears, by the use of proprietary glass cleaner. Never use any form of wax or other body or chromium polish on glass.

3 Maintenance - upholstery and carpets

Mats and carpets should be brushed or vacuum-cleaned regularly, to keep them free of grit. If they are badly stained, remove them from the vehicle for scrubbing or sponging, and make quite sure they are dry before refitting. Seats and interior trim panels can be kept clean by wiping with a damp cloth. If they do become stained (which can be more apparent on light-coloured upholstery), use a little liquid detergent and a soft nail brush to scour the grime out of the grain of the material. Do not forget to keep the headlining clean in the same way as the upholstery. When using liquid cleaners inside the vehicle, do not over-wet the surfaces being cleaned. Excessive damp could get into the seams and padded interior, causing stains, offensive odours or even rot. If the inside of the vehicle gets wet accidentally, it is worthwhile taking some trouble to dry it out properly, particularly where carpets are involved. *Do not leave oil or electric heaters inside the vehicle for this purpose.*

4 Minor body damage - repair

Note: *For more detailed information about bodywork repair, Haynes Publishing produce a book called "The Car Bodywork Repair Manual". This incorporates information on such aspects as rust treatment, painting and glass-fibre repairs, as well as details on more ambitious repairs involving welding and panel beating.*

Repairs of minor scratches in bodywork

If the scratch is very superficial, and does not penetrate to the metal of the bodywork, repair is very simple. Lightly rub the area of the scratch with a paintwork renovator, or a very fine cutting paste, to remove loose paint from the scratch, and to clear the surrounding bodywork of wax polish. Rinse the area with clean water.

Apply touch-up paint to the scratch using a fine paint brush; continue to apply fine layers of paint until the surface of the paint in the scratch is level with the surrounding paintwork. Allow the new paint at least two weeks to harden, then blend it into the surrounding paintwork by rubbing the scratch area with a paintwork renovator or a very fine cutting paste. Finally, apply wax polish.

Where the scratch has penetrated right through to the metal of the bodywork, causing the metal to rust, a different repair technique is required. Remove any loose rust from the bottom of the scratch with a penknife, then apply rust-inhibiting paint, to prevent the formation of rust in the future. Using a rubber or nylon applicator, fill the scratch with bodystopper paste. If required, this paste can be mixed with cellulose thinners, to provide a very thin paste which is ideal for filling narrow scratches. Before the stopper-paste in the scratch hardens, wrap a piece of smooth cotton rag around the top of a finger. Dip the finger in cellulose thinners, and quickly sweep it across the surface of the stopper-paste in the scratch; this will ensure that the surface of the stopper-paste is slightly hollowed. The scratch can now be painted over as described earlier in this Section.

Repairs of dents in bodywork

When deep denting of the vehicle's bodywork has taken place, the first task is to pull the dent out, until the affected bodywork almost attains its original shape. There is little point in trying to restore the original shape completely, as the metal in the damaged area will have stretched on impact, and cannot be reshaped fully to its original contour. It is better to bring the level of the dent up to a point which is about 3 mm below the level of the surrounding bodywork. In cases where the dent is very shallow anyway, it is not worth trying to pull it out at all. If the underside of the dent is accessible, it can be hammered out gently from behind, using a mallet with a wooden or plastic head. Whilst doing this, hold a suitable block of wood firmly against the outside of the panel, to absorb the impact from the hammer blows and thus prevent a large area of the bodywork from being "belled-out".

Should the dent be in a section of the bodywork which has a double skin, or some other factor making it inaccessible from behind, a different technique is called for. Drill several small holes through the metal inside the area - particularly in the deeper section. Then screw long self-tapping screws into the holes, just sufficiently for them to gain a good purchase in the metal. Now the dent can be pulled out by pulling on the protruding heads of the screws with a pair of pliers.

The next stage of the repair is the removal of the paint from the damaged area, and from an inch or so of the surrounding "sound" bodywork. This is accomplished most easily by using a wire brush or abrasive pad on a power drill, although it can be done just as effectively by hand, using sheets of abrasive paper. To complete the preparation for filling, score the surface of the bare metal with a screwdriver or the tang of a file, or alternatively, drill small holes in the affected area. This will provide a really good "key" for the filler paste.

To complete the repair, see the Section on filling and respraying.

Repairs of rust holes or gashes in bodywork

Remove all paint from the affected area, and from an inch or so of the surrounding "sound" bodywork, using an abrasive pad or a wire brush on a power drill. If these are not available, a few sheets of abrasive paper will do the job most effectively. With the paint removed, you will be able to judge the severity of the corrosion, and therefore decide whether to renew the whole panel (if this is possible) or to repair the affected area. New body panels are not as expensive as most people think, and it is often quicker and more satisfactory to fit a new panel than to attempt to repair large areas of corrosion.

Remove all fittings from the affected area, except those which will act as a guide to the original shape of the damaged bodywork (eg headlamp shells etc). Then, using tin snips or a hacksaw blade, remove all loose metal and any other metal badly affected by corrosion. Hammer the edges of the hole inwards, in order to create a slight depression for the filler paste.

Wire-brush the affected area to remove the powdery rust from the surface of the remaining metal. Paint the affected area with rust-inhibiting paint; if the back of the rusted area is accessible, treat this also.

Before filling can take place, it will be necessary to block the hole in some way. This can be achieved by the use of aluminium or plastic mesh, or aluminium tape.

Aluminium or plastic mesh, or glass-fibre matting is probably the best material to use for a large hole. Cut a piece to the approximate size and shape of the hole to be filled, then position it in the hole so that its edges are below the level of the surrounding bodywork. It can be retained in position by several blobs of filler paste around its periphery.

Aluminium tape should be used for small or very narrow holes. Pull a piece off the roll, trim it to the approximate size and shape required, then pull off the backing paper (if used) and stick the tape over the hole; it can be overlapped if the thickness of one piece is insufficient. Burnish down the edges of the tape with the handle of a screwdriver or similar, to ensure that the tape is securely attached to the metal underneath.

Bodywork repairs - filling and respraying

Before using this Section, see the Sections on dent, deep scratch, rust holes and gash repairs.

Many types of bodyfiller are available, but generally speaking, those proprietary kits which contain a tin of filler paste and a tube of resin hardener are best for this type of repair. A wide, flexible plastic or nylon applicator will be found invaluable for imparting a smooth and well-contoured finish to the surface of the filler.

Mix up a little filler on a clean piece of card or board - measure the hardener carefully (follow the maker's instructions on the pack), otherwise the filler will set too rapidly or too slowly. Using the applicator, apply the filler paste to the prepared area; draw the applicator across the surface of the filler to achieve the correct contour and to level the surface. As soon as a contour that approximates to the correct one is achieved, stop working the paste - if you carry on too long, the paste will become sticky and begin to "pick-up" on the applicator. Continue to add thin layers of filler paste at 20-minute intervals, until the level of the filler is just proud of the surrounding bodywork.

Once the filler has hardened, the excess can be removed using a metal plane or file. From then on, progressively-finer grades of abrasive paper should be used, starting with a 40-grade production paper, and finishing with a 400-grade wet-and-dry paper. Always wrap the abrasive paper around a flat rubber, cork, or wooden block - otherwise the surface of the filler will not be completely flat. During the smoothing of the filler surface, the wet-and-dry paper should be periodically rinsed in water. This will ensure that a very smooth finish is imparted to the filler at the final stage.

At this stage, the "dent" should be surrounded by a ring of bare metal, which in turn should be encircled by the finely "feathered" edge of the good paintwork. Rinse the repair area with clean water, until all of the dust produced by the rubbing-down operation has gone.

Spray the whole area with a light coat of - this will show up any imperfections in the surface of the filler. Repair these imperfections with fresh filler paste or bodystopper, and once more smooth the surface with abrasive paper. If bodystopper is used, it can be mixed with cellulose thinners, to form a really thin paste which is ideal for filling small holes. Repeat this spray-and-repair procedure until you are satisfied that the surface of the filler, and the feathered edge of the paintwork, are perfect. Clean the repair area with clean water, and allow to dry fully.

The repair area is now ready for final spraying. Paint spraying must be carried out in a warm, dry, windless and dust-free atmosphere. This condition can be created artificially if you have access to a large indoor working area, but if you are forced to work in the open, you will have to pick your day very carefully. If you are working indoors, dousing the floor in the work area with water will help to settle the dust which would otherwise be in the atmosphere. If the repair area is confined to one body panel, mask off the surrounding panels; this will help to minimise the effects of a slight mis-match in paint colours. Bodywork fittings (eg chrome strips, door handles etc) will also need to be masked off. Use genuine masking tape, and several thicknesses of newspaper, for the masking operations.

Before commencing to spray, agitate the aerosol can thoroughly, then spray a test area (an old tin, or similar) until the technique is mastered. Cover the repair area with a thick coat of primer; the thickness should be built up using several thin layers of paint, rather than one thick one. Using 400 grade wet-and-dry paper, rub down the surface of the primer until it is really smooth. While doing this, the work area should be thoroughly doused with water, and the wet-and-dry paper periodically rinsed in water. Allow to dry before spraying on more paint.

Spray on the top coat, again building up the thickness by using several thin layers of paint. Start spraying in the centre of the repair area, and then, using a circular motion, work outwards until the whole repair area and about 2 inches of the surrounding original paintwork is covered. Remove all masking material 10 to 15 minutes after spraying on the final coat of paint.

Allow the new paint at least two weeks to harden, then, using a paintwork renovator or a very fine cutting paste, blend the edges of the paint into the existing paintwork. Finally, apply wax polish.

Plastic components

With the use of more and more plastic body components by the vehicle manufacturers (eg bumpers. spoilers, and in some cases major body panels), rectification of more serious damage to such items has become a matter of either entrusting repair work to a specialist in this field, or renewing complete components. Repair of such damage by the DIY owner is not really feasible, owing to the cost of the equipment and materials required for effecting such repairs. The basic technique involves making a groove along the line of the crack in the plastic, using a rotary burr in a power drill. The damaged part is then welded back together, using a hot air gun to heat up and fuse a plastic filler rod into the groove. Any excess plastic is then removed, and the area rubbed down to a smooth finish. It is important that a filler rod of the correct plastic is used, as body components can be made of a variety of different types (eg polycarbonate, ABS, polypropylene).

Damage of a less serious nature (abrasions, minor cracks etc) can be repaired by the DIY owner using a two-part epoxy filler repair. Once mixed in equal, this is used in similar fashion to the bodywork filler used on metal panels. The filler is usually cured in twenty to thirty minutes, ready for sanding and painting.

If the owner is renewing a complete component himself, or if he has repaired it with epoxy filler, he will be left with the problem of finding a suitable paint for finishing which is compatible with the type of plastic used. At one time, the use of a universal paint was not possible, owing to the complex range of plastics encountered in body component applications. Standard paints, generally speaking, will not bond to plastic or rubber satisfactorily, but suitable paints to match any plastic or rubber finish, can be obtained from dealers. However, it is now possible to obtain a plastic body parts finishing kit which consists of a pre-primer treatment, a primer and coloured top coat. Full instructions are normally supplied with a kit, but basically, the method of use is to first apply the pre-primer to the component concerned, and allow it to dry for up to 30 minutes. Then the primer is applied, and left to dry for about an hour before finally applying the special-coloured top coat. The result is a correctly-coloured component, where the paint will flex with the plastic or rubber, a property that standard paint does not normally posses.

5 Major body damage - repair

Where serious damage has occurred, or large areas need renewal due to neglect, it means that complete new panels will need welding-in, and this is best left to professionals. If the damage is due to impact, it will also be necessary to check completely the alignment of the bodyshell, and this can only be carried out accurately by a Ford dealer using special jigs. If the body is left misaligned, it is primarily dangerous, as the car will not handle properly, and secondly, uneven stresses will be imposed on the steering, suspension and possibly transmission, causing abnormal wear, or complete failure, particularly to such items as the tyres.

11

6.5 Air inlet resonator box securing bolt (arrowed) – viewed from under the left-hand side of the vehicle

6.6a Remove the screw securing the wheel arch liner to the bumper . . .

6.6b . . . then unscrew the bumper side securing screw

6 Bumpers - removal and refitting

Front bumper

Removal

1 Disconnect the battery negative lead, with reference to Chapter 5A.
2 Remove the radiator grille panel as described in Section 7.
3 Remove the headlights as described in Chapter 12.
4 Apply the handbrake, then jack up the front of the vehicle and support securely on axle stands (see *"Jacking and Vehicle Support"*).
5 Where applicable, unscrew the bolt securing the air inlet resonator box to the body panel, to allow access to the left-hand bumper securing bolt **(see illustration)**.
6 Working on each side of the vehicle in turn, remove the screw securing the wheel arch liner to the front bumper assembly. Pull the wheel arch liners away from the bumper for access to the bumper side securing screws, then unscrew the side securing screws **(see illustrations)**.
7 Where applicable, disconnect the wiring plugs from the front bumper-mounted lights.
8 Working through the headlight apertures, unscrew the two bumper securing nuts (one on each side of the vehicle), then pull the bumper forwards, and withdraw it from the vehicle **(see illustration)**.

Refitting

9 Refitting is a reversal of removal, but refit the headlights with reference to Chapter 12 if necessary.

Rear bumper – Hatchback and Van models

Removal

10 Disconnect the battery negative lead, with reference to Chapter 5A.
11 Working at the rear of the rear wheel arches, unscrew the two bumper securing screws on each side of the vehicle **(see illustration)**.
12 Using a screwdriver, carefully prise the number plate light from the rear bumper and unclip the bulbholder from the light.
13 Working in the luggage compartment, unscrew the two bumper securing nuts, then lift the bumper from the rear of the vehicle **(see illustration)**.

Refitting

14 Refitting is a reversal of removal.

Rear bumper – Courier and Combi models

Removal

15 To improve access, chock the front wheels, then jack up the rear of the vehicle and support on axle stands (see *"Jacking and Vehicle Support"*).
16 Working on each side of the vehicle in turn, unscrew the two bumper lower corner panel securing screws from the rear of the rear wheel arches, then pull the bumper corner panels towards the rear of the vehicle to release them from the main bumper. Withdraw the bumper corner panels **(see illustrations)**.

6.8 Unscrewing a front bumper securing nut

6.11 Rear bumper side securing screws (arrowed) – Hatchback and Van models

6.13 Removing a rear bumper securing nut – Hatchback and Van models

6.16a Remove the securing screws . . .

6.16b . . . and remove the rear bumper lower corner panels – Courier and Combi models

6.17 Rear bumper securing nut (arrowed) – Courier and Combi models

6.18 Right-hand rear bumper mounting bracket bolts (arrowed) – Courier and Combi models

6.19 Rear bumper upper corner panel securing screws (arrowed) – Courier and Combi models

17 Unscrew the now-exposed main bumper securing nuts (one on each side of the vehicle), then withdraw the main bumper from the rear of the vehicle **(see illustration)**.
18 If desired, the bumper mounting brackets can be removed after unscrewing the two bolts securing each bracket to the vehicle body **(see illustration)**. Note that the left-hand bracket bolts also secure the rear exhaust mounting bracket.
19 To remove the bumper upper corner panels, remove the main bumper as described previously, then unscrew the three securing screws in each case, and remove the upper corner panels **(see illustration)**.

Refitting
20 Refitting is a reversal of removal.

7 Radiator grille panel - removal and refitting

Removal
1 Open the bonnet, then pull the grille panel forwards to release it from the four securing clips **(see illustration)**.

Refitting
2 Refitting is a reversal of removal.

8 Bonnet - removal, refitting and adjustment

Removal
1 Open the bonnet, and support it on its stay.
2 Using a marker pen or paint, mark around the hinge positions on the bonnet.
3 Disconnect the windscreen washer fluid hose from the connector in the scuttle at the left-hand side of the engine compartment. Where applicable, release the hose from the bonnet hinge.
4 With the aid of an assistant, support the bonnet, and unscrew the four bolts securing the bonnet to the hinges **(see illustration)**.
5 Lift off the bonnet.

Refitting
6 Align the marks made on the bonnet before removal, with the hinges, then refit and tighten the bonnet securing bolts.
7 Reconnect the windscreen washer fluid hose, and where applicable clip the hose to the bonnet hinge.
8 Check the bonnet adjustment as follows.

Adjustment
9 Close the bonnet, and check that there is an equal gap at each side, between the bonnet and the wing panels. Check also that the bonnet sits flush in relation to the surrounding body panels.
10 The bonnet should close smoothly and positively without excessive pressure. If this is not the case, adjustment will be required.
11 To adjust the bonnet alignment, slacken the bonnet securing bolts, and move the bonnet on the bolts as required (the bolt holes in the hinges are elongated). To adjust the bonnet closure, adjustable bump stops are fitted to the body front panel. These may be raised or lowered by screwing in or out as necessary. If desired, the bonnet lock can be adjusted as described in Section 10.

9 Bonnet release cable - removal and refitting

Removal
1 Working inside the vehicle, remove the steering column shrouds, as described in Section 29.
2 Unclip the inner cable from the bonnet release lever **(see illustration)**.
3 Slide the cable sheath grommet from the steering column lock housing.
4 Working in the engine compartment, remove the front grille panel as described in Section 7.

7.1 Pull the grille panel forwards to release the securing clips (arrowed)

8.4 Unscrewing a bonnet securing bolt

9.2 Unclipping the inner cable from the bonnet release lever

11

9.5 Unclip the bonnet release cable from the lock operating lever (1), and release the cable sheath (2) from the lock body

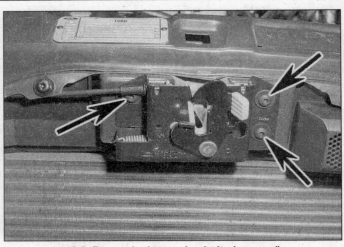

10.3 Bonnet lock securing bolts (arrowed)

5 Unclip the end of the cable from the lock operating lever, then release the cable sheath grommet from the lock body **(see illustration)**.
6 Release the cable from the clips and brackets in the engine compartment, noting its routing.
7 Tie a length of string to the end of the cable at the release lever inside the vehicle, then carefully pull the cable through the bulkhead grommet into the engine compartment.
8 Untie the string from the end of the cable and leave it in position to aid refitting.

Refitting

9 Refitting is a reversal of removal, but tie the string to the release lever end of the cable, and use the string to pull the cable into position. Ensure that the cable is routed as noted before removal, and make sure that the bulkhead grommet is correctly seated.

10 Bonnet lock -
removal and refitting

Removal

1 Remove the front grille panel as described in Section 7.

11.2 Unbolt the door check strap from the door pillar

2 Unclip the bonnet release cable inner sleeve from the lock operating lever, then release the cable sheath grommet from the lock body.
3 Unscrew the securing bolts, and remove the lock assembly **(see illustration)**.

Refitting

4 Refitting is a reversal of removal. If necessary, the position of the lock can be altered to adjust the lock operation, by moving the lock within the elongated holes.

11 Door -
removal and refitting

Removal

1 On models with electrical components mounted in the door, remove the door inner trim panel as described in Section 12, and disconnect the wiring from the components inside the door, noting the routing of the wiring. Pull the wiring grommet from the front edge of the door, and feed the wiring through the hole in the door.
2 Unbolt the door check strap from the door pillar **(see illustration)**.
3 Ensure that the door is adequately

11.4 Prise the retaining clip (arrowed) from the hinge pin

supported, with the aid of an assistant, or using wooden blocks or similar under the bottom edge of the door (take care not to damage the paintwork).
4 Prise off the retaining clips, then drive out the door hinge pins using a suitable drift, and lift the door from the vehicle **(see illustration)**. The lower hinge pin should be driven out upwards, and the upper hinge pin downwards.

Refitting

5 Refitting is a reversal of removal, but check the condition of the hinge pins, and renew if necessary.

12 Door inner trim panel -
removal and refitting

Front door

Removal

1 On models with electrical components inside the door, disconnect the battery negative lead, with reference to Chapter 5A.
2 Prise the cover plug from the centre of the door interior handle surround to expose the securing screw **(see illustration)**.

12.2 Prising the cover plug from the door interior handle surround

12.3 Disconnect the wiring plug from the loudspeaker in the handle surround

3 Prise off the cover, unscrew the securing screw, then withdraw the interior handle surround from the door. Where applicable, disconnect the wiring plug from the loud-speaker mounted in the surround **(see illustration)**.

12.6 Unscrew the securing screw (arrowed) from above the door bin

12.7 Prise off the cover plate for access to the rear trim panel securing screw

12.9b . . . then remove the mirror trim plate

12.4 Removing the window regulator handle

4 On models with manually-operated windows, use a hooked piece of wire or a similar tool to release the window regulator handle securing clip from the shaft. Pull off the regulator handle, and recover the round trim plate **(see illustration)**.
5 Prise out the cover plug, then unscrew the door trim panel securing screw from the armrest **(see illustration)**.
6 Prise out the cover plug, and unscrew the door trim panel securing screw from above the door bin **(see illustration)**.
7 Working at the rear edge of the trim panel, prise off the cover plate, and unscrew the trim panel securing screw **(see illustration)**.
8 Prise out the cover plate, and remove the screw securing the mirror trim plate to the door **(see illustration)**.
9 On models with manually-operated door mirrors, working at the front corner of the door, pull the rubber cover from the mirror

12.8 Prise out the cover plate for access to the mirror trim plate securing screw

12.11 Front door trim panel removed to show securing clips (arrowed)

adjustment lever, then unscrew the plastic collar securing the adjuster lever to the mirror trim plate. Unclip the mirror trim plate, then unclip the mirror adjuster lever from the plate, and remove the plate **(see illustrations)**.
10 On models with electric door mirrors, unclip the mirror trim plate, then disconnect the wiring from the mirror adjustment switch.
11 Work around the edge of the trim panel, and release the securing clips, ideally using a forked tool, then lift up the top edge of the panel, and remove the panel **(see illustration)**.
12 If work is to be carried out on the components inside the door it will be necessary to peel back the protective plastic sheeting from the door. Use a sharp knife to cut the adhesive putty around the edge of the plastic sheeting, then peel the sheeting from the door **(see illustration)**. Do not attempt to peel back the sheeting without cutting the adhesive, as the sheeting will probably tear.

12.5 Unscrewing the trim panel securing screw from the armrest

12.9a Unscrew the collar securing the adjuster lever to the trim plate . . .

12.12 Removing the protective plastic sheeting from the door

11

12.13 Removing the door trim panel mounting bracket

12.16 Unscrewing the interior handle surround securing screw – rear door trim panel

12.19 Rear door trim panel removed to show securing clips (arrowed)

13 If the complete plastic sheeting is to be removed, it will be necessary to drill out the rivets, and remove the trim panel mounting bracket from the door to allow the sheeting to be removed **(see illustration)**. On models with manually-operated windows, recover the insulator from the window winder spindle. It will also be necessary to remove the door-mounted loudspeaker.

Refitting

14 Refitting is a reversal of removal. Where applicable, make sure that the protective plastic sheeting is pushed securely back into position on the door – there should be no need to renew the adhesive, and use new rivets to secure the trim panel mounting bracket.

Rear door

Removal

15 Prise the cover plug from the centre of the door interior handle surround to expose the securing screw.

16 Unscrew the securing screw, then withdraw the interior handle surround from the door **(see illustration)**.

17 Use a hooked piece of wire or a similar tool to release the window regulator handle securing clip from the shaft. Pull off the regulator handle, and recover the round trim plate.

18 Where applicable prise out the cover plate, and unscrew the door trim panel securing screw from the armrest.

19 Using a suitable forked tool, work around the edge of the trim panel, and release the trim panel securing clips, then withdraw the panel from the door **(see illustration)**.

20 If work is to be carried out on the components inside the door it will be necessary to peel back the protective plastic sheeting from the door. Use a sharp knife to cut the adhesive putty around the edge of the plastic sheeting, then peel the sheeting from the door. Do not attempt to peel back the sheeting without cutting the adhesive, as the sheeting will probably tear.

21 If the complete plastic sheeting is to be removed, it will be necessary to drill out the rivets, and remove the trim panel mounting

bracket from the door to allow the sheeting to be removed **(see illustration)**. Recover the insulator from the window winder spindle.

Refitting

22 Refitting is a reversal of removal. Where applicable, make sure that the protective plastic sheeting is pushed securely back into position on the door – there should be no need to renew the adhesive, and use new rivets to secure the trim panel mounting bracket.

---

13 Door handles and lock components - removal and refitting

Door interior handle

Removal

1 Remove the door inner trim panel, and peel back the protective plastic sheeting as described in Section 12.

2 Unclip the handle from the door **(see illustration)**.

3 Move the handle as necessary, and manipulate the nipple on the end of the lock operating cable inner from the handle lever, then release the operating cable from the handle **(see illustration)**. Withdraw the handle.

Refitting

4 Refitting is a reversal of removal.

13.2 Unclip the interior handle from the door

12.21 Drill out the rivets (arrowed) to remove the rear door trim panel mounting bracket

Front door exterior handle

Removal

5 Remove the door inner trim panel, and peel back the protective plastic sheeting as described in Section 12.

6 Working at the rear edge of the door, remove the two screws securing the window upper guide rail/lock shield to the door, then lower the guide rail/lock shield, and manipulate it out through the aperture next to the door lock **(see illustrations)**. Note that the lock shield is secured to the inner door skin with sealant.

7 Working inside the door, remove the two door exterior handle securing screws **(see illustration)**.

13.3 Disconnect the lock operating cable from the handle

13.6a Unscrew the upper . . .

13.6b . . . and lower securing screws . . .

13.6c . . . and remove the window upper guide rail/lock shield

8 Disconnect the lock operating rod from the door lock, then manipulate the rod to disconnect it from the exterior handle. Note the fitted position of the lock operating rod to aid refitting **(see illustrations)**.

9 Withdraw the exterior handle from outside the door.

Refitting

10 Refitting is a reversal of removal, but ensure that the lock operating rod is fitted as noted before removal, and refit the door trim panel with reference to Section 12.

Rear door exterior handle

Removal

11 Remove the door inner trim panel, and peel back the protective plastic sheeting as described in Section 12.

12 Remove the door lock as described later in this Section.

13 Working inside the door, unscrew the two securing screws, then remove the handle from outside the door **(see illustration)**.

Refitting

14 Refitting is a reversal of removal, but refit the door trim panel with reference to Section 12.

Front door lock cylinder

Removal

15 Proceed as described in paragraphs 5 and 6.

16 Prise off the locking clip, and disconnect the lock cylinder operating rod from the lever on the door lock.

17 Where applicable, disconnect the wiring plug from the central locking microswitch attached to the lock cylinder, then unclip the microswitch from the lock cylinder.

18 Using a suitable pin-punch engaged with one of the holes in the lock cylinder retaining plate, tap the retaining plate collar anti-clockwise to release it from the lock cylinder **(see illustration)**.

19 Withdraw the retaining plate, then withdraw the lock cylinder from outside the door **(see illustration)**.

Refitting

20 Refitting is a reversal of removal, bearing in mind the following points.

a) *Tap the retaining plate collar clockwise to secure the lock cylinder – make sure that the retaining plate is correctly fitted.*

b) *Check the operation of the lock mechanism before refitting the door inner trim panel.*

c) *Refit the door trim panel with reference to Section 12.*

13.7 Remove the two exterior handle securing screws (arrowed)

13.8a Disconnect the lock operating rod from the door lock (arrowed) . . .

13.8b . . . then disconnect the rod from the exterior handle

13.13 Rear door exterior handle securing screws (arrowed)

13.18 Engage a pin-punch with one of the holes (arrowed) in the lock cylinder retaining plate

13.19 Removing the front door lock cylinder

11

13.22 Release the lock operating cable from the clips on the door

13.26 Unscrew the three lock securing screws (arrowed)

13.28 Manipulate the lock assembly out through the aperture in the door

Front door lock

Removal

21 Remove the door interior handle, as described previously in this Section.

22 Release the lock operating cable from the clips on the door **(see illustration)**.

23 On certain models, it may be necessary to remove the foam padding from the side impact protection bar inside the door, to enable clearance for the lock to be removed. If the foam padding is removed, note its exact location so that it can be refitted correctly.

24 Working at the rear edge of the door, remove the two screws securing the window upper guide rail/lock shield to the door, then lower the guide rail/lock shield, and manipulate it out though the aperture next to the door lock (see paragraph 6). Note that the lock shield is secured to the inner door skin with sealant.

25 Prise off the locking clips, and disconnect the lock operating rods from the lock.

26 Working at the rear edge of the door, unscrew the three lock securing screws **(see illustration)**.

27 Where applicable, disconnect the wiring plug from the microswitch attached to the lock cylinder, then release the door lock wiring harness clip from the door.

28 Manipulate the lock assembly out through the aperture in the door and, on models with central locking, disconnect the wiring plug from the lock motor **(see illustration)**.

29 Where applicable, unclip the door ajar switch from the top of the lock assembly.

30 To remove the lock operating cable from the lock, proceed as follows **(see illustrations)**.

 a) *Remove the two securing screws, or release the securing clips, as applicable, and withdraw the cover from the lock.*

 b) *Using a small screwdriver, prise the lock operating cable from the lock body. Note that to release the cable sheath collar from the lock body, the plastic fitting on the cable sheath must be turned to align the small cut-out in the plastic fitting with the hole in the lock body.*

31 If desired, on models with central locking, remove the two securing screws, and separate the lock motor from the lock.

Refitting

32 Refitting is a reversal of removal, bearing in mind the following points.

 a) *When reconnecting the lock operating cable, align cut-out in plastic fitting on the cable sheath collar with the hole in the lock body.*

 b) *Check the operation of the lock mechanism before refitting the door inner trim panel.*

 c) *Refit the door trim panel with reference to Section 12.*

Rear door lock

Removal

33 Remove the door interior handle as described previously in this Section.

34 Working at the rear edge of the door, unscrew the three lock securing screws **(see illustration)**.

35 Manipulate the lock out through the aperture in the door and, on models with central locking, disconnect the lock motor wiring plug. Where applicable, unclip the wiring loom from the lock cover.

13.30a Removing the cover from the lock

13.30b Align the cut-out in the plastic end fitting with the hole (arrowed) in the lock body

13.30c Release the inner cable from the lock operating lever

13.34 Rear door lock securing screws (arrowed)

13.38 Disconnecting the lock operating cable from the rear door lock bellcrank

14.4 Front door window glass-to-regulator securing screws (arrowed)

14.7 Prise the weatherseal from the window aperture

14.11 Window regulator securing rivets (arrowed)

36 Remove the two securing screws, and withdraw the cover from the lock.
37 Where applicable, unclip the door ajar switch from the top of the lock assembly.
38 To remove the lock operating cable from the lock, proceed as follows (see illustration).
 a) Remove the two securing screws, or release the securing clips, as applicable, and withdraw the cover from the lock.
 b) Disconnect the cable from the lock bellcrank. To release the cable sheath collar from the lock body, the plastic fitting on the cable sheath must be turned to align the small cut-out in the plastic fitting with the hole in the lock body.
39 If desired, on models with central locking, the lock motor can be separated from the lock after removing the two securing screws.

Refitting

40 Refitting is a reversal of removal, bearing in mind the following points.
 a) When reconnecting the lock operating cable, align cut-out in plastic fitting on the cable sheath with the hole in the lock body.
 b) Check the operation of the lock mechanism before refitting the door inner trim panel.
 c) Refit the door trim panel with reference to Section 12.

14 Door window glass and regulator - removal and refitting

Front door window

Removal

1 Remove the door inner trim panel as described in Section 12.
2 On models with manually-operated windows, temporarily refit the window winder handle. On models with electric windows, temporarily reconnect the battery negative lead, and the door window switch.
3 Make sure that the window is in the fully closed position.
4 Working through the two holes in the door panel, unscrew the two screws securing the

lower edge of the window glass to the regulator mechanism (see illustration).
5 Hold the glass in position in the top of the window aperture, then lower the regulator mechanism.
6 Carefully lower the glass to the bottom of the door.
7 Prise the weatherseal from the lower outside edge of the window aperture (see illustration).
8 Carefully tilt the glass, and withdraw it from the outside of the window aperture.

Refitting

9 Refitting is a reversal of removal, but check the operation of the window regulator mechanism before refitting the door trim panel. Check that the rear edge of the window glass engages with the rear guide channel.

Front door regulator

Note: New rivets will be required to secure the regulator mechanism to the door on refitting.

Removal

10 Remove the door window glass as described previously in this Section.
11 Drill out the rivets securing the regulator mechanism to the door (see illustration).
12 On models with electric windows, working through the lower aperture in the door, disconnect the regulator motor wiring plug.
13 Manipulate the mechanism out through the lower aperture in the door (see illustration).

Refitting

14 Refitting is a reversal of removal, but

14.13 Removing the window regulator mechanism

check the operation of the window regulator mechanism before refitting the door trim panel, and use new rivets to secure the regulator mechanism, and the motor where applicable, to the door.

Rear door window glass

Removal

15 Remove the door inner trim panel as described in Section 12.
16 Temporarily refit the window winder handle, then fully lower the window glass.
17 Remove the window regulator mechanism as described later in this Section.
18 Working at the rear edge of the door, remove the screw securing the fixed rear quarter window trim panel to the door, then remove the trim panel (see illustrations).

14.18a Remove the securing screw (arrowed) . . .

14.18b . . . and remove the trim panel

14.19 Prise the weatherseal from the outside edge of the door

19 Prise the weatherseal from the lower outside edge of the window aperture **(see illustration)**.
20 Unscrew the two upper securing screws, and the centre and lower Torx bolts securing the rear quarter window channel to the door **(see illustrations)**.
21 Withdraw the channel and the rear quarter window from the door as an assembly **(see illustration)**.
22 Carefully tilt the sliding window glass, and withdraw it from the outside of the window aperture.

Refitting

23 Refitting is a reversal of removal, but ensure that the sliding window glass engages with the channel as the channel is refitted, and check the operation of the window regulator mechanism before refitting the door trim panel.

14.20c ... and lower Torx bolts (arrowed)

14.26 Drill out the rivets securing the regulator mechanism to the door

14.20a Unscrew two upper window channel securing screws (arrowed) ...

Rear door regulator

Note: *New rivets will be required to secure the regulator mechanism to the door on refitting.*

Removal

24 Remove the door inner trim panel as described in Section 12.
25 Temporarily refit the window winder handle, then fully lower the window glass.
26 Drill out the four rivets securing the regulator mechanism to the door **(see illustration)**.
27 Manipulate the mechanism out through the lower door aperture, sliding the pad on the regulator arm from the rear of the channel on the bottom of the glass **(see illustrations)**.

Refitting

28 Refitting is a reversal of removal, bearing in mind the following points.

14.21 Withdraw the channel and the rear quarter window as an assembly

14.27a Slide the pad (arrowed) from the rear of the channel on the glass ...

14.20b ... and the centre ...

a) Make sure that the pad on the regulator arm engages correctly with the channel on the bottom of the glass. Fit pad from rear of glass channel.
b) Use new rivets to secure the regulator mechanism to the door.
c) Check the operation of the window regulator mechanism before refitting the door trim panel.

15 Opening rear quarter windows (3-door models) - removal and refitting

Removal

1 Remove the screws securing the handle assembly at the rear of the window glass to the body.
2 Support the glass panel, then prise off the covers, and remove the screws securing the front edge of the glass to the hinges. Lift the glass panel from the vehicle.
3 If desired, the handle and the hinge fasteners can be removed from the glass after prising off the covers, and removing the fasteners.

Refitting

4 Refitting is a reversal of removal.

14.27b ... and withdraw the mechanism through the door aperture

17.4 Prise the washer fluid hose grommet from the tailgate

17.6 Tailgate hinge bolts (arrowed)

17.9 Lever off the tailgate support strut retaining clip

16 Sliding side windows (Combi models) - removal and refitting

Removal

1 Working inside the vehicle, remove the two window locks from the glass panels. Each lock assembly is secured by two screws.
2 Slide the front glass panel fully to the rear.
3 Pull the weatherseal as far as possible from the front part of the window aperture, then slide the rear glass panel fully to the front.
4 Pull the remainder of the weatherseal from the rear part of the window aperture, and withdraw the complete weatherseal.
5 Using a small screwdriver, prise the window glass stop from the upper edge of the window aperture – push the stop towards the front of the vehicle, then prise the stop out from the rear of the clip.
6 Remove the window centre channel from the window aperture.
7 Remove the centre channel support rubber from the upper edge of the window aperture by pulling it out from the rear.
8 The glass panels can now be carefully lifted out from the window aperture.

Refitting

9 Refitting is a reversal of removal, but make sure that the window centre channel components and the weatherseal are correctly refitted.

17 Tailgate and support struts - removal, refitting and adjustment

Tailgate

Removal

1 Disconnect the battery negative lead, with reference to Chapter 5A.
2 Using a pencil or marker pen, mark the position of the hinges on the tailgate to aid refitting.
3 Carefully prise the washer nozzle from the tailgate, and disconnect the nozzle from the end of the washer fluid hose.

4 Prise the rubber grommet from the top edge of the tailgate, then pull the washer fluid hose through, and withdraw the hose from the tailgate (see illustration). If desired, to aid refitting, tie a length of string to the end of the hose before pulling it through, then pull the hose from the tailgate, and untie the string, leaving the string in position in the tailgate.
5 Support the tailgate, and disconnect the support struts, with reference to paragraphs 8 and 9.
6 Ensure that the tailgate is adequately supported, ideally with the aid of an assistant, then unscrew the bolts securing the hinges to the tailgate, and lift the tailgate from the vehicle (see illustration).

Refitting

7 Refitting is a reversal of removal, bearing in mind the following points.
  a) Make sure that the hinges are aligned with the marks made before removal.
  b) Where applicable, use the string to pull the wiring harness and the washer fluid hose into position in the tailgate.
  c) On completion, check the alignment of the tailgate with the surrounding body panels and, if necessary, adjust the position of the tailgate hinges within the elongated holes until satisfactory alignment is achieved.

Support struts

Removal

8 Open the tailgate, and support it in the open position, using a wooden prop or similar

tool. Note that the tailgate is heavy, and will fall closed if either of the support struts are disconnected.
9 Working at the top end of the strut, lever off the retaining clip, and disconnect the end of the strut from the lug on the tailgate (see illustration).
10 Repeat the procedure at the bottom end of the strut, and withdraw the strut.

Refitting

11 Refitting is a reversal of removal.

18 Rear load doors (Courier and Combi models) - removal and refitting

Removal

1 Disconnect the battery negative lead, with reference to Chapter 5A.
2 Where applicable, separate the two halves of the heater rear window wiring connector, then pull the wiring through the grommets in the rear edge of the door.
3 Prise out the two covers for access to the upper door-to-hinge bolts (see illustration).
4 Unscrew the bolts securing the door check strap to the bottom of the door.
5 Support the door, ideally with the aid of an assistant, then unscrew the upper and lower bolts securing the door to the hinges, and carefully lift off the door (see illustration).

Refitting

6 Refitting is a reversal of removal.

18.3 Prise out the covers (arrowed) for access to the upper door-to-hinge bolts

18.5 Rear load door lower door-to-hinge bolts (arrowed)

11

19.2a Unscrew the securing screw . . .

19.2b . . . then prise out the tailgate trim panel securing clip . . .

19.2c . . . and withdraw the trim panel

19 Tailgate lock components - removal and refitting

Lock cylinder

Removal

1 Disconnect the battery negative lead, with reference to Chapter 5A.

2 Unscrew the securing screw, and prise out the clip, then pull the trim panel from the tailgate to release the remaining securing clips **(see illustrations)**.

3 Working inside the tailgate, unscrew the four securing nuts, then withdraw the lock cylinder trim panel/handle from outside the tailgate. Note that two of the nuts also secure the lock operating cable plate **(see illustrations)**.

4 Unclip the lock operating cable from the rear of the lock cylinder.

5 Working inside the tailgate, twist the lock cylinder plastic securing ring anti-clockwise (looking up at the open tailgate) to release it **(see illustration)**.

6 Where applicable, unclip the anti-theft alarm switch from the lock cylinder, by pushing the switch in, and tilting it up, then withdraw the lock cylinder **(see illustration)**.

Refitting

7 Refitting is a reversal of removal, bearing in mind the following points.

a) Check the condition of the seal on the rear of the lock cylinder and renew if necessary.

b) Before fully refitting the lock cylinder, fit the plastic securing ring over the rear of the cylinder.

c) Make sure that the lock operating cable plate is in position on the lock cylinder trim panel/handle studs.

d) Check the operation of the lock mechanism before refitting the tailgate trim panel.

Lock assembly

Removal

8 Proceed as described in paragraphs 1 and 2.

9 Where applicable, unclip the lock operating rod, then unscrew the two lock securing screws **(see illustration)**. Manipulate the lock out from the tailgate and, where applicable, unclip the anti-theft alarm switch from the lock, by pushing the switch in, and tilting it up.

Refitting

10 Refitting is a reversal of removal, but check the operation of the lock mechanism before refitting the tailgate trim panel.

Lock release motor

Removal

11 Proceed as described in paragraphs 1 and 2.

12 Disconnect the lock operating rod.

13 Separate the two halves of the motor wiring connector, then unscrew the screw securing the earth lead to the tailgate.

14 Remove the two motor securing screws, then withdraw the motor from the tailgate.

Refitting

15 Refitting is a reversal of removal, but make sure that the lock operating rod is correctly positioned in the lock lever. Check the operation of the mechanism before refitting the tailgate trim panel.

19.3a Three of the lock cylinder trim panel/handle securing nuts (1), and lock operating cable plate (2)

19.3b Removing the lock cylinder trim panel/handle

19.5 Removing the lock cylinder plastic securing ring

19.6 Removing the lock cylinder

19.9 Lock securing screws (arrowed)

20.1a Prise off the interior handle trim plate . . .

20.1b . . . then prise out the trim panel securing clips

20.2 Unscrewing a mounting plate/relay lever assembly securing screw

20 Rear load door lock components (Courier and Combi models) - removal and refitting

Interior handle

Removal

1 Open the door, then prise off the interior handle trim plate. Prise out the securing clips and remove the door trim panel **(see illustrations)**.

2 Remove the mounting plate/relay lever assembly securing screws, noting the location of the earth wire on one of the screws, and withdraw the mounting plate/relay lever assembly **(see illustration)**.

3 Disconnect the lock operating cables from the relay lever assembly **(see illustration)**.

4 Disconnect the lock operating rod from relay lever assembly.

5 Remove the securing screw, and remove the interior handle, complete with the operating rod **(see illustrations)**.

Refitting

6 Make sure that lugs on relay lever engage with lock on refitting

Lock cylinder/exterior handle assembly

Removal

7 Remove the interior handle as described previously.

8 Turn the lock cylinder retaining clip anti-clockwise, and remove it from the rear of the lock cylinder **(see illustration)**. Recover spacer plate.

9 Turn the lock cylinder/handle assembly clockwise until it can be withdrawn from the door **(see illustration)**.

Refitting

10 Refitting is a reversal of removal, but make sure that the spacer plate is in position under the retaining clip.

Lock assembly

Removal

11 Working at the top or bottom of the door, as applicable, remove two securing screws, then lift out the lock assembly and disconnect the operating cable.

20.3 Disconnecting a lock operating cable from the relay lever assembly

Refitting

12 Refitting is a reversal of removal.

21 Central locking system components - general information

Door lock motor

1 The removal and refitting procedure for the door lock motors is described as part of the door lock removal and refitting procedure in Section 13.

Door lock microswitch

2 Removal and refitting of the microswitches is described as part of the door lock cylinder removal and refitting procedure in Section 13.

20.5a Remove the securing screw (arrowed) . . .

20.5b . . . and remove the interior handle

20.8 Removing the lock cylinder retaining clip

20.9 Removing the lock cylinder/exterior handle assembly

11

21.4 Central locking remote control transmitter battery renewal

1 Cover   3 Contact plate
2 Batteries

Remote control transmitter key batteries - renewal

Note: *If it takes longer than 15 seconds to renew the batteries, the remote control system must be reprogrammed as described later in this Section.*

3 Carefully prise off the transmitter cover, using a small screwdriver.
4 Lift out the batteries and the contact plate **(see illustration)**.
5 Fit the new batteries with the "+" side facing upwards, and the contact plate in between the batteries.
6 Refit the cover.

Remote control transmitter key - reprogramming

7 Insert the ignition key into the ignition switch, and turn the key to position "I". Turn the key back to position "0" as soon as the control light in the clock illuminates. The light will illuminate for 30 seconds, during which the transmitter can be reprogrammed as follows.
8 Point the transmitter towards the interior light in the roof console, then press and hold the front button on the transmitter (nearest the key shaft) depressed. Wait until the light on the transmitter begins to flash, then press the rear button on the transmitter three times (continue to hold the front button depressed).
9 Release the front button. If the lights on the transmitter and the clock flash simultaneously, the reprogramming was successful.

23.3 Removing the door mirror glass

10 To end the procedure, turn the ignition key to position "II".

22 Electric window components - removal and refitting

Window switches

1 Refer to Chapter 12.

Window regulator motors

2 The motors are integral with the regulator assemblies, and if faulty, the complete regulator assembly must be renewed. Removal and refitting of the regulator assemblies is described in Section 14.

23 Exterior mirrors and associated components - removal and refitting

Mirror glass

Removal

1 On models with electric mirrors, disconnect the battery negative lead, with reference to Chapter 5A.
2 Push the inboard edge of the mirror glass fully into the mirror housing, to leave a gap at the outboard edge of the glass.
3 Carefully pull the outboard edge of the glass outwards, and at the same time, pull the glass towards the outboard edge of the housing, until the glass is released from the mirror **(see illustration)**. Where applicable, disconnect the wiring from the glass.

Refitting

4 Where applicable, reconnect the wiring to the glass.
5 Locate the inboard edge of the glass on the mounting in the mirror housing.
6 With the glass laid in position, press the outboard edge of the glass into the housing until an audible click is heard, and the glass locks in position.

Mirror

Removal

7 Remove the door inner trim panel as described in Section 12 - this is necessary for access to the two lower mirror securing bolts.
8 On models with electric mirrors, trace the wiring harness back from the mirror, and separate the two halves of the wiring connector inside the door. Remove the adhesive tape securing the wiring harness to the door.
9 Unscrew the three securing bolts, and withdraw the mirror, complete with wiring harness or adjuster cable (as applicable), from the door.

Refitting

10 Refitting is a reversal of removal.

Electric mirror motor

11 The motor is integral with the mirror, and cannot be renewed separately. If faulty, the complete mirror assembly must be renewed.

Electric mirror switch

12 Switch removal and refitting is described as part of the mirror removal and refitting procedure earlier in this Section.

24 Windscreen, tailgate and fixed window glass - general information

These areas of glass are secured by the tight fit of the weatherseal in the body aperture, and are bonded in position with a special adhesive. Renewal of such fixed glass is a difficult, messy and time-consuming task, which is considered beyond the scope of the home mechanic. It is difficult, unless one has plenty of practice, to obtain a secure, waterproof fit. Furthermore, the task carries a high risk of breakage; this applies especially to the laminated glass windscreen. In view of this, owners are strongly advised to have this sort of work carried out by one of the many specialist windscreen fitters.

25 Sunroof - general information, removal and refitting

General information

1 Two different types of sunroof may be fitted, depending on model. A manually-operated tilting glass panel may be fitted, or an electric sliding canvas roof may be fitted.

Tilting glass sunroof panel

Removal

2 Turn the knob to fully open the sunroof panel.
3 Use a small screwdriver to depress the red locking lever underneath the knob, and release the knob assembly from the bracket on the roof **(see illustration)**.
4 Lift the roof panel to the vertical position, and withdraw it from the roof.

25.3 Depressing the tilting glass sunroof panel locking clip

26.6 Releasing the expansion tank securing clip

26.7 Pull the weatherseal from the bulkhead . . .

26.8 . . . then unclip the cover from the fusebox

Refitting

5 Hold the roof panel vertically, and lower the hinges into the retainers on the roof.

6 Lower the panel, and engage the knob assembly with the bracket on the roof.

Electric sliding canvas sunroof

HAYNES HiNT
If the sunroof mechanism is faulty, and the roof panel is stuck in the open position, the panel can be closed manually as follows.
a) *Remove the blanking plug from the roof console panel.*
b) *Insert the cranked handle supplied with the car in the hole provided in the sunroof motor spindle, then use the handle to turn the motor and close the roof panel.*

26.9a Remove the securing screw (arrowed) . . .

Roof assembly

7 Due to the complexity of the sliding canvas sunroof mechanism, considerable expertise is required to repair, replace or adjust the sunroof components successfully. Removal of the roof first requires the headlining to be removed, which is a tedious operation, and not a task to be undertaken lightly. Therefore, any problems with this type of sunroof should be referred to a Ford dealer.

Roof switch

8 Refer to Chapter 12.

26 Body exterior fittings - removal and refitting

Radiator grille panel

1 Refer to Section 7.

Bumpers

2 Refer to Section 6.

Fuel filler flap

Removal

3 The fuel filler flap is a push-fit into the housing, and is easily broken.

4 Open the flap, and carefully prise the integral hinge from the locating holes in the housing – do not use excessive force.

Refitting

5 Refitting is a reversal of removal.

Scuttle cover panel

Removal

6 Working in the engine compartment, unscrew the coolant expansion tank securing screw, then release the expansion tank securing clip, and move the expansion tank clear of the engine compartment bulkhead, taking care not to strain the coolant hoses (see illustration).

7 Pull the rubber weatherseal from the front edge of the engine compartment bulkhead (see illustration).

8 Unclip the cover from the fusebox at the left-hand side of the engine compartment (see illustration).

9 Where applicable, remove the securing screw, and lift the MAP sensor securing bracket from the bulkhead (see illustrations).

10 Where applicable, pull the oxygen sensor wiring connector from the lug on the bulkhead panel (see illustration).

11 Lift screenwash hoses from slot on right-hand side of panel.

12 Remove the screw securing the panel to the fusebox (see illustration).

13 Remove the screws and remove the three clips securing the panel, then withdraw the panel (see illustrations). Release the speedometer cable grommet from the panel as panel is withdrawn.

26.9b . . . and lift the MAP sensor bracket from the bulkhead

26.10 Pull the oxygen sensor wiring connector from the bulkhead panel

26.12 Removing the screw securing the scuttle cover panel to the fusebox

26.13a Remove the two lower screws and clips (arrowed) . . .

26.13b . . . and the right-hand screw and clip (arrowed) . . .

26.13c . . . and withdraw the scuttle cover panel

Refitting

14 Refitting is a reversal of removal.

Rear spoiler

Removal

15 Open the tailgate, and prise out the four spoiler securing nut covers from the top of the tailgate.
16 Unscrew the four securing nuts, and lift off the spoiler.

Refitting

17 Refitting is a reversal of removal.

Wheel arch liners and engine undershield

18 The wheel arch liners and engine undershield (where applicable) are secured by a combination of self-tapping screws and push-fit clips **(see illustration)**. Removal is self-evident, and normally the clips can be

released by pulling the liner or undershield away from its mountings.

Body trim strips and badges

19 The various body trim strips and badges are held in position with a special adhesive. Removal requires the trim/badge to be heated, to soften the adhesive, and then cut away from the surface. Due to the high risk of damage to the vehicle paintwork during this operation, it is recommended that this task should be entrusted to a Ford dealer.

27 Seats - removal and refitting

Front seat

 Warning: Disconnect the battery negative lead, with reference to Chapter 5A, then wait for two minutes before proceeding.

Removal

1 Pull the side trim panel from the outside edge of the seat then, where applicable, disconnect the now-exposed wiring plug(s) **(see illustrations)**. Unclip the wiring plug(s) from the trim panel.
2 Slide the seat fully rearwards, then unscrew the two front bolts securing the seat rails to the floor **(see illustration)**.
3 Slide the seat fully forwards, then unclip the trim panel from the inner seat rail, and unscrew the three rear bolts securing the

26.18 Front wheel arch liner securing screws (arrowed)

seat rails to the floor (two bolts securing the inner rail, and one bolt securing the outer rail) **(see illustration)**.
4 Lift the seat, complete with the rails, from the vehicle.

Refitting

5 Refitting is a reversal of removal, but tighten the seat mounting bolts to the specified torque.

Rear seat cushion – Hatchback and Van models

Removal

6 Working at the front lower edge of the seat cushion, remove the three screws securing the seat cushion to the floor **(see illustration)**.
7 Lift the front of the seat cushion, and push it sharply towards the rear of the vehicle.
8 Lift up the rear of the cushion, and withdraw it from the vehicle.

27.1a Pull the trim panel from the seat . . .

27.1b . . . then disconnect the wiring plug

27.2 Removing a front seat securing bolt

27.3 Unclip the trim panel from the inner seat rail

27.6 Removing a rear seat cushion securing screw

Refitting

9 Refitting is a reversal of removal.

Rear seat back – Hatchback and Van models

Removal

10 Release the catch, and fold the rear seat back down on top of the cushion.
11 Unscrew the bolts securing the seat back to the hinges, then remove the seat back (see illustration).
12 If desired, the rear seat back catch can now be removed after unscrewing the two securing bolts.

Refitting

13 Refitting is a reversal of removal.

Rear seats – Combi models

Removal

14 The rear seats can be removed as an assembly, after folding the rear seat back

28.2 Unscrew the upper seat belt anchor bolt

28.4 Unscrew the inertia reel anchor bolt (1) and the upper screw (2)

27.11 Removing a rear seat back securing bolt

down, and tilting the complete seat assembly forwards.
15 Release the seat assembly from the locking catches, and withdraw it from the vehicle.

Refitting

16 Refitting is a reversal of removal.

28 Seat belt components - removal and refitting

Front seat belt

Removal

1 On three-door models, unbolt the lower seat belt anchor rail, and slide the seat belt from the rail. On five-door models, unscrew the lower seat belt anchor bolt.
2 Pull off the plastic cover, then unscrew the upper seat belt anchor bolt (see illustration).
3 Remove the centre pillar trim panel and the sill trim panel with reference to Section 29.
4 Unscrew the inertia reel anchor bolt, and the upper screw, than manipulate the inertia reel out from the door pillar, and withdraw the seat belt assembly (see illustration).

Refitting

5 Refitting is a reversal of removal, but tighten the seat belt anchor bolts to the specified torque.

Front seat belt stalk

Removal

6 Remove the front seat (see Section 27).

28.16 Rear seat belt lower anchor bolt (arrowed)

7 On models with front seat belt tensioners, release the tensioner wiring harness from the clips under the seat.
8 Unscrew the bolt securing the stalk assembly to the seat frame. Note that the bolt is captive in the stalk assembly (secured by a paper washer) – do not attempt to remove the bolt from the stalk assembly.
9 Withdraw the assembly from the seat. On models with seat belt tensioners, handle the assembly by holding the tensioner barrel, or the buckle – do not hold the assembly by the stalk.

Refitting

10 Refitting is a reversal of removal, bearing in mind the following points.
a) Make sure that the stalk is angled towards the seat.
b) Tighten the securing bolt to the specified torque.
c) Refit the seat with reference to Section 27.

Front seat belt height adjuster

Removal

11 Pull off the plastic cover, then unscrew the upper seat belt anchor bolt.
12 Remove the centre pillar trim panel with reference to Section 29.
13 Unscrew the two securing bolts, and remove the height adjuster assembly.

Refitting

14 Refitting is a reversal of removal.

Rear inertia reel seat belt

Removal

15 Remove the rear seat cushion as described in Section 27.
16 Unscrew the seat belt lower anchor bolt (see illustration).
17 Pull off the plastic cover, then unscrew the upper seat belt anchor bolt.
18 Working in the luggage compartment, peel back the trim panel for access to the seat belt inertia reel.
19 Unscrew the inertia reel anchor bolt (see illustration).
20 Manipulate the seat belt upper anchor plate down through the hole in the parcel shelf side trim panel, then feed the remainder of the seat belt through the slot, and withdraw the seat belt from the vehicle.

28.19 Rear seat belt inertia reel securing bolt (arrowed)

11

29.3 Withdrawing the upper . . .

29.4 . . . and lower steering column shrouds

Front pillar trim panel

Removal

11 Open the door, and carefully prise the weatherseal from the edge of the door aperture.

12 Carefully prise the trim panel from the pillar to release the three securing clips (one at each end, and one in the centre).

Refitting

13 Refitting is a reversal of removal.

Centre pillar trim panel – Hatchback and Van models

Removal

14 Pull off the plastic cover, then unscrew the upper seat belt anchor bolt.

15 Carefully prise the weatherseal(s) from the edges of the door aperture(s).

16 Carefully prise the trim panel from the pillar to release the three securing clips (one at each end, and one in the centre).

Refitting

17 Refitting is a reversal of removal, but tighten the seat belt anchor bolt to the specified torque.

Centre pillar trim panel – Courier and Combi models

Removal

18 Carefully prise the rear centre pillar trim panel from the pillar to release the two securing clips.

19 Pull off the plastic cover, then unscrew the upper seat belt anchor bolt.

20 Carefully prise the weatherseal from the edges of the door aperture.

21 Carefully prise the trim panel from the pillar to release the three securing clips (one at each end, and one in the centre).

Refitting

22 Refitting is a reversal of removal, but tighten the seat belt anchor bolt to the specified torque.

Rear parcel shelf support panel - Hatchback and Van models

Removal

23 On models with a loudspeaker and/or a luggage compartment light mounted in the rear parcel shelf support panel, disconnect the battery negative lead, with reference to Chapter 5A.

24 Fold down the rear seat back.

25 Unscrew the seat belt lower anchor bolt.

26 Pull off the plastic cover, then unscrew the upper seat belt anchor bolt

27 Working in the luggage compartment, remove the securing clip, and withdraw the luggage compartment side trim panel.

28 Unscrew the securing bolt, and detach the rear seat belt inertia reel from the side of the luggage compartment.

Refitting

21 Refitting is a reversal of removal, but tighten the seat belt anchor bolts to the specified torque.

Rear centre seat belt and seat belt stalks

Removal

22 Remove the rear seat cushion as described in Section 27.

23 Tilt the seat back as necessary for access to the seat belt/stalk anchor bolts.

24 Unscrew the relevant seat belt/stalk anchor bolt(s), and remove the assembly.

Refitting

25 Refitting is a reversal of removal, but tighten the anchor bolt(s) to the specified torque.

29 Interior trim - removal and refitting

General

1 The interior trim panels are secured by a combination of clips and screws. Removal and refitting is generally self-explanatory, noting that it may be necessary to remove or loosen surrounding panels to allow a particular panel to be removed. The following paragraphs describe the removal and refitting of the major panels in more detail.

Door inner trim panels

2 Refer to Section 12.

Steering column shrouds

Removal

3 Working under the lower column shroud, unscrew the five securing screws, then withdraw the upper shroud (see illustration).

4 Unclip and lift off the lower shroud (see illustration).

Refitting

5 Refitting is a reversal of removal.

Sill trim panels

Removal

6 Open the door(s), and carefully prise the weatherseal(s) from the edges of the door aperture(s).

7 Using two small screwdrivers, carefully prise out the trim panel lower securing clips, taking care not to damage the trim panel (see illustration). There are three securing clips on three-door models, and four clips on five-door models.

8 On five-door models, prise out the cover, and remove the securing screw from the rear of the trim panel.

9 Working in the front footwell, tap out the centre pin(s) and prise out the front securing clip(s), or unscrew the securing clip(s), as applicable, then withdraw the trim panel from the sill (see illustration).

Refitting

10 Refitting is a reversal of removal.

29.7 Prising out a sill trim panel lower securing clip

29.9 Removing a sill trim panel front securing clip

29 Disconnect the wiring plugs from the rear loudspeaker and, where applicable, the luggage compartment light (both mounted in the parcel shelf support panel).

30 Peel back the weatherseal(s) from the edge of the parcel shelf support panel.

31 Unscrew the four securing screws (three accessible from the luggage compartment, and one from the passenger compartment), then withdraw the parcel shelf support panel **(see illustrations)**. As the panel is withdrawn, feed the seat belt and, where applicable the wiring, through the holes in the panel.

Refitting

32 Refitting is a reversal of removal, but tighten the seat belt anchor bolts to the specified torque.

Rear pillar trim panel - Hatchback and Van models

Removal

33 Remove the rear parcel shelf support panel, as described previously in this Section.

34 Support the tailgate in the open position, using a wooden prop or similar tool. Note that the tailgate is heavy, and will fall closed if either of the support struts are disconnected.

35 Working at the lower end of the tailgate strut, lever off the retaining clip, and disconnect the end of the strut from the lug on the body.

36 Remove the securing screw from the lower edge of the rear pillar trim panel.

37 Carefully prise the trim panel from the pillar to release the two securing clips (at the top of the panel).

Refitting

38 Refitting is a reversal of removal, but tighten the seat belt anchor bolts to the specified torque.

Lower rear pillar trim panel - 5-door models

Removal

39 Remove the rear seat cushion as described in Section 27, then fold the rear seat back down.

40 Carefully peel back the weatherseal from the edge of the trim panel.

41 Remove the securing screw from the top of the panel, then carefully prise the securing clip from the lower end of the panel, and withdraw the panel.

Refitting

42 Refitting is a reversal of removal.

Luggage compartment side trim panel – Courier and Combi models

Removal

43 Remove the centre pillar trim panel, as described previously in this Section.

44 Remove the securing screw, and withdraw the rear quarter trim panel.

29.31a Three of the rear parcel shelf support panel screws (arrowed) accessible from the luggage compartment . . .

45 Pull off the plastic cover, then unscrew the upper seat belt anchor bolt.

46 Unscrew lower seat belt anchor bolt.

47 Pull the seat belt surround from the trim panel, then manipulate the seat belt through the hole in the panel.

48 Work around the edge of the luggage compartment side trim panel, and release the securing clips (ideally using a forked tool), then withdraw the panel from the vehicle.

Refitting

49 Refitting is a reversal of removal, but tighten the seat belt anchor bolts to the specified torque.

Carpets

50 The passenger compartment floor carpet is in several pieces, and is secured along the edges by screws or various types of clips.

51 Carpet removal and refitting is reasonably straightforward, but time-consuming, due to the fact that all adjoining trim panels must be released, and the seats and centre console must be removed.

Headlining

52 The headlining is clipped to the roof, and can be withdrawn only once all fittings such as the grab handles, sun visors, sunroof, front, centre and rear pillar trim panels, and associated components have been removed. The door, tailgate and sunroof aperture weatherseals will also have to be prised clear.

53 Note that headlining removal requires

30.3 Prise the surround from the gearchange lever gaiter . . .

29.31b . . . and one screw (arrowed) accessible from the passenger compartment

considerable skill and experience if it is to be carried out without damage, and is therefore best entrusted to an expert.

30 Centre console - removal and refitting

Manual transmission models

Removal

1 On models with a remote tailgate release, disconnect the battery negative lead, with reference to Chapter 5A, then carefully prise the tailgate release switch from the centre console, and disconnect the wiring plug.

2 Unscrew the knob from the end of the gearchange lever.

3 Carefully prise the surround from the gearchange lever gaiter **(see illustration)**.

4 Unscrew the two now-exposed centre console rear securing screws **(see illustration)**.

5 Working at the front of the console, prise out the cover plugs (one on each side) to reveal the front securing screws **(see illustration)**. Remove the screws.

6 Withdraw the centre console, and manipulate it over the gearchange lever.

Refitting

7 Refitting is a reversal of removal, but take care not to damage the gearchange lever gaiter.

30.4 . . . and unscrew the two screws (arrowed)

30.5 Prise out the cover plugs for access to the front securing screws

31.8 Prise off the facia side trim panels

31.11 Disconnecting the air bag control unit wiring plug

Automatic transmission models

Removal

8 Disconnect the battery negative lead, with reference to Chapter 5A.

9 On models with an electric tailgate release, carefully prise the tailgate release switch from the centre console, and disconnect the wiring plug.

10 Remove the securing screw, and pull off the gear selector lever knob.

11 Carefully prise off the gear selector lever position indicator cover, and disconnect the wiring plug from the illumination light.

12 Proceed as described in paragraphs 4 to 6.

Refitting

13 Refitting is a reversal of removal.

31	Facia assembly -
	removal and refitting

Removal

Note: *This is a difficult procedure, as the wiring harness and heater/ventilation ducting must be released from the rear of the facia (and attached on refitting) with the facia pulled back from the bulkhead, before the assembly can be removed. Access is very difficult, and it is suggested that this Section is read through thoroughly before starting the procedure.*

1 Disconnect the battery negative lead, with reference to Chapter 5A. Wait for two minutes before carrying out any further work.

2 Remove the centre console as described in Section 30.

3 Remove the steering column assembly as described in Chapter 10.

4 Remove the instrument panel as described in Chapter 12.

5 Remove the radio/cassette player as described in Chapter 12.

6 Remove the heater control unit as described in Chapter 3.

7 Where applicable, remove the passenger's side air bag as described in Chapter 12.

8 Carefully prise the weatherseals from the front edges of the door apertures, then prise off the facia side trim panels **(see illustration)**.

9 Remove the sill trim panels and the front pillar trim panels, as described in Section 29.

10 Where applicable, disconnect the wiring plug(s) from the anti-theft alarm control module in the footwell behind the right-hand sill trim panel.

11 Reach in through the glovebox and prise out the cover panel for access to the air bag control unit. Disconnect the air bag control unit wiring plug **(see illustration)**.

12 Pull the fusebox cover from the facia, then remove the two screws securing the fusebox to the facia. Unclip the fusebox from the facia **(see illustration)**.

13 Work around the facia, and remove the ten facia securing bolts. The bolt locations are as follows **(see illustrations)**.

a) *Two bolts on either side of the facia (revealed by removal of the facia side trim panels).*

b) *Three bolts at the top of the facia - prise out the plastic covers for access.*

31.12 Remove the two screws (arrowed) securing the fusebox to the facia

31.13a Remove the two bolts (arrowed) on either side of the facia . . .

31.13b . . . the three bolts at the top of the facia . . .

31.13c . . . the lower bolts on either side of the floor tunnel . . .

31.13d . . . and the bolt under the facia . . .

31.14 . . . then pull the facia assembly back from the bulkhead

31.15 Heater/ventilation trunking-to-facia securing screws (arrowed)

31.17 Wiring harness-to-facia securing clips (arrowed)

c) *One lower bolt on either side of the floor tunnel (securing the facia mounting brackets to the floor).*

d) *One bolt under the driver's side of the facia (securing the facia to the steering column mounting bracket).*

14 Carefully pull the facia assembly back from the bulkhead, taking care not to strain the wiring harnesses **(see illustration)**. Ensure that the facia is adequately supported to avoid damaging the wiring harnesses.

15 Reach behind the facia, and remove the seven screws securing the heater/ventilation trunking to the facia **(see illustration)**.

16 Working through the radio/cassette player aperture in the front of the facia, remove the remaining screw securing the heater/ventilation trunking to the facia, then remove the heater/ventilation trunking.

17 Again, reach behind the facia and release the clips securing the wiring harnesses to the facia. Note the routing of the harnesses to aid refitting **(see illustration)**.

18 Release the clips and detach the wiring harnesses from the guide rails. Again, not the routing of the harnesses to aid refitting.

19 With the aid of an assistant, lift out the facia, and withdraw it through one of the door apertures.

Refitting

20 Refitting is a reversal of removal, bearing in mind the following points.

a) *Ensure that the wiring harnesses are routed as noted before removal.*

b) *Where applicable, refit the passenger's side air bag as described in Chapter 12.*

c) *Refit the radio/cassette player with reference to Chapter 12.*

d) *Refit the instrument panel with reference to Chapter 12.*

e) *Refit the steering column assembly as described in Chapter 10.*

11

Notes

Chapter 12
Body electrical system

Contents

Degrees of difficulty

Easy, suitable for novice with little experience		Fairly easy, suitable for beginner with some experience		Fairly difficult, suitable for competent DIY mechanic		Difficult, suitable for experienced DIY mechanic		Very difficult, suitable for expert DIY or professional	

Specifications

General

System type ..... 12-volt negative earth

Fuses

Refer to label on fusebox cover

Bulbs	Type	Wattage
Headlight:		
Main beam	H1	55
Dipped beam	H7	55
Front sidelight	Push-fit	5
Front direction indicator light	Bayonet-fit	21
Front direction indicator side repeater light	Push-fit	5
Front foglight	H1	55
Tail/stop light (Courier and Combi models)	Bayonet-fit	5/21
Tail light	Bayonet-fit	5
Stop light	Bayonet-fit	21
Rear direction indicator light	Bayonet-fit	21
Reversing light	Bayonet-fit	21
Rear foglight	Bayonet-fit	21
Number plate light (Hatchback and Van models)	Push-fit	6
Number plate light (Courier and Combi models)	Push-fit	4
Courtesy light	Festoon	10
Map reading lights	Push-fit	5
Luggage compartment light	Push-fit	5
Glovebox light	Push-fit	5

Torque wrench setting	Nm	lbf ft
Air bag electronic control unit screws	6	4

1 General information and precautions

 Warning: Before carrying out any work on the electrical system, read through the precautions given in "Safety first!" at the beginning of this manual, and in Chapter 5.

The electrical system is of 12-volt negative earth type. Power for the lights and all electrical accessories is supplied by a lead/acid type battery, which is charged by the alternator.

This Chapter covers repair and service procedures for the various electrical components not associated with engine. Information on the battery, alternator and starter motor can be found in Chapter 5.

It should be noted that, prior to working on any component in the electrical system, the battery negative terminal should first be disconnected, to prevent the possibility of electrical short-circuits and/or fires.

Caution: Before disconnecting the battery, refer to the information given in Chapter 5A.

2 Electrical fault-finding – general information

Note: *Refer to the precautions given in "Safety first!" and at the beginning of Chapter 5 before starting work. The following tests relate to testing of the main electrical circuits, and should not be used to test delicate electronic circuits (such as anti-lock braking systems), particularly where an electronic control module is used.*

General

1 A typical electrical circuit consists of an electrical component, any switches, relays, motors, fuses, fusible links or circuit breakers related to that component, and the wiring and connectors which link the component to both the battery and the chassis. To help to pinpoint a problem in an electrical circuit, wiring diagrams are included at the end of this Chapter.

2 Before attempting to diagnose an electrical fault, first study the appropriate wiring diagram, to obtain a more complete understanding of the components included in the particular circuit concerned. The possible sources of a fault can be narrowed down by noting whether other components related to the circuit are operating properly. If several components or circuits fail at one time, the problem is likely to be related to a shared fuse or earth connection.

3 Electrical problems usually stem from simple causes, such as loose or corroded connections, a faulty earth connection, a blown fuse, a melted fusible link, or a faulty relay (refer to Section 3 for details of testing relays). Visually inspect the condition of all fuses, wires and connections in a problem circuit before testing the components. Use the wiring diagrams to determine which terminal connections will need to be checked, in order to pinpoint the trouble-spot.

4 The basic tools required for electrical fault-finding include a circuit tester or voltmeter (a 12-volt bulb with a set of test leads can also be used for certain tests); a self-powered test light (sometimes known as a continuity tester); an ohmmeter (to measure resistance); a battery and set of test leads; and a jumper wire, preferably with a circuit breaker or fuse incorporated, which can be used to bypass suspect wires or electrical components. Before attempting to locate a problem with test instruments, use the wiring diagram to determine where to make the connections.

5 To find the source of an intermittent wiring fault (usually due to a poor or dirty connection, or damaged wiring insulation), a "wiggle" test can be performed on the wiring. This involves wiggling the wiring by hand, to see if the fault occurs as the wiring is moved. It should be possible to narrow down the source of the fault to a particular section of wiring. This method of testing can be used in conjunction with any of the tests described in the following sub-Sections.

6 Apart from problems due to poor connections, two basic types of fault can occur in an electrical circuit - open-circuit, or short-circuit.

7 Open-circuit faults are caused by a break somewhere in the circuit, which prevents current from flowing. An open-circuit fault will prevent a component from working, but will not cause the relevant circuit fuse to blow.

8 Short-circuit faults are caused by a "short" somewhere in the circuit, which allows the current flowing in the circuit to "escape" along an alternative route, usually to earth. Short-circuit faults are normally caused by a breakdown in wiring insulation, which allows a feed wire to touch either another wire, or an earthed component such as the bodyshell. A short-circuit fault will normally cause the relevant circuit fuse to blow.

Finding an open-circuit

9 To check for an open-circuit, connect one lead of a circuit tester or voltmeter to either the negative battery terminal or a known good earth.

10 Connect the other lead to a connector in the circuit being tested, preferably nearest to the battery or fuse.

11 Switch on the circuit, bearing in mind that some circuits are live only when the ignition switch is moved to a particular position.

12 If voltage is present (indicated either by the tester bulb lighting or a voltmeter reading, as applicable), this means that the section of the circuit between the relevant connector and the battery is problem-free.

13 Continue to check the remainder of the circuit in the same fashion.

14 When a point is reached at which no voltage is present, the problem must lie between that point and the previous test point with voltage. Most problems can be traced to a broken, corroded or loose connection.

Finding a short-circuit

15 To check for a short-circuit, first disconnect the load(s) from the circuit (loads are the components which draw current from a circuit, such as bulbs, motors, heating elements, etc).

16 Remove the relevant fuse from the circuit, and connect a circuit tester or voltmeter to the fuse connections.

17 Switch on the circuit, bearing in mind that some circuits are live only when the ignition switch is moved to a particular position.

18 If voltage is present (indicated either by the tester bulb lighting or a voltmeter reading, as applicable), this means that there is a short-circuit.

19 If no voltage is present, but the fuse still blows with the load(s) connected, this indicates an internal fault in the load(s).

Finding an earth fault

20 The battery negative terminal is connected to "earth" - the metal of the engine/transmission unit and the car body - and most systems are wired so that they only receive a positive feed, the current returning via the metal of the car body. This means that the component mounting and the body form part of that circuit. Loose or corroded mountings can therefore cause a range of electrical faults, ranging from total failure of a circuit, to a puzzling partial fault. In particular, lights may shine dimly (especially when another circuit sharing the same earth point is in operation), motors (eg wiper motors or the radiator cooling fan motor) may run slowly, and the operation of one circuit may have an apparently-unrelated effect on another. Note that on many vehicles, earth straps are used between certain components, such as the engine/transmission and the body, usually where there is no metal-to-metal contact between components, due to flexible rubber mountings, etc.

21 To check whether a component is properly earthed, disconnect the battery, and connect one lead of an ohmmeter to a known good earth point. Connect the other lead to the wire or earth connection being tested. The resistance reading should be zero; if not, check the connection as follows.

22 If an earth connection is thought to be faulty, dismantle the connection, and clean back to bare metal both the bodyshell and the wire terminal or the component earth connection mating surface. Be careful to remove all traces of dirt and corrosion, then use a knife to trim away any paint, so that a clean metal-to-metal joint is made. On reassembly, tighten the joint fasteners securely; if a wire terminal is being refitted, use serrated washers between the terminal and the bodyshell, to ensure a clean and

3.3 Remove the fusebox cover for access to the fuses. Note the location of the fuse removal tool (arrowed)

3.6 Using the plastic tool, pull the fuse from its location

3.9 Additional fuses are located in the auxiliary fuse/relay box

secure connection. When the connection is remade, prevent the onset of corrosion in the future by applying a coat of petroleum jelly or silicone-based grease, or by spraying on (at regular intervals) a proprietary ignition sealer.

3 Fuses and relays – general information

Fuses

1 Fuses are designed to break a circuit when a predetermined current is reached, in order to protect the components and wiring which could be damaged by excessive current flow. Any excessive current flow will be due to a fault in the circuit, usually a short-circuit (see Section 2).

3.11 To gain access to the relays in the auxiliary fuse/relay box, unclip the main cover

2 The main fuses are located in the fusebox, below the driver's side of the facia.
3 For access to the fuses, pull off the fusebox cover (see illustration).
4 A blown fuse can be recognised from its melted or broken wire.
5 To remove a fuse, first ensure that the relevant circuit is switched off.
6 Using the plastic tool provided on the fusebox cover, pull the fuse from its location (see illustration).
7 Before renewing a blown fuse, trace and rectify the cause, and always use a fuse of the correct rating. Never substitute a fuse of a higher rating, or make temporary repairs using wire or metal foil; more serious damage, or even fire, could result.
8 Note that the fuses are colour-coded as follows. Refer to the markings on the fusebox cover for details of the circuits protected.

Colour	Rating
Orange	5A
Red	10A
Blue	15A
Yellow	20A
Clear or white	25A
Green	30A

9 Additional fuses are located in the auxiliary fuse/relay box, at the rear left-hand corner of the engine compartment (see illustration).

Relays

10 A relay is an electrically-operated switch, which is used for the following reasons:

a) A relay can switch a heavy current remotely from the circuit in which the current is flowing, allowing the use of lighter-gauge wiring and switch contacts.
b) A relay can receive more than one control input, unlike a mechanical switch.
c) A relay can have a timer function - for example, the intermittent wiper relay.

11 Most of the relays are located under the facia, at the rear of the main fusebox. Additional relays are located in the auxiliary fuse/relay box, at the rear left-hand corner of the engine compartment (see illustration).
12 Access to the relays in the fusebox can be obtained by removing the two securing screws, then releasing the securing clips, and lowering the fusebox from the facia (see illustrations).
13 If a circuit or system controlled by a relay develops a fault, and the relay is suspect, operate the system. If the relay is functioning, it should be possible to hear it "click" as it is energised. If this is the case, the fault lies with the components or wiring of the system. If the relay is not being energised, then either the relay is not receiving a main supply or a switching voltage, or the relay itself is faulty. Testing is by the substitution of a known good unit, but be careful - while some relays are identical in appearance and in operation, others look similar but perform different functions.
14 To remove a relay, first ensure that the relevant circuit is switched off. The relay can then simply be pulled out from the socket, and pushed back into position.

3.12a Remove the two securing screws . . .

3.12b . . . then release the securing clips . . .

3.12c . . . and lower the fusebox from the facia

3.15 Removing the direction indicator/hazard flasher relay

15 The direction indicator/hazard flasher relay is plugged into the bottom of the steering column combination switch assembly, and can be removed after removing the switch assembly as described in Section 4 (see illustration).

4.2 Disconnecting the wiring plug from the anti-theft immobiliser transceiver unit

4.6a Separate the two halves of the ignition switch wiring connector . . .

4.9 Disconnect the combination switch wiring plugs . . .

4 Switches – removal and refitting

Note: *Disconnect the battery negative lead, with reference to Chapter 5A before removing any switch, and reconnect the lead after refitting the switch.*

Ignition switch/ steering column lock

Steering column lock cylinder

1 Remove the steering column shrouds as described in Chapter 11.
2 Where applicable, disconnect the wiring plug and remove the securing screw, then withdraw the anti-theft immobiliser transceiver unit from the ignition switch/ steering lock assembly (see illustration).

4.4 Removing the steering lock cylinder

4.6b . . . then release the securing clips . . .

4.10 . . . then remove the securing screw . . .

3 Insert the ignition key, and turn it to position "I".
4 Using a small screwdriver, depress the locking pin at the top of the lock housing, then pull out the lock cylinder using the key (see illustration).
5 To refit the lock cylinder, push the assembly into the lock housing, until the locking pin engages, then turn the ignition key to position "0" and withdraw the key.

Ignition switch

Caution: Do not remove the ignition switch whilst the steering column lock cylinder is removed.

6 To remove the ignition switch, separate the two halves of the wiring connector, then release the securing clips using a small screwdriver, and withdraw the switch from the end of the lock housing (see illustrations).
7 Refitting is a reversal of removal, but make sure that the plunger on the lock engages correctly with the switch wiper.

Steering column combination switch assembly

8 Remove the steering column shrouds as described in Chapter 11.
9 Disconnect the wiring plugs from the rear of the switches (see illustration).
10 Remove the securing screw from the top of the switch assembly (see illustration).
11 Lift the switch assembly from the steering column (see illustration).
12 If desired, the direction indicator/hazard flasher relay can now be unplugged from the bottom of the switch.
13 Refitting is a reversal of removal.

4.6c . . . and withdraw the switch

4.11 . . . and lift the switch assembly from the steering column

4.15 Pushing out a switch from the facia

Facia-mounted pushbutton switches

14 Remove the clock/temperature display as described in Section 13.
15 Working through the clock/temperature gauge aperture, push out the relevant switch, then disconnect the wiring plug **(see illustration)**.
16 Refitting is a reversal of removal.

Headlight adjustment switch

17 Carefully prise the switch from the facia using a small screwdriver, and disconnect the wiring plug.
18 Refitting is a reversal of removal.

Heater blower motor switch

19 Refer to Chapter 3.

Stop light switch and handbrake "on" warning light switch

20 Refer to Chapter 9.

Electric window switches

21 Remove the door inner trim panel as described in Chapter 11.
22 Disconnect the wiring plug from the switch, then push the switch out from the trim panel.
23 Refitting is a reversal of removal.

Electric mirror switch

24 Refer to Chapter 11.

Remote tailgate release switch and electric sunroof switch

25 Carefully prise the switch from the housing, and disconnect the wiring plug.

5.3 Removing the headlight bulb cover

4.28 Door pillar-mounted courtesy light switch securing screw (arrowed)

26 Refitting is a reversal of removal.

Courtesy light switches

Door pillar-mounted switch

27 Where applicable, pull the rubber cover from the switch.
28 Unscrew the switch securing screw, then pull the switch from the door pillar, and disconnect the wiring plug **(see illustration)**.
29 It is advisable to tape or tie the switch wiring in position, to prevent it from dropping down into the door pillar.
30 Refitting is a reversal of removal.

Light-mounted switches

31 The switches are integral with the light units, and cannot be renewed separately.

Glovebox light switch

32 Open the glovebox, and prise out the switch/light unit, then disconnect the wiring plug.
33 Refitting is a reversal of removal.

Luggage compartment light switch

34 The switch is integral with the tailgate electrical contact plate at the rear of the passenger compartment.
35 Open the tailgate, and prise the assembly from the body panel, then disconnect the wiring plugs **(see illustration)**.
36 Refitting is a reversal of removal.

5.4 Disconnect the wiring plug . . .

4.35 Prising out the luggage compartment light switch/contact plate assembly

5 Bulbs (exterior lights) – renewal

1 Whenever a bulb is renewed, note the following points.
a) *Disconnect the battery negative lead before starting work. See Chapter 5A.*
b) *Remember that, if the light has just been in use, the bulb may be extremely hot.*
c) *Always check the bulb contacts and holder, ensuring that there is clean metal-to metal contact between the bulb and its live(s) and earth. Clean off any corrosion or dirt before fitting a new bulb.*
d) *Wherever bayonet-type bulbs are fitted (see Specifications), ensure that the live contact(s) bear firmly against the bulb contact.*
e) *Always ensure that the new bulb is of the correct rating, and that it is completely clean before fitting it; this applies particularly to headlight/foglight bulbs (see below).*

Headlight

2 Remove the headlight (see Section 7).
3 Release the securing clips from each side of the headlight rear cover, then pull off the cover **(see illustration)**.
4 Pull the wiring plug from the rear of the relevant bulb (separate main and dipped beam bulbs are fitted) **(see illustration)**.
5 Release the spring clip by compressing its ends, then withdraw the relevant bulb **(see illustration)**.

5.5 . . . then release the spring clip and withdraw the bulb

12

5.11 Removing the sidelight bulb from the bulbholder

5.15 Removing the direction indicator light cover from the headlight assembly

5.16 Removing the front direction indicator light bulb from the bulbholder

6 When handling the new bulb, use a tissue or clean cloth, to avoid touching the glass with the fingers; moisture and grease from the skin can cause blackening and rapid failure of this type of bulb. If the glass is accidentally touched, wipe it clean using methylated spirit.
7 Install the new bulb, ensuring that its locating tabs are correctly seated in the light cut-outs. Secure the bulb in position with the spring clip, and reconnect the wiring plug.
8 Refit the cover, and secure with the clips, then refit the headlight as described in Section 7.

Front sidelight

9 Remove the headlight as described in Section 7.
10 Release the securing clips from each side of the headlight rear cover, then pull off the cover.

5.24 Use a screwdriver to remove the direction indicator side repeater light

5.25 Turn the bulbholder anti-clockwise to remove it from the lens

11 Pull the bulbholder from the rear of the light. The bulb is a push-fit in the bulbholder **(see illustration)**.
12 Fit the new bulb using a reversal of the removal procedure.
13 Refit the headlight as described in Section 7.

Front direction indicator light

14 Remove the headlight as described in Section 7.
15 Release the securing clip, then pull the direction indicator light cover (the round cover) from the rear of the headlight **(see illustration)**.
16 Twist the bulbholder anti-clockwise to remove it from the light unit. The bulb is a bayonet-fit in the bulbholder **(see illustration)**.
17 Fit the new bulb using a reversal of the removal procedure, then refit the headlight as described in Section 7.

Front foglight

18 Remove the foglight as described in Section 7.
19 Pull the rubber cover from the rear of the light unit.
20 Release the securing clip, and pull the bulb from the light.
21 When handling the new bulb, use a tissue or clean cloth, to avoid touching the glass with the fingers; moisture and grease from the skin can cause blackening and rapid failure of this type of bulb. If the glass is accidentally touched, wipe it clean using methylated spirit.

5.28 Press the locking tabs to remove the rear light bulbholder – Hatchback and Van models

22 Fit the new bulb using a reversal of the removal procedure. Ensure that the flat on the bulb locates against the shoulder in the light unit.
23 Refit the foglight with reference to Section 7.

Front direction indicator side repeater light

24 Using a screwdriver (rest the screwdriver on a piece of rag to protect the paintwork), push the complete light assembly sideways, and pull it from the wing panel **(see illustration)**.
25 Turn the bulbholder anti-clockwise to remove it from the lens. The bulb is a push-fit in the bulbholder **(see illustration)**.
26 Fit the new bulb using a reversal of the removal procedure.

Rear lights – Hatchback and Van models

27 Open the tailgate, then release the securing clip, and pull the luggage compartment trim panel back from the rear of the light unit.
28 Press the locking tabs at the centre of the bulbholder together, and remove the bulbholder **(see illustration)**.
29 The bulbs are a bayonet-fit in the bulbholder **(see illustration)**.
30 Fit the new bulb using a reversal of the removal procedure.

5.29 The bulbs are a bayonet-fit in the bulbholder – Hatchback and Van models

5.32 Unscrew the rear light securing nuts (arrowed) – Courier and Combi models

5.33 Remove the light assembly . . .

5.34 . . . then unclip the bulbholder – Courier and Combi models

5.35 The bulbs are a bayonet-fit – Courier and Combi models

5.37 Prise the rear number plate light unit from the bumper . . .

5.38 . . . and twist the bulbholder anti-clockwise to remove it – Hatchback and Van models

Rear lights – Courier and Combi models

31 Open the rear doors, and turn the securing clip at the top of the light rear cover anti-clockwise to release it. Withdraw the cover.
32 Unscrew the two now-exposed nuts securing the light unit to the body (**see illustration**).
33 Working outside the vehicle, pull the lower end of the light unit out slightly, then press down, and withdraw the complete light assembly (**see illustration**).
34 Squeeze the upper and lower bulbholder securing clips, and remove the bulbholder from the light unit (**see illustration**).
35 The bulbs are a bayonet-fit in the bulbholder (**see illustration**).
36 Fit the new bulb using a reversal of the removal procedure.

Rear number plate light – Hatchback and Van models

37 Carefully prise the light unit from the rear bumper using screwdriver (**see illustration**).
38 Twist the bulbholder anti-clockwise, and remove it from the light unit (**see illustration**).
39 The bulb is a push-fit in the bulbholder.
40 Fit the new bulb using a reversal of removal procedure.

Rear number plate light – Courier and Combi models

41 Carefully prise the light unit from the rear door.
42 Pull the bulbholder from the rear of the light unit (**see illustration**). The bulb is a bayonet-fit in the bulbholder.
43 Refitting is a reversal of removal.

6   Bulbs (interior lights) – renewal

General

1 Refer to Section 5, paragraph 1.

Courtesy lights

2 Carefully prise the lens from the light unit (see illustration).
3 Pull the bulb from the sprung contacts (**see illustration**).
4 Fit the new bulb using a reversal of the removal procedure.

Map reading lights

5 Carefully prise the light unit from the roof console, and disconnect the wiring plugs.

5.42 Pull the bulbholder from the rear number plate light – Courier and Combi models

6.2 Prise off the lens . . .

6.3 . . . for access to the courtesy light bulb

6.11 Removing the luggage compartment light bulb

6 Slide the contact plate back from the bulb, and withdraw the bulb.
7 Fit the new bulb using a reversal of the removal procedure.

Glovebox light

8 Open the glovebox, and pull the bulb from the switch/light assembly.
9 Fit the new bulb using a reversal of the removal procedure.

Luggage compartment light

10 Carefully prise the light unit out from the trim panel.
11 The bulb can now be reached from the back of the light unit. The bulb is a push-fit in the bulbholder **(see illustration)**. If necessary, the bulbholder can be removed by twisting anti-clockwise.
12 Fit the new bulb using a reversal of the removal procedure.

7.2 Remove the screw (arrowed) securing the outboard headlight mounting bracket to the body panel

7.3 Remove the two screws securing the inner edge of the headlight

6.14 Removing an instrument panel warning light bulb

Instrument panel illumination and warning light bulbs

13 Remove the instrument panel as described in Section 10.
14 Twist the relevant bulbholder anti-clockwise to remove it from the rear of the panel **(see illustration)**.
15 The bulbs are integral with the bulbholders.
16 Fit the new bulb using a reversal of the removal procedure. Refit the instrument panel with reference to Section 10.

Clock/temperature display illumination bulb

17 The bulb is integral with the clock/temperature display unit, and cannot be renewed separately.

Pushbutton switch illumination bulbs

18 The bulbs are integral with the switches, and cannot be renewed separately.

Cigarette lighter illumination bulb

19 Open the ashtray.
20 Working at the rear of the ashtray, Disconnect the cigarette lighter wiring plugs.
21 Squeeze the rear corners of the ashtray to release the securing lugs, then pull the ashtray from the facia.
22 Working at the rear of the assembly, carefully prise the bulbholder from the cigarette lighter body. The bulb is a push-fit in the bulbholder.

7.5 Disconnecting the headlight wiring plug

23 Fit the new bulb using a reversal of the removal procedure.

Heater/ventilation control unit illumination bulbs

24 Remove the heater control unit as described in Chapter 3.
25 Twist the relevant bulbholder anti-clockwise and remove it from the rear of the panel. The bulbs are integral with the bulbholders.
26 Fit the new bulb using a reversal of the removal procedure.

Heater blower motor switch illumination bulb

27 Pull the knob from the blower switch for access to the bulb.
28 The bulb is a push-fit in the switch.
29 Fit the new bulb using a reversal of the removal procedure.

7   Exterior light units – removal and refitting

Note: *Disconnect the battery negative lead, with reference to Chapter 5A before removing any light unit, and reconnect the lead after refitting the unit.*

Headlight

Removal

Caution: Do not unscrew the Torx screw on the headlight housing.
1 Remove the radiator grille panel as described in Chapter 11.
2 Remove the screw securing the outboard headlight mounting bracket to the body panel **(see illustration)**.
3 Remove the two securing screws from the inner edge of the headlight **(see illustration)**.
4 Withdraw the headlight by moving it towards the centre of the vehicle, and forwards.
5 Disconnect the wiring plug, and withdraw the headlight **(see illustration)**.
6 Note that if desired, the headlight lens can be removed after releasing the metal securing clips around the edge of the lens.

7.7 Make sure that the locating lug (arrowed) engages with the hole in the inner wing panel

7.15 Rear light unit securing nuts (arrowed) – Hatchback and Van models

Refitting

7 Refitting is a reversal of removal, but make sure that the locating lug on the headlight engages with the corresponding hole in the inner wing panel and, on completion, have the headlight beam alignment checked at the earliest opportunity **(see illustration)**.

Front direction indicator light

8 The front direction indicator light is integral with the headlight.

Front foglight

Removal

9 Working at the top of the light unit, unscrew the securing screw. Where applicable, also remove the securing screw from the lower, outer corner of the light.
10 Pull the light unit from the bumper.

Refitting

11 Refitting is a reversal of removal.

Front direction indicator side repeater light

12 The procedure is described as part of the bulb renewal procedure in Section 5.

Rear lights – Hatchback and Van models

Note: *A new rubber seal should be used on refitting.*

Removal

13 Open the tailgate, then release the securing clip, and pull the luggage compartment trim panel back from the rear of the light unit.
14 Disconnect the wiring plug from the rear of the bulbholder. If desired, unclip the bulbholder from the light unit.
15 Unscrew the three securing nuts, and withdraw the light unit from the rear of the vehicle **(see illustration)**. Recover the rubber seal.

Refitting

16 Refitting is a reversal of removal, but use a new rubber seal, and make sure that the seal is seated correctly.

Rear lights – Courier and Combi models

17 The procedure is described as part of the bulb renewal procedure in Section 5.

Rear number plate light

18 The procedure is described as part of the bulb renewal procedure in Section 5.

---

8 Headlight beam adjustment components – removal and refitting

Adjuster switch

1 Refer to Section 4.

Adjuster motor

Removal

2 If necessary for access, remove the headlight as described in Section 7.
3 Release the securing clips from each side of the headlight rear cover, then pull off the cover.
4 Disconnect the wiring plug from the rear of the motor.
5 Twist the motor anti-clockwise, and pull it from the headlight.

Refitting

6 Refitting is a reversal of removal but, where applicable, refit the headlight with reference to Section 7.

---

9 Headlight beam alignment – general information

1 All later vehicles are equipped with a four-position electrical vertical beam adjuster unit - this can be used to adjust the headlight beam, to compensate for the relevant load which the vehicle is carrying. An adjuster switch is provided on the facia. The adjuster switch should be positioned as follows, according to the load being carried in the vehicle. Refer to the vehicle handbook for further information.
2 Accurate adjustment of the headlight beam is only possible using optical beam-setting equipment, and this work should therefore be carried out by a Ford dealer or suitably-equipped workshop.
3 For reference, the headlights can be finely adjusted by rotating the adjuster screws fitted

9.3 Headlight beam adjustment screws

1 Vertical alignment screw
2 Horizontal alignment screw

to the top of each light unit. The screws are accessible through the top of the body front panel. The vertical adjustment screw is mounted at the inner end of the headlight. The horizontal adjustment screw is mounted at the outer end of the headlight **(see illustration)**. Note if the vertical adjustment is altered, this will affect the horizontal adjustment, which will have to be adjusted also.

---

10 Instrument panel – removal and refitting

Removal

Caution: When the instrument panel has been removed, do not rest it face down on the lens.

1 Disconnect the battery negative lead, with reference to Chapter 5A.
2 Remove the steering column shrouds, with reference to Chapter 11 if necessary.
3 Remove the steering column combination switch assembly as described in Section 4.
4 Working at the passenger's side edge of the instrument panel/heater/ventilation nozzle/switch trim panel, prise out the cover to expose the trim panel securing screw. Remove the securing screw **(see illustration)**.
5 Working above the instrument panel, unscrew the remaining trim panel securing screws **(see illustration)**.

10.4 Prise out the cover to expose the instrument panel/heater/ventilation nozzle/switch trim panel securing screw (arrowed)

10.5 Unscrew the remaining trim panel securing screws

10.6 Ease the trim panel forwards to release the retaining clips (arrowed)

10.7 Speedometer cable grommets (arrowed) at inner and outer bulkhead – viewed with scuttle cover panel and wiper motor removed for clarity

10.9a Unscrew the upper . . .

10.9b . . . and lower instrument panel securing screws (arrowed)

6 Ease the trim panel forwards to release the retaining clips at the bottom of the panel, then pull the panel forwards and disconnect the wiring plugs from the switches and clock/temperature display (where applicable) mounted in the panel. Withdraw the panel **(see illustration)**.

7 Working in the scuttle at the rear of the engine compartment, prise the speedometer cable grommet from the inner bulkhead – if desired, to improve access, remove the windscreen wiper motor and linkage as described in Section 19 **(see illustration)**.

8 Prise the grommet from the outer bulkhead at the rear of the engine compartment. Note the routing of the speedometer cable to ensure correct refitting.

9 Working inside the vehicle, remove the four instrument panel securing screws **(see illustrations)**.

10 The speedometer cable must now be disconnected from the transmission. On most models, access is easiest from under the vehicle. If desired, apply the handbrake, then jack up the front of the vehicle and support securely on axle stands (see "Jacking and Vehicle Support").

11 If necessary, counterhold the vehicle speed sensor at the transmission using a suitable spanner, then unscrew the securing nut, and disconnect the end of the speedometer cable from the transmission **(see illustration)**. Again, note the routing of the speedometer cable to aid refitting.

12 Where applicable, lower the vehicle to the ground.

13 Working inside the vehicle, carefully ease the instrument panel forwards from the facia (if necessary, push the speedometer cable through the bulkhead as the instrument panel is withdrawn), then release the securing clip, and disconnect the speedometer cable from the rear of the panel.

14 Disconnect the wiring plugs from the rear of the instrument panel, then remove the panel **(see illustration)**.

Refitting

15 Refitting is a reversal of removal, bearing in mind the following points.
- a) Ensure that the speedometer cable is routed as noted before removal.
- b) Ensure that the speedometer cable grommets are correctly located in the inner and outer bulkhead panels.
- c) Make sure that the speedometer cable securing clip engages correctly with the back of the speedometer.
- d) Pull the speedometer cable through into the engine compartment as the instrument panel is refitted.

11 Instrument panel components – removal and refitting

1 With the instrument panel removed as described in Section 10, proceed as follows.

Lens assembly

2 Working at the top of the instrument panel, twist the two bulbholders anti-clockwise, and remove them from the panel **(see illustration)**.

3 Release the four lens retaining lugs, and remove the lens assembly **(see illustrations)**.

4 Refitting is a reversal of removal.

Tachometer

5 Remove the lens assembly as described previously in this Section.

6 Unscrew the two securing screws, and withdraw the tachometer. Note that one of the securing screws also secures the speedometer **(see illustration)**.

10.11 Disconnecting the speedometer cable (arrowed) from the transmission

10.14 Removing the instrument panel

11.2 Remove the bulbholders from the top of the panel

11.3a Two of the lens securing clips (arrowed)

11.3b Removing the lens assembly from the instrument panel

11.6 Instrument securing screws (arrowed)

Fuel/temperature gauge assembly

7 Remove the lens assembly as described previously in this Section.

8 Remove the two securing screws and withdraw the gauge assembly (one of the screws also secures the speedometer). Note that the fuel gauge and the temperature gauge cannot be separated.

9 Refitting is a reversal of removal.

Speedometer

10 Remove the fuel/temperature gauge assembly and the tachometer as described previously in this Section, then lift out the speedometer.

Illumination/warning light bulbs

11 Twist the bulbholders anti-clockwise to remove them from the panel. The bulbs are integral with the bulbholders.

12 Refit by twisting clockwise to lock the bulb in position.

12 Cigarette lighter – removal and refitting

Removal

1 Disconnect the battery negative lead, with reference to Chapter 5A.

2 Open the ashtray, and pull out the ashtray liner.

3 Pull out the cigarette lighter element.

4 Working at the rear of the ashtray, Disconnect the cigarette lighter wiring plugs.

5 Squeeze the rear corners of the ashtray to release the securing lugs, then pull the ashtray from the facia.

6 Working at the rear of the assembly, carefully prise the bulbholder from the cigarette lighter body.

7 Remove the cigarette lighter body as follows.

a) Rotate the cigarette lighter body approximately 30° clockwise.

b) Push the rear of the body forwards approximately 10 mm.

c) Rotate the body back to its original position.

d) Push the body forwards, and remove it from the ashtray.

8 The illumination ring can now be pulled from the ashtray.

Refitting

9 Refitting is a reversal of removal.

13 Clock/temperature display – removal and refitting

Removal

1 Disconnect the battery negative lead, with reference to Chapter 5A.

2 Using a small screwdriver or similar tool, carefully prise the clock/temperature display from the facia – take care not to damage the facia trim.

3 Disconnect the wiring plug(s) and withdraw the unit (see illustration).

Refitting

4 Refitting is a reversal of removal.

14 Auxiliary warning system components – information, removal and refitting

General information

1 Certain models are equipped with an auxiliary warning system.

2 This system comprises a number of sensors, and four warning devices as follows.

a) Ice warning – an air temperature sensor provides information which is displayed by the clock/temperature display. Two warning lights in the display (orange and red) will illuminate, depending on the outside temperature. The orange light will illuminate when the air temperature is between ½ and 4°C, and the red light will illuminate when the air temperature is below ½°C.

b) Low fuel warning – a warning light will illuminate when around 8 litres of fuel remain in the tank. The signal is provided by the fuel level sender unit (see Chapter 4).

c) Low washer fluid level – a warning light will illuminate when the washer fluid level requires topping up. The signal is provided by a float and reed switch in the fluid reservoir.

d) Door/tailgate/bonnet ajar warning – a warning light will illuminate if a door, the tailgate or the bonnet is not fully shut. The signals are provided by switches which are shared with the central locking and alarm systems.

Fuel level sender unit

3 Refer to Chapter 4.

Door/tailgate/bonnet ajar switches

4 The door and tailgate ajar switches are mounted on the locks, and the locks must be removed for access to the switches. The bonnet ajar switch is mounted on the body front panel under the bonnet.

Air temperature sensor

Removal

5 Disconnect the battery negative lead, with reference to Chapter 5A.

6 Apply the handbrake, then jack up the front of the vehicle and support securely on axle stands (see "Jacking and Vehicle Support").

7 Remove the two securing screws, and withdraw the lower grille panel from the front bumper.

8 Separate the two halves of the air temperature sensor wiring connector.

13.3 Removing the clock/temperature display from the facia

14.9 Unclip the auxiliary warning system air temperature sensor from the front panel

14.15 Using a screwdriver, carefully prise the auxiliary warning system washer fluid level sensor from the reservoir

14.20 Disconnect the auxiliary warning system control unit wiring plug (arrowed)

9 Unclip the sensor from the front panel (see illustration).

Refitting

10 Refitting is a reversal of removal.

Washer fluid level sensor

Removal

11 Disconnect the battery negative lead, with reference to Chapter 5A.

12 Remove the right-hand front wheel trim or the wheel centre plate (alloy wheels), then slacken the wheel nuts. Apply the handbrake, then jack up the front of the vehicle, and support securely on axle stands (see "Jacking and Vehicle Support"). Remove the roadwheel.

13 Remove the wheel arch liner, with reference to Chapter 11 if necessary.

14 Working at the rear of the wheel arch, locate the sensor wiring connector, then manipulate the connector as necessary to enable the two halves to be separated.

15 Using a screwdriver, carefully prise the sensor from the side of the reservoir (see illustration). Have a suitable container ready to catch escaping fluid. Take care not to damage the rubber grommet.

Refitting

16 Refitting is a reversal of removal.

Control unit

Removal

17 Disconnect the battery negative lead, with reference to Chapter 5A.

15.4 Headlight warning buzzer location (arrowed) in fuse/relay box

18 Remove the centre console as described in Chapter 11.

19 Release the wiring harness from the upper control unit securing clip.

20 Disconnect the control unit wiring plug (see illustration).

21 Release the control unit from the securing clips, and withdraw it from the bracket.

Refitting

22 Refitting is a reversal of removal.

15 Lights on warning buzzer – removal and refitting

Removal

1 Disconnect the battery negative lead, with reference to Chapter 5A.

2 Working at the driver's side of the facia, pull off the fusebox cover.

3 Remove the two securing screws, and pull the fusebox forward from the facia to expose the relays.

4 The headlight warning buzzer is located at the lower right-hand corner of the relay panel (see illustration). Pull the buzzer from the panel to remove it.

Refitting

5 Refitting is a reversal of removal.

16 Horn – removal and refitting

Removal

1 The horn is located under the left-hand corner of the front bumper.

2 Disconnect the battery negative lead, with reference to Chapter 5A.

3 Disconnect the wiring plug from the horn.

4 Unscrew the securing nut, and remove the horn from its mounting bracket (see illustration).

Refitting

5 Refitting is a reversal of removal.

17 Speedometer cable – removal and refitting

Removal

1 Remove the instrument panel as described in Section 10, then withdraw the cable through the bulkhead panels into the engine compartment.

2 Release the cable from any brackets or clips, noting its routing, then withdraw the cable from the vehicle.

Refitting

3 Refitting is a reversal of removal, but ensure that the cable is routed as noted before removal, and refit the instrument panel as described in Section 10.

18 Wiper arm – removal and refitting

Removal

1 Operate the wiper motor, then switch it off so that the wiper arm returns to the at-rest position.

> **HAYNES HINT** *Stick a piece of masking tape along the edge of the wiper blade, to use as an alignment aid on refitting.*

16.4 Horn wiring plug (1) and horn securing nut (2)

18.2 Unscrew the securing nut and washer . . .

2 Lift up the wiper arm spindle nut cover, then slacken and remove the spindle nut. Recover the washer **(see illustration)**.
3 Lift the blade off the glass, and pull the wiper arm off its spindle. Note that on some models, the wiper arms may be very tight on the spindle splines - it should be possible to lever the arm off the spindle, using a flat-bladed screwdriver (take care not to damage the scuttle cover panel) **(see illustration)**.

Refitting

4 Ensure that the wiper arm and spindle splines are clean and dry, then refit the arm to the spindle. Where applicable, align the wiper blade with the tape fitted on removal.

18.3 . . . and withdraw the wiper arm

5 Refit the spindle nut, tightening it securely, and clip the nut cover back into position.

19 Windscreen wiper motor and linkage – removal and refitting

Removal

1 Remove the wiper arms as described in Section 18.
2 Prise off the covers, then unscrew and remove the nuts securing the wiper arm drive spindles to the body panel **(see illustrations)**. Lift off the washers and spacer plates.

3 Remove the scuttle cover panel as described in Chapter 11.
4 Disconnect the wiper motor wiring plug **(see illustration)**.
5 Unscrew the two bolts securing the wiper motor mounting plate **(see illustration)**.
6 Manipulate the wiper motor/linkage assembly out from the scuttle **(see illustration)**.
7 If desired, the motor can be removed from the linkage as follows **(see illustration)**.
a) Make alignment marks on the linkage drive link and the motor spindle, then unscrew the spindle nut.
b) Unscrew the three bolts securing the motor to the mounting plate, then withdraw the motor from the linkage assembly.

Refitting

8 Refitting is a reversal of removal, bearing in mind the following points.
a) Ensure that the motor is in the "parked" position before refitting.
b) If the motor has been removed from the linkage, ensure that the marks made on the linkage drive link and motor spindle are aligned on refitting.
c) Refit the wiper arms with reference to Section 18.

19.2a Prise off the covers . . .

19.2b . . . and unscrew the wiper arm drive spindle securing nuts

19.4 Disconnect the wiper motor wiring plug

19.5 Unscrew the securing bolts . . .

19.6 . . . and withdraw the wiper motor/linkage assembly from the scuttle

19.7 Wiper motor-to-linkage mounting details

1 Motor-to-drive link spindle nut
2 Motor securing bolts

12

20.2a Unscrewing the tailgate trim panel securing screw

20.2b Removing the tailgate trim panel

20.4 Tailgate wiper motor mounting details

1 Earth lead securing bolt
2 Wiper motor securing bolts

20.5 Disconnecting the tailgate wiper motor wiring connector

20 Tailgate wiper motor – removal and refitting

Removal

1 Disconnect the battery negative lead, with reference to Chapter 5A.
2 Unscrew the tailgate trim panel securing screw, and prise out the plastic surround, then prise around the edge of the trim panel to release the remaining retaining clips, and withdraw the tailgate trim panel **(see illustrations)**.
3 Remove the wiper arm as described in Section 18.
4 Unscrew the bolt securing the wiper motor earth lead to the tailgate **(see illustration)**.
5 Separate the two halves of the wiper motor wiring connector **(see illustration)**.

21.2a Remove the screw (arrowed) . . .

20.6 Withdrawing the tailgate wiper motor

6 Unscrew the three securing bolts, and withdraw the motor assembly from the tailgate **(see illustration)**.

Refitting

7 Refitting is a reversal of removal, but refit the wiper arm with reference to Section 18.

21 Windscreen/tailgate washer system components – removal and refitting

Washer fluid reservoir

Removal

1 Disconnect the battery negative lead, with reference to Chapter 5A.
2 Working in the engine compartment, remove the screw securing the coolant expansion tank, then release the securing clip

21.2b . . . and release the clip securing the coolant expansion tank

using a screwdriver, and move the expansion tank to one side, clear of the washer fluid reservoir filler neck **(see illustrations)**. There is no need to disconnect the coolant hoses from the expansion tank.
3 Pull the washer fluid reservoir filler neck from the reservoir **(see illustration)**.
4 Remove the right-hand front wheel trim or the wheel centre plate (alloy wheels), then slacken the wheel nuts. Apply the handbrake, then jack up the front of the vehicle, and support securely on axle stands (see *"Jacking and Vehicle Support"*). Remove the roadwheel.
5 Remove the wheel arch liner, with reference to Chapter 11 if necessary.
6 Place a suitable container beneath the reservoir, then drain the fluid from the reservoir into the container, by disconnecting the fluid hose(s) from the pump(s) in the reservoir.
7 Partially open the front door, then unscrew the two reservoir securing nuts, which are accessible at the rear of the door pillar **(see illustration)**.
8 Support the reservoir then, working under the wheel arch, unscrew the reservoir securing bolt **(see illustration)**.
9 Lower the reservoir, and disconnect the fluid pump wiring plug(s), the remaining fluid hose(s) and, where applicable, the fluid level sensor wiring plug. Release the clips securing the hoses and wiring harness(es) to the reservoir, then feed the hoses and harness(es)

21.3 Pull the washer fluid reservoir filler neck from the reservoir

21.7 One of the washer fluid reservoir securing nuts (arrowed)

21.8 Washer fluid reservoir securing bolt location (arrowed)

21.9a Disconnect the motor wiring plug . . .

21.9b . . . and release the clips securing the hoses and wiring to the reservoir

21.19 Removing the windscreen washer nozzle

21.21 Removing the tailgate washer nozzle

through the hole in the top of the reservoir, and withdraw the reservoir from under the wheel arch **(see illustrations)**.

Refitting

10 Refitting is a reversal of removal, bearing in mind the following points.

  a) *Check the condition of the filler neck O-ring, and renew if necessary.*

  b) *Make sure that the fluid hose(s) and the filler neck are securely reconnected to the reservoir.*

Washer fluid pump

Removal

11 Disconnect the battery negative lead, with reference to Chapter 5A.

12 Proceed as described in paragraphs 4 to 6. Note that in some cases, it may prove easier to remove the reservoir as described previously in this Section for access to the pump.

13 If not already done, disconnect the fluid hose(s) from the pump, then disconnect the pump wiring plug.

14 Pull the pump from the reservoir, and recover the rubber sealing grommet.

Refitting

15 Examine the rubber sealing grommet, and renew if necessary.

16 Refitting is a reversal of removal, but take care not to push the grommet into the reservoir when refitting the pump. Make sure that the pump is securely fitted in its sealing grommet, and make sure that the fluid hose(s) are securely reconnected.

Windscreen washer nozzle

Removal

17 Open the bonnet and, where applicable, prise out the securing clips, and pull back the underbonnet insulation for access to the washer nozzle.

18 Working under the bonnet, carefully pull the fluid hose end fitting from the washer nozzle.

19 Carefully prise the washer nozzle from the outside of the bonnet **(see illustration)**.

Refitting

20 Refitting is a reversal of removal, but make sure that the fluid hose end fitting is securely reconnected to the nozzle.

Tailgate washer nozzle

Removal

21 Carefully prise the nozzle from the top of

22.4 Using DIN removal tools to remove the radio/cassette player

the tailgate, taking care not to damage the paintwork **(see illustration)**.

22 Disconnect the fluid hose, and remove the nozzle. Take care not to allow the hose to drop down into the tailgate.

Refitting

23 Refitting is a reversal of removal, but make sure that the fluid hose is securely reconnected.

---

22 Radio/cassette player – removal and refitting

Note: *On models with a security-coded radio/cassette player, once the battery has been disconnected, the unit cannot be re-activated until the appropriate security code has been entered. Do not remove the unit unless the appropriate code is known. The following information applies to radio/cassette players having standard DIN fixings. Two DIN removal tools will be required for this operation.*

Removal

1 Disconnect the battery negative lead, with reference to Chapter 5A.

2 Insert the DIN removal tools into the holes on each side of the radio/cassette player, and push them until they click into place.

3 Pull the tools gently to the left and right to release the locking tangs.

4 Gently pull the radio/cassette player from the facia, using the removal tools **(see illustration)**.

22.5 Disconnect the wiring plugs and the aerial lead from the rear of the radio/cassette player unit

5 Disconnect the wiring plugs and the aerial lead, and withdraw the unit (see illustration).

Refitting

6 Reconnect the wiring plugs and the aerial lead, then push the unit into its housing until the securing clips engage.
7 On completion, reconnect the battery negative lead and, where applicable enter the security code.

23 Loudspeakers – removal and refitting

Main front door-mounted loudspeakers

Removal

1 Remove the relevant door inner trim panel, as described in Chapter 11.
2 Unscrew the four loudspeaker securing screws, then withdraw the loudspeaker from the door and disconnect the wiring plug (see illustration).

Refitting

3 Refitting is a reversal of removal.

Front door-mounted high-frequency ("tweeter") loudspeakers

Removal

4 The loudspeaker is integral with the door interior handle surround.

5 Prise off the cover, unscrew the securing screw, then withdraw the interior handle surround from the door. Disconnect the wiring plug from the loudspeaker mounted in the surround, then remove the surround/loudspeaker assembly (see illustrations).

Refitting

6 Refitting is a reversal of removal.

Rear parcel shelf-mounted loudspeakers

Removal

7 Disconnect the battery negative lead, with reference to Chapter 5A.
8 If removing the right-hand loudspeaker, working in the luggage compartment, remove the luggage compartment light from the rear parcel shelf support panel, by prising the light out and disconnecting the wiring plug.
9 Remove the two securing screws, then withdraw the loudspeaker sideways from the parcel shelf, and disconnect the wiring plug.

Refitting

10 Refitting is a reversal of removal, but make sure that the lugs on the loudspeaker engage correctly with the slots in the trim panel.

24 Radio aerial – removal and refitting

Removal

1 Disconnect the battery negative lead, with reference to Chapter 5A.
2 Carefully prise the courtesy light assembly from the roof console. Disconnect the wiring plugs, and remove the courtesy light assembly (note that the light assembly incorporates the remote control receiver for the central locking system, where applicable).
3 Unscrew the now-exposed securing screw, and disconnect the aerial lead from the base of the aerial (see illustration).
4 Withdraw the aerial from the roof panel. Note that the aerial mast can be unscrewed from the aerial body if desired.

23.2 Removing a main front door-mounted loudspeaker

Refitting

5 Refitting is a reversal of removal.

25 Anti-theft alarm system and engine immobiliser – general information

Certain vehicles are equipped with an anti-theft alarm system and/or and engine immobiliser system. Various types of system may be fitted depending on vehicle specification, and market. The anti-theft alarm system, is automatically activated by the central locking system (manually, or via the remote control, where applicable). The engine immobiliser system is operated by a coded unit in the ignition key – the engine can only be started using one of the ignition keys originally supplied with the car when new.
The alarm system has switches on the bonnet, tailgate and each of the doors.
Any faults with the system should be referred to a Ford dealer.

26 Airbag system – general information, precautions and system de-activation

General information

A driver's side air bag is fitted as standard equipment on some models, and is available as an option on others. The air bag is fitted to the steering wheel centre pad.

23.5a Prise off the cover for access to the handle surround/loudspeaker securing screw

23.5b Removing the handle surround/"tweeter" loudspeaker

24.3 Radio aerial securing screw (arrowed)

Similarly, a passenger's side air bag is also fitted as standard equipment, or as an option, depending on model.

The system is armed only when the ignition is switched on, however, a reserve power source maintains a power supply to the system in the event of a break in the main electrical supply. The system is activated by a "g" sensor (deceleration sensor), incorporated in the electronic control unit. Note that the electronic control unit also controls the front seat belt tensioners.

The air bags are inflated by gas generators, which force the bags out from their locations in the steering wheel, and the passenger's side facia, where applicable.

Precautions

Warning: The following precautions must be observed when working on vehicles equipped with an air bag system, to prevent the possibility of personal injury.

General precautions

The following precautions **must** be observed when carrying out work on a vehicle equipped with an air bag.
a) Do not disconnect the battery with the engine running.
b) Before carrying out any work in the vicinity of the air bag, removal of any of the air bag components, or any welding work on the vehicle, de-activate the system as described in the following sub-Section.
c) Do not attempt to test any of the air bag system circuits using test meters or any other test equipment.
d) If the air bag warning light comes on, or any fault in the system is suspected, consult a Ford dealer without delay. **Do not** attempt to carry out fault diagnosis, or any dismantling of the components.

Precautions to be taken when handling an air bag

a) Transport the air bag by itself, bag upward.
b) Do not put your arms around the air bag.
c) Carry the air bag close to the body, bag outward.
d) Do not drop the air bag or expose it to impacts.
e) Do not attempt to dismantle the air bag unit.
f) Do not connect any form of electrical equipment to any part of the air bag circuit.

Precautions to be taken when storing an air bag unit

a) Store the unit in a cupboard with the air bag upward.
b) Do not expose the air bag to temperatures above 80°C.
c) Do not expose the air bag to flames.
d) Do not attempt to dispose of the air bag - consult a Ford dealer.
e) Never refit an air bag which is known to be faulty or damaged.

27.4 Unscrewing a driver's air bag unit securing screw

De-activation of air bag system

The system must be de-activated as follows, before carrying out any work on the air bag components or surrounding area.
a) Switch off the ignition.
b) Remove the ignition key.
c) Switch off all electrical equipment.
d) Disconnect the battery negative lead, with reference to Chapter 5A.
e) Insulate the battery negative terminal and the end of the battery negative lead to prevent any possibility of contact.
f) Wait for at least two minutes before carrying out any further work.

27 Airbag system components – removal and refitting

Driver's side air bag unit

Warning: Refer to the precautions given in Section 26 before attempting to carry out work on the air bag components.

Removal

1 The air bag unit is an integral part of the steering wheel centre pad.
2 De-activate the air bag system as described in Section 26.
3 Move the steering wheel as necessary for access to the two air bag unit securing screws. The screws are located at the rear of the steering wheel centre pad.

27.11 Release the passenger's side air bag cover securing clips

27.6 Disconnecting the air bag unit wiring connector

4 Remove the two air bag unit securing screws (see illustration).
5 Gently ease the air bag unit from the steering wheel.
6 Lift the air bag unit from the steering wheel, then unclip the air bag wiring harness from the rear of the air bag unit (note the harness routing), and disconnect the wiring connector from the rear of the air bag unit (see illustration).
7 Withdraw the air bag unit, and store it in a safe place, with reference to the precautions given in Section 26.

Refitting

8 Refitting is a reversal of removal, but make sure that the wiring harness is routed as noted before removal, and make sure that the wiring connector is securely reconnected.

Passenger's side air bag unit

Warning: Refer to the precautions given in Section 26 before attempting to carry out work on the air bag components.

Removal

9 De-activate the air bag system as described in Section 26.
10 Carefully prise the passenger's side heating/ventilation nozzle from the facia.
11 Working through the heating/ventilation nozzle housing, release the outer clips securing the air bag cover. If a tool is used to release the clips, ensure that the tool always points towards the centre of the air bag cover, **not** into the facia towards the air bag (see illustration).
12 Work around the edge of the air bag cover, and release the remaining securing clips, then lift the cover from the facia.
13 Unscrew the nut and the Torx screw securing the air bag cover strap to the facia, then withdraw the cover and strap (see illustration).
14 Unscrew the three Torx bolts securing the air bag, then carefully lift the air bag from the facia (see illustration).
15 Disconnect the two wiring connectors from the rear of the air bag, noting the routing of the wiring, then withdraw the air bag from the facia,

27.13 Unscrew the nut and Torx screw securing the air bag cover strap

27.14 Unscrew the three air bag securing bolts (arrowed)

27.15 Disconnect the air bag wiring connectors (arrowed)

27.22 Disconnect the wiring connectors from the rotary switch assembly

and store it in a safe place, with reference to the precautions given in Section 26 **(see illustration)**.

Refitting

16 Refitting is a reversal of removal, bearing in mind the following points.

a) *Make sure that the wiring harness is routed as noted before removal.*

b) *Make sure that the wiring connectors are securely reconnected.*

c) *Make sure that the air bag cover strap is not twisted.*

Electronic control unit

17 In order to remove the air bag electronic control unit, it is necessary to drill an access hole into the facia to reach one of the control unit securing screws. Due to the risk of damage to the control unit during this operation, it is recommended that removal and refitting of the control unit is entrusted to a Ford dealer.

Air bag rotary switch

Removal

18 Disconnect the battery negative lead, with reference to Chapter 5A.

19 Remove the steering column shrouds, with reference to Chapter 11 if necessary.

20 Remove the driver's side air bag unit as described previously in this Section.

21 Remove the steering wheel as described in Chapter 10.

22 Disconnect the wiring connectors from the rotary switch assembly **(see illustration)**.

23 Carefully release the three retaining lugs, then withdraw the rotary switch from the steering column **(see illustration)**.

Refitting

Caution: The rotary switch centralising procedure described in the following paragraphs must be carried out before refitting the assembly. If there is any doubt about the centralisation of the switch, repeat the centralising procedure.

24 Depress the locking pin at the lower left-hand corner of the rotary switch **(see illustration)**.

25 Rotate the inner switch rotor fully anti-clockwise against the outer rotor until tight.

26 Rotate the inner switch rotor approximately 3½ turns clockwise, then release the locking pin. Ensure that the inner rotor is locked in position.

27 Refit the switch using a reversal of the removal procedure, then refit the steering wheel as described in Chapter 10, and refit the driver's side air bag as described previously in this Section.

27.23 Release the three rotary switch assembly retaining lugs (arrowed)

27.24 Depress the locking pin (arrowed) to centralise the rotary switch (viewed with switch fitted to steering wheel)

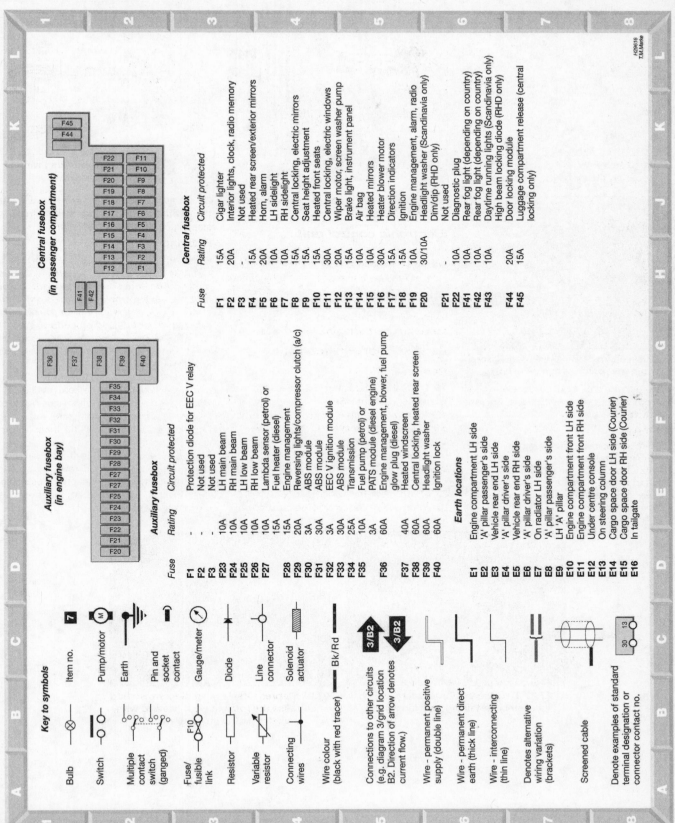

Central fusebox (in passenger compartment)

F45
F44

F22	F11
F21	F10
F20	F9
F19	F8
F18	F7
F17	F6
F16	F5
F15	F4
F14	F3
F13	F2
F12	F1

F41 F42

Auxiliary fusebox (in engine bay)

F36 F37 F38 F39 F40

F35
F34
F33
F32
F31
F30
F29
F28
F27
F27
F25
F24
F23
F22
F21
F20

Central fusebox

Fuse	Rating	Circuit protected
F1	15A	Cigar lighter
F2	20A	Interior lights, clock, radio memory
F3	-	Not used
F4	15A	Heated rear screen/exterior mirrors
F5	20A	Horn, alarm
F6	10A	LH sidelight
F7	10A	RH sidelight
F8	15A	Central locking, electric mirrors
F9	15A	Seat height adjustment
F10	15A	Heated front seats
F11	30A	Central locking, electric windows
F12	20A	Wiper motor, screen washer pump
F13	15A	Brake light, instrument panel
F14	10A	Air bag
F15	10A	Heated mirrors
F16	30A	Heater blower motor
F17	15A	Direction indicators
F18	15A	Ignition
F19	10A	Engine management, alarm, radio
F20	30/10A	Headlight washer (Scandinavia only)
		Dim/dip (RHD only)
F21	-	Not used
F22	10A	Diagnostic plug
F41	10A	Rear fog light (depending on country)
F42	10A	Rear fog light (depending on country)
F43	10A	Daytime running lights (Scandinavia only)
		High beam locking diode (RHD only)
F44	20A	Door locking module
F45	15A	Luggage compartment release (central locking only)

Auxiliary fusebox

Fuse	Rating	Circuit protected
F1	-	Protection diode for EEC V relay
F2	-	Not used
F3	-	Not used
F23	10A	LH main beam
F24	10A	RH main beam
F25	10A	LH low beam
F26	10A	RH low beam
F27	10A	Lambda sensor (petrol) or
		Fuel heater (diesel)
F28	15A	Engine management
F29	20A	Reversing lights/compressor clutch (a/c)
F30	3A	ABS module
F31	30A	ABS module
F32	3A	EEC V ignition module
F33	30A	ABS module
F34	25A	Transmission
F35	10A	Fuel pump (petrol) or
		PATS module (diesel engine)
F36	60A	Engine management, blower, fuel pump
		glow plug (diesel)
F37	40A	Heated windscreen
F38	60A	Central locking, heated rear screen
F39	60A	Headlight washer
F40	60A	Ignition lock

Earth locations

E1	Engine compartment LH side
E2	'A' pillar passenger's side
E3	Vehicle rear end LH side
E4	'A' pillar driver's side
E5	Vehicle rear end RH side
E6	'A' pillar driver's side
E7	On radiator LH side
E8	'A' pillar passenger's side
E9	LH 'A' pillar
E10	Engine compartment front LH side
E11	Engine compartment front RH side
E12	Under centre console
E13	On steering column
E14	Cargo space door LH side (Courier)
E15	Cargo space door RH side (Courier)
E16	In tailgate

Key to symbols

- Bulb
- Switch
- Multiple contact switch (ganged)
- Fuse/fusible link — F10
- Resistor
- Variable resistor
- Connecting wires
- Wire colour (black with red tracer) — Bk/Rd
- Connections to other circuits (e.g. diagram 3/grid location B2. Direction of arrow denotes current flow.) — 3/B2
- Wire – permanent positive supply (double line)
- Wire – permanent direct earth (thick line)
- Wire – interconnecting (thin line)
- Denotes alternative wiring variation (brackets)
- Screened cable
- Denote examples of standard terminal designation or connector contact no. — 30 13
- Item no. — 7
- Pump/motor — M
- Earth
- Pin and socket contact
- Gauge/meter
- Diode
- Line connector
- Solenoid actuator

H29616
T.M.Merrie

Diagram 1 : Information for wiring diagrams

12

Starting, charging, and fuel heater - Diesel

Alternator warning light

4/D5

Auxiliary fusebox

Wire colours

Bk	Black	Og	Orange
Bn	Brown	Rd	Red
Bu	Blue	Sr	Silver
Gn	Green	Vt	Violet
Gy	Grey	Wh	White
Lg	Light green	Ye	Yellow
Pk	Pink	Na	Natural

H29617
T.M.Marks

Anti-theft Central locking module

12

Auxiliary fusebox

Central fusebox

Cigar lighter and clock

Interior illumination

9/H2

11

Central fusebox

Auxiliary fusebox

Horn

Starting and charging - petrol

Auxiliary fusebox

Bk/Bu (manual)

P,R,N,D

Fuel injection ECU

6/G6

Alternator warning light/ heated windscreen

4/D5, 11/E5

Wh/Bu (Bk)

Fuel injection ECU

6/C7

Note, wire colours in brackets denote 1.25/1.4 Zetec models

Key to items

1 Battery
2 Starter motor
3 Alternator
4 Ignition switch
5 Starter inhibitor switch (auto. trans.)
6 Starter relay
7 Fuel heater relay (Diesel)
8 Fuel heater (Diesel)
9 Horn
10 Multifunction switch (part of)
   e = horn switch
11 Cigar lighter
12 Clock

Diagram 2 : Starting, charging, (fuel heater - Diesel), horn, cigar lighter and clock

H29618
T.M.Maña

Engine cooling fan

ABS and TCS

Diesel/fuel injection ECU

5/G3,6/B7

Diesel/fuel injection ECU

5/G3,6/B6

Without A/C

With A/C

Central fusebox

F18

Auxiliary fusebox

Central fusebox

Stop light switch

TCS/ABS warning light

Auxiliary fusebox

Data link connector

Wire colours

Bk	Black	**Og**	Orange
Bn	Brown	**Rd**	Red
Bu	Blue	**Sr**	Silver
Gn	Green	**Vt**	Violet
Gy	Grey	**Wh**	White
Lg	Light green	**Ye**	Yellow
Pk	Pink	**Na**	Natural

Key to items

1   Battery
4   Ignition switch
14 ABS control module
    a = TCS solenoid valve
    b = inlet LH front ABS solenoid valve
    c = outlet LH front ABS solenoid valve
    d = inlet RH front ABS solenoid valve
    e = inlet LH rear ABS solenoid valve
    f = inlet RH rear ABS solenoid valve
    g = outlet RH front ABS solenoid valve
    h = ABS control unit
    i = outlet LH rear ABS solenoid valve
    j = outlet RH rear ABS solenoid valve
    k = ABS pump

15 LH rear wheel sensor
16 LH front wheel sensor
17 RH rear wheel sensor
18 RH front wheel sensor
19 High speed cooling fan relay (with A/C)
20 Cooling fan relay
21 Cooling fan resistor (with A/C)
22 Cooling fan
23 Power hold relay
24 Diode
25 Wheel sensors

Diagram 3 : ABS/TCS and engine cooling fan

12

Diagram 4 : Warning lights and gauges

Key to items

1 Battery
4 Ignition switch
27 Instrument cluster
  a = direction indicator warning light
  b = high beam warning light
  c = instrument illumination
  d = tachometer
  e = airbag warning light
  f = alternator warning light
  g = oil pressure warning light
  h = glow plug warning light (diesel)
  i = fuel gauge
  j = low fuel warning light
  k = low washer fluid warning light
  l = TCS warning light
  m = ABS warning light
  n = temperature gauge
  o = catalyst warning light
  p = door ajar warning light
  q = low brake fluid/handbrake
     warning light
28 Fuel tank unit
  a = fuel pump (fuel injection only)
  b = fuel gauge sender unit
  c = fuel level switch (auxiliary
     warning only)
29 Oil pressure switch
30 Auxiliary warning module
31 Low washer fluid level switch
32 Coolant temperature sender unit
33 Low brake fluid switch
34 Inertia switch
35 Hand brake switch

Wire colours

Bk	Black	**Og**	Orange	
Bn	Brown	**Rd**	Red	
Bu	Blue	**Sr**	Silver	
Gn	Green	**Vt**	Violet	
Gy	Grey	**Wh**	White	
Lg	Light green	**Ye**	Yellow	
Pk	Pink	**Na**	Natural	

H29679
T.M.Marke

Key to items

1 Battery
4 Ignition switch
23 Power hold relay
24 Diode
38 Preglow relay
39 Diesel ECU
40 Engine coolant temperature sensor
41 Barometric absolute pressure sensor
42 EGR valve position sensor
43 Dual pressure switch
44 Idle speed motor
45 Pump unit
  a = partial load advance solenoid
  b = fuel lever variable resistor
  c = cold start solenoid
  d = fuel shut-off solenoid
46 EGR solenoid
47 Crankshaft position sensor
48 Glow plugs

Wire colours

Bk	Black	Og	Orange
Bn	Brown	Rd	Red
Bu	Blue	Sr	Silver
Gn	Green	Vt	Violet
Gy	Grey	Wh	White
Lg	Light green	Ye	Yellow
Pk	Pink	Na	Natural

Diagram 5 : Diesel engine management

Key to items

1 Battery	54 Air flow sensor
4 Ignition switch	55 Crankshaft position sensor
23 Power hold relay	56 Camshaft position sensor
24 Diode	57 Canister purge solenoid valve
50 Fuel injection ECU	58 Idle speed control valve
51 Idle speed control valve	59 Throttle position sensor
52 Vehicle speed sensor	60 Engine coolant temp. sensor
53 Air temp. sensor	61 Power steering pressure switch
62 Clutch pedal switch	66 Dual pressure switch
63 Transmission switch	67 EGR solenoid
64 Fuel pump relay	68 Ignition coil
65 Lambda sensor	69 Fuel injectors

Wire colours

Bk Black	Og Orange		
Bn Brown	Rd Red		
Bu Blue	Sr Silver		
Gn Green	Vt Violet		
Gy Grey	Wh White		
Lg Light green	Ye Yellow		
Pk Pink	Na Natural		

Diagram 6 : Petrol engine management

Note, wire colours in brackets denote 1.25/1.4 Zetec models

H29821 T.M.Marke

Central fusebox
Auxiliary fusebox
Inertia switch
Starter inhibitor switch
Data link connector
Air cond.
Tachometer
Alternator
Cooling fan relay
High speed cooling fan relay
Catalyst warning light

H29622
T.M.Marke

Key to items

1 Battery
4 Ignition switch
72 Dip beam relay
73 Main beam relay
74 Dim/Dip relay 1
75 Dim/Dip relay 2
76 Combination switch (part of)
    d = side/headlight switch
    h = headlight main/dip/flash switch

77 LH headlight assembly
78 RH headlight assembly
79 Headlight levelling switch
80 Main beam blocking diode

Wire colours

Bk	Black	**Og**	Orange
Bn	Brown	**Rd**	Red
Bu	Blue	**Sr**	Silver
Gn	Green	**Vt**	Violet
Gy	Grey	**Wh**	White
Lg	Light green	**Ye**	Yellow
Pk	Pink	**Na**	Natural

Main beam warning light

Central fusebox

Auxiliary fusebox

Diagram 7 : Exterior lighting - headlights and headlight levelling

12

Diagram 8 : Exterior lighting

Wire colours

Bk	Black	Og	Orange
Bn	Brown	Rd	Red
Bu	Blue	Sr	Silver
Gn	Green	Vt	Violet
Gy	Grey	Wh	White
Lg	Light green	Ye	Yellow
Pk	Pink	Na	Natural

Key to items

1	Battery	88	RH number plate light
4	Ignition switch	89	Reversing light switch
5	Starter inhibitor switch (auto. trans.)	90	Stop light switch
76	Combination switch (part of)	91	LH stop and reversing light
	a = hazard warning switch	92	RH stop light
	b = hazard warning indicator	93	Ignition relay
	c = direction indicator switch	94	LH front direction indicator
	d = side/headlight switch	95	LH rear direction indicator
83	LH sidelight	96	LH direction indicator side repeater
84	RH sidelight	97	RH front direction indicator
85	LH tail light	98	RH rear direction indicator
86	RH tail light	99	RH direction indicator side repeater
87	LH number plate light	100	Direction indicator flasher relay

Stop and reversing lights

Side, tail and number plate lights

Direction indicators and hazard warning

Diagram 9 : Exterior lighting continued and interior lighting

Wire colours

Bk	Black	Og	Orange
Bn	Brown	Rd	Red
Bu	Blue	Sr	Silver
Gn	Green	Vt	Violet
Gy	Grey	Wh	White
Lg	Light green	Ye	Yellow
Pk	Pink	Na	Natural

Key to items

1	Battery
4	Ignition switch
76	Combination switch (part of) d = side/headlight switch
103	RH rear foglight
104	Rear foglight switch
105	LH front foglight
106	RH front foglight
107	Front foglight switch
108	Front foglight relay
109	Auxiliary relay
110	Interior light delay relay
111	Link (without delay)
112	Lights on warning buzzer
113	Interior/map reading light
114	Glovebox light
115	Luggage compartment light
116	Tailgate contact plate
117	Gearshift illumination light
118	Driver's door switch
119	Passenger's door switch
120	Driver's rear door switch
121	Passenger's rear door switch

Interior lighting

Front and rear foglights

12

Key to items

1	Battery
4	Ignition switch
76	Combination switch (part of)
	f = front washer switch
	g = rear wash/wipe switch
	j = front wiper switch
93	Ignition relay
124	Rear wiper relay
125	Front wiper switch
126	Rear wiper switch
127	Tailgate contact plate
128	Front/rear washer pump
129	Heater blower motor
130	Heater blower resistors
131	Heater blower switch
132	Sunroof switch
133	Sunroof motor

Wire colours

Bk	Black	Og	Orange
Bn	Brown	Rd	Red
Bu	Blue	Sr	Silver
Gn	Green	Vt	Violet
Gy	Grey	Wh	White
Lg	Light green	Ye	Yellow
Pk	Pink	Na	Natural

Heater blower

Power sunroof

Front and rear wash/wipe

H29625
T.M.Marke

Diagram 10 : Wash/wipe, heater blower and sunroof

Key to items

1	Battery	137	Heated rear window
4	Ignition switch	138	Heated windscreen relay
76	Combination switch (part of)	139	Heated windscreen
	d = side/headlight switch	140	Heated windscreen switch
127	Tailgate contact plate	141	Mirror control switch
135	Heated rear window switch	142	Driver's mirror assembly
136	Heated rear window relay	143	Passenger's mirror assembly

Electric mirrors

Front/rear heated screens

Wire colours

Bk	Black	Og	Orange
Bn	Brown	Rd	Red
Bu	Blue	Sr	Silver
Gn	Green	Vt	Violet
Gy	Grey	Wh	White
Lg	Light green	Ye	Yellow
Pk	Pink	Na	Natural

Diagram 11 : Heated front/rear screens and electric mirrors

H29626
T.M.Marks

12

Wire colours

Bk	Black	Og	Orange
Bn	Brown	Rd	Red
Bu	Blue	Sr	Silver
Gn	Green	Vt	Violet
Gy	Grey	Wh	White
Lg	Light green	Ye	Yellow
Pk	Pink	Na	Natural

Diagram 12 : Electric windows, tailgate release, central locking and radio/cassette

Key to items

1	Battery
4	Ignition switch
93	Ignition relay
145	Driver's window switch
146	Passenger's side window switch
147	Driver's side motor
148	Passenger's side motor
149	Tailgate release switch
150	Tailgate release motor
151	Passenger's door lock motor
152	Passenger's rear door lock motor
153	Driver's door lock
154	Driver's rear door lock
155	Radio/cassette unit
156	LH rear speaker
157	RH rear speaker
158	LH front speaker 1 and 2
158	RH front speaker 1 and 2

H29627
T.M.Merke

Dimensions and Weights

Note: *All figures are approximate, and may vary according to model. Refer to manufacturer's data for exact figures.*

Dimensions

Overall length:
  Hatchback and Van models . . . . 3828 mm
  Courier and Combi models . . . . 4115 mm
Overall width (excluding mirrors):
  Hatchback and Van models . . . . 1634 mm
  Courier and Combi models . . . . 1650 mm
Overall height (unladen):
  Hatchback models . . . . 1334 to 1409 mm
  Van models . . . . 1334 to 1377 mm
  Courier models . . . . 1804 to 1835 mm
  Combi models . . . . 1788 to 1819 mm
Wheelbase . . . . 2700 mm
  Hatchback and Van models . . . . 2446 mm
  Courier and Combi models . . . . 2700 mm

Weights

Kerb weight:
  Hatchback and Van models:
    Petrol models . . . . 1005 to 1159 kg
    Diesel models . . . . 1089 to 1218 kg
  Courier and Combi models:
    Petrol models . . . . 995 to 1215 kg
    Diesel models . . . . 1081 to 1301 kg
Maximum gross vehicle weight:
  Hatchback and Van models:
    Petrol models . . . . 1415 to 1485 kg
    Diesel models . . . . 1510 to 1550 kg
  Courier and Combi models:
    Petrol models . . . . 1310 to 1625 kg
    Diesel models . . . . 1400 to 1715 kg
Maximum towing weights . . . . Refer to your Ford dealer
Maximum trailer nose weight . . . . 50 kg
Maximum roof rack load . . . . 75 kg

Conversion factors

Length (distance)

Inches (in)	x 25.4	= Millimetres (mm)	x 0.0394	=	Inches (in)
Feet (ft)	x 0.305	= Metres (m)	x 3.281	=	Feet (ft)
Miles	x 1.609	= Kilometres (km)	x 0.621	=	Miles

Volume (capacity)

Cubic inches (cu in; in³)	x 16.387	= Cubic centimetres (cc; cm³)	x 0.061	=	Cubic inches (cu in; in³)
Imperial pints (Imp pt)	x 0.568	= Litres (l)	x 1.76	=	Imperial pints (Imp pt)
Imperial quarts (Imp qt)	x 1.137	= Litres (l)	x 0.88	=	Imperial quarts (Imp qt)
Imperial quarts (Imp qt)	x 1.201	= US quarts (US qt)	x 0.833	=	Imperial quarts (Imp qt)
US quarts (US qt)	x 0.946	= Litres (l)	x 1.057	=	US quarts (US qt)
Imperial gallons (Imp gal)	x 4.546	= Litres (l)	x 0.22	=	Imperial gallons (Imp gal)
Imperial gallons (Imp gal)	x 1.201	= US gallons (US gal)	x 0.833	=	Imperial gallons (Imp gal)
US gallons (US gal)	x 3.785	= Litres (l)	x 0.264	=	US gallons (US gal)

Mass (weight)

Ounces (oz)	x 28.35	= Grams (g)	x 0.035	=	Ounces (oz)
Pounds (lb)	x 0.454	= Kilograms (kg)	x 2.205	=	Pounds (lb)

Force

Ounces-force (ozf; oz)	x 0.278	= Newtons (N)	x 3.6	=	Ounces-force (ozf; oz)
Pounds-force (lbf; lb)	x 4.448	= Newtons (N)	x 0.225	=	Pounds-force (lbf; lb)
Newtons (N)	x 0.1	= Kilograms-force (kgf; kg)	x 9.81	=	Newtons (N)

Pressure

Pounds-force per square inch (psi; lbf/in²; lb/in²)	x 0.070	= Kilograms-force per square centimetre (kgf/cm²; kg/cm²)	x 14.223	=	Pounds-force per square inch (psi; lbf/in²; lb/in²)
Pounds-force per square inch (psi; lbf/in²; lb/in²)	x 0.068	= Atmospheres (atm)	x 14.696	=	Pounds-force per square inch (psi; lbf/in²; lb/in²)
Pounds-force per square inch (psi; lbf/in²; lb/in²)	x 0.069	= Bars	x 14.5	=	Pounds-force per square inch (psi; lbf/in²; lb/in²)
Pounds-force per square inch (psi; lbf/in²; lb/in²)	x 6.895	= Kilopascals (kPa)	x 0.145	=	Pounds-force per square inch (psi; lbf/in²; lb/in²)
Kilopascals (kPa)	x 0.01	= Kilograms-force per square centimetre (kgf/cm²; kg/cm²)	x 98.1	=	Kilopascals (kPa)
Millibar (mbar)	x 100	= Pascals (Pa)	x 0.01	=	Millibar (mbar)
Millibar (mbar)	x 0.0145	= Pounds-force per square inch (psi; lbf/in²; lb/in²)	x 68.947	=	Millibar (mbar)
Millibar (mbar)	x 0.75	= Millimetres of mercury (mmHg)	x 1.333	=	Millibar (mbar)
Millibar (mbar)	x 0.401	= Inches of water (inH₂O)	x 2.491	=	Millibar (mbar)
Millimetres of mercury (mmHg)	x 0.535	= Inches of water (inH₂O)	x 1.868	=	Millimetres of mercury (mmHg)
Inches of water (inH₂O)	x 0.036	= Pounds-force per square inch (psi; lbf/in²; lb/in²)	x 27.68	=	Inches of water (inH₂O)

Torque (moment of force)

Pounds-force inches (lbf in; lb in)	x 1.152	= Kilograms-force centimetre (kgf cm; kg cm)	x 0.868	=	Pounds-force inches (lbf in; lb in)
Pounds-force inches (lbf in; lb in)	x 0.113	= Newton metres (Nm)	x 8.85	=	Pounds-force inches (lbf in; lb in)
Pounds-force inches (lbf in; lb in)	x 0.083	= Pounds-force feet (lbf ft; lb ft)	x 12	=	Pounds-force inches (lbf in; lb in)
Pounds-force feet (lbf ft; lb ft)	x 0.138	= Kilograms-force metres (kgf m; kg m)	x 7.233	=	Pounds-force feet (lbf ft; lb ft)
Pounds-force feet (lbf ft; lb ft)	x 1.356	= Newton metres (Nm)	x 0.738	=	Pounds-force feet (lbf ft; lb ft)
Newton metres (Nm)	x 0.102	= Kilograms-force metres (kgf m; kg m)	x 9.804	=	Newton metres (Nm)

Power

Horsepower (hp)	x 745.7	= Watts (W)	x 0.0013	=	Horsepower (hp)

Velocity (speed)

Miles per hour (miles/hr; mph)	x 1.609	= Kilometres per hour (km/hr; kph)	x 0.621	=	Miles per hour (miles/hr; mph)

Fuel consumption*

Miles per gallon (mpg)	x 0.354	= Kilometres per litre (km/l)	x 2.825	=	Miles per gallon (mpg)

Temperature

Degrees Fahrenheit = (°C x 1.8) + 32   Degrees Celsius (Degrees Centigrade; °C) = (°F - 32) x 0.56

It is common practice to convert from miles per gallon (mpg) to litres/100 kilometres (l/100km), where mpg x l/100 km = 282

Spare parts are available from many sources, including maker's appointed garages, accessory shops, and motor factors. To be sure of obtaining the correct parts, it will sometimes be necessary to quote the vehicle identification number. If possible, it can also be useful to take the old parts along for positive identification. Items such as starter motors and alternators may be available under a service exchange scheme - any parts returned should be clean.

Our advice regarding spare parts is as follows.

Officially appointed garages

This is the best source of parts which are peculiar to your car, and which are not otherwise generally available (eg, badges, interior trim, certain body panels, etc). It is also the only place at which you should buy parts if the vehicle is still under warranty.

Accessory shops

These are very good places to buy materials and components needed for the maintenance of your car (oil, air and fuel filters, light bulbs, drivebelts, greases, brake pads, touch-up paint, etc). Components of this nature sold by a reputable shop are usually of the same standard as those used by the car manufacturer.

Besides components, these shops also sell tools and general accessories, usually have convenient opening hours, charge lower prices, and can often be found close to home. Some accessory shops have parts counters where components needed for almost any repair job can be purchased or ordered.

Motor factors

Good factors will stock all the more important components which wear out comparatively quickly, and can sometimes supply individual components needed for the overhaul of a larger assembly (eg, brake seals and hydraulic parts, bearing shells, pistons, valves). They may also handle work such as cylinder block reboring, crankshaft regrinding, etc.

Tyre and exhaust specialists

These outlets may be independent, or members of a local or national chain. They frequently offer competitive prices when compared with a main dealer or local garage, but it will pay to obtain several quotes before making a decision. When researching prices, also ask what "extras" may be added - for instance fitting a new valve and balancing the wheel are both commonly charged on top of the price of a new tyre.

Other sources

Beware of parts or materials obtained from market stalls, car boot sales or similar outlets. Such items are not invariably sub-standard, but there is little chance of compensation if they do prove unsatisfactory. in the case of safety-critical components such as brake pads, there is the risk not only of financial loss, but also of an accident causing injury or death.

Second-hand components or assemblies obtained from a car breaker can be a good buy in some circumstances, but this sort of purchase is best made by the experienced DIY mechanic.

Vehicle Identification

Modifications are a continuing and unpublicised process in vehicle manufacture, quite apart from major model changes. Spare parts manuals and lists are compiled upon a numerical basis, the individual vehicle identification numbers being essential to correct identification of the component concerned.

When ordering spare parts, always give as much information as possible. Quote the car model, year of manufacture and registration, chassis and engine numbers as appropriate.

The *Vehicle Identification Number (VIN)* plate is riveted to the bonnet lock crossmember and is visible once the bonnet has been opened. The vehicle identification (chassis) number is also stamped onto the floor of the passenger compartment, between the right-hand front seat and the door, and also onto the top left-hand corner of the facia assembly. The number on the floor can be viewed by lifting the flap in the carpet and the number on the facia is visible through the windscreen **(see illustrations)**.

The engine number can be found on the front of the cylinder block. On models fitted with the Zetec-SE petrol engine, the number is on the right-hand side whereas on all other models it can be found on the left-hand side of the block

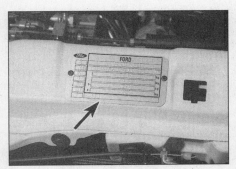

Vehicle identification plate location (arrowed)

VIN number (arrowed) stamped on floor in passenger compartment

VIN number (arrowed) on facia assembly

Whenever servicing, repair or overhaul work is carried out on the car or its components, observe the following procedures and instructions. This will assist in carrying out the operation efficiently and to a professional standard of workmanship.

Joint mating faces and gaskets

When separating components at their mating faces, never insert screwdrivers or similar implements into the joint between the faces in order to prise them apart. This can cause severe damage which results in oil leaks, coolant leaks, etc upon reassembly. Separation is usually achieved by tapping along the joint with a soft-faced hammer in order to break the seal. However, note that this method may not be suitable where dowels are used for component location.

Where a gasket is used between the mating faces of two components, a new one must be fitted on reassembly; fit it dry unless otherwise stated in the repair procedure. Make sure that the mating faces are clean and dry, with all traces of old gasket removed. When cleaning a joint face, use a tool which is unlikely to score or damage the face, and remove any burrs or nicks with an oilstone or fine file.

Make sure that tapped holes are cleaned with a pipe cleaner, and keep them free of jointing compound, if this is being used, unless specifically instructed otherwise.

Ensure that all orifices, channels or pipes are clear, and blow through them, preferably using compressed air.

Oil seals

Oil seals can be removed by levering them out with a wide flat-bladed screwdriver or similar implement. Alternatively, a number of self-tapping screws may be screwed into the seal, and these used as a purchase for pliers or some similar device in order to pull the seal free.

Whenever an oil seal is removed from its working location, either individually or as part of an assembly, it should be renewed.

The very fine sealing lip of the seal is easily damaged, and will not seal if the surface it contacts is not completely clean and free from scratches, nicks or grooves. If the original sealing surface of the component cannot be restored, and the manufacturer has not made provision for slight relocation of the seal relative to the sealing surface, the component should be renewed.

Protect the lips of the seal from any surface which may damage them in the course of fitting. Use tape or a conical sleeve where possible. Lubricate the seal lips with oil before fitting and, on dual-lipped seals, fill the space between the lips with grease.

Unless otherwise stated, oil seals must be fitted with their sealing lips toward the lubricant to be sealed.

Use a tubular drift or block of wood of the appropriate size to install the seal and, if the seal housing is shouldered, drive the seal down to the shoulder. If the seal housing is unshouldered, the seal should be fitted with its face flush with the housing top face (unless otherwise instructed).

Screw threads and fastenings

Seized nuts, bolts and screws are quite a common occurrence where corrosion has set in, and the use of penetrating oil or releasing fluid will often overcome this problem if the offending item is soaked for a while before attempting to release it. The use of an impact driver may also provide a means of releasing such stubborn fastening devices, when used in conjunction with the appropriate screwdriver bit or socket. If none of these methods works, it may be necessary to resort to the careful application of heat, or the use of a hacksaw or nut splitter device.

Studs are usually removed by locking two nuts together on the threaded part, and then using a spanner on the lower nut to unscrew the stud. Studs or bolts which have broken off below the surface of the component in which they are mounted can sometimes be removed using a stud extractor. Always ensure that a blind tapped hole is completely free from oil, grease, water or other fluid before installing the bolt or stud. Failure to do this could cause the housing to crack due to the hydraulic action of the bolt or stud as it is screwed in.

When tightening a castellated nut to accept a split pin, tighten the nut to the specified torque, where applicable, and then tighten further to the next split pin hole. Never slacken the nut to align the split pin hole, unless stated in the repair procedure.

When checking or retightening a nut or bolt to a specified torque setting, slacken the nut or bolt by a quarter of a turn, and then retighten to the specified setting. However, this should not be attempted where angular tightening has been used.

For some screw fastenings, notably cylinder head bolts or nuts, torque wrench settings are no longer specified for the latter stages of tightening, "angle-tightening" being called up instead. Typically, a fairly low torque wrench setting will be applied to the bolts/nuts in the correct sequence, followed by one or more stages of tightening through specified angles.

Locknuts, locktabs and washers

Any fastening which will rotate against a component or housing during tightening should always have a washer between it and the relevant component or housing.

Spring or split washers should always be renewed when they are used to lock a critical component such as a big-end bearing retaining bolt or nut. Locktabs which are folded over to retain a nut or bolt should always be renewed.

Self-locking nuts can be re-used in non-critical areas, providing resistance can be felt when the locking portion passes over the bolt or stud thread. However, it should be noted that self-locking stiffnuts tend to lose their effectiveness after long periods of use, and should then be renewed as a matter of course.

Split pins must always be replaced with new ones of the correct size for the hole.

When thread-locking compound is found on the threads of a fastener which is to be re-used, it should be cleaned off with a wire brush and solvent, and fresh compound applied on reassembly.

Special tools

Some repair procedures in this manual entail the use of special tools such as a press, two or three-legged pullers, spring compressors, etc. Wherever possible, suitable readily-available alternatives to the manufacturer's special tools are described, and are shown in use. In some instances, where no alternative is possible, it has been necessary to resort to the use of a manufacturer's tool, and this has been done for reasons of safety as well as the efficient completion of the repair operation. Unless you are highly-skilled and have a thorough understanding of the procedures described, never attempt to bypass the use of any special tool when the procedure described specifies its use. Not only is there a very great risk of personal injury, but expensive damage could be caused to the components involved.

Environmental considerations

When disposing of used engine oil, brake fluid, antifreeze, etc, give due consideration to any detrimental environmental effects. Do not, for instance, pour any of the above liquids down drains into the general sewage system, or onto the ground to soak away. Many local council refuse tips provide a facility for waste oil disposal, as do some garages. If none of these facilities are available, consult your local Environmental Health Department, or the National Rivers Authority, for further advice.

With the universal tightening-up of legislation regarding the emission of environmentally-harmful substances from motor vehicles, most vehicles have tamperproof devices fitted to the main adjustment points of the fuel system. These devices are primarily designed to prevent unqualified persons from adjusting the fuel/air mixture, with the chance of a consequent increase in toxic emissions. If such devices are found during servicing or overhaul, they should, wherever possible, be renewed or refitted in accordance with the manufacturer's requirements or current legislation.

Note: It is antisocial and illegal to dump oil down the drain. To find the location of your local oil recycling bank, call this number free.

The jack supplied with the vehicle tool kit should only be used for changing the roadwheels - see *"Wheel changing"* at the front of this manual. When carrying out any other kind of work, raise the vehicle using a hydraulic (or "trolley") jack, and always supplement the jack with axle stands positioned under the vehicle jacking points.

To raise the front of the vehicle, position the jack head underneath the reinforced sections of the body, next to the front jacking points for use with the vehicle jack **(see illustration)**. Support the vehicle with axle stands and slotted wooden blocks positioned under the reinforced sections of the body, just inboard of the sill panels.

To raise the rear of the vehicle, position the jack head under the reinforced sections of the sill panels (the same points as used for the wheelchanging jack). Lift the vehicle to the required height and support it on axle stands positioned underneath the rear suspension assembly mounting points.

The jack supplied with the vehicle locates with the jacking points on the sills. Ensure that the jack head is correctly engaged before attempting to raise the vehicle.

Never work under, around, or near a raised vehicle, unless it is adequately supported in at least two places with axle stands.

Jacking points and axle stand locations

A *Jacking points for use with vehicle jack*   B *Jacking points for use with hydraulic jack*   C *Axle stand locations*

Tools and working facilities

Introduction

A selection of good tools is a fundamental requirement for anyone contemplating the maintenance and repair of a motor vehicle. For the owner who does not possess any, their purchase will prove a considerable expense, offsetting some of the savings made by doing-it-yourself. However, provided that the tools purchased meet the relevant national safety standards and are of good quality, they will last for many years and prove an extremely worthwhile investment.

To help the average owner to decide which tools are needed to carry out the various tasks detailed in this manual, we have compiled three lists of tools under the following headings: *Maintenance and minor repair, Repair and overhaul*, and *Special*. Newcomers to practical mechanics should start off with the *Maintenance and minor repair* tool kit, and confine themselves to the simpler jobs around the vehicle. Then, as confidence and experience grow, more difficult tasks can be undertaken, with extra tools being purchased as, and when, they are needed. In this way, a *Maintenance and minor repair* tool kit can be built up into a *Repair and overhaul* tool kit over a considerable period of time, without any major cash outlays. The experienced do-it-yourselfer will have a tool kit good enough for most repair and overhaul procedures, and will add tools from the *Special* category when it is felt that the expense is justified by the amount of use to which these tools will be put.

Maintenance and minor repair tool kit

The tools given in this list should be considered as a minimum requirement if routine maintenance, servicing and minor repair operations are to be undertaken. We recommend the purchase of combination spanners (ring one end, open-ended the other); although more expensive than open-ended ones, they do give the advantages of both types of spanner.

☐ *Combination spanners:*
   Metric - 8 to 19 mm inclusive
☐ *Adjustable spanner - 35 mm jaw (approx.)*
☐ *Spark plug spanner (with rubber insert) - petrol models*
☐ *Spark plug gap adjustment tool - petrol models*
☐ *Set of feeler gauges*
☐ *Brake bleed nipple spanner*
☐ *Screwdrivers:*
   Flat blade - 100 mm long x 6 mm dia
   Cross blade - 100 mm long x 6 mm dia
   Torx - various sizes (not all vehicles)
☐ *Combination pliers*
☐ *Hacksaw (junior)*
☐ *Tyre pump*
☐ *Tyre pressure gauge*
☐ *Oil can*
☐ *Oil filter removal tool*
☐ *Fine emery cloth*
☐ *Wire brush (small)*
☐ *Funnel (medium size)*
☐ *Sump drain plug key (not all vehicles)*

Repair and overhaul tool kit

These tools are virtually essential for anyone undertaking any major repairs to a motor vehicle, and are additional to those given in the *Maintenance and minor repair* list. Included in this list is a comprehensive set of sockets. Although these are expensive, they will be found invaluable as they are so versatile - particularly if various drives are included in the set. We recommend the half-inch square-drive type, as this can be used with most proprietary torque wrenches.

The tools in this list will sometimes need to be supplemented by tools from the *Special* list:

☐ *Sockets (or box spanners) to cover range in previous list (including Torx sockets)*
☐ *Reversible ratchet drive (for use with sockets)*
☐ *Extension piece, 250 mm (for use with sockets)*
☐ *Universal joint (for use with sockets)*
☐ *Flexible handle or sliding T "breaker bar" (for use with sockets)*
☐ *Torque wrench (for use with sockets)*
☐ *Self-locking grips*
☐ *Ball pein hammer*
☐ *Soft-faced mallet (plastic or rubber)*
☐ *Screwdrivers:*
   Flat blade - long & sturdy, short (chubby), and narrow (electrician's) types
   Cross blade – long & sturdy, and short (chubby) types
☐ *Pliers:*
   Long-nosed
   Side cutters (electrician's)
   Circlip (internal and external)
☐ *Cold chisel - 25 mm*
☐ *Scriber*
☐ *Scraper*
☐ *Centre-punch*
☐ *Pin punch*
☐ *Hacksaw*
☐ *Brake hose clamp*
☐ *Brake/clutch bleeding kit*
☐ *Selection of twist drills*
☐ *Steel rule/straight-edge*
☐ *Allen keys (inc. splined/Torx type)*
☐ *Selection of files*
☐ *Wire brush*
☐ *Axle stands*
☐ *Jack (strong trolley or hydraulic type)*
☐ *Light with extension lead*
☐ *Universal electrical multi-meter*

Sockets and reversible ratchet drive

Brake bleeding kit

Torx key, socket and bit

Hose clamp

Angular-tightening gauge

Special tools

The tools in this list are those which are not used regularly, are expensive to buy, or which need to be used in accordance with their manufacturers' instructions. Unless relatively difficult mechanical jobs are undertaken frequently, it will not be economic to buy many of these tools. Where this is the case, you could consider clubbing together with friends (or joining a motorists' club) to make a joint purchase, or borrowing the tools against a deposit from a local garage or tool hire specialist. It is worth noting that many of the larger DIY superstores now carry a large range of special tools for hire at modest rates.

The following list contains only those tools and instruments freely available to the public, and not those special tools produced by the vehicle manufacturer specifically for its dealer network. You will find occasional references to these manufacturers' special tools in the text of this manual. Generally, an alternative method of doing the job without the vehicle manufacturers' special tool is given. However, sometimes there is no alternative to using them. Where this is the case and the relevant tool cannot be bought or borrowed, you will have to entrust the work to a dealer.

- ☐ Angular-tightening gauge
- ☐ Valve spring compressor
- ☐ Valve grinding tool
- ☐ Piston ring compressor
- ☐ Piston ring removal/installation tool
- ☐ Cylinder bore hone
- ☐ Balljoint separator
- ☐ Coil spring compressors (where applicable)
- ☐ Two/three-legged hub and bearing puller
- ☐ Impact screwdriver
- ☐ Micrometer and/or vernier calipers
- ☐ Dial gauge
- ☐ Stroboscopic timing light
- ☐ Dwell angle meter/tachometer
- ☐ Fault code reader
- ☐ Cylinder compression gauge
- ☐ Hand-operated vacuum pump and gauge
- ☐ Clutch plate alignment set
- ☐ Brake shoe steady spring cup removal tool
- ☐ Bush and bearing removal/installation set
- ☐ Stud extractors
- ☐ Tap and die set
- ☐ Lifting tackle
- ☐ Trolley jack

Buying tools

Reputable motor accessory shops and superstores often offer excellent quality tools at discount prices, so it pays to shop around.

Remember, you don't have to buy the most expensive items on the shelf, but it is always advisable to steer clear of the very cheap tools. Beware of 'bargains' offered on market stalls or at car boot sales. There are plenty of good tools around at reasonable prices, but always aim to purchase items which meet the relevant national safety standards. If in doubt, ask the proprietor or manager of the shop for advice before making a purchase.

Care and maintenance of tools

Having purchased a reasonable tool kit, it is necessary to keep the tools in a clean and serviceable condition. After use, always wipe off any dirt, grease and metal particles using a clean, dry cloth, before putting the tools away. Never leave them lying around after they have been used. A simple tool rack on the garage or workshop wall for items such as screwdrivers and pliers is a good idea. Store all normal spanners and sockets in a metal box. Any measuring instruments, gauges, meters, etc, must be carefully stored where they cannot be damaged or become rusty.

Take a little care when tools are used. Hammer heads inevitably become marked, and screwdrivers lose the keen edge on their blades from time to time. A little timely attention with emery cloth or a file will soon restore items like this to a good finish.

Working facilities

Not to be forgotten when discussing tools is the workshop itself. If anything more than routine maintenance is to be carried out, a suitable working area becomes essential.

It is appreciated that many an owner-mechanic is forced by circumstances to remove an engine or similar item without the benefit of a garage or workshop. Having done this, any repairs should always be done under the cover of a roof.

Wherever possible, any dismantling should be done on a clean, flat workbench or table at a suitable working height.

Any workbench needs a vice; one with a jaw opening of 100 mm is suitable for most jobs. As mentioned previously, some clean dry storage space is also required for tools, as well as for any lubricants, cleaning fluids, touch-up paints etc, which become necessary.

Another item which may be required, and which has a much more general usage, is an electric drill with a chuck capacity of at least 8 mm. This, together with a good range of twist drills, is virtually essential for fitting accessories.

Last, but not least, always keep a supply of old newspapers and clean, lint-free rags available, and try to keep any working area as clean as possible.

Micrometers

Dial test indicator ("dial gauge")

Strap wrench

Compression tester

Fault code reader

This is a guide to getting your vehicle through the MOT test. Obviously it will not be possible to examine the vehicle to the same standard as the professional MOT tester. However, working through the following checks will enable you to identify any problem areas before submitting the vehicle for the test.

Where a testable component is in borderline condition, the tester has discretion in deciding whether to pass or fail it. The basis of such discretion is whether the tester would be happy for a close relative or friend to use the vehicle with the component in that condition. If the vehicle presented is clean and evidently well cared for, the tester may be more inclined to pass a borderline component than if the vehicle is scruffy and apparently neglected.

It has only been possible to summarise the test requirements here, based on the regulations in force at the time of printing. Test standards are becoming increasingly stringent, although there are some exemptions for older vehicles.

An assistant will be needed to help carry out some of these checks.

The checks have been sub-divided into four categories, as follows:

1 Checks carried out **FROM THE DRIVER'S SEAT**

2 Checks carried out **WITH THE VEHICLE ON THE GROUND**

3 Checks carried out **WITH THE VEHICLE RAISED AND THE WHEELS FREE TO TURN**

4 Checks carried out on **YOUR VEHICLE'S EXHAUST EMISSION SYSTEM**

1 Checks carried out **FROM THE DRIVER'S SEAT**

Handbrake

☐ Test the operation of the handbrake. Excessive travel (too many clicks) indicates incorrect brake or cable adjustment.
☐ Check that the handbrake cannot be released by tapping the lever sideways. Check the security of the lever mountings.

Footbrake

☐ Depress the brake pedal and check that it does not creep down to the floor, indicating a master cylinder fault. Release the pedal, wait a few seconds, then depress it again. If the pedal travels nearly to the floor before firm resistance is felt, brake adjustment or repair is necessary. If the pedal feels spongy, there is air in the hydraulic system which must be removed by bleeding.

☐ Check that the brake pedal is secure and in good condition. Check also for signs of fluid leaks on the pedal, floor or carpets, which would indicate failed seals in the brake master cylinder.
☐ Check the servo unit (when applicable) by operating the brake pedal several times, then keeping the pedal depressed and starting the engine. As the engine starts, the pedal will move down slightly. If not, the vacuum hose or the servo itself may be faulty.

Steering wheel and column

☐ Examine the steering wheel for fractures or looseness of the hub, spokes or rim.
☐ Move the steering wheel from side to side and then up and down. Check that the steering wheel is not loose on the column, indicating wear or a loose retaining nut. Continue moving the steering wheel as before, but also turn it slightly from left to right.
☐ Check that the steering wheel is not loose on the column, and that there is no abnormal

movement of the steering wheel, indicating wear in the column support bearings or couplings.

Windscreen, mirrors and sunvisor

☐ The windscreen must be free of cracks or other significant damage within the driver's field of view. (Small stone chips are acceptable.) Rear view mirrors must be secure, intact, and capable of being adjusted.

☐ The driver's sunvisor must be capable of being stored in the "up" position.

Seat belts and seats

Note: *The following checks are applicable to all seat belts, front and rear.*

☐ Examine the webbing of all the belts (including rear belts if fitted) for cuts, serious fraying or deterioration. Fasten and unfasten each belt to check the buckles. If applicable, check the retracting mechanism. Check the security of all seat belt mountings accessible from inside the vehicle.

☐ Seat belts with pre-tensioners, once activated, have a "flag" or similar showing on the seat belt stalk. This, in itself, is not a reason for test failure.

☐ The front seats themselves must be securely attached and the backrests must lock in the upright position.

Doors

☐ Both front doors must be able to be opened and closed from outside and inside, and must latch securely when closed.

2 Checks carried out WITH THE VEHICLE ON THE GROUND

Vehicle identification

☐ Number plates must be in good condition, secure and legible, with letters and numbers correctly spaced – spacing at (A) should be at least twice that at (B).

☐ The VIN plate and/or homologation plate must be legible.

Electrical equipment

☐ Switch on the ignition and check the operation of the horn.

☐ Check the windscreen washers and wipers, examining the wiper blades; renew damaged or perished blades. Also check the operation of the stop-lights.

☐ Check the operation of the sidelights and number plate lights. The lenses and reflectors must be secure, clean and undamaged.

☐ Check the operation and alignment of the headlights. The headlight reflectors must not be tarnished and the lenses must be undamaged.

☐ Switch on the ignition and check the operation of the direction indicators (including the instrument panel tell-tale) and the hazard warning lights. Operation of the sidelights and stop-lights must not affect the indicators - if it does, the cause is usually a bad earth at the rear light cluster.

☐ Check the operation of the rear foglight(s), including the warning light on the instrument panel or in the switch.

☐ The ABS warning light must illuminate in accordance with the manufacturers' design. For most vehicles, the ABS warning light should illuminate when the ignition is switched on, and (if the system is operating properly) extinguish after a few seconds. Refer to the owner's handbook.

Footbrake

☐ Examine the master cylinder, brake pipes and servo unit for leaks, loose mountings, corrosion or other damage.

☐ The fluid reservoir must be secure and the fluid level must be between the upper (A) and lower (B) markings.

☐ Inspect both front brake flexible hoses for cracks or deterioration of the rubber. Turn the steering from lock to lock, and ensure that the hoses do not contact the wheel, tyre, or any part of the steering or suspension mechanism. With the brake pedal firmly depressed, check the hoses for bulges or leaks under pressure.

Steering and suspension

☐ Have your assistant turn the steering wheel from side to side slightly, up to the point where the steering gear just begins to transmit this movement to the roadwheels. Check for excessive free play between the steering wheel and the steering gear, indicating wear or insecurity of the steering column joints, the column-to-steering gear coupling, or the steering gear itself.

☐ Have your assistant turn the steering wheel more vigorously in each direction, so that the roadwheels just begin to turn. As this is done, examine all the steering joints, linkages, fittings and attachments. Renew any component that shows signs of wear or damage. On vehicles with power steering, check the security and condition of the steering pump, drivebelt and hoses.

☐ Check that the vehicle is standing level, and at approximately the correct ride height.

Shock absorbers

☐ Depress each corner of the vehicle in turn, then release it. The vehicle should rise and then settle in its normal position. If the vehicle continues to rise and fall, the shock absorber is defective. A shock absorber which has seized will also cause the vehicle to fail.

Exhaust system

☐ Start the engine. With your assistant holding a rag over the tailpipe, check the entire system for leaks. Repair or renew leaking sections.

3 Checks carried out **WITH THE VEHICLE RAISED AND THE WHEELS FREE TO TURN**

Jack up the front and rear of the vehicle, and securely support it on axle stands. Position the stands clear of the suspension assemblies. Ensure that the wheels are clear of the ground and that the steering can be turned from lock to lock.

Steering mechanism

☐ Have your assistant turn the steering from lock to lock. Check that the steering turns smoothly, and that no part of the steering mechanism, including a wheel or tyre, fouls any brake hose or pipe or any part of the body structure.
☐ Examine the steering rack rubber gaiters for damage or insecurity of the retaining clips. If power steering is fitted, check for signs of damage or leakage of the fluid hoses, pipes or connections. Also check for excessive stiffness or binding of the steering, a missing split pin or locking device, or severe corrosion of the body structure within 30 cm of any steering component attachment point.

Front and rear suspension and wheel bearings

☐ Starting at the front right-hand side, grasp the roadwheel at the 3 o'clock and 9 o'clock positions and rock gently but firmly. Check for free play or insecurity at the wheel bearings, suspension balljoints, or suspension mountings, pivots and attachments.
☐ Now grasp the wheel at the 12 o'clock and 6 o'clock positions and repeat the previous inspection. Spin the wheel, and check for roughness or tightness of the front wheel bearing.

☐ If excess free play is suspected at a component pivot point, this can be confirmed by using a large screwdriver or similar tool and levering between the mounting and the component attachment. This will confirm whether the wear is in the pivot bush, its retaining bolt, or in the mounting itself (the bolt holes can often become elongated).

☐ Carry out all the above checks at the other front wheel, and then at both rear wheels.

Springs and shock absorbers

☐ Examine the suspension struts (when applicable) for serious fluid leakage, corrosion, or damage to the casing. Also check the security of the mounting points.
☐ If coil springs are fitted, check that the spring ends locate in their seats, and that the spring is not corroded, cracked or broken.
☐ If leaf springs are fitted, check that all leaves are intact, that the axle is securely attached to each spring, and that there is no deterioration of the spring eye mountings, bushes, and shackles.

☐ The same general checks apply to vehicles fitted with other suspension types, such as torsion bars, hydraulic displacer units, etc. Ensure that all mountings and attachments are secure, that there are no signs of excessive wear, corrosion or damage, and (on hydraulic types) that there are no fluid leaks or damaged pipes.
☐ Inspect the shock absorbers for signs of serious fluid leakage. Check for wear of the mounting bushes or attachments, or damage to the body of the unit.

Driveshafts (fwd vehicles only)

☐ Rotate each front wheel in turn and inspect the constant velocity joint gaiters for splits or damage. Also check that each driveshaft is straight and undamaged.

Braking system

☐ If possible without dismantling, check brake pad wear and disc condition. Ensure that the friction lining material has not worn excessively, (A) and that the discs are not fractured, pitted, scored or badly worn (B).

☐ Examine all the rigid brake pipes underneath the vehicle, and the flexible hose(s) at the rear. Look for corrosion, chafing or insecurity of the pipes, and for signs of bulging under pressure, chafing, splits or deterioration of the flexible hoses.
☐ Look for signs of fluid leaks at the brake calipers or on the brake backplates. Repair or renew leaking components.
☐ Slowly spin each wheel, while your assistant depresses and releases the footbrake. Ensure that each brake is operating and does not bind when the pedal is released.

☐ Examine the handbrake mechanism, checking for frayed or broken cables, excessive corrosion, or wear or insecurity of the linkage. Check that the mechanism works on each relevant wheel, and releases fully, without binding.

☐ It is not possible to test brake efficiency without special equipment, but a road test can be carried out later to check that the vehicle pulls up in a straight line.

Fuel and exhaust systems

☐ Inspect the fuel tank (including the filler cap), fuel pipes, hoses and unions. All components must be secure and free from leaks.

☐ Examine the exhaust system over its entire length, checking for any damaged, broken or missing mountings, security of the retaining clamps and rust or corrosion.

Wheels and tyres

☐ Examine the sidewalls and tread area of each tyre in turn. Check for cuts, tears, lumps, bulges, separation of the tread, and exposure of the ply or cord due to wear or damage. Check that the tyre bead is correctly seated on the wheel rim, that the valve is sound and properly seated, and that the wheel is not distorted or damaged.

☐ Check that the tyres are of the correct size for the vehicle, that they are of the same size and type on each axle, and that the pressures are correct.

☐ Check the tyre tread depth. The legal minimum at the time of writing is 1.6 mm over at least three-quarters of the tread width. Abnormal tread wear may indicate incorrect front wheel alignment.

Body corrosion

☐ Check the condition of the entire vehicle structure for signs of corrosion in load-bearing areas. (These include chassis box sections, side sills, cross-members, pillars, and all suspension, steering, braking system and seat belt mountings and anchorages.) Any corrosion which has seriously reduced the thickness of a load-bearing area is likely to cause the vehicle to fail. In this case professional repairs are likely to be needed.

☐ Damage or corrosion which causes sharp or otherwise dangerous edges to be exposed will also cause the vehicle to fail.

4 Checks carried out on **YOUR VEHICLE'S EXHAUST EMISSION SYSTEM**

Petrol models

☐ Have the engine at normal operating temperature, and make sure that it is in good tune (ignition system in good order, air filter element clean, etc).

☐ Before any measurements are carried out, raise the engine speed to around 2500 rpm, and hold it at this speed for 20 seconds. Allow the engine speed to return to idle, and watch for smoke emissions from the exhaust tailpipe. If the idle speed is obviously much too high, or if dense blue or clearly-visible black smoke comes from the tailpipe for more than 5 seconds, the vehicle will fail. As a rule of thumb, blue smoke signifies oil being burnt (engine wear) while black smoke signifies unburnt fuel (dirty air cleaner element, or other carburettor or fuel system fault).

☐ An exhaust gas analyser capable of measuring carbon monoxide (CO) and hydrocarbons (HC) is now needed. If such an instrument cannot be hired or borrowed, a local garage may agree to perform the check for a small fee.

CO emissions (mixture)

☐ At the time of writing, for vehicles first used between 1st August 1975 and 31st July 1986 (P to C registration), the CO level must not exceed 4.5% by volume. For vehicles first used between 1st August 1986 and 31st July 1992 (D to J registration), the CO level must not exceed 3.5% by volume. Vehicles first used after 1st August 1992 (K registration) must conform to the manufacturer's specification. The MOT tester has access to a DOT database or emissions handbook, which lists the CO and HC limits for each make and model of vehicle. The CO level is measured with the engine at idle speed, and at "fast idle". The following limits are given as a general guide:

At idle speed -
   CO level no more than 0.5%
At "fast idle" (2500 to 3000 rpm) -
   CO level no more than 0.3%
   (Minimum oil temperature 60°C)

☐ If the CO level cannot be reduced far enough to pass the test (and the fuel and ignition systems are otherwise in good condition) then the carburettor is badly worn, or there is some problem in the fuel injection system or catalytic converter (as applicable).

HC emissions

☐ With the CO within limits, HC emissions for vehicles first used between 1st August 1975 and 31st July 1992 (P to J registration) must not exceed 1200 ppm. Vehicles first used after 1st August 1992 (K registration) must conform to the manufacturer's specification. The MOT tester has access to a DOT database or emissions handbook, which lists the CO and HC limits for each make and model of vehicle. The HC level is measured with the engine at "fast idle". The following is given as a general guide:

At "fast idle" (2500 to 3000 rpm) -
   HC level no more than 200 ppm
   (Minimum oil temperature 60°C)

☐ Excessive HC emissions are caused by incomplete combustion, the causes of which can include oil being burnt, mechanical wear and ignition/fuel system malfunction.

Diesel models

☐ The only emission test applicable to Diesel engines is the measuring of exhaust smoke density. The test involves accelerating the engine several times to its maximum unloaded speed.

Note: *It is of the utmost importance that the engine timing belt is in good condition before the test is carried out.*

☐ The limits for Diesel engine exhaust smoke, introduced in September 1995 are:
Vehicles first used before 1st August 1979:
   Exempt from metered smoke testing, but must not emit "dense blue or clearly visible black smoke for a period of more than 5 seconds at idle" or "dense blue or clearly visible black smoke during acceleration which would obscure the view of other road users".
Non-turbocharged vehicles first used after
   1st August 1979: 2.5m^{-1}
Turbocharged vehicles first used after
   1st August 1979: 3.0m^{-1}

☐ Excessive smoke can be caused by a dirty air cleaner element. Otherwise, professional advice may be needed to find the cause.

Engine

- [ ] Engine fails to rotate when attempting to start
- [ ] Engine rotates, but will not start
- [ ] Engine difficult to start when cold
- [ ] Engine difficult to start when hot
- [ ] Starter motor noisy or excessively-rough in engagement
- [ ] Engine starts, but stops immediately
- [ ] Engine idles erratically
- [ ] Engine misfires at idle speed
- [ ] Engine misfires throughout the driving speed range
- [ ] Engine hesitates on acceleration
- [ ] Engine stalls
- [ ] Engine lacks power
- [ ] Engine backfires
- [ ] Oil pressure warning light illuminated with engine running
- [ ] Engine runs-on after switching off
- [ ] Engine noises

Cooling system

- [ ] Overheating
- [ ] Overcooling
- [ ] External coolant leakage
- [ ] Internal coolant leakage
- [ ] Corrosion

Fuel and exhaust systems

- [ ] Excessive fuel consumption
- [ ] Fuel leakage and/or fuel odour
- [ ] Excessive noise or fumes from exhaust system

Clutch

- [ ] Pedal travels to floor - no pressure or very little resistance
- [ ] Clutch fails to disengage (unable to select gears).
- [ ] Clutch slips (engine speed increases, with no increase in vehicle speed).
- [ ] Judder as clutch is engaged
- [ ] Noise when depressing or releasing clutch pedal

Manual transmission

- [ ] Noisy in neutral with engine running
- [ ] Noisy in one particular gear
- [ ] Difficulty engaging gears
- [ ] Jumps out of gear
- [ ] Vibration
- [ ] Lubricant leaks

Automatic transmission

- [ ] Fluid leakage
- [ ] Transmission fluid brown, or has burned smell
- [ ] General gear selection problems
- [ ] Transmission will not downshift (kickdown) with accelerator pedal fully depressed
- [ ] Engine will not start in any gear, or starts in gears other than Park or Neutral
- [ ] Transmission slips, shifts roughly, is noisy, or has no drive in forward or reverse gears

Driveshafts

- [ ] Vibration when accelerating or decelerating
- [ ] Clicking or knocking noise on turns (at slow speed on full-lock)

Braking system

- [ ] Vehicle pulls to one side under braking
- [ ] Noise (grinding or high-pitched squeal) when brakes applied
- [ ] Excessive brake pedal travel
- [ ] Brake pedal feels spongy when depressed
- [ ] Excessive brake pedal effort required to stop vehicle
- [ ] Judder felt through brake pedal or steering wheel when braking
- [ ] Brakes binding
- [ ] Rear wheels locking under normal braking

Suspension and steering

- [ ] Vehicle pulls to one side
- [ ] Wheel wobble and vibration
- [ ] Excessive pitching and/or rolling around corners, or during braking
- [ ] Wandering or general instability
- [ ] Excessively-stiff steering
- [ ] Excessive play in steering
- [ ] Lack of power assistance
- [ ] Tyre wear excessive

Electrical system

- [ ] Battery will not hold a charge for more than a few days
- [ ] Ignition/no-charge warning light remains illuminated with engine running
- [ ] Ignition/no-charge warning light fails to come on
- [ ] Lights inoperative
- [ ] Instrument readings inaccurate or erratic
- [ ] Horn inoperative, or unsatisfactory in operation
- [ ] Windscreen wipers inoperative, or unsatisfactory in operation
- [ ] Windscreen washers inoperative, or unsatisfactory in operation
- [ ] Electric windows inoperative, or unsatisfactory in operation
- [ ] Central locking system inoperative, or unsatisfactory in operation

Introduction

The vehicle owner who does his or her own maintenance according to the recommended service schedules should not have to use this section of the manual very often. Modern component reliability is such that, provided those items subject to wear or deterioration are inspected or renewed at the specified intervals, sudden failure is comparatively rare. Faults do not usually just happen as a result of sudden failure, but develop over a period of time. Major mechanical failures in particular are usually preceded by characteristic symptoms over hundreds or even thousands of miles. Those components which do occasionally fail without warning are often small and easily carried in the vehicle.

With any fault-finding, the first step is to decide where to begin investigations. Sometimes this is obvious, but on other occasions, a little detective work will be necessary. The owner who makes half a dozen haphazard adjustments or replacements may be successful in curing a fault (or its symptoms), but will be none the wiser if the fault recurs, and ultimately may have spent more time and money than was necessary. A calm and logical approach will be found to be more satisfactory in the long run. Always take into account any warning signs or abnormalities that may have been noticed in the period preceding the fault - power loss, high or low gauge readings, unusual smells, etc - and remember that failure of components such as fuses or spark plugs may only be pointers to some underlying fault.

The pages which follow provide an easy-reference guide to the more common problems which may occur during the operation of the vehicle. These problems and their possible causes are grouped under headings denoting various components or systems, such as Engine, Cooling system, etc. The Chapter and/or Section which deals with the problem is also shown in brackets.

Whatever the fault, certain basic principles apply. These are as follows:

Verify the fault. This is simply a matter of being sure that you know what the symptoms are before starting work. This is particularly important if you are investigating a fault for someone else, who may not have described it very accurately.

Don't overlook the obvious. For example, if the vehicle won't start, is there fuel in the tank? (Don't take anyone else's word on this particular point, and don't trust the fuel gauge either!) If an electrical fault is indicated, look for loose or broken wires before digging out the test gear.

Cure the disease, not the symptom. Substituting a flat battery with a fully-charged one will get you off the hard shoulder, but if the underlying cause is not attended to, the new battery will go the same way. Similarly, changing oil-fouled spark plugs for a new set will get you moving again, but remember that the reason for the fouling (if it wasn't simply an incorrect grade of plug) will have to be established and corrected.

Don't take anything for granted. Particularly, don't forget that a "new" component may itself be defective (especially if it's been rattling around in the boot for months), and don't leave components out of a fault diagnosis sequence just because they are new or recently-fitted. When you do finally diagnose a difficult fault, you'll probably realise that all the evidence was there from the start.

Engine

Engine fails to rotate when attempting to start

☐ Battery terminal connections loose or corroded (see *"Weekly checks"*)
☐ Battery discharged or faulty (Chapter 5A)
☐ Broken, loose or disconnected wiring in the starting circuit (Chapter 5A)
☐ Defective starter solenoid or switch (Chapter 5A)
☐ Defective starter motor (Chapter 5A)
☐ Starter pinion or flywheel ring gear teeth loose or broken (Chapters 2 and 5A)
☐ Engine earth strap broken or disconnected (Chapter 5A)

Engine rotates, but will not start

☐ Fuel cut-off switch energised (Chapter 4A).
☐ Fuel tank empty
☐ Battery discharged (engine rotates slowly) (Chapter 5A)
☐ Battery terminal connections loose or corroded (see *"Weekly checks"*)
☐ Ignition components damp or damaged - petrol models (Chapters 1 and 5B)
☐ Broken, loose or disconnected wiring in the ignition circuit - petrol models (Chapters 1A and 5B)
☐ Worn, faulty or incorrectly-gapped spark plugs - petrol models (Chapter 1A)
☐ Preheating system faulty - diesel models (Chapter 5C)
☐ Fuel injection system fault - petrol models (Chapter 4A)
☐ Stop solenoid faulty - diesel models (Chapter 4B)
☐ Air in fuel system - diesel models (Chapter 4B)
☐ Major mechanical failure (eg camshaft drive) (Chapter 2)

Engine difficult to start when cold

☐ Battery discharged (Chapter 5A)
☐ Battery terminal connections loose or corroded (see *"Weekly checks"*)
☐ Worn, faulty or incorrectly-gapped spark plugs - petrol models (Chapter 1A)
☐ Preheating system faulty - diesel models (Chapter 5C)
☐ Fuel injection system fault - petrol models (Chapter 4A)
☐ Other ignition system fault - petrol models (Chapters 1A and 5B)
☐ Low cylinder compressions (Chapter 2)

Engine difficult to start when hot

☐ Air filter element dirty or clogged (Chapter 1)
☐ Fuel injection system fault - petrol models (Chapter 4A)
☐ Low cylinder compressions (Chapter 2)

Starter motor noisy or excessively-rough in engagement

☐ Starter pinion or flywheel ring gear teeth loose or broken (Chapters 2 and 5A)
☐ Starter motor mounting bolts loose or missing (Chapter 5A)
☐ Starter motor internal components worn or damaged (Chapter 5A)

Engine starts, but stops immediately

☐ Loose or faulty electrical connections in the ignition circuit - petrol models (Chapters 1A and 5B)
☐ Vacuum leak at the throttle body or inlet manifold - petrol models (Chapter 4A)
☐ Blocked injector/fuel injection system fault - petrol models (Chapter 4A)

Engine idles erratically

☐ Air filter element clogged (Chapter 1)
☐ Vacuum leak at the throttle body, inlet manifold or associated hoses - petrol models (Chapter 4A)
☐ Worn, faulty or incorrectly-gapped spark plugs - petrol models (Chapter 1A)
☐ Uneven or low cylinder compressions (Chapter 2)
☐ Camshaft lobes worn (Chapter 2)
☐ Timing belt/chain incorrectly fitted (Chapter 2)
☐ Blocked injector/fuel injection system fault - petrol models (Chapter 4A)
☐ Faulty injector(s) - diesel models (Chapter 4B)

Engine misfires at idle speed

☐ Worn, faulty or incorrectly-gapped spark plugs - petrol models (Chapter 1A)
☐ Faulty spark plug HT leads (where fitted) - petrol models (Chapter 1A)
☐ Vacuum leak at the throttle body, inlet manifold or associated hoses - petrol models (Chapter 4A)
☐ Blocked injector/fuel injection system fault - petrol models (Chapter 4A)
☐ Faulty injector(s) - diesel models (Chapter 4B)
☐ Uneven or low cylinder compressions (Chapter 2)
☐ Disconnected, leaking, or perished crankcase ventilation hoses (Chapter 4C)

Engine misfires throughout the driving speed range

☐ Fuel filter choked (Chapter 1)
☐ Fuel pump faulty, or delivery pressure low (Chapter 4)
☐ Fuel tank vent blocked, or fuel pipes restricted (Chapter 4)
☐ Vacuum leak at the throttle body, inlet manifold or associated hoses - petrol models (Chapter 4A)
☐ Worn, faulty or incorrectly-gapped spark plugs - petrol models (Chapter 1A)
☐ Faulty spark plug HT leads (where fitted) - petrol models (Chapter 1A)
☐ Faulty injector(s) - diesel models (Chapter 4B)
☐ Faulty ignition coil - petrol models (Chapter 5A)
☐ Uneven or low cylinder compressions (Chapter 2)
☐ Blocked injector/fuel injection system fault - petrol models (Chapter 4A)

Engine (continued)

Engine hesitates on acceleration

- [ ] Worn, faulty or incorrectly-gapped spark plugs - petrol models (Chapter 1A)
- [ ] Vacuum leak at the throttle body, inlet manifold or associated hoses (Chapter 4)
- [ ] Blocked injector/fuel injection system fault - petrol models (Chapter 4A)
- [ ] Faulty injector(s) - diesel models (Chapter 4B)

Engine stalls

- [ ] Vacuum leak at the throttle body, inlet manifold or associated hoses - petrol models (Chapter 4A)
- [ ] Fuel filter choked (Chapter 1)
- [ ] Fuel pump faulty, or delivery pressure low - petrol models (Chapter 4A)
- [ ] Fuel tank vent blocked, or fuel pipes restricted (Chapter 4)
- [ ] Blocked injector/fuel injection system fault - petrol models (Chapter 4A)
- [ ] Faulty injector(s) - diesel models (Chapter 4B)

Engine lacks power

- [ ] Timing belt/chain incorrectly fitted (Chapter 2)
- [ ] Fuel filter choked (Chapter 1)
- [ ] Fuel pump faulty, or delivery pressure low (Chapter 4)
- [ ] Uneven or low cylinder compressions (Chapter 2)
- [ ] Worn, faulty or incorrectly-gapped spark plugs - petrol models (Chapter 1A)
- [ ] Vacuum leak at the throttle body, inlet manifold or associated hoses - petrol models (Chapter 4A)
- [ ] Blocked injector/fuel injection system fault - petrol models (Chapter 4A)
- [ ] Faulty injector(s) - diesel models (Chapter 4B)
- [ ] Injection pump timing incorrect - diesel models (Chapter 4B)
- [ ] Brakes binding (Chapters 1 and 9)
- [ ] Clutch slipping (Chapter 6)

Engine backfires

- [ ] Timing belt incorrectly fitted (Chapter 2)
- [ ] Vacuum leak at the throttle body, inlet manifold or associated hoses - petrol models (Chapter 4A)
- [ ] Blocked injector/fuel injection system fault - petrol models (Chapter 4A)

Oil pressure warning light illuminated with engine running

- [ ] Low oil level, or incorrect oil grade (see "Weekly checks")

- [ ] Faulty oil pressure sensor (Chapter 5A)
- [ ] Worn engine bearings and/or oil pump (Chapter 2)
- [ ] High engine operating temperature (Chapter 3)
- [ ] Oil pressure relief valve defective (Chapter 2)
- [ ] Oil pick-up strainer clogged (Chapter 2)

Engine runs-on after switching off

- [ ] Excessive carbon build-up in engine (Chapter 2)
- [ ] High engine operating temperature (Chapter 3)
- [ ] Fuel injection system fault - petrol models (Chapter 4A)
- [ ] Faulty stop solenoid - diesel models (Chapter 4B)

Engine noises

Pre-ignition (pinking) or knocking during acceleration or under load

- [ ] Ignition timing incorrect/ignition system fault - petrol models (Chapters 1A and 5A)
- [ ] Incorrect grade of spark plug - petrol models (Chapter 1A)
- [ ] Incorrect grade of fuel (Chapter 4)
- [ ] Vacuum leak at the throttle body, inlet manifold or associated hoses - petrol models (Chapter 4A)
- [ ] Excessive carbon build-up in engine (Chapter 2)
- [ ] Blocked injector/fuel injection system fault - petrol models (Chapter 4A)

Whistling or wheezing noises

- [ ] Leaking inlet manifold or throttle body gasket - petrol models (Chapter 4A)
- [ ] Leaking exhaust manifold gasket or pipe-to-manifold joint (Chapter 4)
- [ ] Leaking vacuum hose (Chapters 4, 5 and 9)
- [ ] Blowing cylinder head gasket (Chapter 2)

Tapping or rattling noises

- [ ] Worn valve gear or camshaft (Chapter 2)
- [ ] Ancillary component fault (coolant pump, alternator, etc) (Chapters 3, 5, etc)

Knocking or thumping noises

- [ ] Worn big-end bearings (regular heavy knocking, perhaps less under load) (Chapter 2)
- [ ] Worn main bearings (rumbling and knocking, perhaps worsening under load) (Chapter 2)
- [ ] Piston slap (most noticeable when cold) (Chapter 2)
- [ ] Ancillary component fault (coolant pump, alternator, etc) (Chapters 3, 5A, etc)

Cooling system

Overheating

- [ ] Insufficient coolant in system (see "Weekly checks")
- [ ] Thermostat faulty (Chapter 3)
- [ ] Radiator core blocked, or grille restricted (Chapter 3)
- [ ] Cooling fan faulty (Chapter 3)
- [ ] Inaccurate temperature gauge sender unit (Chapter 3)
- [ ] Airlock in cooling system (Chapter 3)
- [ ] Pressure cap faulty (Chapter 3)

Overcooling

- [ ] Thermostat faulty (Chapter 3)
- [ ] Inaccurate temperature gauge sender unit (Chapter 3)
- [ ] Cooling fan faulty (Chapter 3)

External coolant leakage

- [ ] Deteriorated or damaged hoses or hose clips (Chapter 1)

- [ ] Radiator core or heater matrix leaking (Chapter 3)
- [ ] Pressure cap faulty (Chapter 3)
- [ ] Coolant pump internal seal leaking (Chapter 3)
- [ ] Coolant pump-to-block seal leaking (Chapter 3)
- [ ] Boiling due to overheating (Chapter 3)
- [ ] Core plug leaking (Chapter 2)

Internal coolant leakage

- [ ] Leaking cylinder head gasket (Chapter 2)
- [ ] Cracked cylinder head or cylinder block (Chapter 2)

Corrosion

- [ ] Infrequent draining and flushing (Chapter 1)
- [ ] Incorrect coolant mixture or inappropriate coolant type (see "Weekly checks")

Fuel and exhaust systems

Excessive fuel consumption
- [ ] Air filter element dirty or clogged (Chapter 1)
- [ ] Fuel injection system fault - petrol models (Chapter 4A)
- [ ] Faulty injector(s) - diesel models (Chapter 4B)
- [ ] Ignition timing incorrect/ignition system fault - petrol models (Chapters 1A and 5A)
- [ ] Tyres under-inflated (see *"Weekly checks"*)

Fuel leakage and/or fuel odour
- [ ] Damaged or corroded fuel tank, pipes or connections (Chapter 4)

Excessive noise or fumes from exhaust system
- [ ] Leaking exhaust system or manifold joints (Chapters 1 and 4)
- [ ] Leaking, corroded or damaged silencers or pipe (Chapters 1 and 4)
- [ ] Broken mountings causing body or suspension contact (Chapter 1)

Clutch

Pedal travels to floor - no pressure or very little resistance
- [ ] Air in hydraulic system/faulty master or slave cylinder (Chapter 6)
- [ ] Faulty hydraulic release system (Chapter 6)
- [ ] Broken clutch release bearing or fork (Chapter 6)
- [ ] Broken diaphragm spring in clutch pressure plate (Chapter 6)

Clutch fails to disengage (unable to select gears)
- [ ] Air in hydraulic system/faulty master or slave cylinder (Chapter 6)
- [ ] Faulty hydraulic release system (Chapter 6)
- [ ] Clutch disc sticking on gearbox input shaft splines (Chapter 6)
- [ ] Clutch disc sticking to flywheel or pressure plate (Chapter 6)
- [ ] Faulty pressure plate assembly (Chapter 6)
- [ ] Clutch release mechanism worn or incorrectly assembled (Chapter 6)

Clutch slips (engine speed increases, with no increase in vehicle speed)
- [ ] Faulty hydraulic release system (Chapter 6)
- [ ] Clutch disc linings excessively worn (Chapter 6)
- [ ] Clutch disc linings contaminated with oil or grease (Chapter 6)
- [ ] Faulty pressure plate or weak diaphragm spring (Chapter 6)

Judder as clutch is engaged
- [ ] Clutch disc linings contaminated with oil or grease (Chapter 6)
- [ ] Clutch disc linings excessively worn (Chapter 6)
- [ ] Faulty or distorted pressure plate or diaphragm spring (Chapter 6).
- [ ] Worn or loose engine or gearbox mountings (Chapter 2)
- [ ] Clutch disc hub or gearbox input shaft splines worn (Chapter 6)

Noise when depressing or releasing clutch pedal
- [ ] Worn clutch release bearing (Chapter 6)
- [ ] Worn or dry clutch pedal bushes (Chapter 6)
- [ ] Faulty pressure plate assembly (Chapter 6)
- [ ] Pressure plate diaphragm spring broken (Chapter 6)
- [ ] Broken clutch disc cushioning springs (Chapter 6)

Manual transmission

Noisy in neutral with engine running
- [ ] Input shaft bearings worn (noise apparent with clutch pedal released, but not when depressed) (Chapter 7A)*
- [ ] Clutch release bearing worn (noise apparent with clutch pedal depressed, possibly less when released) (Chapter 6)

Noisy in one particular gear
- [ ] Worn, damaged or chipped gear teeth (Chapter 7A)*

Difficulty engaging gears
- [ ] Clutch fault (Chapter 6)
- [ ] Worn or damaged gearchange linkage/cable (Chapter 7A)
- [ ] Worn synchroniser units (Chapter 7A)*

Jumps out of gear
- [ ] Worn or damaged gearchange linkage/cable (Chapter 7A)

- [ ] Worn synchroniser units (Chapter 7A)*
- [ ] Worn selector forks (Chapter 7A)*

Vibration
- [ ] Lack of oil (Chapter 1)
- [ ] Worn bearings (Chapter 7A)*

Lubricant leaks
- [ ] Leaking differential output oil seal (Chapter 7A)
- [ ] Leaking housing joint (Chapter 7A)*
- [ ] Leaking input shaft oil seal (Chapter 7A)*

Although the corrective action necessary to remedy the symptoms described is beyond the scope of the home mechanic, the above information should be helpful in isolating the cause of the condition, so that the owner can communicate clearly with a professional mechanic.

Automatic transmission

Note: *Due to the complexity of the automatic transmission, it is difficult for the home mechanic to properly diagnose and service this unit. For problems other than the following, the vehicle should be taken to a dealer service department or automatic transmission specialist. Do not be too hasty in removing the transmission if a fault is suspected, as most of the testing is carried out with the unit still fitted.*

Fluid leakage

☐ Automatic transmission fluid is usually dark in colour. Fluid leaks should not be confused with engine oil, which can easily be blown onto the transmission by airflow.
☐ To determine the source of a leak, first remove all built-up dirt and grime from the transmission housing and surrounding areas using a degreasing agent, or by steam-cleaning. Drive the vehicle at low speed, so airflow will not blow the leak far from its source. Raise and support the vehicle, and determine where the leak is coming from. The following are common areas of leakage:
a) Oil pan (Chapter 1A and 7B)
b) Dipstick tube (Chapter 1A and 7B)
c) Transmission-to-fluid cooler unions (Chapter 7B)

Transmission fluid brown, or has burned smell

☐ Transmission fluid level low (Chapter 1A)

General gear selection problems

☐ Chapter 7B deals with checking the selector cable on automatic transmissions. The following are common problems which may be caused by a faulty cable:
a) Engine starting in gears other than Park or Neutral.
b) Indicator panel indicating a gear other than the one actually being used.
c) Vehicle moves when in Park or Neutral.
d) Poor gear shift quality or erratic gear changes.

Engine will not start in any gear, or starts in gears other than Park or Neutral

☐ Incorrect starter/inhibitor (multi-function) switch adjustment (Chapter 7B)
☐ Incorrect selector cable adjustment (Chapter 7B)

Transmission slips, shifts roughly, is noisy, or has no drive in forward or reverse gears

☐ There are many probable causes for the above problems, but the home mechanic should be concerned with only one possibility - fluid level. Before taking the vehicle to a dealer or transmission specialist, check the fluid level and condition of the fluid as described in Chapter 1A. Correct the fluid level as necessary, or change the fluid if needed. If the problem persists, professional help will be necessary.

Driveshafts

Vibration when accelerating or decelerating

☐ Worn inner constant velocity joint (Chapter 8)
☐ Bent or distorted driveshaft (Chapter 8)
☐ Worn intermediate bearing (Chapter 8)

Clicking or knocking noise on turns (at slow speed on full-lock)

☐ Worn outer constant velocity joint (Chapter 8)
☐ Lack of constant velocity joint lubricant, possibly due to damaged gaiter (Chapter 8)
☐ Worn intermediate bearing (Chapter 8)

Braking system

Note: *Before assuming that a brake problem exists, make sure that the tyres are in good condition and correctly inflated, that the front wheel alignment is correct, and that the vehicle is not loaded with weight in an unequal manner. Apart from checking the condition of all pipe and hose connections, any faults occurring on the anti-lock braking system should be referred to a Ford dealer for diagnosis.*

Vehicle pulls to one side under braking

☐ Worn, defective, damaged or contaminated brake pads/shoes on one side (Chapters 1 and 9)
☐ Seized or partially-seized brake caliper piston/wheel cylinder (Chapters 1 and 9)
☐ A mixture of brake pad/shoe lining materials fitted between sides (Chapters 1 and 9)
☐ Brake caliper/backplate mounting bolts loose (Chapter 9)
☐ Worn or damaged steering or suspension components (Chapters 1 and 10)

Noise (grinding or high-pitched squeal) when brakes applied

☐ Brake pad/shoe friction lining material worn down to metal backing (Chapters 1 and 9)
☐ Excessive corrosion of brake disc/drum (may be apparent after the vehicle has been standing for some time (Chapters 1 and 9)
☐ Foreign object (stone chipping, etc) trapped between brake disc and shield (Chapters 1 and 9)

Excessive brake pedal travel

☐ Faulty master cylinder (Chapter 9)
☐ Air in hydraulic system (Chapters 1 and 9)
☐ Faulty vacuum servo unit (Chapter 9)

Brake pedal feels spongy when depressed

☐ Air in hydraulic system (Chapters 1 and 9)
☐ Deteriorated flexible rubber brake hoses (Chapters 1 and 9)
☐ Master cylinder mounting nuts loose (Chapter 9)
☐ Faulty master cylinder (Chapter 9)

Excessive brake pedal effort required to stop vehicle

☐ Faulty vacuum servo unit (Chapter 9)
☐ Disconnected, damaged or insecure brake servo vacuum hose (Chapter 9)
☐ Primary or secondary hydraulic circuit failure (Chapter 9)
☐ Seized brake caliper/wheel cylinder piston (Chapter 9)
☐ Brake pads/shoes incorrectly fitted (Chapters 1 and 9)
☐ Incorrect grade of brake pads/shoes fitted (Chapters 1 and 9)
☐ Brake pad/shoe linings contaminated (Chapters 1 and 9)
☐ Faulty vacuum pump - diesel models (Chapter 9)

Judder felt through brake pedal or steering wheel when braking

☐ Excessive run-out or distortion of discs/drums (Chapters 1 and 9)
☐ Brake pad/shoe linings worn (Chapters 1 and 9)
☐ Brake caliper/backplate mounting bolts loose (Chapter 9)
☐ Wear in suspension or steering components or mountings (Chapters 1 and 10)

Brakes binding

☐ Seized brake caliper/wheel cylinder piston (Chapter 9)
☐ Incorrectly-adjusted handbrake mechanism (Chapter 9)
☐ Faulty master cylinder (Chapter 9)

Rear wheels locking under normal braking

☐ Rear brake shoe linings contaminated (Chapters 1 and 9)
☐ Rear brake drums warped (Chapters 1 and 9)

Suspension and steering

Note: *Before diagnosing suspension or steering faults, be sure that the trouble is not due to incorrect tyre pressures, mixtures of tyre types, or binding brakes.*

Vehicle pulls to one side

☐ Defective tyre (see *"Weekly checks"*)
☐ Excessive wear in suspension or steering components (Chapters 1 and 10)
☐ Incorrect front wheel alignment (Chapter 10)
☐ Accident damage to steering or suspension components (Chapter 1)

Wheel wobble and vibration

☐ Front roadwheels out of balance (vibration felt mainly through the steering wheel) (Chapters 1 and 10)
☐ Rear roadwheels out of balance (vibration felt throughout the vehicle) (see *"Weekly checks"* and Chapter 10)
☐ Roadwheels damaged or distorted (Chapters 1 and 10)
☐ Faulty or damaged tyre (see *"Weekly checks"*)
☐ Worn steering or suspension joints, bushes or components (Chapters 1 and 10)
☐ Wheel bolts loose (Chapters 1 and 10)

Excessive pitching and/or rolling around corners, or during braking

☐ Defective shock absorbers (Chapters 1 and 10)
☐ Broken or weak spring and/or suspension component (Chapters 1 and 10)
☐ Worn or damaged anti-roll bar or mountings (Chapter 10)

Wandering or general instability

☐ Incorrect front wheel alignment (Chapter 10)
☐ Worn steering or suspension joints, bushes or components (Chapters 1 and 10)
☐ Roadwheels out of balance (Chapters 1 and 10)
☐ Faulty or damaged tyre (see *"Weekly checks"*)
☐ Wheel bolts loose (Chapters 1 and 10)
☐ Defective shock absorbers (Chapters 1 and 10)

Excessively-stiff steering

☐ Seized steering linkage balljoint or suspension balljoint (Chapters 1 and 10)

☐ Broken or incorrectly-adjusted auxiliary drivebelt (Chapter 1)
☐ Incorrect front wheel alignment (Chapter 10)
☐ Steering gear damaged (Chapter 10)

Excessive play in steering

☐ Worn steering column/intermediate shaft joints (Chapter 10)
☐ Worn track rod balljoints (Chapters 1 and 10)
☐ Worn steering gear (Chapter 10)
☐ Worn steering or suspension joints, bushes or components (Chapters 1 and 10)

Lack of power assistance

☐ Broken or incorrectly-adjusted auxiliary drivebelt (Chapter 1)
☐ Incorrect power steering fluid level (see *"Weekly checks"*)
☐ Restriction in power steering fluid hoses (Chapter 1)
☐ Faulty power steering pump (Chapter 10)
☐ Faulty steering gear (Chapter 10)

Tyre wear excessive

Tyres worn on inside or outside edges

☐ Tyres under-inflated (wear on both edges) (see *"Weekly checks"*)
☐ Incorrect camber or castor angles (wear on one edge only) (Chapter 10)
☐ Worn steering or suspension joints, bushes or components (Chapters 1 and 10)
☐ Excessively-hard cornering
☐ Accident damage

Tyre treads exhibit feathered edges

☐ Incorrect toe-setting (Chapter 10)

Tyres worn in centre of tread

☐ Tyres over-inflated (see *"Weekly checks"*)

Tyres worn on inside and outside edges

☐ Tyres under-inflated (see *"Weekly checks"*)

Tyres worn unevenly

☐ Tyres/wheels out of balance (see *"Weekly checks"*)
☐ Excessive wheel or tyre run-out
☐ Worn shock absorbers (Chapters 1 and 10)
☐ Faulty tyre (see *"Weekly checks"*)

Electrical system

Note: *For problems associated with the starting system, refer to the faults listed under "Engine" earlier in this Section.*

Battery will not hold a charge for more than a few days

- [ ] Battery defective internally (Chapter 5A)
- [ ] Battery terminal connections loose or corroded (see *"Weekly checks"*)
- [ ] Auxiliary drivebelt worn or incorrectly adjusted (Chapter 1)
- [ ] Alternator not charging at correct output (Chapter 5A)
- [ ] Alternator or voltage regulator faulty (Chapter 5A)
- [ ] Short-circuit causing continual battery drain (Chapters 5 and 12)

Ignition/no-charge warning light remains illuminated with engine running

- [ ] Auxiliary drivebelt broken, worn, or incorrectly adjusted (Chapter 1)
- [ ] Internal fault in alternator or voltage regulator (Chapter 5A)
- [ ] Broken, disconnected, or loose wiring in charging circuit (Chapter 5A)

Ignition/no-charge warning light fails to come on

- [ ] Warning light bulb blown (Chapter 12)
- [ ] Broken, disconnected, or loose wiring in warning light circuit (Chapter 12)
- [ ] Alternator faulty (Chapter 5A)

Lights inoperative

- [ ] Bulb blown (Chapter 12)
- [ ] Corrosion of bulb or bulbholder contacts (Chapter 12)
- [ ] Blown fuse (Chapter 12)
- [ ] Faulty relay (Chapter 12)
- [ ] Broken, loose, or disconnected wiring (Chapter 12)
- [ ] Faulty switch (Chapter 12)

Instrument readings inaccurate or erratic

Instrument readings increase with engine speed

- [ ] Faulty voltage regulator (Chapter 12)

Fuel or temperature gauges give no reading

- [ ] Faulty gauge sender unit (Chapters 3 and 4)
- [ ] Wiring open-circuit (Chapter 12)
- [ ] Faulty gauge (Chapter 12)

Fuel or temperature gauges give continuous maximum reading

- [ ] Faulty gauge sender unit (Chapters 3 and 4)
- [ ] Wiring short-circuit (Chapter 12)
- [ ] Faulty gauge (Chapter 12)

Horn inoperative, or unsatisfactory in operation

Horn operates all the time

- [ ] Horn push either earthed or stuck down (Chapter 12)
- [ ] Horn cable-to-horn push earthed (Chapter 12)

Horn fails to operate

- [ ] Blown fuse (Chapter 12)
- [ ] Cable or cable connections loose, broken or disconnected (Chapter 12)
- [ ] Faulty horn (Chapter 12)

Horn emits intermittent or unsatisfactory sound

- [ ] Cable connections loose (Chapter 12)
- [ ] Horn mountings loose (Chapter 12)
- [ ] Faulty horn (Chapter 12)

Windscreen wipers inoperative, or unsatisfactory in operation

Wipers fail to operate, or operate very slowly

- [ ] Wiper blades stuck to screen, or linkage seized or binding (Chapter 12)
- [ ] Blown fuse (Chapter 12)
- [ ] Cable or cable connections loose, broken or disconnected (Chapter 12)
- [ ] Faulty relay (Chapter 12)
- [ ] Faulty wiper motor (Chapter 12)

Wiper blades sweep over too large or too small an area of the glass

- [ ] Wiper arms incorrectly positioned on spindles (Chapter 12)
- [ ] Excessive wear of wiper linkage (Chapter 12)
- [ ] Wiper motor or linkage mountings loose or insecure (Chapter 12)

Wiper blades fail to clean the glass effectively

- [ ] Wiper blade rubbers worn or perished (see *"Weekly checks"*)
- [ ] Wiper arm tension springs broken, or arm pivots seized (Chapter 12)
- [ ] Insufficient windscreen washer additive to adequately remove road film (see *"Weekly checks"*)

Windscreen washers inoperative, or unsatisfactory in operation

One or more washer jets inoperative

- [ ] Blocked washer jet
- [ ] Disconnected, kinked or restricted fluid hose (Chapter 12)
- [ ] Insufficient fluid in washer reservoir (see *"Weekly checks"*)

Washer pump fails to operate

- [ ] Broken or disconnected wiring or connections (Chapter 12)
- [ ] Blown fuse (Chapter 12)
- [ ] Faulty washer switch (Chapter 12)
- [ ] Faulty washer pump (Chapter 12)

Washer pump runs for some time before fluid is emitted from jets

- [ ] Faulty one-way valve in fluid supply hose (Chapter 12)

Electric windows inoperative, or unsatisfactory in operation

Window glass will only move in one direction

- [ ] Faulty switch (Chapter 12)

Window glass slow to move

- [ ] Regulator seized or damaged, or in need of lubrication (Chapter 11)
- [ ] Door internal components or trim fouling regulator (Chapter 11)
- [ ] Faulty motor (Chapter 11)

Window glass fails to move

- [ ] Blown fuse (Chapter 12)
- [ ] Faulty relay (Chapter 12)
- [ ] Broken or disconnected wiring or connections (Chapter 12)
- [ ] Faulty motor (Chapter 11)

Central locking system inoperative, or unsatisfactory in operation

Complete system failure

- [ ] Blown fuse (Chapter 12)
- [ ] Faulty relay (Chapter 12)
- [ ] Broken or disconnected wiring or connections (Chapter 12)
- [ ] Faulty motor (Chapter 11)

Latch locks but will not unlock, or unlocks but will not lock

- [ ] Faulty master switch (Chapter 12)
- [ ] Broken or disconnected latch operating rods or levers (Chapter 11)
- [ ] Faulty relay (Chapter 12)
- [ ] Faulty motor (Chapter 11)

One solenoid/motor fails to operate

- [ ] Broken or disconnected wiring or connections (Chapter 12)
- [ ] Faulty operating assembly (Chapter 11)
- [ ] Broken, binding or disconnected latch operating rods or levers (Chapter 11)
- [ ] Fault in door latch (Chapter 11)

A

ABS (Anti-lock brake system) A system, usually electronically controlled, that senses incipient wheel lockup during braking and relieves hydraulic pressure at wheels that are about to skid.

Air bag An inflatable bag hidden in the steering wheel (driver's side) or the dash or glovebox (passenger side). In a head-on collision, the bags inflate, preventing the driver and front passenger from being thrown forward into the steering wheel or windscreen.

Air cleaner A metal or plastic housing, containing a filter element, which removes dust and dirt from the air being drawn into the engine.

Air filter element The actual filter in an air cleaner system, usually manufactured from pleated paper and requiring renewal at regular intervals.

Air filter

Allen key A hexagonal wrench which fits into a recessed hexagonal hole.

Alligator clip A long-nosed spring-loaded metal clip with meshing teeth. Used to make temporary electrical connections.

Alternator A component in the electrical system which converts mechanical energy from a drivebelt into electrical energy to charge the battery and to operate the starting system, ignition system and electrical accessories.

Alternator (exploded view)

Ampere (amp) A unit of measurement for the flow of electric current. One amp is the amount of current produced by one volt acting through a resistance of one ohm.

Anaerobic sealer A substance used to prevent bolts and screws from loosening. Anaerobic means that it does not require oxygen for activation. The Loctite brand is widely used.

Antifreeze A substance (usually ethylene glycol) mixed with water, and added to a vehicle's cooling system, to prevent freezing of the coolant in winter. Antifreeze also contains chemicals to inhibit corrosion and the formation of rust and other deposits that would tend to clog the radiator and coolant passages and reduce cooling efficiency.

Anti-seize compound A coating that reduces the risk of seizing on fasteners that are subjected to high temperatures, such as exhaust manifold bolts and nuts.

Anti-seize compound

Asbestos A natural fibrous mineral with great heat resistance, commonly used in the composition of brake friction materials. Asbestos is a health hazard and the dust created by brake systems should never be inhaled or ingested.

Axle A shaft on which a wheel revolves, or which revolves with a wheel. Also, a solid beam that connects the two wheels at one end of the vehicle. An axle which also transmits power to the wheels is known as a live axle.

Axle assembly

Axleshaft A single rotating shaft, on either side of the differential, which delivers power from the final drive assembly to the drive wheels. Also called a driveshaft or a halfshaft.

B

Ball bearing An anti-friction bearing consisting of a hardened inner and outer race with hardened steel balls between two races.

Bearing

Bearing The curved surface on a shaft or in a bore, or the part assembled into either, that permits relative motion between them with minimum wear and friction.

Big-end bearing The bearing in the end of the connecting rod that's attached to the crankshaft.

Bleed nipple A valve on a brake wheel cylinder, caliper or other hydraulic component that is opened to purge the hydraulic system of air. Also called a bleed screw.

Brake bleeding

Brake bleeding Procedure for removing air from lines of a hydraulic brake system.

Brake disc The component of a disc brake that rotates with the wheels.

Brake drum The component of a drum brake that rotates with the wheels.

Brake linings The friction material which contacts the brake disc or drum to retard the vehicle's speed. The linings are bonded or riveted to the brake pads or shoes.

Brake pads The replaceable friction pads that pinch the brake disc when the brakes are applied. Brake pads consist of a friction material bonded or riveted to a rigid backing plate.

Brake shoe The crescent-shaped carrier to which the brake linings are mounted and which forces the lining against the rotating drum during braking.

Braking systems For more information on braking systems, consult the *Haynes Automotive Brake Manual*.

Breaker bar A long socket wrench handle providing greater leverage.

Bulkhead The insulated partition between the engine and the passenger compartment.

C

Caliper The non-rotating part of a disc-brake assembly that straddles the disc and carries the brake pads. The caliper also contains the hydraulic components that cause the pads to pinch the disc when the brakes are applied. A caliper is also a measuring tool that can be set to measure inside or outside dimensions of an object.

Camshaft A rotating shaft on which a series of cam lobes operate the valve mechanisms. The camshaft may be driven by gears, by sprockets and chain or by sprockets and a belt.

Canister A container in an evaporative emission control system; contains activated charcoal granules to trap vapours from the fuel system.

Canister

Carburettor A device which mixes fuel with air in the proper proportions to provide a desired power output from a spark ignition internal combustion engine.

Carburettor

Castellated Resembling the parapets along the top of a castle wall. For example, a castellated balljoint stud nut.

Castellated nut

Castor In wheel alignment, the backward or forward tilt of the steering axis. Castor is positive when the steering axis is inclined rearward at the top.

Catalytic converter A silencer-like device in the exhaust system which converts certain pollutants in the exhaust gases into less harmful substances.

Catalytic converter

Circlip A ring-shaped clip used to prevent endwise movement of cylindrical parts and shafts. An internal circlip is installed in a groove in a housing; an external circlip fits into a groove on the outside of a cylindrical piece such as a shaft.

Clearance The amount of space between two parts. For example, between a piston and a cylinder, between a bearing and a journal, etc.

Coil spring A spiral of elastic steel found in various sizes throughout a vehicle, for example as a springing medium in the suspension and in the valve train.

Compression Reduction in volume, and increase in pressure and temperature, of a gas, caused by squeezing it into a smaller space.

Compression ratio The relationship between cylinder volume when the piston is at top dead centre and cylinder volume when the piston is at bottom dead centre.

Constant velocity (CV) joint A type of universal joint that cancels out vibrations caused by driving power being transmitted through an angle.

Core plug A disc or cup-shaped metal device inserted in a hole in a casting through which core was removed when the casting was formed. Also known as a freeze plug or expansion plug.

Crankcase The lower part of the engine block in which the crankshaft rotates.

Crankshaft The main rotating member, or shaft, running the length of the crankcase, with offset "throws" to which the connecting rods are attached.

Crankshaft assembly

Crocodile clip See Alligator clip

D

Diagnostic code Code numbers obtained by accessing the diagnostic mode of an engine management computer. This code can be used to determine the area in the system where a malfunction may be located.

Disc brake A brake design incorporating a rotating disc onto which brake pads are squeezed. The resulting friction converts the energy of a moving vehicle into heat.

Double-overhead cam (DOHC) An engine that uses two overhead camshafts, usually one for the intake valves and one for the exhaust valves.

Drivebelt(s) The belt(s) used to drive accessories such as the alternator, water pump, power steering pump, air conditioning compressor, etc. off the crankshaft pulley.

Accessory drivebelts

Driveshaft Any shaft used to transmit motion. Commonly used when referring to the axleshafts on a front wheel drive vehicle.

Driveshaft

Drum brake A type of brake using a drum-shaped metal cylinder attached to the inner surface of the wheel. When the brake pedal is pressed, curved brake shoes with friction linings press against the inside of the drum to slow or stop the vehicle.

Drum brake assembly

E

EGR valve A valve used to introduce exhaust gases into the intake air stream.

EGR valve

Electronic control unit (ECU) A computer which controls (for instance) ignition and fuel injection systems, or an anti-lock braking system. For more information refer to the *Haynes Automotive Electrical and Electronic Systems Manual.*

Electronic Fuel Injection (EFI) A computer controlled fuel system that distributes fuel through an injector located in each intake port of the engine.

Emergency brake A braking system, independent of the main hydraulic system, that can be used to slow or stop the vehicle if the primary brakes fail, or to hold the vehicle stationary even though the brake pedal isn't depressed. It usually consists of a hand lever that actuates either front or rear brakes mechanically through a series of cables and linkages. Also known as a handbrake or parking brake.

Endfloat The amount of lengthwise movement between two parts. As applied to a crankshaft, the distance that the crankshaft can move forward and back in the cylinder block.

Engine management system (EMS) A computer controlled system which manages the fuel injection and the ignition systems in an integrated fashion.

Exhaust manifold A part with several passages through which exhaust gases leave the engine combustion chambers and enter the exhaust pipe.

Exhaust manifold

F

Fan clutch A viscous (fluid) drive coupling device which permits variable engine fan speeds in relation to engine speeds.

Feeler blade A thin strip or blade of hardened steel, ground to an exact thickness, used to check or measure clearances between parts.

Feeler blade

Firing order The order in which the engine cylinders fire, or deliver their power strokes, beginning with the number one cylinder.

Flywheel A heavy spinning wheel in which energy is absorbed and stored by means of momentum. On cars, the flywheel is attached to the crankshaft to smooth out firing impulses.

Free play The amount of travel before any action takes place. The "looseness" in a linkage, or an assembly of parts, between the initial application of force and actual movement. For example, the distance the brake pedal moves before the pistons in the master cylinder are actuated.

Fuse An electrical device which protects a circuit against accidental overload. The typical fuse contains a soft piece of metal which is calibrated to melt at a predetermined current flow (expressed as amps) and break the circuit.

Fusible link A circuit protection device consisting of a conductor surrounded by heat-resistant insulation. The conductor is smaller than the wire it protects, so it acts as the weakest link in the circuit. Unlike a blown fuse, a failed fusible link must frequently be cut from the wire for replacement.

G

Gap The distance the spark must travel in jumping from the centre electrode to the side

Adjusting spark plug gap

electrode in a spark plug. Also refers to the spacing between the points in a contact breaker assembly in a conventional points-type ignition, or to the distance between the reluctor or rotor and the pickup coil in an electronic ignition.

Gasket Any thin, soft material - usually cork, cardboard, asbestos or soft metal - installed between two metal surfaces to ensure a good seal. For instance, the cylinder head gasket seals the joint between the block and the cylinder head.

Gasket

Gauge An instrument panel display used to monitor engine conditions. A gauge with a movable pointer on a dial or a fixed scale is an analogue gauge. A gauge with a numerical readout is called a digital gauge.

H

Halfshaft A rotating shaft that transmits power from the final drive unit to a drive wheel, usually when referring to a live rear axle.

Harmonic balancer A device designed to reduce torsion or twisting vibration in the crankshaft. May be incorporated in the crankshaft pulley. Also known as a vibration damper.

Hone An abrasive tool for correcting small irregularities or differences in diameter in an engine cylinder, brake cylinder, etc.

Hydraulic tappet A tappet that utilises hydraulic pressure from the engine's lubrication system to maintain zero clearance (constant contact with both camshaft and valve stem). Automatically adjusts to variation in valve stem length. Hydraulic tappets also reduce valve noise.

I

Ignition timing The moment at which the spark plug fires, usually expressed in the number of crankshaft degrees before the piston reaches the top of its stroke.

Inlet manifold A tube or housing with passages through which flows the air-fuel mixture (carburettor vehicles and vehicles with throttle body injection) or air only (port fuel-injected vehicles) to the port openings in the cylinder head.

J

Jump start Starting the engine of a vehicle with a discharged or weak battery by attaching jump leads from the weak battery to a charged or helper battery.

L

Load Sensing Proportioning Valve (LSPV) A brake hydraulic system control valve that works like a proportioning valve, but also takes into consideration the amount of weight carried by the rear axle.
Locknut A nut used to lock an adjustment nut, or other threaded component, in place. For example, a locknut is employed to keep the adjusting nut on the rocker arm in position.
Lockwasher A form of washer designed to prevent an attaching nut from working loose.

M

MacPherson strut A type of front suspension system devised by Earle MacPherson at Ford of England. In its original form, a simple lateral link with the anti-roll bar creates the lower control arm. A long strut - an integral coil spring and shock absorber - is mounted between the body and the steering knuckle. Many modern so-called MacPherson strut systems use a conventional lower A-arm and don't rely on the anti-roll bar for location.
Multimeter An electrical test instrument with the capability to measure voltage, current and resistance.

N

NOx Oxides of Nitrogen. A common toxic pollutant emitted by petrol and diesel engines at higher temperatures.

O

Ohm The unit of electrical resistance. One volt applied to a resistance of one ohm will produce a current of one amp.
Ohmmeter An instrument for measuring electrical resistance.
O-ring A type of sealing ring made of a special rubber-like material; in use, the O-ring is compressed into a groove to provide the sealing action.

O-ring

Overhead cam (ohc) engine An engine with the camshaft(s) located on top of the cylinder head(s).
Overhead valve (ohv) engine An engine with the valves located in the cylinder head, but with the camshaft located in the engine block.
Oxygen sensor A device installed in the engine exhaust manifold, which senses the oxygen content in the exhaust and converts this information into an electric current. Also called a Lambda sensor.

P

Phillips screw A type of screw head having a cross instead of a slot for a corresponding type of screwdriver.
Plastigage A thin strip of plastic thread, available in different sizes, used for measuring clearances. For example, a strip of Plastigage is laid across a bearing journal. The parts are assembled and dismantled; the width of the crushed strip indicates the clearance between journal and bearing.

Plastigage

Propeller shaft The long hollow tube with universal joints at both ends that carries power from the transmission to the differential on front-engined rear wheel drive vehicles.
Proportioning valve A hydraulic control valve which limits the amount of pressure to the rear brakes during panic stops to prevent wheel lock-up.

R

Rack-and-pinion steering A steering system with a pinion gear on the end of the steering shaft that mates with a rack (think of a geared wheel opened up and laid flat). When the steering wheel is turned, the pinion turns, moving the rack to the left or right. This movement is transmitted through the track rods to the steering arms at the wheels.
Radiator A liquid-to-air heat transfer device designed to reduce the temperature of the coolant in an internal combustion engine cooling system.
Refrigerant Any substance used as a heat transfer agent in an air-conditioning system. R-12 has been the principle refrigerant for many years; recently, however, manufacturers have begun using R-134a, a non-CFC substance that is considered less harmful to the ozone in the upper atmosphere.
Rocker arm A lever arm that rocks on a shaft or pivots on a stud. In an overhead valve engine, the rocker arm converts the upward movement of the pushrod into a downward movement to open a valve.
Rotor In a distributor, the rotating device inside the cap that connects the centre electrode and the outer terminals as it turns, distributing the high voltage from the coil secondary winding to the proper spark plug. Also, that part of an alternator which rotates inside the stator. Also, the rotating assembly of a turbocharger, including the compressor wheel, shaft and turbine wheel.
Runout The amount of wobble (in-and-out movement) of a gear or wheel as it's rotated. The amount a shaft rotates "out-of-true." The out-of-round condition of a rotating part.

S

Sealant A liquid or paste used to prevent leakage at a joint. Sometimes used in conjunction with a gasket.
Sealed beam lamp An older headlight design which integrates the reflector, lens and filaments into a hermetically-sealed one-piece unit. When a filament burns out or the lens cracks, the entire unit is simply replaced.
Serpentine drivebelt A single, long, wide accessory drivebelt that's used on some newer vehicles to drive all the accessories, instead of a series of smaller, shorter belts. Serpentine drivebelts are usually tensioned by an automatic tensioner.

Serpentine drivebelt

Shim Thin spacer, commonly used to adjust the clearance or relative positions between two parts. For example, shims inserted into or under bucket tappets control valve clearances. Clearance is adjusted by changing the thickness of the shim.
Slide hammer A special puller that screws into or hooks onto a component such as a shaft or bearing; a heavy sliding handle on the shaft bottoms against the end of the shaft to knock the component free.
Sprocket A tooth or projection on the periphery of a wheel, shaped to engage with a chain or drivebelt. Commonly used to refer to the sprocket wheel itself.
Starter inhibitor switch On vehicles with an

automatic transmission, a switch that prevents starting if the vehicle is not in Neutral or Park.

Strut See MacPherson strut.

T

Tappet A cylindrical component which transmits motion from the cam to the valve stem, either directly or via a pushrod and rocker arm. Also called a cam follower.

Thermostat A heat-controlled valve that regulates the flow of coolant between the cylinder block and the radiator, so maintaining optimum engine operating temperature. A thermostat is also used in some air cleaners in which the temperature is regulated.

Thrust bearing The bearing in the clutch assembly that is moved in to the release levers by clutch pedal action to disengage the clutch. Also referred to as a release bearing.

Timing belt A toothed belt which drives the camshaft. Serious engine damage may result if it breaks in service.

Timing chain A chain which drives the camshaft.

Toe-in The amount the front wheels are closer together at the front than at the rear. On rear wheel drive vehicles, a slight amount of toe-in is usually specified to keep the front wheels running parallel on the road by offsetting other forces that tend to spread the wheels apart.

Toe-out The amount the front wheels are closer together at the rear than at the front. On front wheel drive vehicles, a slight amount of toe-out is usually specified.

Tools For full information on choosing and using tools, refer to the *Haynes Automotive Tools Manual*.

Tracer A stripe of a second colour applied to a wire insulator to distinguish that wire from another one with the same colour insulator.

Tune-up A process of accurate and careful adjustments and parts replacement to obtain the best possible engine performance.

Turbocharger A centrifugal device, driven by exhaust gases, that pressurises the intake air. Normally used to increase the power output from a given engine displacement, but can also be used primarily to reduce exhaust emissions (as on VW's "Umwelt" Diesel engine).

U

Universal joint or U-joint A double-pivoted connection for transmitting power from a driving to a driven shaft through an angle. A U-joint consists of two Y-shaped yokes and a cross-shaped member called the spider.

V

Valve A device through which the flow of liquid, gas, vacuum, or loose material in bulk may be started, stopped, or regulated by a movable part that opens, shuts, or partially obstructs one or more ports or passageways. A valve is also the movable part of such a device.

Valve clearance The clearance between the valve tip (the end of the valve stem) and the rocker arm or tappet. The valve clearance is measured when the valve is closed.

Vernier caliper A precision measuring instrument that measures inside and outside dimensions. Not quite as accurate as a micrometer, but more convenient.

Viscosity The thickness of a liquid or its resistance to flow.

Volt A unit for expressing electrical "pressure" in a circuit. One volt that will produce a current of one ampere through a resistance of one ohm.

W

Welding Various processes used to join metal items by heating the areas to be joined to a molten state and fusing them together. For more information refer to the *Haynes Automotive Welding Manual*.

Wiring diagram A drawing portraying the components and wires in a vehicle's electrical system, using standardised symbols. For more information refer to the *Haynes Automotive Electrical and Electronic Systems Manual*.

Note: References throughout this index are in the form - "Chapter number" • "Page number"

Haynes Manuals – The Complete List

Title	Book No.
ALFA ROMEO	
Alfa Romeo Alfasud/Sprint (74 - 88) up to F	0292
Alfa Romeo Alfetta (73 - 87) up to E	0531
ALFA ROMEO	
Audi 80 (72 - Feb 79) up to T	0207
Audi 80, 90 (79 - Oct 86) up to D & Coupe (81 - Nov 88) up to F	0605
Audi 80, 90 (Oct 86 - 90) D to H & Coupe (Nov 88 - 90) F to H	1491
Audi 100 (Oct 82 - 90) up to H & 200 (Feb 84 - Oct 89) A to G	0907
Audi 100 & A6 Petrol & Diesel (May 91 - May 97) H to P	3504
Audi A4 (95 - Feb 00) M to V	3575
AUSTIN	
Austin/MG/Rover Maestro 1.3 & 1.6 (83 - 95) up to M	0922
Austin/MG Metro (80 - May 90) up to G	0718
Austin/Rover Montego 1.3 & 1.6 (84 - 94) A to L	1066
Austin/MG/Rover Montego 2.0 (84 - 95) A to M	1067
Mini (59 - 69) up to H	0527
Mini (69 - Oct 96) up to P	0646
Austin/Rover 2.0 litre Diesel Engine (86 - 93) C to L	1857
BEDFORD	
Bedford CF (69 - 87) up to E	0163
Bedford/Vauxhall Rascal & Suzuki Supercarry (86 - Oct 94) C to M	3015
BMW	
BMW 316, 320 & 320i (4-cyl) (75 - Feb 83) up to Y	0276
BMW 320, 320i, 323i & 325i (6-cyl) (Oct 77 - Sept 87) up to E	0815
BMW 3-Series (Apr 91 - 96) H to N	3210
BMW 3- & 5-Series (sohc) (81 - 91) up to J	1948
BMW 520i & 525e (Oct 81 - June 88) up to E	1560
BMW 525, 528 & 528i (73 - Sept 81) up to X	0632
CITROEN	
Citroën 2CV, Ami & Dyane (67 - 90) up to H	0196
Citroën AX Petrol & Diesel (87 - 97) D to P	3014
Citroën BX (83 - 94) A to L	0908
Citroën C15 Van Petrol & Diesel (89 - Oct 98) F to S	3509
Citroën CX (75 - 88) up to F	0528
Citroën Saxo Petrol & Diesel (96 - 98) N to S	3506
Citroën Visa (79 - 88) up to F	0620
Citroën Xantia Petrol & Diesel (93 - 98) K to S	3082
Citroën XM Petrol & Diesel (89 - 98) G to R	3451
Citroën ZX Diesel (91 - 93) J to L	1922
Citroën ZX Petrol (91 - 94) H to M	1881
Citroën 1.7 & 1.9 litre Diesel Engine (84 - 96) A to N	1379
COLT	
Colt/Mitsubishi 1200, 1250 & 1400 (79 - May 84) up to A	0600
FIAT	
Fiat 500 (57 - 73) up to M	0090
Fiat Cinquecento (93 - 98) K to R	3501
Fiat Panda (81 - 95) up to M	0793
Fiat Punto Petrol & Diesel (94 - Oct 99) L to V	3251
Fiat Regata (84 - 88) A to F	1167
Fiat Tipo (88 - 91) E to J	1625
Fiat Uno (83 - 95) up to M	0923
Fiat X1/9 (74 - 89) up to G	0273
FORD	
Ford Capri II (& III) 1.6 & 2.0 (74 - 87) up to E	0283
Ford Capri II (& III) 2.8 & 3.0 (74 - 87) up to E	1309
Ford Cortina Mk IV (& V) 1.6 & 2.0 (76 - 83) up to A	0343
Ford Escort (75 - Aug 80) up to V	0280
Ford Escort (Sept 80 - Sept 90) up to H	0686
Ford Escort & Orion (Sept 90 - 97) H to P	1737
Ford Escort Mk II Mexico, RS 1600 & RS 2000 (75 - 80) up to W	0735
Ford Fiesta (76 - Aug 83) up to Y	0334
Ford Fiesta (Aug 83 - Feb 89) A to F	1030
Ford Fiesta (Feb 89 - Oct 95) F to N	1595
Ford Fiesta Petrol & Diesel (Oct 95 - 97) N to R	3397
Ford Granada (Sept 77 - Feb 85) up to B	0481
Ford Granada & Scorpio (Mar 85 - 94) B to M	1245
Ford Ka (96 - 99) P to T	3570
Ford Mondeo Petrol (93 - 99) K to T	1923
Ford Mondeo Diesel (93 - 96) L to N	3465
Ford Orion (83 - Sept 90) up to H	1009
Ford Sierra 4 cyl. (82 - 93) up to K	0903
Ford Sierra V6 (82 - 91) up to J	0904
Ford Transit Petrol (Mk 2) (78 - Jan 86) up to C	0719
Ford Transit Petrol (Mk 3) (Feb 86 - 89) C to G	1468
Ford Transit Diesel (Feb 86 - 99) C to T	3019
Ford 1.6 & 1.8 litre Diesel Engine (84 - 96) A to N	1172
Ford 2.1, 2.3 & 2.5 litre Diesel Engine (77 - 90) up to H	1606
FREIGHT ROVER	
Freight Rover Sherpa (74 - 87) up to E	0463
HILLMAN	
Hillman Avenger (70 - 82) up to Y	0037
HONDA	
Honda Accord (76 - Feb 84) up to A	0351
Honda Civic (Feb 84 - Oct 87) A to E	1226
Honda Civic (Nov 91 - 96) J to N	3199
HYUNDAI	
Hyundai Pony (85 - 94) C to M	3398
JAGUAR	
Jaguar E Type (61 - 72) up to L	0140
Jaguar MkI & II, 240 & 340 (55 - 69) up to H	0098
Jaguar XJ6, XJ & Sovereign; Daimler Sovereign (68 - Oct 86) up to D	0242
Jaguar XJ6 & Sovereign (Oct 86 - Sept 94) D to M	3261
Jaguar XJ12, XJS & Sovereign; Daimler Double Six (72 - 88) up to F	0478
JEEP	
Jeep Cherokee Petrol (93 - 96) K to N	1943
LADA	
Lada 1200, 1300, 1500 & 1600 (74 - 91) up to J	0413
Lada Samara (87 - 91) D to J	1610
LAND ROVER	
Land Rover 90, 110 & Defender Diesel (83 - 95) up to N	3017
Land Rover Discovery Diesel (89 - 95) G to N	3016
Land Rover Series IIA & III Diesel (58 - 85) up to C	0529
Land Rover Series II, IIA & III Petrol (58 - 85) up to C	0314
MAZDA	
Mazda 323 (Mar 81 - Oct 89) up to G	1608
Mazda 323 (Oct 89 - 98) G to R	3455
Mazda 626 (May 83 - Sept 87) up to E	0929
Mazda B-1600, B-1800 & B-2000 Pick-up (72 - 88) up to F	0267
MERCEDES BENZ	
Mercedes-Benz 190, 190E & 190D Petrol & Diesel (83 - 93) A to L	3450
Mercedes-Benz 200, 240, 300 Diesel (Oct 76 - 85) up to C	1114
Mercedes-Benz 250 & 280 (68 - 72) up to L	0346
Mercedes-Benz 250 & 280 (123 Series) (Oct 76 - 84) up to B	0677
Mercedes-Benz 124 Series (85 - Aug 93) C to K	3253
MG	
MGB (62 - 80) up to W	0111
MG Midget & AH Sprite (58 - 80) up to W	0265
MITSUBISHI	
Mitsubishi Shogun & L200 Pick-Ups (83 - 94) up to M	1944
MORRIS	
Morris Ital 1.3 (80 - 84) up to B	0705
Morris Minor 1000 (56 - 71) up to K	0024
NISSAN	
Nissan Bluebird (May 84 - Mar 86) A to C	1223
Nissan Bluebird (Mar 86 - 90) C to H	1473
Nissan Cherry (Sept 82 - 86) up to D	1031
Nissan Micra (83 - Jan 93) up to K	0931
Nissan Micra (93 - 99) K to T	3254
Nissan Primera (90 - Aug 99) H to T	1851
Nissan Stanza (82 - 86) up to D	0824
Nissan Sunny (May 82 - Oct 86) up to D	0895
Nissan Sunny (Oct 86 - Mar 91) D to H	1378
Nissan Sunny (Apr 91 - 95) H to N	3219
OPEL	
Opel Ascona & Manta (B Series) (Sept 75 - 88) up to F	0316
Opel Ascona (81 - 88) *(Not available in UK see Vauxhall Cavalier 0812)*	3215
Opel Astra (Oct 91 - Feb 98) *(Not available in UK see Vauxhall Astra 1832)*	3156
Opel Calibra (90 - 98) *(See Vauxhall/Opel Calibra Book No. 3502)*	
Opel Corsa (83 - Mar 93) *(Not available in UK see Vauxhall Nova 0909)*	3160
Opel Corsa (Mar 93 - 97) *(Not available in UK see Vauxhall Corsa 1985)*	3159
Opel Frontera Petrol & Diesel (91 - 98) *(See Vauxhall/Opel Frontera Book No. 3454)*	
Opel Kadett (Nov 79 - Oct 84)	0634
Opel Kadett (Oct 84 - Oct 91) *(Not available in UK see Vauxhall Astra & Belmont 1136)*	3196
Opel Omega & Senator (86 - 94) *(Not available in UK see Vauxhall Carlton & Senator 1469)*	3157
Opel Omega (94 - 99) *(See Vauxhall/Opel Omega Book No. 3510)*	
Opel Rekord (Feb 78 - Oct 86) up to D	0543

Title	Book No
Opel Vectra (Oct 88 - Oct 95)	
(Not available in UK see Vauxhall Cavalier 1570)	3158
Opel Vectra Petrol & Diesel (95 - 98)	
(Not available in UK see Vauxhall Vectra 3396)	3523
PEUGEOT	
Peugeot 106 Petrol & Diesel (91 - 98) J to S	1882
Peugeot 205 (83 - 95) A to N	0932
Peugeot 305 (78 - 89) up to G	0538
Peugeot 306 Petrol & Diesel (93 - 99) K to T	3073
Peugeot 309 (86 - 93) C to K	1266
Peugeot 405 Petrol (88 - 96) E to N	1559
Peugeot 405 Diesel (88 - 96) E to N	3198
Peugeot 406 Petrol & Diesel (96 - 97) N to R	3394
Peugeot 505 (79 - 89) up to G	0762
Peugeot 1.7/1.8 & 1.9 litre Diesel Engine (82 - 96) up to N	0950
Peugeot 2.0, 2.1, 2.3 & 2.5 litre Diesel Engines (74 - 90) up to H	1607
PORSCHE	
Porsche 911 (65 - 85) up to C	0264
Porsche 924 & 924 Turbo (76 - 85) up to C	0397
PROTON	
Proton (89 - 97) F to P	3255
RANGE ROVER	
Range Rover V8 (70 - Oct 92) up to K	0606
RELIANT	
Reliant Robin & Kitten (73 - 83) up to A	0436
RENAULT	
Renault 5 (Feb 85 - 96) B to N	1219
Renault 9 & 11 (82 - 89) up to F	0822
Renault 18 (79 - 86) up to D	0598
Renault 19 Petrol (89 - 94) F to M	1646
Renault 19 Diesel (89 - 95) F to N	1946
Renault 21 (86 - 94) C to M	1397
Renault 25 (84 - 92) B to K	1228
Renault Clio Petrol (91 - May 98) H to R	1853
Renault Clio Diesel (91 - June 96) H to N	3031
Renault Espace Petrol & Diesel (85 - 96) C to N	3197
Renault Fuego (80 - 86) up to C	0764
Renault Laguna Petrol & Diesel (94 - 96) L to P	3252
Renault Mégane & Scénic Petrol & Diesel (96 - 98) N to R	3395
ROVER	
Rover 213 & 216 (84 - 89) A to G	1116
Rover 214 & 414 (89 - 96) G to N	1689
Rover 216 & 416 (89 - 96) G to N	1830
Rover 211, 214, 216, 218 & 220 Petrol & Diesel (Dec 95 - 98) N to R	3399
Rover 414, 416 & 420 Petrol & Diesel (May 95 - 98) M to R	3453
Rover 618, 620 & 623 (93 - 97) K to P	3257
Rover 820, 825 & 827 (86 - 95) D to N	1380
Rover 3500 (76 - 87) up to E	0365
Rover Metro, 111 & 114 (May 90 - 96) G to N	1711
SAAB	
Saab 90, 99 & 900 (79 - Oct 93) up to L	0765
Saab 900 (Oct 93 - 98) L to R	3512
Saab 9000 (4-cyl) (85 - 95) C to N	1686

Title	Book No
SEAT	
Seat Ibiza & Cordoba Petrol & Diesel (Oct 93 - Oct 99) L to V	3571
Seat Ibiza & Malaga (85 - 92) B to K	1609
SKODA	
Skoda Estelle (77 - 89) up to G	0604
Skoda Favorit (89 - 96) F to N	1801
Skoda Felicia Petrol & Diesel (95 - 99) M to T	3505
SUBARU	
Subaru 1600 & 1800 (Nov 79 - 90) up to H	0995
SUZUKI	
Suzuki SJ Series, Samurai & Vitara (4-cyl) (82 - 97) up to P	1942
Suzuki Supercarry (86 - Oct 94) C to M	3015
TALBOT	
Talbot Alpine, Solara, Minx & Rapier (75 - 86) up to D	0337
Talbot Horizon (78 - 86) up to D	0473
Talbot Samba (82 - 86) up to D	0823
TOYOTA	
Toyota Carina E (May 92 - 97) J to P	3256
Toyota Corolla (Sept 83 - Sept 87) A to E	1024
Toyota Corolla (80 - 85) up to C	0683
Toyota Corolla (Sept 87 - Aug 92) E to K	1683
Toyota Corolla (Aug 92 - 97) K to P	3259
Toyota Hi-Ace & Hi-Lux (69 - Oct 83) up to A	0304
TRIUMPH	
Triumph Acclaim (81 - 84) up to B	0792
Triumph GT6 & Vitesse (62 - 74) up to N	0112
Triumph Spitfire (62 - 81) up to X	0113
Triumph Stag (70 - 78) up to T	0441
Triumph TR7 (75 - 82) up to Y	0322
VAUXHALL	
Vauxhall Astra (80 - Oct 84) up to B	0635
Vauxhall Astra & Belmont (Oct 84 - Oct 91) B to J	1136
Vauxhall Astra (Oct 91 - Feb 98) J to R	1832
Vauxhall/Opel Calibra (90 - 98) G to S	3502
Vauxhall Carlton (Oct 78 - Oct 86) up to D	0480
Vauxhall Carlton & Senator (Nov 86 - 94) D to L	1469
Vauxhall Cavalier 1600, 1900 & 2000 (75 - July 81) up to W	0315
Vauxhall Cavalier (81 - Oct 88) up to F	0812
Vauxhall Cavalier (Oct 88 - 95) F to N	1570
Vauxhall Chevette (75 - 84) up to B	0285
Vauxhall Corsa (Mar 93 - 97) K to R	1985
Vauxhall/Opel Frontera Petrol & Diesel (91 - Sept 98) J to S	3454
Vauxhall Nova (83 - 93) up to K	0909
Vauxhall/Opel Omega (94 - 99) L to T	3510
Vauxhall Vectra Petrol & Diesel (95 - 98) N to R	3396
Vauxhall/Opel 1.5, 1.6 & 1.7 litre Diesel Engine (82 - 96) up to N	1222
VOLKSWAGEN	
Volkswagen Beetle 1200 (54 - 77) up to S	0036
Volkswagen Beetle 1300 & 1500 (65 - 75) up to P	0039
Volkswagen Beetle 1302 & 1302S (70 - 72) up to L	0110
Volkswagen Beetle 1303, 1303S & GT (72 - 75) up to P	0159

Title	Book No.
Volkswagen Golf & Jetta Mk 1 1.1 & 1.3 (74 - 84) up to A	0716
Volkswagen Golf, Jetta & Scirocco Mk 1 1.5,1.6 & 1.8 (74 - 84) up to A	0726
Volkswagen Golf & Jetta Mk 1 Diesel (78 - 84) up to A	0451
Volkswagen Golf & Jetta Mk 2 (Mar 84 - Feb 92) A to J	1081
Volkswagen Golf & Vento Petrol & Diesel (Feb 92 - 96) J to N	3097
Volkswagen LT vans & light trucks (76 - 87) up to E	0637
Volkswagen Passat & Santana (Sept 81 - May 88) up to E	0814
Volkswagen Passat Petrol & Diesel (May 88 - 96) E to P	3498
Volkswagen Polo & Derby (76 - Jan 82) up to X	0335
Volkswagen Polo (82 - Oct 90) up to H	0813
Volkswagen Polo (Nov 90 - Aug 94) H to L	3245
Volkswagen Polo Hatchback Petrol & Diesel (94 - 99) M to S	3500
Volkswagen Scirocco (82 - 90) up to H	1224
Volkswagen Transporter 1600 (68 - 79) up to V	0082
Volkswagen Transporter 1700, 1800 & 2000 (72 - 79) up to V	0226
Volkswagen Transporter (air-cooled) (79 - 82) up to Y	0638
Volkswagen Transporter (water-cooled) (82 - 90) up to H	3452
VOLVO	
Volvo 142, 144 & 145 (66 - 74) up to N	0129
Volvo 240 Series (74 - 93) up to K	0270
Volvo 262, 264 & 260/265 (75 - 85) up to C	0400
Volvo 340, 343, 345 & 360 (76 - 91) up to J	0715
Volvo 440, 460 & 480 (87 - 97) D to P	1691
Volvo 740 & 760 (82 - 91) up to J	1258
Volvo 850 (92 - 96) J to P	3260
Volvo 940 (90 - 96) H to N	3249
Volvo S40 & V40 (96 - 99) N to V	3569
Volvo S70, V70 & C70 (96 - 99) P to V	3573
YUGO/ZASTAVA	
Yugo/Zastava (81 - 90) up to H	1453
AUTOMOTIVE TECHBOOKS	
Automotive Brake Manual	3050
Automotive Carburettor Manual	3288
Automotive Diagnostic Fault Codes Manual	3472
Automotive Diesel Engine Service Guide	3286
Automotive Disc Brake Manual	3542
Automotive Electrical and Electronic Systems Manual	3049
Automotive Engine Management and Fuel Injection Systems Manual	3344
Automotive Gearbox Overhaul Manual	3473
Automotive Service Summaries Manual	3475
Automotive Timing Belts Manual – Austin/Rover	3549
Automotive Timing Belts Manual - Ford	3474
Automotive Timing Belts Manual – Peugeot/Citroën	3568
Automotive Timing Belts Manual – Vauxhall/Opel	3577
Automotive Welding Manual	3053
In-Car Entertainment Manual (3rd Edition)	3363
OTHER TITLES	
Haynes Diesel Engine Systems & Data Book (91 -00)	3548
Haynes Petrol Models Data Book (94 - 00)	3718

CL09.04/00

Preserving Our Motoring Heritage

< The Model J Duesenberg Derham Tourster. Only eight of these magnificent cars were ever built – this is the only example to be found outside the United States of America

Almost every car you've ever loved, loathed or desired is gathered under one roof at the Haynes Motor Museum. Over 300 immaculately presented cars and motorbikes represent every aspect of our motoring heritage, from elegant reminders of bygone days, such as the superb Model J Duesenberg to curiosities like the bug-eyed BMW Isetta. There are also many old friends and flames. Perhaps you remember the 1959 Ford Popular that you did your courting in? The magnificent 'Red Collection' is a spectacle of classic sports cars including AC, Alfa Romeo, Austin Healey, Ferrari, Lamborghini, Maserati, MG, Riley, Porsche and Triumph.

A Perfect Day Out

Each and every vehicle at the Haynes Motor Museum has played its part in the history and culture of Motoring. Today, they make a wonderful spectacle and a great day out for all the family. Bring the kids, bring Mum and Dad, but above all bring your camera to capture those golden memories for ever. You will also find an impressive array of motoring memorabilia, a comfortable 70 seat video cinema and one of the most extensive transport book shops in Britain. The Pit Stop Cafe serves everything from a cup of tea to wholesome, home-made meals or, if you prefer, you can enjoy the large picnic area nestled in the beautiful rural surroundings of Somerset.

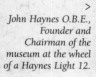

> John Haynes O.B.E., Founder and Chairman of the museum at the wheel of a Haynes Light 12.

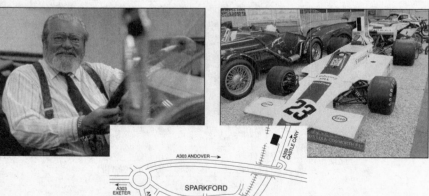

< Graham Hill's Lola Cosworth Formula 1 car next to a 1934 Riley Sports.

The Museum is situated on the A359 Yeovil to Frome road at Sparkford, just off the A303 in Somerset. It is about 40 miles south of Bristol, and 25 minutes drive from the M5 intersection at Taunton.

Open 9.30am - 5.30pm (10.00am - 4.00pm Winter) 7 days a week, *except Christmas Day, Boxing Day and New Years Day*

Special rates available for schools, coach parties and outings Charitable Trust No. 292048